Life Sciences

MW00902604

continued

CALCULUS

and Its Applications

SECOND EDITION

Daniel D. Benice

HOUGHTON MIFFLIN COMPANY   BOSTON   NEW YORK

Senior Sponsoring Editor: Maureen O'Connor
Development Editor: Lenore Parens
Associate Editor: Dawn Nuttall
Senior Project Editor: Maria Morelli
Editorial Assistant: Christian Zbriskie
Senior Production/Design Coordinator: Priscilla Bailey
Marketing Manager: Charles Cavaliere

Custom Publishing Editor: Jan Scipio
Custom Publishing Production Manager: Kathleen McCourt
Custom Publishing Project Coordinator: Kim Gavrilles

Chapter 1: Don Smentzer/Tony Stone Images; *Chapter 2:* Art Montes De Oca/FPG International;
Chapter 3: Glyn Kirk/Tony Stone Images; *Chapter 4:* Raymond Gehman/National Geographic Image
Collection; *Chapter 5:* © 1996 Lauren Greenfield; *Chapter 6:* © 1996 John Marshall; *Chapter 7:*
Chris Johns/National Geographic Image Collection; *Chapter 8:* Patrick Donehue/Tony Stone Images;
Chapter 9: © 1996 John Marshall; *Chapter 10:* John Lund/Tony Stone Images; *Chapter 11:* Gary
Benson/Tony Stone Images; *Chapter 12:* Keith Dannemiller/SABA.

Cover Designer: Galen B. Murphy
Cover Art: Photodisc

Printed in the United States of America.

ISBN-13: 978-0-618-40070-6
ISBN-10: 0-618-40070-2

N-02365

5   6   7   8   9 –CCI– 09   08   07   06

 Houghton Mifflin
Custom Publishing

222 Berkeley Street • Boston, MA 02116

Address all correspondence and order information to the above address.

CONTENTS

CHAPTER

DERIVATIVES   103

CHAPTER

ADDITIONAL APPLICATIONS OF THE DERIVATIVE   184

CHAPTER

PROBABILITY AND CALCULUS   410

CHAPTER

DIFFERENTIAL EQUATIONS   443

CHAPTER

PREFACE

The second edition of *Calculus and Its Applications* provides a one- or two-semester introduction to calculus for students of business, economics, management, social sciences, life sciences, and other fields. Building on the success of the first edition, the text offers a motivated, comprehensive, applications-oriented approach to the subject. Crafted with care and experience, this book offers instructors and students an ideal combination of content, level, writing style, and modern features.

NEW IN THIS EDITION

Many changes have been made in response to instructors who want to see certain new elements become part of the applied calculus course. The following changes have been made to reflect the AMATYC, MAA, and NCTM standards and proposals. (Detailed explanation follows in the features section.)

1. The number of *technology exercises* has been tripled and their variety has been expanded.
2. The number of *writing exercises* has been doubled.
3. More *real-life mathematical models* have been used.
4. *Chapter openers* offer students a glimpse into how mathematics is used in everyday life.
5. *Projects and essays* have been created for each chapter.
6. More *conceptual exercises* have been added.

The content, approach, and flexibility make this a text that can rightfully be considered by nearly all instructors, from conservative to reform.

FEATURES

Technology Exercises: The number of technology exercises has been tripled. These quality exercises teach concepts and expand understanding. Furthermore, they add an extra dimension and excitement to the study of calculus by offering visual perspectives and problem-solving approaches that are unavailable with conventional techniques. Most sections contain a group of exercises that are designed to be solved with a graphing calculator (or computer software). For examples of technology exercises, see pages 131, 197–198, 220–221, and 320–321. Within the technology exercise sets, you will find *Notes* that provide assistance in using graphing calculators and offer samples of the potential of computer algebra systems such as *Maple* and *Mathematica*.

Writing Exercises: The number of writing exercises (marked **W** in the text) has been doubled. Such questions force students to think and to have a good grasp of the subject. There are literally hundreds of exercises that require students to provide written explanations. A sample of writing exercises can be seen on pages 218–220, 245, and 297. These innovative questions address proposals and standards from AMATYC, MAA, NCTM and others who support writing across the curriculum.

Real-Life Mathematical Models: Throughout the book you will find equations and functions that are mathematical models for real data. To view a few models that are new to this edition, see Example 6 on page 282, Example 9 on page 291, and Example 3 on page 340. Sometimes the model is given as a graph (rather than an equation) of a function, as with Exercise 50 on page 55, Example 3 on page 71, and Exercise 44 on page 245. Still another form in which the model may appear is as the data itself, as in Exercise 74 on page 218, which begins with Karl von Frisch's original dancing-bees data.

Chapter Openers: The chapter openers illustrate calculus in the real world and serve to pique student interest. Colorful photos depict scenes from work environments, sports settings, and nature. Accompanying captions explain the sometimes surprising relevance of the photos to the material in the chapter.

In addition, margin notes in each chapter describe the accomplishments of people active in using calculus-related mathematics. In each instance, there is an opportunity for a follow up reading activity, either via a specific book that is described or by simply reading more about the person noted.

Projects and Essays: Projects and essays have been created and placed at the end of each chapter. The projects involve research, writing, and cooperative work in areas such as applications, historical topics, and extensions of the mathematics. They are well thought out, interesting, and doable. For examples see pages 101–102, 182–183, 247, and 409.

Conceptual Exercises: Besides writing exercises and technology exercises, other types of exercises have been significantly increased in number, including:

(a) Graph interpretation exercises

(b) Real-world applications exercises

(c) Graph-related exercises

(d) Challenging exercises

(e) Review exercises

(f) Calculator exercises (denoted by calculator logo 🖩)

PEDAGOGY   Instructors who have used the first edition of this book have found that it really works—both for them and for their students.

- *Students* can read and understand the book. Explanations are carefully presented. Examples illustrate ideas and techniques. Extra steps, explanations, and annotations help avoid confusion. *Instructors* are pleased that the mathematics is solid and honest and that the organization makes it easy for students to locate concepts, definitions, theorems, and examples when they are studying or doing homework exercises.

- The huge number of exercises have been carefully constructed and gently graduated. *Students* gain confidence as they actively master skills and learn concepts. *Instructors* can teach at the level they prefer.

- The examples and exercises demonstrate real-world use of calculus. The opportunity to apply calculus concepts and skills creates interest, involvement, reinforcement, and thinking. *Students* soon discover that calculus is exciting mathematics. *Instructors* have consistently praised the quality and variety of applications.

- *Students* get to see basic economics functions presented together in one section (Section 1.5). After rates of change are examined (in Section 3.3), *instructors* can present marginal analysis thoroughly and without interruption (Section 3.4).

CONTENT AND ORGANIZATION

The text offers comprehensive coverage of the calculus topics appropriate for the course. Since there is always the need to tailor a textbook to fit your specific course, we present here a guide that will help you to select the sections and topic sequence that will be best for your class.

The first four sections of Chapter 1 constitute a review of algebra and accordingly can be covered in class or omitted if the students are already familiar with the material. By contrast, Section 1.5 (Functions in Economics) introduces and explains key concepts that will be used in business applications throughout the book.

Since calculus cannot be understood without some knowledge of limits, Chapter 2 offers a pragmatic study of this important topic. If time constraints or personal preference demand that you get to the derivative quickly, cover only Section 2.1 (Introduction to Limits) and then go directly to Chapter 3 (Derivatives). Other sections of Chapter 2 can be covered as needed and as time permits. Another alternative is to present Sections 2.1 through 2.3 and return later as needed to limits at infinity (2.4) and infinite limits (2.5).

Chapter 3 introduces the derivative. You will want to present Sections 3.1–3.8 in sequence. Notice that Section 3.4 offers thorough coverage of the marginal concepts. Section 3.9 (Related Rates) can be omitted if it is not considered part of your course.

Chapter 4 presents applications of the derivative. The sections should be studied in sequence. Elasticity of demand (Section 4.6) can be omitted, although many business calculus courses consider the topic essential.

Chapter 5 presents the exponential and logarithmic functions. The sections should be covered in sequence.

Chapter 6 covers integration. Sections 6.1–6.4 should be taught in sequence. The three remaining sections offer applications and can be presented in any order. Note that in Section 6.5 the application of integration to finding the average value of a function and the volume of a solid of revolution are not essential to the continuity of the chapter or the text. Section 6.6 (Surplus) is an important business topic, but it can be omitted or studied later without loss of continuity.

Integration by substitution (Section 7.1) is an important extension of the integration ideas presented in Chapter 6. The remainder of Chapter 7 includes standard topics that can be covered or omitted to fit the nature of your course.

Chapter 8 presents probability from a calculus standpoint. If desired, Section 8.3 can be omitted without loss of continuity.

Chapter 9 presents differential equations. The order of Sections 9.3 and 9.4 can be interchanged, or the sections can be omitted if desired.

The sections of Chapter 10 (Multivariable Calculus) are arranged in a fairly standard order. However, you can rearrange the sequence or omit sections. The only restrictions are that Sections 10.1 and 10.2 must be presented first and that Section 10.3 must be covered before 10.5.

Many students taking this course have never studied trigonometry. Consequently, what seems like a simple review (Sections 11.1 and 11.2) may in fact serve as an introduction to trigonometry for some students. The sections of Chapter 11 should be covered in sequence.

It is intended that Sections 12.1 through 12.5 be presented in order. However, you could extract Section 12.4 (Taylor Series) and cover it independently. Section 12.5 uses material from 12.3 and 12.4. The sections on Newton's method (12.6) and L'Hôpital's rule (12.7) can be taught independently of Sections 12.1–12.5.

SUPPLEMENTS FOR THE INSTRUCTOR

Instructor's Resource Manual with Testing Program: The Instructor's Resource Manual contains several lab or group activities that can be worked using a graphing calculator or other graphing utility. These activities have been written specifically for this text. The Testing Program contains a printed test bank of all items in the computerized test generator plus two chapter tests for each chapter. Answers to all test questions are included.

Computerized Test Generator: The Computerized Test Generator contains more than 2000 test questions, organized by section to follow topics in the text. Over one-third are applications questions. The instructor can choose between multiple-choice and free-response answer formats. It is available for the IBM PC and compatible computers and for the Macintosh. DOS and Windows versions provide **on-line testing** and **gradebook** functions.

Solutions Manual: The Solutions Manual contains complete solutions to all exercises.

SUPPLEMENTS FOR THE STUDENT

Student Solutions Manual: The Student Solutions Manual contains complete solutions to all odd-numbered exercises.

Math Assistant Software: Math Assistant Software is available for the Macintosh and IBM PC (and compatibles). This package easily plots algebraic and trigonometric functions.

ACKNOWLEDGMENTS

I would like to express my genuine appreciation to the reviewers listed here. Their constructive comments have made a significant impact on the quality of this text. I am grateful for the support and encouragement they have offered.

Second edition reviewers: Paul Allen, *University of Alabama;* Howard I. Dwyer, *University of Wisconsin, Platteville;* John A. Frohliger, *St. Norbert College,* WI; Pauline Graveline, *Canton College of Technology,* NY; James Hassed, *University of Colorado;* John Haverhals, *Bradley University,* IL; Richard Leedy, *Polk Community College,* FL; Jackie LeFebvre, *Illinois Central College;* Robert R. Molina, *Alma College,* MI; Mark Nugent, *University of Missouri, St. Louis;* Georgia B. Pyrros, *University of Delaware;* George W. Schultz, St. *Petersburg Jr. College,* FL; Jean M. Shutters, *Harrisburg Area Community College,* PA; William Lee Truman, *Pembroke State University,* NC; Elizabeth E. White, *Trident Technical College,* SC; Ming Xue, *Massachusetts Institute of Technology.*

First edition reviewers: Daniel D. Anderson, *University of Iowa;* Ronald Barnes, *University of Houston, downtown campus,* TX; Margaret Russell Berkes, *University of Vermont, Montpelier;* George R. Bradley, *Duquesne University,* PA; Michael J. Bradley, *Merrimack College,* MA; Gabriel B. Costa, *Seton Hall University,* NJ; Sam Councilman, *California State University;* Preston Dinkins, *Southern University,* LA; John Erbland, *University of Hartford,* CT; Gerald K. Goff, *Oklahoma State University;* Kwang Chul Ha,

Illinois State University; Gerald Higdon, *Fitchburg State College,* MA; Joel W. Irish, *University of Southern Maine;* Thomas Judson, *University of Portland,* OR; Donald LaTorre, *Clemson University,* SC; Robert Levine, *Community College of Allegheny County,* PA; Norman Martin, *Northern Arizona University;* Michael E. Mays, *West Virginia University;* Reginald Mazeres, *Tennessee Technological University;* Patsy N. Newman, *Richard Bland College,* VA; R. Glen Powers, *Western Kentucky University;* Michael Schramm, *LeMoyne College,* NY; Jean M. Shutters, *Harrisburg Area Community College,* PA; Ronald Smith, *Edison Community College,* FL; Kenneth W. Spackman, *University of North Carolina, Wilmington;* Robert F. Sutherland, *Bridgewater State College,* MA; Arnold R. Vobach, *University of Houston,* TX; Terry J. Walters, *University of Tennessee at Chattanooga;* Jan E. Wynn, *Brigham Young University,* UT; Earl Zwick, *Indiana State University*

I would like to give special thanks to Jean Shutters at Harrisburg Area Community College, PA for revising the *Instructor's Resource Manual with Testing Program* and to Christopher Pladdy at Nicholls State University, LA for updating the *Solutions Manual* and *Student Solutions Manual*.

It was a pleasure working with the professionals at Houghton Mifflin: Maria Morelli (Senior Project Editor), Lenore Parens (Development Editor), Maureen O'Connor (Senior Sponsoring Editor), and Dawn Nuttall (Associate Editor).

DANIEL D. BENICE

FUNCTIONS

1

Contractors under budget pressure must decide how many carpenters to hire; masons calculate the proportions of sand to cement when mixing mortar; inspectors determine the property taxes families must pay after adding rooms to their homes.

Algebraic functions are fundamental tools for construction and many other professions. Likewise, they are the basis of the more complicated mathematical operations you will encounter in calculus.

*T*his chapter is intended to prepare you for a successful exploration of the ideas and applications of elementary calculus. We have included some algebra review, an introduction to functions and graphs, and a presentation of the functions used in business and economics. Because the material presented here will be used throughout the book, it is important that you become familiar with it.

1.1 *REAL NUMBERS AND ALGEBRA REVIEW*

Have you ever wondered why certain words are used in mathematics? Why are quadratic equations called that? Just what does "quadratic" have to do with x^2? Steven Schwartzman has the answers in his book *The Words of Mathematics* which explains the origins, literal meanings, and mathematical connections of more than 1500 words.

By using this valuable resource, you can share the excitement of an enthusiastic teacher of mathematics and linguistics. You will find that even some of the more common-seeming words of mathematics have interesting origins, perhaps surprising for such words as factor, exponent, algebra, fraction, notation, and radical.

The study of elementary calculus requires a knowledge of the real number system. The real numbers can be considered points on a line. To every real number there corresponds one point. To every point there corresponds one real number. (See Figure 1.)

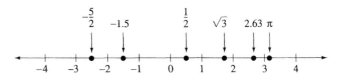

Figure 1 The real number line

Inequalities can be used to compare real numbers. The symbols used are $>$ (greater than), $<$ (less than), $\geq$ (greater than or equal to), and $\leq$ (less than or equal to). For example, $x > 3$ (x is greater than 3) and $y \leq -2$ (y is less than or equal to -2).

In some applications it is useful to combine two inequalities in order to express an **interval.** For example,

$$2 < x < 5$$

combines the inequalities $2 < x$ and $x < 5$ and represents all real numbers between 2 and 5. The notation $(2, 5)$ is used to denote such an **open interval** that excludes the endpoints. Graphically, the interval is shown as

The inequality $2 \leq x \leq 5$ expresses a **closed interval,** one in which the endpoints are included. The interval is denoted $[2, 5]$ and is shown graphically as

The two intervals $(2, 5)$ and $[2, 5]$ and others are shown in Figure 2. A parenthesis is used to indicate that an endpoint is not included. A bracket is used to indicate that an endpoint is included. Intervals such as $(2, 5]$ and $[2, 5)$ are called **half-open intervals.** The symbol ∞ (infinity) is used to specify that the interval extends infinitely far to the right. Similarly, $-\infty$ (minus infinity) is used to specify that an interval extends infinitely far to the left. Because ∞ does not represent a number, it is never included in the interval, and thus, a parenthesis is always used with that symbol.

inequality	interval notation	graph
$2 < x < 5$	$(2, 5)$	
$2 \le x \le 5$	$[2, 5]$	
$2 < x \le 5$	$(2, 5]$	
$2 \le x < 5$	$[2, 5)$	
$x > 2$	$(2, \infty)$	
$x \le 5$	$(-\infty, 5]$	

Figure 2 Intervals

This section continues with a brief review of *linear inequalities*, which you will see have intervals for solutions. Some calculus problems require the solution of inequalities. You should recall that linear inequalities are solved in much the same way as linear equations. But there is one key difference.

If both sides of an inequality are multiplied or divided by a negative number, the direction of the inequality is reversed: $>$ becomes $<$, and $<$ becomes $>$.

EXAMPLE 1 Solve the inequality $-3(2 + x) + x \ge 14$.

SOLUTION When the expression on the left side is multiplied out, the inequality becomes

$$-6 - 3x + x \ge 14$$
$$-6 - 2x \ge 14 \qquad \text{after simplifying}$$
$$-2x \ge 20 \qquad \text{adding 6 to both sides}$$
$$x \le -10 \qquad \text{dividing both sides by } -2$$

Notice that division of both sides by a negative number (-2) resulted in a reversal of the direction of the inequality. The $\ge$ became $\le$. The solution is $x \le -10$ or $(-\infty, -10]$. ♦

Next, we provide a brief review of exponents, quadratic equations and rational expressions.

Exponents and Radicals

Recall the concept of exponent: $x^2 = x \cdot x$ and $x^3 = x \cdot x \cdot x$. In general,

---

Exponent

If x is any real number and n is a positive integer, then

$$x^n = x \cdot x \cdot x \cdots x \qquad n \text{ factors of } x$$

Here x is called the **base** and n is called the **exponent** or **power.**

Negative Exponents

If x is any nonzero real number and n is a positive integer, then

$$x^{-n} = \frac{1}{x^n} \qquad \frac{1}{x^{-n}} = x^n$$

The next example shows the value of changing negative exponents to positive exponents for calculation purposes.

EXAMPLE 2   Evaluate.   **(a)** 2^{-3} **(b)** $\dfrac{1}{4^{-2}}$

SOLUTION   **(a)** $2^{-3} = \dfrac{1}{2^3} = \dfrac{1}{8}$ **(b)** $\dfrac{1}{4^{-2}} = 4^2 = 16$ ◆

Note

Beginning in Chapter 3, you will see the occasional need to change from positive exponents to negative exponents in order to use calculus operations. An expression such as $1/x^4$ would be changed to x^{-4}.

Several important properties of exponents are given next.

Properties of Exponents

If x and y are real numbers and m and n are integers, then

$$x^0 = 1 \qquad x \neq 0$$

$$x^m \cdot x^n = x^{m+n}$$

$$(x^m)^n = x^{mn}$$

$$(x \cdot y)^m = x^m y^m$$

$$\left(\frac{x}{y}\right)^m = \frac{x^m}{y^m} \qquad y \neq 0$$

$$\frac{x^m}{x^n} = x^{m-n} \qquad x \neq 0$$

EXAMPLE 3   Use the properties of exponents to simplify each expression.

(a) $x^5 \cdot x^3$ (b) $(a^4)^6$ (c) $(2x)^4$ (d) $\left(\dfrac{a}{b}\right)^{10}$ (e) $\dfrac{x^{12}}{x^5}$ (f) $5x^0$

SOLUTION   (a) $x^5 \cdot x^3 = x^{5+3} = x^8$ (b) $(a^4)^6 = a^{4 \cdot 6} = a^{24}$

(c) $(2x)^4 = 2^4 x^4 = 16x^4$ (d) $\left(\dfrac{a}{b}\right)^{10} = \dfrac{a^{10}}{b^{10}}$

(e) $\dfrac{x^{12}}{x^5} = x^{12-5} = x^7$ (f) $5x^0 = 5 \cdot x^0 = 5 \cdot 1 = 5$ ◆

Exponent notation can be extended to radicals. The idea that $\sqrt{x} \cdot \sqrt{x} = x$ suggests using $x^{1/2}$ as the exponent notation of $\sqrt{x}$, since $x^{1/2} \cdot x^{1/2} = x$ would be consistent with a known property of exponents.

Exponent Form of Radicals

$$x^{1/2} = \sqrt{x} \qquad x \geq 0$$

$$x^{1/3} = \sqrt[3]{x} \qquad \text{all } x$$

$$x^{1/n} = \sqrt[n]{x} \qquad x \geq 0 \text{ when } n \text{ even}$$

$$x^{1/n} = \sqrt[n]{x} \qquad \text{all } x \text{ when } n \text{ odd}$$

Here is an example that demonstrates numerical computation.

EXAMPLE 4   Evaluate.   **(a)** $9^{1/2}$ **(b)** $8^{1/3}$

SOLUTION   **(a)** $9^{1/2} = \sqrt{9} = 3$ **(b)** $8^{1/3} = \sqrt[3]{8} = 2$ ◆

Rational Exponents

$$x^{m/n} = (x^{1/n})^m \quad \text{or} \quad (x^m)^{1/n}$$

$$x \geq 0 \text{ when } n \text{ is even}$$

The form $(x^{1/n})^m$ is usually easier to work with in numerical situations, because the number whose root you seek is usually smaller. This idea is demonstrated next.

EXAMPLE 5   Evaluate $64^{3/2}$ two different ways. Compare.

SOLUTION
$$64^{3/2} = (64^{1/2})^3 = (8)^3 = 512 \qquad \text{easier}$$

$$64^{3/2} = (64^3)^{1/2} = (262{,}144)^{1/2} = 512 \qquad \text{harder} \qquad ◆$$

Negative fractional exponents are a natural extension.

EXAMPLE 6   Evaluate.   **(a)** $9^{-1/2}$ **(b)** $16^{-3/2}$

SOLUTION   **(a)** $9^{-1/2} = \dfrac{1}{9^{1/2}} = \dfrac{1}{3}$ **(b)** $16^{-3/2} = \dfrac{1}{16^{3/2}} = \dfrac{1}{(16^{1/2})^3} = \dfrac{1}{(4)^3} = \dfrac{1}{64}$ ◆

Recall that numbers such as $\sqrt{2}$ and $\sqrt{7}$ are irrational numbers. This means that a fraction such as

$$\frac{5}{\sqrt{2}}$$

has an irrational denominator. You can make this denominator a rational number (that is, *rationalize the denominator*) by multiplying the denominator by $\sqrt{2}$. Of course, you must also multiply the numerator by $\sqrt{2}$ to avoid changing the value of the fraction. Here is the procedure.

$$\frac{5}{\sqrt{2}} = \frac{5}{\sqrt{2}} \cdot \frac{\sqrt{2}}{\sqrt{2}} = \frac{5\sqrt{2}}{2}$$

Quadratic Equations

An expression of the form $ax^2 + bx + c$, where $a \neq 0$, is called **quadratic** in x. Such expressions can sometimes be readily factored. For example,

$$x^2 + 7x + 10 = (x + 5)(x + 2)$$

Recall that in the factoring, x and x are selected to yield x^2 when multiplied. The $+5$ and $+2$ are chosen because their product is the $+10$ of the original expression and their sum is the $+7$ of the $+7x$.

EXAMPLE 7 Factor.   **(a)** $2x^2 - 4x - 30$ **(b)** $3x^2 - 11x + 6$ **(c)** $x^2 - 49$

SOLUTION   **(a)** $2x^2 - 4x - 30 = 2(x^2 - 2x - 15) = 2(x - 5)(x + 3)$

           (b) $3x^2 - 11x + 6 = (3x - 2)(x - 3)$

           (c) $x^2 - 49 = (x + 7)(x - 7)$ ◆

A *quadratic equation* can be solved by factoring if the quadratic expression can be factored.

EXAMPLE 8 Solve the quadratic equation $5x^2 + 2x - 3 = 0$.

SOLUTION We begin by factoring the quadratic expression.

$$(5x - 3)(x + 1) = 0$$

If either factor is zero, then the product will be zero. So, set each factor equal to zero to solve the equation.

$$
\begin{array}{c|c}
5x - 3 = 0 & x + 1 = 0 \\
5x = 3 & x = -1 \\
x = 3/5 &
\end{array}
$$

The solutions of the quadratic equation are 3/5 and -1.   ◆

If the quadratic expression cannot be factored or if you are having trouble factoring it, use the **quadratic formula** to solve the equation.

Quadratic Formula

If $ax^2 + bx + c = 0$ and $a \neq 0$, then

$$x = \frac{-b \pm \sqrt{b^2 - 4ac}}{2a}$$

The symbol $\pm$ is read "plus or minus."

EXAMPLE 9 Solve the quadratic equation $x^2 + 5x + 2 = 0$.

SOLUTION The equation $x^2 + 5x + 2 = 0$ cannot be solved by factoring using integers. We will use the quadratic formula, with $a = 1$, $b = 5$, and $c = 2$.

$$x = \frac{-b \pm \sqrt{b^2 - 4ac}}{2a} = \frac{-5 \pm \sqrt{25 - 4(1)(2)}}{2(1)} = \frac{-5 \pm \sqrt{17}}{2}$$

If desired, the fraction containing the two solutions can be split into two fractions in order to display or compute each solution separately.

$$x = \frac{-5 + \sqrt{17}}{2}, \quad x = \frac{-5 - \sqrt{17}}{2} \qquad \text{alternative form} \qquad \blacklozenge$$

EXAMPLE 10 Solve the equation $x^2 - 4x = 1$.

SOLUTION We note that this is a quadratic equation. However, it looks different because the expression is not set equal to zero. *Whether we are solving by factoring or by formula, quadratic equations must be in an "equals zero" form before we can proceed.* In this case, we can add -1 to both sides to get the desired form.

$$x^2 - 4x - 1 = 0$$

The expression cannot be factored using integers, so we will use the quadratic formula. Here $a = 1$, $b = -4$, and $c = -1$.

$$x = \frac{-(-4) \pm \sqrt{(-4)^2 - 4(1)(-1)}}{2(1)} = \frac{4 \pm \sqrt{16 + 4}}{2} = \frac{4 \pm \sqrt{20}}{2}$$

But $\sqrt{20}$ can be simplified, and the fraction will then reduce. To begin,

$$\sqrt{20} = \sqrt{4 \cdot 5} = \sqrt{4}\sqrt{5} = 2\sqrt{5}$$

So we have

$$x = \frac{4 \pm 2\sqrt{5}}{2} = \frac{2(2 \pm \sqrt{5})}{2} = 2 \pm \sqrt{5}$$

The *factor* of 2 in the numerator was eliminated by division by the *factor* of 2 in the denominator (since $2 \div 2 = 1$). The result is a simplified form. $\qquad \blacklozenge$

Quadratic expressions are examples of **polynomials.** A polynomial expression is a sum of terms (one or more) of the form ax^n, where a is a real number and n is a nonnegative integer. Examples of polynomials include $5x + 12$, $x^2 - 9x + 17$, $4x^3 - 2$, and x^6.

Rational Expressions (Fractions)

You will need to work with algebraic fractions in calculus. When the numerator and denominator expressions are polynomials, the fraction is called a **rational expression.** Such an expression is not defined when the denominator polynomial is equal to zero.

Fractions are *reduced* by factoring. Like factors can be eliminated by division.

EXAMPLE 11 Reduce $\dfrac{x^2 + 7x}{x^2 - x}$.

SOLUTION $\dfrac{x^2 + 7x}{x^2 - x} = \dfrac{x(x + 7)}{x(x - 1)} = \dfrac{x + 7}{x - 1} \qquad \blacklozenge$

Fractions can be *added* or *subtracted* by obtaining a common denominator.

EXAMPLE 12 Add $\dfrac{3}{x} + \dfrac{5}{x+1}$.

SOLUTION $\dfrac{3}{x} + \dfrac{5}{x+1} = \dfrac{3}{x} \cdot \dfrac{x+1}{x+1} + \dfrac{5}{x+1} \cdot \dfrac{x}{x}$

$$= \dfrac{3x+3}{x(x+1)} + \dfrac{5x}{x(x+1)} = \dfrac{8x+3}{x(x+1)} \qquad \blacklozenge$$

Fractions are *multiplied* by multiplying numerator by numerator and denominator by denominator. Reduce before you multiply.

EXAMPLE 13 Multiply $\dfrac{3}{x^2-1} \cdot \dfrac{x+1}{7}$.

SOLUTION $\dfrac{3}{x^2-1} \cdot \dfrac{x+1}{7} = \dfrac{3}{(x+1)(x-1)} \cdot \dfrac{(x+1)}{7} = \dfrac{3}{7x-7} \qquad \blacklozenge$

Division of fractions is accomplished by inverting the divisor fraction and changing the process to multiplication.

EXAMPLE 14 Divide $\dfrac{4}{x} \div \dfrac{3}{5x}$.

SOLUTION $\dfrac{4}{x} \div \dfrac{3}{5x} = \dfrac{4}{x} \cdot \dfrac{5x}{3} = \dfrac{4}{\cancel{x}} \cdot \dfrac{5 \cdot \cancel{x}}{3} = \dfrac{20}{3} \qquad \blacklozenge$

If the numerator or denominator of a fraction contains a fraction, then the entire expression is called a **complex fraction.** Such fractions can be simplified by determining the least common denominator of all the fractions within the complex fraction *and then* multiplying *each term* of the complex fraction by that common denominator. Consider

$$\dfrac{1 + \dfrac{1}{x}}{\dfrac{x}{y} - 2} \qquad \text{The fractions within are } \dfrac{1}{x} \text{ and } \dfrac{x}{y}.$$

The least common denominator is xy, so multiply each term by xy. The result is

$$\dfrac{xy \cdot 1 + xy \cdot \dfrac{1}{x}}{xy \cdot \dfrac{x}{y} - xy \cdot 2} \qquad \text{or} \qquad \dfrac{xy + y}{x^2 - 2xy} \qquad \blacklozenge$$

Equations containing fractions can be solved by multiplying both sides (all terms) by the least common denominator of the fractions present.

EXAMPLE 15 Solve the equation.

$$\dfrac{x+1}{x} + \dfrac{1}{3} = \dfrac{5}{x}$$

SOLUTION Multiply both sides (all terms) by the least common denominator, $3x$.

$$3x \cdot \frac{x+1}{x} + 3x \cdot \frac{1}{3} = 3x \cdot \frac{5}{x}$$

which simplifies to

$$3(x+1) + x = 3 \cdot 5$$
$$3x + 3 + x = 15$$
$$4x + 3 = 15$$
$$4x = 12$$
$$x = 3$$

The solution is 3, but check it in the original equation. (Any time both sides of an equation are multiplied by an unknown quantity, the "solution" produced may be *extraneous*; that is, it may not be a solution of the original equation.)   ♦

1.1 Exercises

In Exercises 1–10, write each inequality using interval notation.

1. $5 \le x \le 9$

2. $-1 \le x < 4$

3. $x \ge 6$

4. $3 < x \le 8$

5. $x < 0$

6. $x > 0$

7. $x > -2$

8. $t \le -4$

9. $t < \pi$

10. $t \ge \sqrt{2}$

In Exercises 11–20, write each interval as an inequality.

11. $[0, \infty)$

12. $(4, 19)$

13. $[1, 75]$

14. $(0, 100]$

15. $(-\infty, -2)$

16. $[7, \infty)$

17. $(-5, \infty)$

18. $(-\infty, 2)$

19. $[\pi, 7)$

20. $[-3, 7)$

Solve each linear inequality given in Exercises 21–28.

21. $5x - 1 \le 29$

22. $4x - 3 \ge 33$

23. $3x \ge 0$

24. $x - 2 < 0$

25. $1 - 8x \le 0$

26. $5 - 2x \ge 6$

27. $5(y + 1) < 13$

28. $4(t + 3) > 17$

W 29. Explain what is wrong with the notation $(3, \infty]$.

W 30. In terms of real numbers, what is the meaning of $(-\infty, \infty)$?

In Exercises 31–42, use properties of exponents to simplify the expression. Do not leave negative exponents in your answer. Assume the variables are never equal to zero.

31. $x^{12} \cdot x^5$

32. $t^4 t^{10}$

33. $(b^7)^3$

34. $(y^5)^8$

35. $\dfrac{x^{14}}{x^8}$

36. $\dfrac{t^{19}}{t^7}$

37. $2 \cdot x^0$

38. $(2x)^0$

39. x^{-3}

40. y^{-7}

41. $\dfrac{7}{x^{-2}}$

42. $\dfrac{x^{-4}}{2}$

Evaluate each expression in Exercises 43–56. Do not use a calculator.

43. 3^{-2}

44. 2^{-4}

45. $49^{1/2}$

46. $25^{1/2}$

47. $27^{1/3}$

48. $64^{1/3}$

49. $16^{-1/2}$

50. $8^{-1/3}$

51. $4^{3/2}$

52. $16^{3/2}$ **53.** $27^{2/3}$ **54.** $64^{2/3}$

55. $9^{-3/2}$ **56.** $8^{-2/3}$

In Exercises 57–62, use a calculator to evaluate each expression. Round the result to four decimal places.

57. $2^{3.5}$ **58.** $6^{1.9}$ **59.** $15^{2.6}$

60. $11^{4.2}$ **61.** $4.3^{.04}$ **62.** $12.9^{.01}$

Rationalize the denominator of each expression in Exercises 63–68.

63. $\dfrac{4}{\sqrt{3}}$ **64.** $\dfrac{7}{\sqrt{2}}$ **65.** $\dfrac{2}{\sqrt{5}}$

66. $\dfrac{3}{\sqrt{7}}$ **67.** $\dfrac{6}{\sqrt{3}}$ **68.** $\dfrac{12}{\sqrt{2}}$

Use factoring to solve each quadratic equation in Exercises 69–82.

69. $x^2 - 64 = 0$ **70.** $y^2 - 1 = 0$

71. $x^2 - 9x = 0$ **72.** $n^2 + 4n = 0$

73. $y^2 + 9y + 14 = 0$ **74.** $x^2 - x - 6 = 0$

75. $x^2 - 2x - 8 = 0$ **76.** $x^2 + 2x - 3 = 0$

77. $2t^2 - 6t - 20 = 0$ **78.** $2y^2 - 14y + 24 = 0$

79. $3x^2 - 10x - 8 = 0$ **80.** $2x^2 + 3x - 5 = 0$

81. $2x^2 + x = 6$ **82.** $3x^2 - 10x = -8$

Use the quadratic formula to solve each quadratic equation in Exercises 83–92.

83. $x^2 + 3x + 1 = 0$ **84.** $x^2 + 5x - 1 = 0$

85. $t^2 - 2t - 4 = 0$ **86.** $x^2 - 2x - 2 = 0$

87. $x^2 - 4x - 2 = 0$ **88.** $y^2 + 6y + 2 = 0$

89. $4y^2 + 10y - 5 = 0$ **90.** $3x^2 + 6x - 2 = 0$

91. $2x^2 + 6x = 3$ **92.** $2y^2 - 4y = 5$

Reduce each fraction in Exercises 93–100.

93. $\dfrac{x^2 - 9}{x + 3}$ **94.** $\dfrac{x + 1}{x^2 - 1}$

95. $\dfrac{x^2 - 4x}{x^2 - 16}$ **96.** $\dfrac{x^2 - 4}{x - 2}$

97. $\dfrac{2x - 10}{3x - 15}$ **98.** $\dfrac{2x^2 - 10x}{3x}$

99. $\dfrac{x}{x^2 + 5x}$ **100.** $\dfrac{x^2}{x^3}$

In Exercises 101–106, add or subtract the fractions as indicated.

101. $\dfrac{2}{x} + \dfrac{5}{3x}$ **102.** $\dfrac{1}{4x} + \dfrac{6}{x}$

103. $\dfrac{7}{x - 1} + \dfrac{1}{x}$ **104.** $\dfrac{3}{x - 4} + \dfrac{5}{x}$

105. $\dfrac{3}{2x} - \dfrac{5}{x + 2}$ **106.** $\dfrac{1}{x - 3} - \dfrac{2}{3x}$

In Exercises 107–114, multiply or divide as indicated.

107. $\dfrac{x + 1}{2x + 2} \cdot \dfrac{2x}{x - 1}$ **108.** $\dfrac{3}{7x} \cdot \dfrac{x^2}{4}$

109. $\dfrac{x}{x - 4} \div \dfrac{2}{5x - 20}$ **110.** $\dfrac{x}{x + 3} \div \dfrac{2x}{x + 3}$

111. $\dfrac{3x - 12}{3x} \cdot \dfrac{5x}{x^2 - 16}$ **112.** $\dfrac{5}{2x + 4} \cdot \dfrac{x^2 + 2x}{3x}$

113. $\dfrac{x^2 + x}{2} \div \dfrac{x^2 - 1}{8x}$ **114.** $\dfrac{x + 8}{8x} \div \dfrac{x + 2}{2x}$

In Exercises 115–118, simplify each complex fraction.

115. $\dfrac{\dfrac{x}{2} + x}{1 - \dfrac{x}{2}}$ **116.** $\dfrac{\dfrac{a}{b} + \dfrac{b}{a}}{7}$

117. $\dfrac{\dfrac{3}{x} + h}{x + \dfrac{1}{h}}$ **118.** $\dfrac{3x + \dfrac{2}{y}}{5 - \dfrac{1}{3}}$

In Exercises 119–122, solve each equation.

119. $\dfrac{x + 1}{3} + \dfrac{x}{2} = 7$ **120.** $\dfrac{x}{4} - 3 = \dfrac{x - 2}{2}$

121. $2 - \dfrac{1}{x} = \dfrac{x + 2}{x}$ **122.** $\dfrac{3}{x} + 4 = \dfrac{x + 1}{x}$

W 123. The quadratic formula is used to solve equations of the form $ax^2 + bx + c = 0$, where $a \neq 0$.

    (a) Considering $ax^2 + bx + c = 0$ as a quadratic equation, explain why a cannot be 0.

    (b) Looking at the quadratic formula, explain why a cannot be 0.

W 124. Consider the expression

$$\frac{5}{\sqrt{2}}$$

(a) Which part of the fraction contains an irrational number?

(b) Explain how you can change the form of the fraction so that the irrational number will no longer appear in that part of the fraction.

1.2 │ INTRODUCTION TO FUNCTIONS

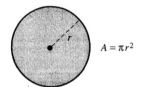

$A = \pi r^2$

You probably recall the geometry formula $A = \pi r^2$, which says that the area A of the region within a circle is equal to π times the square of the radius r.

The equation $A = \pi r^2$ defines a correspondence between two variables, r and A. For every nonnegative value of r there is a corresponding value of A. The formula $A = \pi r^2$ provides the rule of correspondence; it indicates how to compute the A value that corresponds to any particular r value supplied. The correspondence can be viewed as

$$r \xrightarrow{\ \pi r^2\ } A$$

$$0 \longrightarrow 0$$

$$1 \longrightarrow \pi \qquad \text{approximately } 3.14$$

$$2 \longrightarrow 4\pi \qquad \text{approximately } 12.56$$

$$.5 \longrightarrow .25\pi \qquad \text{approximately } .785$$

The area example, using $A = \pi r^2$, provides an introduction to the concept of **function.** Here the function is a rule that assigns one A value to each r value. (A is a function of r.) The equation $y = 2x + 1$ also defines a function; for every x value supplied there is one y value. (y is a function of x.)

$$x \xrightarrow{\ 2x + 1\ } y$$

$$0 \longrightarrow 1$$

$$3 \longrightarrow 7$$

$$.5 \longrightarrow 2$$

$$-2 \longrightarrow -3$$

In general,

Function

A **function** is a rule of correspondence by which each element of one set (X) is assigned to exactly one element of the other set (Y).

If the elements of the first set are values of x and the elements of the second set are values of y, then we have a correspondence between x and y:

$$x \longrightarrow y$$

The variable x is called the **independent variable,** and y is called the **dependent variable.**

The Swiss mathematician Leonhard Euler (1707–1783) suggested the use of function notation for certain applications, many of which arise in calculus. Functions are named by letters, with the letter f being the most popular.

If the function is named f and the independent variable is x, then the **function notation** $f(x)$ can be used instead of y. Thus, $y = 2x + 1$ becomes $f(x) = 2x + 1$. The $f(x)$ is read "f of x" or "f at x." It is the value of f at x. The relationship can be considered as follows:

$$x \xrightarrow{\ f\ } 2x + 1$$

$f(x) = 2x + 1$ is a rule that assigns to any number x the function value $2x + 1$. If $x = 3$, the function value is $2(3) + 1$, or 7. This can be seen as

$$3 \xrightarrow{\ f\ } 7 \quad \text{or as} \quad f(3) = 7$$

Alternatively, if $f(x) = 2x + 1$, then $f(3) = 2(3) + 1 = 7$.

Note

When $y = 2x + 1$ is written in function notation as $f(x) = 2x + 1$, the *function* is f, not $f(x)$. Keep in mind that $f(x)$ is the *value* that corresponds to a particular x. The equation $f(x) = 2x + 1$ *defines* or *gives* the function, but the function is f, not $f(x)$. At times we may choose to use an informal abbreviated statement such as "function $f(x) = \ldots$" rather than the more formal and complete statement "function *defined by* (*or given by*) $f(x) = \ldots$"

EXAMPLE 1 Let function f be defined by $f(x) = 5x^2 - 4x + 8$. Determine each value.

 (a) $f(0)$ **(b)** $f(2)$ **(c)** $f(-2)$ **(d)** $f(x + 1)$

SOLUTION **(a)** $f(0) = 5(0)^2 - 4(0) + 8 = 0 - 0 + 8 = 8$

(b) $f(2) = 5(2)^2 - 4(2) + 8 = 5 \cdot 4 - 8 + 8 = 20$

(c) $f(-2) = 5(-2)^2 - 4(-2) + 8 = 5 \cdot 4 + 8 + 8 = 36$

(d) $f(x + 1) = 5(x + 1)^2 - 4(x + 1) + 8$
$$= 5(x^2 + 2x + 1) - 4x - 4 + 8$$
$$= 5x^2 + 10x + 5 - 4x - 4 + 8$$
$$= 5x^2 + 6x + 9 \qquad \blacklozenge$$

EXAMPLE 2   Let function f be defined by $f(x) = 5x - 9$. Determine each value.

(a) $f(x + h)$ **(b)** $f(x + h) - f(x)$

SOLUTION   **(a)** To compute $f(x + h)$, replace x by $x + h$ in $f(x) = 5x - 9$.

$$f(x + h) = 5(x + h) - 9$$
$$= 5x + 5h - 9$$

(b) To compute $f(x + h) - f(x)$, subtract $f(x)$ from $f(x + h)$. We already know the value of $f(x + h)$ from part (a).

$$f(x + h) - f(x) = (5x + 5h - 9) - (5x - 9)$$
$$= 5x + 5h - 9 - 5x + 9$$
$$= 5h \qquad \blacklozenge$$

The letters used to name functions are often chosen to fit applications: R for revenue, C for cost, P for profit, v for velocity, etc.

EXAMPLE 3   **COST OF BOOKS**

APPLIED

If $C(x) = 12x$ gives the cost in dollars of x books, what is the cost of 5 books?

SOLUTION   Because $C(x) = 12x$ is the cost of x books, the cost of 5 books is $C(5)$.

$$C(5) = 12(5) = 60$$

We conclude that the cost of 5 books is \$60. $\qquad \blacklozenge$

EXAMPLE 4   **CONCENTRATION OF MEDICINE**

APPLIED

The concentration K of a particular medicine in the bloodstream t hours after it has been swallowed is given next. Find the concentration of the medicine after 2 hours.

$$K(t) = \frac{.03t}{1 + t^2} \qquad t \geq 0$$

SOLUTION   After 2 hours, the concentration is $K(2)$, namely,

$$K(2) = \frac{.03(2)}{1 + (2)^2} = \frac{.06}{5} = .012$$

After 2 hours the concentration of the medicine is .012 (or 1.2%). $\qquad \blacklozenge$

The set of all possible values of the independent variable x is called the **domain** of the function. (The corresponding set of all possible values of the dependent variable y is called the **range**.) For $f(x) = 2x + 1$, x can be any real number, because when any real number is used for x there will be a corresponding real number $f(x)$, or y. The domain of this function f includes all the real numbers.

If a function gives the distance traveled by a rocket for any time t, then t cannot be negative, because time cannot be negative. There will be further restriction on the domain of such a function, since the flight cannot go on indefinitely. If the flight lasts 20 seconds, then the domain will be t such that $0 \le t \le 20$, or [0, 20] using interval notation.

In addition to the nature of an application, there are other concerns that can restrict the domain of a function.

1. *Division by zero is not defined.* In view of this, any value of x that creates division by zero cannot be in the domain of a function. There would be no $f(x)$ corresponding to such an x.

2. *Square roots of negative numbers are not real numbers.* Thus, any value of x creating the square root of a negative number cannot be in the domain of a function. There would be no real $f(x)$ corresponding to such an x.

EXAMPLE 5   Find the domain of $f(x) = \dfrac{1}{x - 4}$.

SOLUTION   If $x = 4$, division by zero results. Since division by zero is not defined, no f value is produced if 4 is used for x. Thus, 4 is not in the domain of f. This means that the domain of f is all the real numbers except 4. We can write this simply as $x \ne 4$.   ◆

EXAMPLE 6   Find the domain of $g(x) = \sqrt{x - 1}$.

SOLUTION   If $x - 1$ is negative, the result is the square root of a negative number. Since the square root of a negative number is not a real number, no g value will be produced in such instances. This means that the domain is all x values for which $x - 1 \ge 0$. Solving this linear inequality yields $x \ge 1$. Thus, the domain of g is $x \ge 1$, or the interval [1, ∞).   ◆

A **zero** of a function f is any real number x for which $f(x) = 0$.

EXAMPLE 7   Find the zeros of each function.

   (a) $f(x) = 5x - 20$ **(b)** $f(x) = x^2 + 5x - 14$

SOLUTION   **(a)** Given $f(x) = 5x - 20$, it follows that $f(x) = 0$ when $5x - 20 = 0$. Solving $5x - 20 = 0$ yields $x = 4$. The (only) zero of this function is 4.

   (b) Given $f(x) = x^2 + 5x - 14$, it follows that $f(x) = 0$ when $x^2 + 5x - 14 = 0$. This quadratic equation can be solved by factoring.

$$x^2 + 5x - 14 = 0$$
$$(x + 7)(x - 2) = 0$$
$$x = -7, \; x = 2$$

We conclude that the zeros of this function are -7 and 2.   ◆

The section closes with a note on composition of functions. If f and g are functions, then the **composite functions** $f \circ g$ and $g \circ f$ are defined as follows:

$$(f \circ g)(x) = f(g(x)) \qquad\qquad (g \circ f)(x) = g(f(x))$$

The notation $f(g(x))$ is read "f of g of x." $f(g(x))$ is a function of a function.

EXAMPLE 8   If $f(x) = 5x - 2$ and $g(x) = x^2 + 1$, find   **(a)** $(f \circ g)(x)$ **(b)** $(g \circ f)(x)$.

SOLUTION   **(a)** $(f \circ g)(x) = f(g(x))$

$$= f(x^2 + 1)$$
$$= 5(x^2 + 1) - 2$$
$$= 5x^2 + 5 - 2$$
$$= 5x^2 + 3$$

(b) $(g \circ f)(x) = g(f(x))$

$$= g(5x - 2)$$
$$= (5x - 2)^2 + 1$$
$$= 25x^2 - 20x + 4 + 1$$
$$= 25x^2 - 20x + 5 \qquad\blacklozenge$$

1.2   Exercises

In Exercises 1–10, find $f(0)$, $f(1)$, $f(2)$, and $f(-1)$.

1. $f(x) = 5x + 7$
2. $f(x) = 1 - 5x$
3. $f(x) = x^2 + 3x + 1$
4. $f(x) = 3x^2 - 6x + 4$
5. $f(x) = -x^2 + 5$
6. $f(x) = x^2 - 9x$
7. $f(x) = 6$
8. $f(x) = -2$
9. $f(x) = \sqrt{x + 1}$
10. $f(x) = \sqrt{x + 2}$

In Exercises 11–16, find $f(x + 2)$ and $f(x - 3)$.

11. $f(x) = x^2 - 3x + 7$
12. $f(x) = x^2 + 10x$
13. $f(x) = 4x^2 + 9x$
14. $f(x) = 3x^2 - 5x + 2$
15. $f(x) = \dfrac{x + 5}{x - 7}$
16. $f(x) = \dfrac{x - 6}{x + 1}$

In Exercises 17–20, find $f(x + h)$ and $f(x + h) - f(x)$.

17. $f(x) = 3x - 4$
18. $f(x) = 2x - 1$
19. $f(x) = -9x + 2$
20. $f(x) = -5x + 3$

In Exercises 21–22, find $f(.4)$, $f(.25)$ and $f(-1.8)$.

21. $f(x) = 1.75x - 4.1x^3$
22. $f(x) = \sqrt{3x + 7.99}$

23. *(COST)* If $C(x) = 32x$ is the cost in dollars of producing x radios, what is the cost of making 8 radios?

24. *(REVENUE)* Suppose that the total revenue a business receives from the sale of x bolts is

$$R(x) = 3x + \frac{1000}{x} \quad \text{cents}$$

What is the total revenue from the sale of 250 bolts?

25. *(TEMPERATURE)* After x seconds, the temperature of a metal plate undergoing a finishing process will be

$$T(x) = -2x^2 + 64x + 65 \quad \text{degrees Fahrenheit}$$

(a) What is the temperature after 10 seconds?
(b) What is the temperature at the beginning?

26. *(ROCKET FLIGHT)* A toy rocket is launched vertically upward with initial velocity of 200 feet per second. Its distance s (in feet) from the ground at any time t (in seconds) is $s(t) = -16t^2 + 200t$. How high is the rocket after 5 seconds?

27. *(PROFIT)* A manufacturer of telephones determines that the profit from producing and selling x telephones is given by $P(x) = .01x^2 + 60x - 500$ dollars. What is the profit on the production and sale of 1000 telephones?

28. (*FENCE PERIMETER*) A rectangular fence is to be constructed so that its length is $3x + 2$ meters and its width is x meters. If P is the function that gives the perimeter, determine $P(x)$.

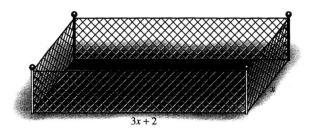

$3x + 2$

29. (*BACTERIA GROWTH*) A colony of bacteria is placed into a growth-inhibiting environment. The number of bacteria present at any time t (hours) is given by

$$n(t) = 1000 + 20t + t^2$$

(a) How many bacteria are present after 1 hour?
(b) How many bacteria are present after 10 hours?
(c) What is the value of t at the start, and how many bacteria are present then?

30. (*BALLOON VOLUME*) The volume of a spherical balloon can be expressed as a function of its radius.

$$V(r) = \frac{4}{3}\pi r^3$$

where V is the volume and r is the radius. How much air is in a spherical balloon that is blown up to have a radius of 10 inches? (Use 3.14 for π and round your result to the nearest cubic inch.)

31. (*MEDICINE DOSAGE*) One method used to calculate the children's dosage of medicines gives the child's dosage as a function of age.

$$D(c) = \frac{c + 1}{24} \cdot a$$

where a = the adult dosage, c = the child's age in years, and D = the child's dosage.
(a) Write the formula for $D(c)$, assuming the adult dosage of a particular drug is 400 milligrams.
(b) Compute $D(8)$, again assuming that the adult dosage is 400 milligrams.
W **(c)** Explain the meaning of $D(8)$ in part (b).

32. (*AIR POLLUTION*) A city's environmental advisors conclude that the amount of carbon monoxide in the air (in parts per million) is given by the function

$$f(x) = 1 + .003x^{1.5}$$

where x is the number of thousands of automobiles driven in the city.
(a) Determine the level of carbon monoxide when 100,000 cars are driven in the city.
(b) What is the level of carbon monoxide when 1,000,000 cars are driven in the city?

In Exercises 33–46, determine the domain of each function.

33. $f(x) = x^2 + 5$ **34.** $f(x) = 1 - 5x$

35. $f(x) = \sqrt{x - 2}$ **36.** $f(x) = \sqrt{x + 5}$

37. $f(x) = \dfrac{1}{x + 3}$ **38.** $g(x) = \sqrt{5x}$

39. $g(x) = \dfrac{1}{x(x - 1)}$ **40.** $f(x) = \dfrac{x}{x^2 + x}$

41. $f(x) = \sqrt{3x - 2}$ **42.** $g(x) = \sqrt{3 - 5x}$

43. $g(x) = (x + 1)^{1/2}$ **44.** $f(x) = x^3$

45. $g(x) = \dfrac{x}{x^2}$ **46.** $f(x) = \dfrac{x^3}{x}$

In Exercises 47–54, find the zeros of each function.

47. $f(x) = 2x + 6$ **48.** $f(x) = 3x - 2$

49. $f(x) = x^2 - 9$ **50.** $f(x) = 2x^2 - 50$

51. $f(x) = x^2 - 9x + 20$ **52.** $f(x) = x^2 - x - 12$

53. $f(x) = x^2 + 5x - 2$ **54.** $f(x) = x^2 - 7x + 3$

In Exercises 55–60, determine $(f \circ g)(x)$ and $(g \circ f)(x)$.

55. $f(x) = 3x + 1$, $g(x) = 7x$

56. $f(x) = 2x - 1$, $g(x) = x + 6$

57. $f(x) = x^2 + 2x$, $g(x) = x - 1$

58. $f(x) = x^2 - 7x + 10$, $g(x) = x + 4$

59. $f(x) = \dfrac{1}{x}$, $g(x) = 3x$

60. $f(x) = 2x$, $g(x) = \dfrac{7}{x}$

W 61. Do f and $f(x)$ mean the same thing? If not, explain the difference in meaning.

W 62. Consider the function $f(x) = x(2x + 3)$.

(a) Explain why the domain of the function is all the real numbers.

(b) Suppose now that x represents the length of one side of a rectangle and $2x + 3$ represents the length of another side of the rectangle. What is the domain of the function f in this application setting? Explain.

1.3 | *LINEAR FUNCTIONS*

In algebra, you obtained the graph of a *straight line* by determining points from the equation of the line. For example, given $y = 2x + 1$, you can let x be 0, 1, and 2 (or any other numbers) and then determine each corresponding y value from the equation. Once two or more points have been obtained, they can be plotted in the xy plane, and a straight line can be passed through them. See Figure 3.

x	$y = 2x + 1$	points
0	1	(0, 1)
1	3	(1, 3)
2	5	(2, 5)

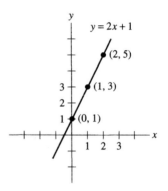

Figure 3

The graphs of equations such as $y = 3$ and $y = -1$ are *horizontal lines*. (See Figure 4.) In particular, the graph of $y = 0$ is the x axis. Note that the line $y = 3$ is horizontal because for every x value, the y value is 3. Points on the line include (0, 3), (1, 3), (2, 3), and so on.

Horizontal Lines

If c is any real number, then

$$y = c$$

is the equation of a horizontal line.

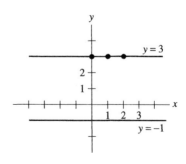

Figure 4 Horizontal lines

The graphs of equations such as $x = 4$ and $x = -3$ are *vertical lines*. (See Figure 5.) In particular, the graph of $x = 0$ is the y axis. Note that the line $x = 4$ is vertical because for every y value, the x value is 4. Points on the line include $(4, 0)$, $(4, 1)$, $(4, 2)$, and so on.

Vertical Lines

If c is any real number, then

$$x = c$$

is the equation of a vertical line.

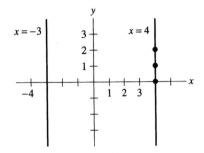

Figure 5 Vertical lines

The steepness or inclination or **slope** of a straight line can be formally defined and measured. In order to include the intuitive notion that the steeper the line, the greater the magnitude of its slope, the slope of a straight line is defined to be the change in y divided by the change in x between any two distinct points (x_1, y_1) and (x_2, y_2) on the line.

Slope of a Straight Line

$$\text{slope } (m) = \frac{y_2 - y_1}{x_2 - x_1} \qquad x_1 \neq x_2$$

where (x_1, y_1) and (x_2, y_2) are points on the line. See Figure 6.

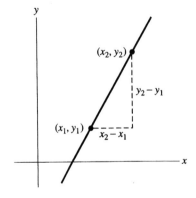

Figure 6 The slope of a line

In many instances, we will want to use the notation Δy (read as "delta y") for the change in y and Δx ("delta x") for the change in x. Using this notation, the definition of slope becomes

---

Slope (*m*) of a Line

$$m = \frac{\Delta y}{\Delta x} \qquad \Delta x \neq 0$$

EXAMPLE 1 Determine the slope of the line that passes through the given points.

(a) (2, 4) and (3, 1)   (b) (5, 2) and (8, 4)

SOLUTION (a) $m = \dfrac{\Delta y}{\Delta x} = \dfrac{y_2 - y_1}{x_2 - x_1} = \dfrac{1 - 4}{3 - 2} = \dfrac{-3}{1} = -3$

The slope of the line is -3. The graph is shown in Figure 7.

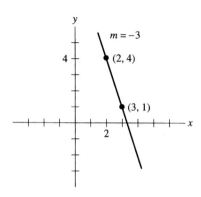

Figure 7

(b) $m = \dfrac{\Delta y}{\Delta x} = \dfrac{y_2 - y_1}{x_2 - x_1} = \dfrac{4 - 2}{8 - 5} = \dfrac{2}{3}$

The slope of the line is 2/3. The graph is shown in Figure 8.

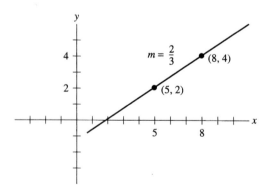

Figure 8   ◆

The example just completed demonstrates the following result.

Sign of the Slope

1. Lines with *negative slope* fall as they go from left to right.

2. Lines with *positive slope* rise as they go from left to right.

We will now digress briefly to present the concept of y intercept. Then we will be prepared to determine a special form for the equation of a straight line—a form involving both slope and y intercept.

The **y intercept** of a straight line is the point where the line crosses the y axis. (*Note*: Some mathematicians consider the y intercept to be merely the y coordinate of that point, since x is always 0 there.) The y intercept of the graph of any function is the point where the graph crosses the y axis. See Figure 9.

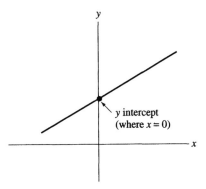

Figure 9 The y intercept

The y intercept of the line $y = 4x - 5$ is determined by letting $x = 0$ in the equation of the line. If $x = 0$, we have

$$y = 4(0) - 5 = 0 - 5 = -5$$

Thus, the y intercept of the line $y = 4x - 5$ is $(0, -5)$ or -5.

There are two very useful forms of the equation of a straight line. We can now proceed to determine both of them.

If a line with slope m passes through point (x_1, y_1) and if (x, y) can be any other point on the line, then by the definition of slope,

$$m = \frac{y - y_1}{x - x_1}$$

Multiplying both sides by $x - x_1$ yields the **point-slope form** of the equation.

Equation of a Straight Line

Point-Slope Form

$$y - y_1 = m(x - x_1)$$

$(x_1, y_1) =$ a point on the line $\qquad m =$ slope

Another form of the equation of a straight line can be obtained by considering

$y - y_1 = m(x - x_1)$ with (x_1, y_1) being the y intercept. If $(0, b)$ is used to represent the y intercept, then $x_1 = 0$, $y_1 = b$, and we have

$$y - b = m(x - 0)$$
$$y - b = mx \qquad \text{after multiplying}$$
$$y = mx + b \qquad \text{solving for } y$$

This is the **slope-intercept form** of the equation of a straight line.

Equation of a Straight Line

Slope-Intercept Form

$$y = mx + b$$

$m =$ slope $(0, b) = y$ intercept

EXAMPLE 2   Determine the slope and y intercept of each line.

(a) $y = 7x - 3$ **(b)** $y = -x + 6$ **(c)** $2y - 3x = 10$

SOLUTION   **(a)** The equation $y = 7x - 3$ is already in the form $y = mx + b$, from which we can see that $m = 7$ and $b = -3$. Thus, the slope is 7 and the y intercept is -3 or $(0, -3)$.

(b) The equation $y = -x + 6$ or $y = -1x + 6$ is in the form $y = mx + b$. Here $m = -1$ and $b = 6$. Thus, the slope is -1 and the y intercept is 6 or $(0, 6)$.

(c) The equation $2y - 3x = 10$ is not in the form $y = mx + b$. However, if we add $3x$ to both sides and then divide both sides by 2, we have the desired form, namely,

$$y = \frac{3}{2}x + 5$$

From this form it is clear that the slope is 3/2 and the y intercept is 5 or $(0, 5)$.   ◆

EXAMPLE 3   Determine the equation of the line having slope 2 and y intercept $(0, -6)$.

SOLUTION   Since the slope is 2, we know that $y = mx + b$ is $y = 2x + b$. Furthermore, given that the y intercept is $(0, -6)$, we know that $b = -6$. Thus, the equation of the line is

$$y = 2x - 6$$ ◆

The next two examples show two different ways of solving the same problem.

EXAMPLE 4   Determine the equation of the line having slope 5 and passing through the point $(3, 24)$. Use the slope-intercept form.

SOLUTION   Because the slope of the line is 5, we know that $y = mx + b$ is

$$y = 5x + b$$

Unlike in Example 3, we do not know the y intercept. But the value of b can be determined. Since the point $(3, 24)$ is on the line, it must be true that together $x = 3$ and $y = 24$ satisfy the equation of the line. Substituting 3 for x and 24 for y into the equation $y = 5x + b$ will determine b.

$$24 = 5(3) + b$$
$$24 = 15 + b$$
$$b = 9$$

Now we know the equation of the line, namely,

$$y = 5x + 9 \qquad \blacklozenge$$

EXAMPLE 5   Determine the equation of the line having slope 5 and passing through the point $(3, 24)$. Use the point-slope form.

SOLUTION   Using the given point $(3, 24)$ and slope 5, the point-slope form is

$$y - y_1 = m(x - x_1)$$
$$y - 24 = 5(x - 3)$$

Rather than leave this unfinished equation, we will manipulate it into the more function-like form $y = mx + b$. In steps,

$$y - 24 = 5x - 15$$
$$y = 5x + 9 \qquad \blacklozenge$$

APPLIED

EXAMPLE 6   *A SOCIAL WORKER'S STUDY*

A social worker has been studying data on child abuse that her colleagues have collected over a 3-year period. Based on the 3-year figures, she concludes that child abuse in her region is increasing linearly. Among the data is the fact that there were 230 known cases during the second year and 250 known cases during the third year.

(a) Determine the equation of the line ($y = mx + b$ form) that passes through the two data points $(2, 230)$ and $(3, 250)$.

(b) If child abuse continues to increase linearly according to the equation derived in part (a), how many cases will there be next year (the fourth year)?

SOLUTION   **(a)** The equation of the line is of the form $y = mx + b$. Slope m can be computed as follows:

$$m = \frac{\Delta y}{\Delta x} = \frac{250 - 230}{3 - 2} = \frac{20}{1} = 20$$

Because the slope is 20, the line will have the form

$$y = 20x + b$$

The value of b can be determined by using either point, (2, 230) or (3, 250), in the equation $y = 20x + b$, as in Example 4. Either way, the result is $b = 190$. Thus, the equation of the line is

$$y = 20x + 190$$

(b) To determine the number of cases in the fourth year (assuming that the pattern continues), let $x = 4$ in the equation $y = 20x + 190$.

$$y = 20(4) + 190 = 270$$

We conclude that there will be 270 cases next year if child abuse continues to increase linearly according to the derived equation. ◆

From the intuitive notion of slope as a measure of steepness or inclination, it follows that

Parallel Lines

1. If two distinct lines have the same slope, then they are *parallel*.

2. If two lines are *parallel*, then they have the same slope.

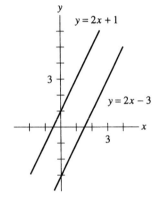

Figure 10 Parallel lines

The lines $y = 2x + 1$ and $y = 2x - 3$ are parallel; each line has a slope of 2. (See Figure 10.) By contrast, the lines $y = 3x + 2$ and $y = 2x + 1$ are not parallel; their slopes are not the same.

The section ends with a note about functions. We have been using equations of the form $y = mx + b$. Such equations define **linear functions.** Using function notation, we have $f(x) = mx + b$.

Linear Function f

$$f(x) = mx + b$$

$m =$ slope $b = y$ intercept

1.3 Exercises

In Exercises 1–8, obtain a few points and draw the graph of the given line.

1. $y = x + 2$ **2.** $y = x - 3$

3. $y = 3x - 2$ **4.** $y = 2x - 3$

5. $y = -x + 1$ **6.** $y = -x - 1$

7. $y = 5 - 2x$ **8.** $y = 1 - 3x$

In Exercises 9–14, determine the slope of the line that passes through the points and sketch a graph of the line.

9. (2, 4) and (6, 16)   **10.** (5, 2) and (7, 3)

11. (1, 5) and (3, 1)   **12.** (1, −3) and (4, 1)

13. (4, 9) and (7, 9)   **14.** (−2, 6) and (1, 11)

In Exercises 15–18, determine the slope of the line.

15.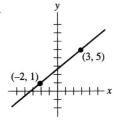

16.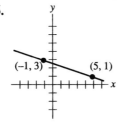

17.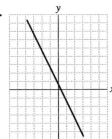

18.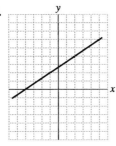

19. Determine the slope of the line that passes through the points (2.71, 8.64) and (1.85, 10.32).

20. Determine the slope of the line that passes through the points (5.23, −1.91) and (7.14, 2.36).

In Exercises 21–30, determine the slope and y intercept of each line.

21. $y = 5x + 3$ **22.** $y = 4x - 1$

23. $y = x - 9$ **24.** $y = -x + 2$

25. $y = 1 - 7x$ **26.** $y = 4 + 3x$

27. $y = 3$ **28.** $y = -2$

29. $y - 8x = 6$ **30.** $y + 2x = 7$

In Exercises 31–40, determine the equation of the line having the given slope and y intercept.

31. $m = -2$, (0, 4)   **32.** $m = 1$, (0, 0)

33. $m = 5$, (0, −3)   **34.** $m = -1$, (0, −2)

35. $m = 0$, (0, −1)   **36.** $m = 0$, (0, 5)

37. $m = \frac{2}{3}$, $\left(0, \frac{1}{2}\right)$ **38.** $m = -\frac{3}{7}$, $\left(0, \frac{1}{4}\right)$

39. $m = 1.8$, (0, 2.4)   **40.** $m = 5.3$, (0, 1.7)

In Exercises 41–46, determine the equation of the line having the given slope and passing through the given point.

41. $m = 3$, (1, 8)   **42.** $m = 4$, (2, 3)

43. $m = -2$, (5, −3)   **44.** $m = -3$, (−1, 4)

45. $m = -1$, (−3, 0)   **46.** $m = 9$, (0, −8)

47. Determine the equation of the line that is parallel to the line $y = 3x + 5$ and passes through the point (2, −4).

48. (*CELSIUS/FAHRENHEIT*) There is a linear relationship between temperature given in Celsius (°C) and in Fahrenheit (°F). Water freezes at 0°C or 32°F. Water boils at 100°C or 212°F. Consider the points (0, 32) and (100, 212), which are of the form (C, F).
(a) Using the points given, determine the slope.
(b) Determine the F intercept.
(c) Write the equation of the line.

49. (*ENTOMOLOGY*) Entomologists have found that the number of chirps per minute (y) made by a cricket depends on the temperature (x) in degrees Fahrenheit and that the relationship is linear. Consider the points (40, 0) and (60, 80).

W (a) Explain the meaning of the point (60, 80) in this setting.

(b) Find the equation of the line that describes the relationship.

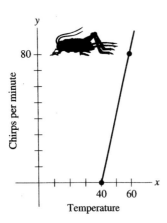

50. (**WATER TEMPERATURE**) Suppose the temperature of the water in a swimming pool between 1 p.m. and 6 p.m. is a linear function of time. At 1 p.m. the water is 70°F, and at 6 p.m. the water is 85°F. Let t be the time in hours and y be the temperature.

(a) Using the information given, list the two known points of the form (t, y). Let $t = 0$ be 1 p.m.

(b) Find the equation of the line (of form $y = mt + b$) on which the two points lie.

(c) Use the equation from part (b) to determine the water temperature at 2 p.m.

(d) At what time was the water temperature 80°?

51. (**DEPRECIATION**) Straight-line (linear) depreciation of equipment purchased by businesses is described by the equation

$$y = C - \frac{C - S}{n}t$$

where t is the time in years, y is the value in dollars of the asset after t years, n is the useful life in years, C is the original cost in dollars, and S is the scrap (resale) value in dollars of the asset.

(a) Your company purchases a machine for $3400. If the scrap value is $400 and the useful life is 15 years, determine the linear equation of form $y = mt + b$ that describes the machine's value at any time.

(b) What will be the value of the machine after 8 years?

52. (**TAXI FARE**) The taxi fare is $1.00, plus 50¢ per quarter mile. If F is the taxi fare and x is the number of quarter miles, find the linear equation that describes such taxi fares.

53. (**APPRECIATION**) A jewelry store guarantees its customers that the value of all diamonds bought from them will appreciate linearly and that purchasers can trade them in at any time at the appreciated value. On a $2000 diamond, they guarantee an appreciation of $100 per year.

W (a) Consider $y = mx + b$. If x is the number of years since purchase and b is the original purchase price, what do m and y represent?

(b) Using the known m and b, write the linear equation that describes this situation.

(c) Use the linear equation determined in part (b) to find the guaranteed value of the diamond after 7 years.

(d) Use the linear equation obtained in part (b) to determine in how many years the guaranteed value of the diamond will be $3200.

W 54. (a) Find two points such that the slope of the line through them is undefined.

(b) Explain why the slope is undefined.

(c) What word would you use to describe the line through the two points [from part (a)]?

W 55. At the beginning of the section, it is stated that "to obtain the graph of $y = 2x + 1$, you can let x be 0, 1, and 2 (or other numbers) and then determine each corresponding y value." Explain why you can use *any real number* for x in this equation. Include the word "domain" in your explanation.

W 56. (**UV INDEX**) On a June morning, the UV (ultraviolet ray) index in Naples, Florida, was as follows:

time (x)	UV index (y)
6	0
7	.5
8	1
9	2
10	4

Is this relationship between the UV index and time *linear*?
Explain.

W 57. *(FUND GROWTH)* A utility mutual fund and a growth
mutual fund have both been operating for 2 years. The
tables at the right show the share price y in dollars at time t
in years for functions u and g. Which function, u or g, is
more nearly linear? Explain.

utility "*u*"			growth "*g*"	
t	*y*		*t*	*y*
0	10.00		0	10.00
1	10.70		1	11.65
2	11.50		2	12.80

1.4 | *GRAPHS OF FUNCTIONS*

Figure 11
René Descartes (1596–1650)

In Section 1.3 the graph of a linear function was obtained by determining points from the
equation. The points were then plotted, and a straight line was passed through them. This
natural union of algebra and geometry that provides a geometric image of an algebraic
equation was developed by the French mathematician René Descartes. His work on such
"analytic geometry" was published in 1637 and helped lead to the development of calculus
less than 50 years later. The rectangular coordinate system used for plotting points is also
known as the *Cartesian* coordinate system—named for Descartes.

When function notation is used, the equation $y = 2x + 1$ is written $f(x) = 2x + 1$.
The $f(x)$ means the same as y, so for graphing purposes the points (x, y) become $(x, f(x))$,
and $f(x)$ is the second coordinate when the first coordinate is x.

Consider the graph shown in Figure 12. Can you see from the graph that $f(4) = 7$; that
is, when $x = 4$, the value of $f(x)$ is 7? [This follows from the fact that the point $(4, 7)$ is on
the graph of f.] Also note that $f(0) = 3$; that is, when $x = 0$, the value of y is 3. Finally, is
it clear that $f(-5) = 0$?

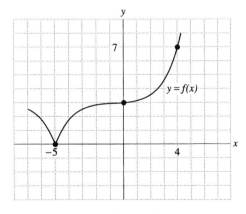

Figure 12

EXAMPLE 1   **TOWN POPULATION GROWTH**

The graph in Figure 13 shows the population of a small town over a 20-year period.

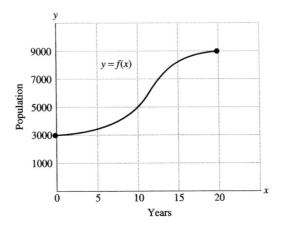

Figure 13

(a) Determine $f(10)$.   **(b)** Is $f(5) > f(15)$?

(c) Compute $f(20) - f(0)$. What does the result represent?

SOLUTION   **(a)** Since $f(10)$ is the y value when $x = 10$, look for the y coordinate where $x = 10$. Clearly, when $x = 10$, $y = 5000$. That is, $f(10) = 5000$.

(b) From the graph, it appears that $f(5)$ is between 3000 and 4000, whereas $f(15)$ is more than 7000. Thus, $f(5)$ is not greater than $f(15)$. Alternatively, we can just look at the graph briefly to see that the curve is higher at $x = 15$ than it is at $x = 5$, which means that $f(15) > f(5)$.

(c) $f(20) - f(0) = 9000 - 3000 = 6000$, which is the increase in population during the 20-year period.   ◆

The remainder of this section offers a variety of graphs of functions. Keep in mind that the **graph of a function** f is the set of all points $(x, f(x))$ satisfying the equation that defines the function. Ordinarily, we obtain only a few points of a graph from the equation. Then we draw the curve or line (the graph) through those points.

The definition of a function says that for *every* x there is *one* y. The graphical interpretation of this idea is considered in the **vertical line test:** If a vertical line crosses a curve in two or more places, then the curve is not the graph of a function. (After all, in that case there would be two or more y values corresponding to a particular x. See Figure 14.)

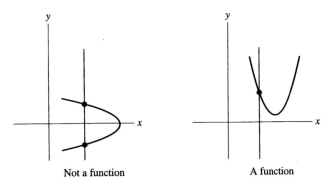

Not a function   A function

Figure 14 Vertical line test

Presented next are some special graphs—graphs of basic functions that will appear throughout the study of calculus.

Square Function

$$f(x) = x^2$$

The domain of the square function consists of all the real numbers. Using 0, 1, −1, 2, −2, etc. for x will yield some points. A smooth curve can then be passed through the points. The graph of $f(x) = x^2$ is an example of a *parabola*. See Figure 15.

some points

x	y
0	0
±1	1
±2	4
±3	9

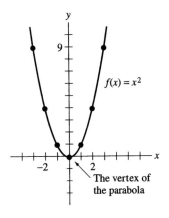

$f(x) = x^2$

The vertex of the parabola

Figure 15

The **square function** is one special example of a **quadratic function.** The graph of any quadratic function is a parabola.

Quadratic Functions

$$f(x) = ax^2 + bx + c \qquad a \neq 0$$

The x coordinate of the *vertex* of
$f(x) = ax^2 + bx + c$ is

$$x = -\frac{b}{2a}$$

The vertex is the highest or lowest point on
the graph of a quadratic function. It is the
point where the graph turns around.

The statement about the x coordinate of the vertex can be proved easily using the calculus
presented in Chapter 4. Furthermore, we can show that the parabola opens upward when
$a > 0$ and downward when $a < 0$.

An easy way to graph a quadratic function is to use the vertex and at least two points on
each side of it.

EXAMPLE 2 Sketch the graph of $f(x) = x^2 - 6x + 7$.

SOLUTION Clearly f is a quadratic function. Here $a = 1$ and $b = -6$. Thus, the x coordinate of the
vertex is

$$x = -\frac{b}{2a} = -\frac{-6}{2(1)} = 3$$

Since $f(3) = (3)^2 - 6(3) + 7 = -2$, the vertex is $(3, -2)$. By letting x be 1, 2, 4, and 5,
we obtain two points on each side of the vertex, namely, $(1, 2)$, $(2, -1)$, $(4, -1)$, and
$(5, 2)$. The graph is shown in Figure 16. ◆

Next, consider the **square root function.**

Square Root Function

$$f(x) = \sqrt{x}$$

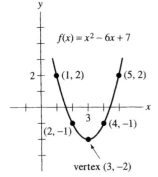

Figure 16

The domain of the square root function consists of all the nonnegative real numbers
(that is, $x \geq 0$). Because the square root of a negative number is not a real number, no
negative numbers can have corresponding functional values. Points and the graph of
$f(x) = \sqrt{x}$ are shown in Figure 17.

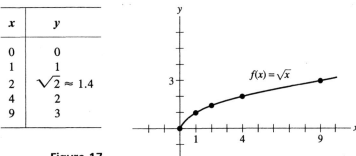

x	y
0	0
1	1
2	$\sqrt{2} \approx 1.4$
4	2
9	3

Figure 17

The numbers 0, 1, 4, and 9 were chosen for x because they are perfect squares. But, we could have chosen such numbers as 3, 5, 6, 7, and 8 and approximated each square root (as was done with 2). The symbol $\approx$ is used to mean *approximately equal to*.

$\approx$ means "approximately equal to."

The **cube function** is presented next.

Cube Function

$$f(x) = x^3$$

The domain of the cube function consists of all the real numbers. See Figure 18.

x	y
0	0
1	1
2	8
-1	-1
-2	-8

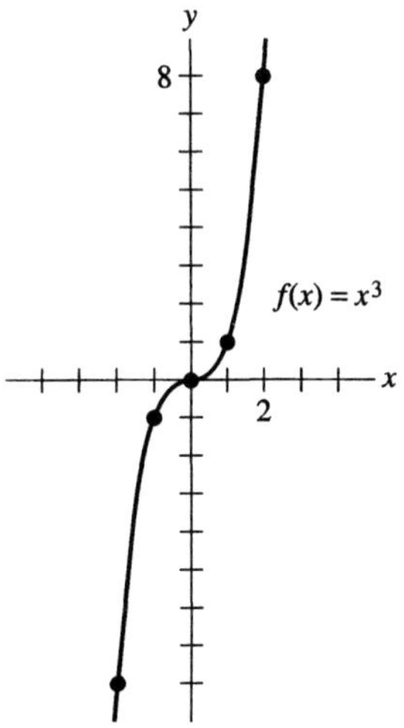

$f(x) = x^3$

Figure 18

The **reciprocal function** is presented next. The graph offers an example of a curve called a *hyperbola*.

Reciprocal Function

$$f(x) = \frac{1}{x}$$

The domain consists of all the real numbers except 0, because if x were 0, division by zero would occur. The choice of numbers near 0 (that is, near the number for which f is not defined) leads to particularly helpful points. See Figure 19.

x	y
1	1
2	1/2
3	1/3
1/2	2
1/3	3

x	y
-1	-1
-2	$-1/2$
-3	$-1/3$
$-1/2$	-2
$-1/3$	-3

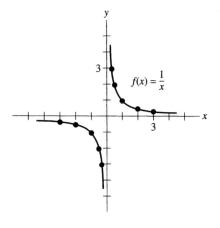

Figure 19

Recall the concept of **absolute value,** denoted | |. The absolute value of any real number is the magnitude of the number. Thus, $|+7| = 7$, $|-7| = 7$, and $|0| = 0$. The absolute value function is presented next, and its graph is shown in Figure 20.

Absolute Value Function

$$f(x) = |x|$$

The domain of the absolute value function consists of all the real numbers.

x	y
0	0
1	1
2	2
3	3

x	y
−1	1
−2	2
−3	3

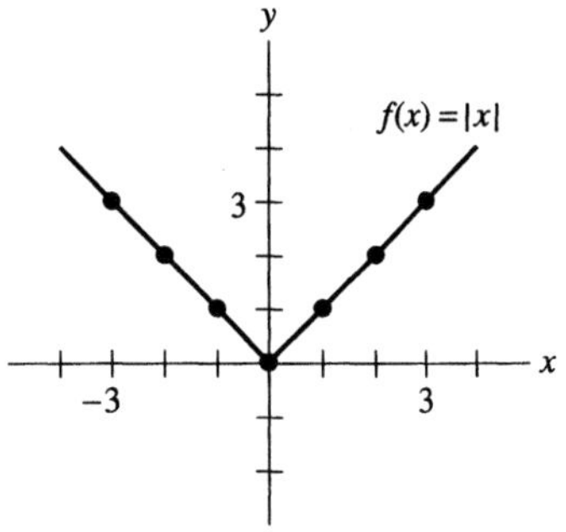

Figure 20 The absolute value function

Absolute value can be defined algebraically in a way that leads naturally to the use of a **two-piece function** or **two-part function.** Such **piecewise functions** will be needed for the study of limits and continuity in Chapter 2. We can say that

$$|x| = x \qquad \text{when } x \geq 0$$

$$|x| = -x \quad \text{when } x < 0$$

The second statement above says that when x is a negative number (that is, when $x < 0$), $|x|$ will be the opposite signed number. For example, if $x = -6$, then $|x| = -x = -(-6) = 6$. Thus, we have the following formal definition of $|x|$.

$$|x| = \begin{cases} x & x \geq 0 \\ -x & x < 0 \end{cases}$$

To continue, let us graph the two-part function

$$f(x) = \begin{cases} x & x \geq 0 \\ -x & x < 0 \end{cases}$$

The notation of this function is understood to mean

$$f(x) = x \qquad \text{when } x \geq 0$$
$$f(x) = -x \quad \text{when } x < 0$$

When using x values that are nonnegative, $f(x)$ is computed using $f(x) = x$. When using x values that are negative, $f(x)$ is computed using $f(x) = -x$. Some points and the graph are shown in Figure 21.

x	$f(x)$
1	1
2	2
3	3
0	0

x	$f(x)$
-1	1
-2	2
-3	3

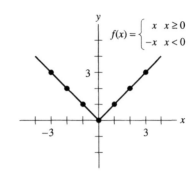

$$f(x) = \begin{cases} x & x \geq 0 \\ -x & x < 0 \end{cases}$$

Figure 21

EXAMPLE 3 Sketch the graph of

$$f(x) = \begin{cases} x + 3 & x < 0 \\ 4 & 0 \leq x \leq 7 \end{cases}$$

SOLUTION Some points and the graph are shown in Figure 22.

x	$f(x) = x + 3$
-1	2
-2	1
-3	0
-4	-1

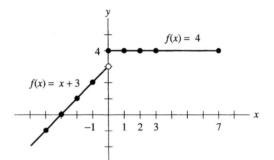

x	$f(x) = 4$
0	4
1	4
2	4
3	4

Figure 22

♦

    The small circle at (0, 3) indicates that the left portion of the graph does not include (0, 3). After all, when $x = 0$, $f(x) = 4$. Accordingly, the right portion begins at (0, 4), as shown by the solid dot at (0, 4). The graph ends at (7, 4) because f is not defined for x beyond 7. For example, $f(8)$ is not defined.

EXAMPLE 4 Sketch the graph of

$$f(x) = \begin{cases} x^2 & x \leq 0 \\ x + 1 & x > 0 \end{cases}$$

SOLUTION Figure 23 shows some points and the graph of the function. The solid dot at $(0, 0)$ indicates that $(0, 0)$ is on the graph. The small circle at $(0, 1)$ indicates that the right portion of the graph does not include the point $(0, 1)$.

x	$f(x) = x^2$
0	0
-1	1
-2	4

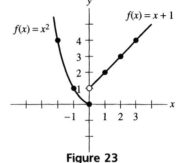

Figure 23

x	$f(x) = x + 1$
1	2
2	3
3	4

♦

APPLIED

EXAMPLE 5 *PAYING VOLUNTEERS FOR AN EXPERIMENT*

A psychologist needs volunteers for an experiment. She offers to pay $8 per hour for volunteers who work up to 5 hours. Those who work more than 5 hours are paid $10 per hour for the additional hours. Let x represent the number of hours worked, and write the function V that describes a volunteer's pay.

SOLUTION For x between 0 and 5, the pay is $8 per hour times the number of hours, x.

$$V(x) = 8x \qquad \text{for } 0 \le x \le 5$$

When x is greater than 5, the person makes $8 per hour for 5 hours ($40 total) plus $10 per hour for each hour above the 5 hours. The number of hours above 5 hours is $x - 5$ hours, so the earnings would be $40 + 10(x - 5)$ dollars for those who work more than 5 hours. The expression simplifies, and we have

$$V(x) = 10x - 10 \qquad \text{for } x > 5$$

The two parts can be combined to give the entire definition of V.

$$V(x) = \begin{cases} 8x & 0 \le x \le 5 \\ 10x - 10 & x > 5 \end{cases}$$

♦

Translation and Reflection (optional)

Consider that $x^2 + 3$ is 3 more than x^2. It follows that the y values of $y = x^2 + 3$ will be 3 more than the y values of $y = x^2$—for the same x. In turn, the graph of $y = x^2 + 3$ will be the same shape as, *but 3 units above,* the graph of $y = x^2$. See Figure 24. Similarly, the graph of $y = x^2 - 2$ will be the same shape as, *but 2 units below,* the graph of $y = x^2$. See Figure 25.

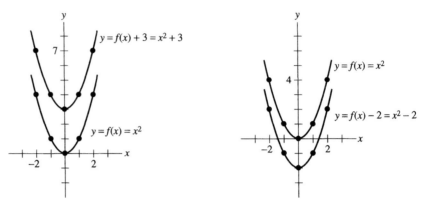

Figure 24   **Figure 25**

An awareness of such *vertical translations* (up or down) of familiar graphs can be helpful in drawing other graphs. For example, if you know the graph of $y = x^2$, then graphing $y = x^2 + 3$ is an easy matter. Simply draw the graph of $y = x^2$ and shift it up 3 units, point for point. Similarly, the graph of $y = x^2 - 2$ can be drawn by shifting the graph of $y = x^2$ down 2 units. In general, for $c > 0$, the graph of $y = f(x) + c$ is c units above the graph of $y = f(x)$ and the graph of $y = f(x) - c$ is c units below the graph of $y = f(x)$.

The concept of *reflection* is presented next. To compare the graphs of $y = x^2$ and $y = -x^2$, note first that points for the graph of $y = -x^2$ can be obtained from points for the graph of $y = x^2$ simply by changing the sign of the y coordinates. (After all, $-x^2$ means $-1 \cdot x^2$.)

x	$y = x^2$	$y = -x^2$
0	0	0
± 1	1	-1
± 2	4	-4
± 3	9	-9

The graphs are shown in Figure 26.

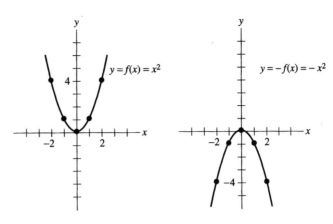

Figure 26

The sign change created by placing a minus in front of the x^2 resulted in a *reflection* of the graph across the x axis. In general, the graph of $y = -f(x)$ is a reflection across the x axis of the graph of $y = f(x)$.

1.4 Exercises

1. Answer the following questions based on the graph shown below.

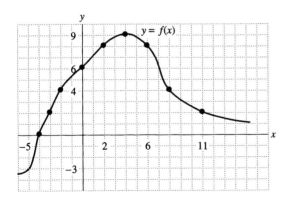

   (a) What is y when $x = 6$?
   (b) What is $f(0)$?
   (c) Determine x for which $f(x) = 0$.
   (d) Determine $f(11)$.
   (e) Find x for which $f(x) = 8$.

2. Based on the graph shown in Exercise 1, label each of the following statements as true or false.
   (a) $f(2) = 5$ (b) $f(-1) = 8$
   (c) $f(4) = 9$ (d) $f(8) = 4$
   (e) $f(-5) > 0$ (f) $f(-3) > 0$
   (g) $f(13) = 5$ (h) $f(1) > f(3)$
   (i) $f(10) < f(-1)$ (j) $f(0) \geq 6$

3. **(DISTANCE)** Answer the questions based on the following graph of a 1-hour boat ride.

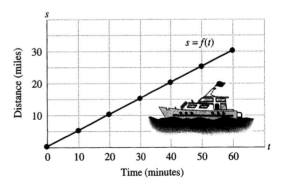

(a) Determine $s(60)$.

(b) How many miles were traveled in the first 10 minutes?

(c) For what t is $s(t) = 20$?

(d) Determine m and b in the linear function given by $s(t) = mt + b$.

(e) What is the domain of function s?

4. Answer the questions based on the graph shown.

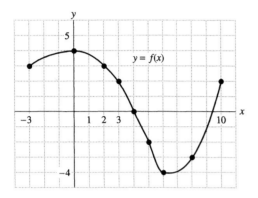

(a) What is the domain of f?

(b) What is the value of $f(5)$?

(c) For what x is $f(x) = 3$?

(d) What is the largest value that $f(x)$ can be?

(e) What is the smallest value that $f(x)$ can be?

5. *(MEMORIZATION)* Psychologists have conducted studies on the retention of memorized material. In the graph shown below, functions N and S both give the amount *forgotten* as a function of time t over a 2-week period after memorization has been completed. N represents nonsense words, and S represents the words of a song.

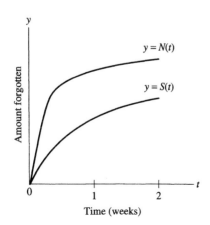

(a) For what value of t is $N(t) = S(t)$?

(b) Complete the following sentence. $N(t) > S(t)$ for t _____.

W **(c)** Explain in nonmathematical words the meaning of the completed sentence in part (b).

6. *(STOCK MARKET)* Function J (graphed below) describes the Dow Jones Industrial Average (DJIA) during a day's trading session (10 a.m. to 4 p.m.). Here x is the time on a 24-hour clock: 1 p.m. = 13, 2 p.m. = 14, 3 p.m. = 15, and 4 p.m. = 16. Consider the DJIA for the day.

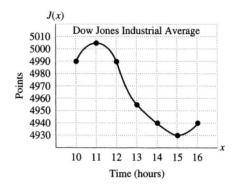

(a) Determine $J(16)$.

(b) Determine x for which $J(x) = 4955$.

(c) At what time did $J(x)$ reach its minimum value?

(d) What was the amount of gain or loss in the DJIA?

7. *(CITY POPULATION)* A sociologist has put together the graphs of two functions (shown below) that show the population growth in two different cities over a period of 30 years. Function n describes the growth in a selected northeastern U.S. city, and function w describes the growth in a particular western U.S. city.

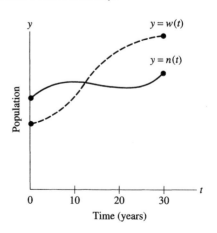

(a) Which city had the greater initial population?

W **(b)** Is it true that $w(15) > n(15)$? Explain.

W **(c)** Is it true that $n(5) < w(5)$? Explain.

8. Refer to the figure and complete the following statements by using inequalities involving x.

    (a) $f(x) > g(x)$ when _____.

    (b) $f(x) < g(x)$ when _____.

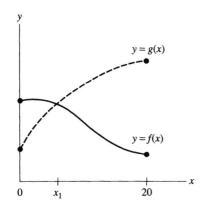

In Exercises 9–14, determine which curves are graphs of functions.

9.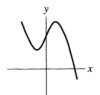

10.

11.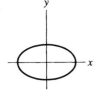

12.

13.

14.

In Exercises 15–22, sketch the graph of the given quadratic function.

15. $f(x) = x^2 - 4x + 5$

16. $f(x) = x^2 - 6x + 10$

17. $f(x) = x^2 + 6x + 6$

18. $f(x) = x^2 + 8x + 10$

19. $y = -x^2 + 2x$

20. $y = -x^2 - 4x - 6$

21. $y = 2x^2 - 8x + 5$

22. $y = 2x^2 - 4x - 1$

In Exercises 23–32, sketch the graph of each two-piece function.

23. $f(x) = \begin{cases} x^2 & x \geq 0 \\ 2 & x < 0 \end{cases}$

24. $f(x) = \begin{cases} x & x \geq 2 \\ -1 & x < 2 \end{cases}$

25. $f(x) = \begin{cases} \sqrt{x} & x \geq 0 \\ x & x < 0 \end{cases}$

26. $f(x) = \begin{cases} \sqrt{x} & x > 0 \\ x^3 & x \leq 0 \end{cases}$

27. $f(x) = \begin{cases} \dfrac{1}{x} & x > 0 \\ 1 & x \leq 0 \end{cases}$

28. $f(x) = \begin{cases} 3 & x > 0 \\ |x| & x \leq 0 \end{cases}$

29. $f(x) = \begin{cases} 3 & x \geq 1 \\ -2 & x < 1 \end{cases}$

30. $f(x) = \begin{cases} -x & x \geq 0 \\ x & x < 0 \end{cases}$

31. **(WORKER'S PAY)** Workers at a fast-food restaurant earn $5 per hour for the first 40 hours in a week and then $7.50 per hour for additional hours. Let x be the number of hours worked in a week, and write the two-piece function W that describes a worker's pay.

32. **(TRAIN SPEED)** A passenger train travels continuously for 10 hours. For the first 4 hours, the train travels at an average speed of 70 miles per hour. The remainder of the trip is at night, and the train goes an average of 58 miles per hour. Use t for time (in hours) and A for average speed (in miles per hour). Write the two-part function A that describes the train's average speed during the 10-hour ride.

W **33.** Explain the meaning of $f(2) = 8$. You may use x and y in your explanation, but do not use f or $f(x)$.

W **34.** Suppose that $f(x_1) > f(x_2)$. Does this mean that $x_1 > x_2$? Explain.

W **35.** **(INSECT POPULATION)** Let function P give the insect population at any time t in months. Let $t = 0$ represent *now*. Explain the meaning of the expression $P(6) - P(0)$ in this setting.

W **36.** Consider the graph that follows. Is this the graph of a function? Explain.

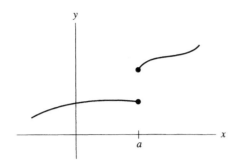

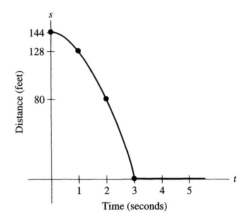

W 37. (COURSE LOAD) Consider the function $y = N(t)$, which gives the number of courses that a student is taking this semester. A semester is 15 weeks.

   (a) Describe the graph, assuming the student does not drop or add any courses during the semester.

   (b) Describe the graph, assuming the student drops a course after 4 weeks.

   (c) Describe the graph, assuming the student adds a course after 1 week and then drops a course after 3 weeks.

38. (FALLING OBJECT) A ball dropped from a height of 144 feet falls according to

$$s = -16t^2 + 144$$

where s is its distance above the ground (in feet) and t is the time (in seconds). After 3 seconds, it hits the mud below. (See the following graph.)

Create a two-piece function that defines s for the first 5 seconds after the ball has been dropped.

Use translations and reflections of the basic graphs $y = x^2$, $y = \sqrt{x}$, $y = x^3$, $y = |x|$, and $y = 1/x$ to sketch the graph of each function given in Exercises 39–46.

39. $y = \sqrt{x} + 2$ **40.** $y = \sqrt{x} - 1$

41. $y = -\dfrac{1}{x}$ **42.** $y = \dfrac{1}{x} + 1$

43. $y = x^2 - 3$ **44.** $y = x^3 + 1$

45. $y = -|x|$ **46.** $y = |x| - 3$

 TECHNOLOGY *E X E R C I S E S*

Note Your graphing utility has a standard *window* or *range* setting, which is usually the interval $[-10,10]$ for x and $[-10,10]$ for y. However, you can change the interval when needed or when called for in the exercises.

1. Study the graph of $f(x) = x^3 + 5x^2 + 3x - 5$ on the interval $[-10,10]$.

   (a) How many zeros does f have in the interval? (The concept of a *zero* of a function was introduced in Section 1.2, page 15.)

   (b) To the nearest integer, what is the smallest zero of f in the interval?

2. Study the graph of $f(x) = x^3 + 3x^2 - x - 10$ on the interval $[-10,10]$.

   (a) How many zeros does f have in the interval?

   (b) How many positive zeros does f have in the interval?

(c) How many negative zeros does f have in the interval?

3. Study the graph of $f(x) = 2x^3 - x^2 + 5x + 1$ on the interval $[-5, 5]$.

   (a) How many zeros of f are found between 0 and 1?

   (b) Use **Zoom In** and **Trace** as needed to estimate to the nearest tenth the negative zero of f.

4. Graph the function. Then zoom and trace as needed to determine for what values of x the given function is positive.

$$f(x) = 1.98 - x^{1.5}$$

5. For what values of x is the given function negative?

$$f(x) = x^3 + x^2 - 6x$$

6. To the nearest tenth, determine all values of x for which $f(x) = g(x)$, given that $f(x) = x^2 - 4x + 5$ and $g(x) = x + 2$. To accomplish this, graph both functions together using the standard range. Note the points of intersection, and then zoom in on each point of intersection separately.

7. To the nearest tenth, determine all values of x for which $f(x) = g(x)$, given that $f(x) = x - 1.7\sqrt{x}$ and $g(x) = 4.8 - .6x$.

8. Graph $y = x^3 - 4x^2 + 3x - 5$. To the nearest tenth, what is the smallest value of y (lowest that the graph reaches) for x values chosen in the interval $[0, 4]$?

9. Graph $y = x^3 + x^2 - 8x - 9.2$. To the nearest tenth, what is the largest value of y (highest that the graph reaches) for x values chosen in $[-5, 2]$?

Note   **ABS** is used to graph absolute value functions just as the $\sqrt{}$ key is used to graph square root functions. Use **ABS** in Exercises 10 and 11.

10. Graph $f(x) = |2x|$ and $g(x) = |x - 3.2|$ and determine, to the nearest tenth, the x values for which $f(x) = g(x)$.

11. Graph $f(x) = 5 - |x|$ and $g(x) = |1.3x|$ and determine, to the nearest tenth, the x values for which $f(x) = g(x)$.

Note   Software known as a *computer algebra system* can be used to display graphs, perform numerical calculation, accomplish algebraic manipulation, and carry out calculus operations. *Mathematica* and *Maple* are two popular systems. The graph of $y = x^2$ for x between -2 and 2 can be obtained by using the following commands.

Mathematica:	`Plot [x^2, {x, -2, 2}]`
Maple:	`plot (x^2, x = -2..2);`

If you have access to such a system, graph $y = \sqrt{x}$, $y = x^3$, $y = 1/x$, and $y = |x|$ and compare the results with the graphs in the text. Also, try Exercises 19 and 21.

1.5 | ***FUNCTIONS IN ECONOMICS***

Functions that provide information about cost, revenue, and profit can be of great value to management. This section offers an introduction to the **cost function** (C), **revenue function** (R), and **profit function** (P) as well as a presentation of supply and demand concepts. We begin by establishing the notation for three important types of functions. Using x for the number of units produced or sold, we have

---

Cost, Revenue, Profit

$C(x)$ = the total *cost* of producing x units

$R(x)$ = the total *revenue* from the sale of x units

$P(x)$ = the total *profit* from the production and sale of x units

---

APPLIED

EXAMPLE 1 **COST OF PRODUCING RADIOS**

Assume that the cost of producing x radios is $C(x) = .4x^2 + 7x + 95$ dollars.

(a) Find the cost of producing 20 radios.

(b) Determine the cost of producing the 20th radio.

(c) Determine the cost of producing 0 radios.

SOLUTION **(a)** The cost of producing 20 radios is $C(20)$.

$$C(20) = .4(20)^2 + 7(20) + 95 = 160 + 140 + 95 = 395$$

The cost of producing 20 radios is $395.

(b) The cost of producing the 20th radio can be determined by subtracting the cost of the first 19 radios from the cost of the first 20 radios. That cost is

$$C(20) - C(19) = (395) - [.4(19)^2 + 7(19) + 95]$$
$$= 395 - 372.40 = 22.60$$

The 20th radio costs $22.60 to produce.

(c) The cost of producing 0 radios is $C(0)$.

$$C(0) = .4(0)^2 + 7(0) + 95 = 95$$

The cost of producing 0 radios is $95. ◆

The cost of producing no units [see Example 1, part (c)] is called the **fixed cost** or **overhead.** Such cost can vary from nearly zero to large amounts. Overhead can include such things as rent, tooling, training, insurance, equipment purchase, research, design, and other expenses that exist regardless of how many units are produced.

$$C(0) = \text{fixed cost or overhead}$$

A profit function P is sometimes given directly, but other times it may be necessary to determine profit as revenue minus cost.

$$\text{Profit} = \text{Revenue} - \text{Cost}$$
$$P(x) = R(x) - C(x)$$

APPLIED

EXAMPLE 2 *PROFIT ON THE MANUFACTURE AND SALE OF RADIOS*

It costs a manufacturer $C(x) = .4x^2 + 7x + 95$ dollars to produce x radios. They can be sold at \$40 each; that is, revenue from the sale of x radios is $R(x) = 40x$ dollars.

(a) Determine the profit function.

(b) What is the profit on the manufacture and sale of 25 radios?

(c) What is the profit on the manufacture and sale of 2 radios?

SOLUTION **(a)** Using $P(x) = R(x) - C(x)$, we have

$$P(x) = (40x) - (.4x^2 + 7x + 95)$$
$$P(x) = -.4x^2 + 33x - 95 \qquad \text{when simplified}$$

(b) The profit on the manufacture and sale of 25 radios is $P(25)$.

$$P(25) = -.4(25)^2 + 33(25) - 95 = 480$$

The manufacture and sale of 25 radios yields a profit of \$480.

(c) The profit on the manufacture and sale of 2 radios is $P(2)$.

$$P(2) = -.4(2)^2 + 33(2) - 95 = -30.6$$

The *minus* (negative profit) indicates a *loss*. The company would *lose* \$30.60 on the manufacture and sale of just 2 radios. ◆

In parts (b) and (c) of Example 2, profit could have been computed by evaluating the cost and revenue functions separately. In (b), $R(25) = 1000$ and $C(25) = 520$. Then $P(25) = R(25) - C(25) = 480$, which demonstrates that $P(x) > 0$ when $R(x) > C(x)$. In (c), $R(2) = 80$ and $C(2) = 110.60$. Then $P(2) = R(2) - C(2) = -30.6$, which demonstrates that $P(x) < 0$ when $C(x) > R(x)$. In general,

$$\textit{Profit} \quad \text{when } R(x) > C(x)$$
$$\textit{Loss} \quad \text{when } C(x) > R(x)$$

It is natural to wonder what the profit will be when $R(x) = C(x)$. Because $P(x) = R(x) - C(x)$, clearly $P(x) = 0$ when $R(x) = C(x)$. The company will break even when $P(x) = 0$. Thus, x for which $R(x) = C(x)$ is called the *break-even quantity*. The point of intersection of the graphs of $y = R(x)$ and $y = C(x)$ is called the **break-even point.** See Figure 27. Knowing how many units must be sold in order to break even is important to managers when they consider production and marketing of new products.

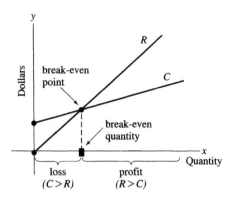

Figure 27

The next two examples show an algebraic approach to determining the break-even quantity.

EXAMPLE 3   *BREAK-EVEN QUANTITY*

APPLIED

A manufacturer of plastic containers for compact disks has the profit function

$$P(x) = .3x - 150 \quad \text{dollars}$$

where x is the number of CD containers produced and sold. How many containers must be made and sold in order to break even?

SOLUTION   To break even, profit must be zero. That is,

$$.3x - 150 = 0$$
$$.3x = 150$$
$$x = \frac{150}{.3} = 500$$

Thus, 500 CD containers must be manufactured and sold for this company to break even.

Figure 28 shows a graph of the profit function.

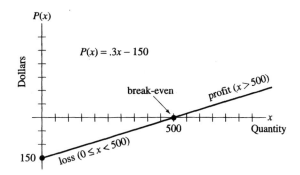

Figure 28   ◆

EXAMPLE 4 **BREAK-EVEN QUANTITY**

Assume that cost and revenue (in dollars) are given by

$$C(x) = 20x + 1250 \qquad R(x) = 50x - .1x^2$$

for $0 \le x \le 400$. For what quantity x will this business break even?

SOLUTION It will break even when $R(x) = C(x)$; that is, when

$$50x - .1x^2 = 20x + 1250 \qquad \text{or} \qquad .1x^2 - 30x + 1250 = 0$$

The quadratic equation can be solved by factoring (which you may find difficult), or by the quadratic formula as

$$x = \frac{30 \pm \sqrt{900 - 4(.1)(1250)}}{2(.1)} = \frac{30 \pm 20}{.2}$$

which leads to

$$x = \frac{50}{.2} = 250 \qquad \text{and} \qquad x = \frac{10}{.2} = 50$$

We conclude that *the business will break even when the quantity produced and sold is either 50 or 250 units*. (When $x < 50$ units, cost is greater than revenue, and a loss results. When $50 < x < 250$, revenue is greater than cost, and a profit results. When $x > 250$, cost is greater than revenue, and a loss results.)   ◆

Note

In Example 4, the square root was $\sqrt{900 - 500}$ or $\sqrt{400}$, which is exactly 20. If instead it had been $\sqrt{300}$, then a calculator approximation (such as 17.3) would be used to continue the procedure in order to determine the quantity x.

Price Functions

Consumers know that often there is a relationship between the price of an item and the demand for it. When the price is high, the demand is low. When the price is lower, consumer demand is greater. The relationship between the price per unit p and the quantity demanded x may be given by a **demand equation.**

EXAMPLE 5   *PRICE AND DEMAND*

Assume that for some product, the equation

$$p = 80 - .2x \quad \text{dollars}$$

gives the relationship between the price per unit p and the quantity x demanded. If the price of this product is set at \$70 per unit, then the quantity demanded is x such that

$$70 = 80 - .2x$$
$$x = 50 \quad \text{quantity demanded}$$

If the price is lowered to \$65, then we have

$$65 = 80 - .2x$$
$$x = 75 \quad \text{quantity demanded}$$

This example shows the typical relationship between price and quantity demanded: the lower the price, the greater the demand.   ◆

The relationship $p = 80 - .2x$ might have been stated as $p + .2x = 80$ or as $.2x = 80 - p$. However, the form $p = 80 - .2x$ was chosen in anticipation of using the equation as a **price function** p and using the price function to construct a total revenue function R.

Revenue

x = number of units (quantity)

p or $p(x)$ = price per unit

$R(x) = x \cdot p$ = total revenue from the sale of x units

EXAMPLE 6   *CONSTRUCTING A REVENUE FUNCTION*

Use the demand equation $p = 80 - .2x$ to construct the revenue function, and then find the total revenue from the sale of 90 units.

SOLUTION   The equation $p = 80 - .2x$ can be written as $p(x) = 80 - .2x$, using function notation to emphasize its price-function nature. Then

$$R(x) = x \cdot p(x)$$

becomes

$$R(x) = x(80 - .2x)$$
$$R(x) = 80x - .2x^2 \qquad \text{when simplified}$$

The revenue from the sale of 90 units is then

$$R(90) = 80(90) - .2(90)^2 = 5580$$

The revenue function is $R(x) = 80x - .2x^2$, and the revenue from the sale of 90 units is $5580. ♦

The relationship between the price per unit paid to a supplier and the number of items being supplied may be given by a **supply equation.** Ordinarily, the quantity x supplied will be greater when the price p is higher and less when the price is lower.

EXAMPLE 7   PRICE AND SUPPLY

Assume that the relationship between the price p (in dollars) per unit and the quantity x supplied is given by the equation

$$p = .02x + 3$$

(a) Find the number of units supplied when the price is $4.00 per unit.

(b) Find the number of units supplied when the price is $4.50 per unit.

SOLUTION   **(a)** When the price is $4 per unit, we have

$$4 = .02x + 3$$
$$x = 50$$

50 units will be supplied at a price of $4 each.

(b) When the price is $4.50 per unit, we have

$$4.50 = .02x + 3$$
$$x = 75$$

75 units will be supplied when the price is $4.50 per unit. ♦

The supply equation $p = .02x + 3$ defines a price function. (We could write it as $p(x) = .02x + 3$ to emphasize the point.) The total cost function C can be constructed from the price function p.

Cost

x = number of units (quantity)

p or $p(x)$ = price per unit

$C(x) = x \cdot p$ = total cost to supply x units

APPLIED

EXAMPLE 8 *CONSTRUCTING A COST FUNCTION*

Use the supply equation $p = .02x + 3$ to construct the cost function, and then find the total cost of supplying 85 units.

SOLUTION The equation $p = .02x + 3$ can be written as $p(x) = .02x + 3$, using function notation to emphasize its price-function nature. Then

$$C(x) = x \cdot p(x)$$
$$C(x) = x(.02x + 3) \qquad \text{using } p(x) = .02x + 3$$
$$C(x) = .02x^2 + 3x \qquad \text{the cost function}$$

The cost of supplying 85 units is then

$$C(85) = .02(85)^2 + 3(85) = 399.50 \qquad \text{or \$399.50} \qquad \blacklozenge$$

Note

Because price functions are used for both supply and demand, each time one arises there will be an indication of whether it is a supply equation or a demand equation. An alternative approach, which avoids ambiguity, is to use D or $D(x)$ for demand and S or $S(x)$ for supply.

$$p = S(x) \qquad \text{supply}$$
$$p = D(x) \qquad \text{demand}$$

The market for a product will be in a state of *equilibrium* when the quantity supplied (or produced) is equal to the quantity demanded. The point (x, p) for which equilibrium exists is called the **equilibrium point** and will be designated as (x_e, p_e). See Figure 29.

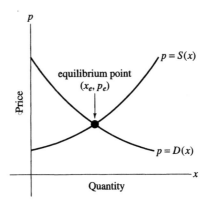

Figure 29 Supply and demand—and the equilibrium point

EXAMPLE 9 **SUPPLY, DEMAND, AND EQUILIBRIUM**

Suppose the demand equation for a product is $p = 17 - .2x$ (dollars) and the supply equation is $p = .4x + 8$ (dollars).

(a) Find the equilibrium quantity. **(b)** Find the equilibrium price.

(c) Determine the equilibrium point.

SOLUTION **(a)** The quantity for which equilibrium will exist is the value of x for which supply and demand are equal. In other words, we seek x such that

$$.4x + 8 = 17 - .2x$$

or

$$.6x = 9$$
$$x = 15$$

The equilibrium quantity is 15.

(b) The price at market equilibrium is the p value corresponding to the equilibrium quantity, 15. Either equation (supply or demand) can be used to obtain p by using 15 for x. From the demand equation $p = 17 - .2x$, we have

$$p = 17 - .2(15) = 17 - 3 = 14$$

The equilibrium price is $14.

(c) The equilibrium point (x_e, p_e) has as its coordinates the equilibrium quantity x_e and the equilibrium price p_e. Thus, based on parts (a) and (b), we have

$$(x_e, p_e) = (15, 14)$$ ◆

1.5 Exercises

1. (COST) Suppose the cost of producing x umbrellas is $C(x) = .1x^2 + 5x + 210$ dollars.
(a) Find the cost of producing 25 umbrellas.
(b) Find the cost of producing the 25th umbrella.
(c) Determine the fixed cost or overhead.

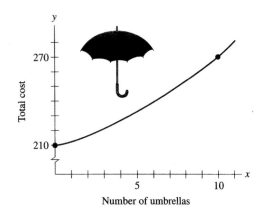

Number of umbrellas

2. (COST) Suppose $C(x) = .2x^2 + 17x + 95$ is the cost (in dollars) of making x wheel covers.
(a) What is the cost of making 20 wheel covers?
(b) Find the cost of making the 10th wheel cover.
(c) What is the fixed cost?

3. (COST) If the cost of producing x lamps is given by $C(x) = 35x + 195$ dollars, how many lamps can be produced for $1000?

4. (COST) A calculator manufacturer determines that the cost to make each calculator is $3 and the fixed cost is $1200. Determine the cost function—that is, the total cost of producing x calculators.

5. (REVENUE) A manufacturer of automobile batteries finds that the revenue from the sale of x batteries is $27x - .01x^2$ dollars for $0 \leq x \leq 2000$.
(a) How much revenue is derived from the sale of 100 batteries?
(b) What is the revenue obtained from the sale of the 100th battery?

6. (REVENUE) A cigar box distributor's revenue is

$$R(x) = 1.35x \text{ dollars}$$

where x is the number of boxes sold.

(a) How much revenue is obtained from selling 5 boxes?
(b) What is the revenue obtained from the sale of the 5th box?
(c) What is the revenue obtained from the sale of the 8th box?

7. (PROFIT) Consider that it costs a TV manufacturer $C(x) = .1x^2 + 150x + 1000$ dollars to produce x TV sets. The revenue from the sale of x TV sets is $R(x) = 280x$ dollars.
(a) Determine the profit function.
(b) What is the profit on the manufacture and sale of 50 TV sets?

8. (PROFIT) If revenue from the sale of x carpets is $R(x) = 90x$ and the cost to obtain the carpets is $C(x) = 50x + .03x^2$, determine the profit function.

9. (PROFIT) A tire maker can produce x tires at a cost of $29 + .02x$ dollars *per tire*. The company can sell the tires at $54 each.
(a) Determine the cost function.
(b) Determine the revenue function.
(c) Determine the profit function.

10. (PROFIT) A manufacturer of felt-tip pens can produce x boxes of pens for $2.4 + .01x$ dollars *per box*. The company can sell the pens at $3.59 per box.
(a) Determine the cost function.
(b) Determine the revenue function.
(c) Determine the profit function.

11. (PROFIT) If x barrels can be produced at a cost of $6 each and sold at a price of $15 - .02x$ dollars each, determine the profit function P.

12. (PROFIT) If x jackets can be produced at a cost of $.01x + 19$ dollars each and sold at a price of $50 each, determine the profit function P.

13. (BREAK-EVEN QUANTITY) A travel agent determines that her monthly profit on the sale of x dollars worth of airline tickets is $P(x) = .1x - 410$ dollars.
(a) What is her profit on $5800 in monthly airline ticket sales?
(b) How much is her loss if sales are only $2000?
(c) What must her monthly sales be in order to break even?

14. (BREAK-EVEN QUANTITY) The management of a publishing company informs the marketing department that the profit function is $P(x) = .08x - 15,200$ dollars, where x is the number of dollars of sales.

W **(a)** How would management react to sales of $100,000?
(b) How many dollars of sales are needed to break even?

W **15.** **(PROFIT)** Suppose you know the cost and revenue functions for a particular business. Explain how you would use $C(x)$ and $R(x)$ to determine the company's profit from the sale of the 75th unit. Use words rather than expressions or equations.

W **16.** **(COST)** $C(x)$ is the cost of producing x limousines.
(a) What is the meaning of the following expression: $C(45) - C(43)$?
(b) What is the meaning of $C(2)$?

W **17.** **(PROFIT)** Consider the accompanying graph of the cost and revenue functions given. As usual, P is the corresponding profit function.

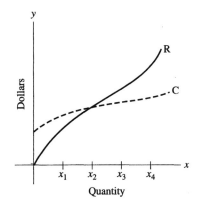

Quantity

(a) Is $P(x) > 0$ when $x < x_1$? Explain.
(b) Which is the greatest of $P(x_1)$, $P(x_2)$, $P(x_3)$, and $P(x_4)$? Why?
(c) Which is the smallest of $P(x_1)$, $P(x_2)$, $P(x_3)$, and $P(x_4)$? Why?

18. **(COST)** Consider three sources of costs in producing clocks to ship. The fixed costs are $1400. The total variable cost of producing x clocks is $.1x^2 + 14x$ dollars. Additionally, the boxes used to ship the clocks cost $1.25 each.
(a) Determine the cost function that includes all three considerations.
(b) Determine the complete cost of producing 62 clocks in boxes, ready to ship.

19. **(DEMAND)** Suppose the equation $p = 90 - .02x$ gives the relationship between the price (in dollars) per unit and the quantity x demanded. If the price is set at $52 per unit, what is the quantity demanded?

20. **(DEMAND)** If $p = -.04x + 72$ is the relationship between the price per unit (in dollars) and the quantity x demanded, what is the quantity demanded when the price is $50 per unit?

21. **(DEMAND AND REVENUE)** Use the demand equation $p = 50 - .1x$ dollars to construct the revenue function, and then find the total revenue from the sale of 40 units.

22. **(DEMAND AND REVENUE)** Let the demand equation be $p = 34 - .3x$ dollars.
(a) Determine $R(x)$.　　**(b)** Determine $R(15)$.

23. **(SUPPLY)** Assume that the equation $p = .3x + 17$ gives the relationship between the price (in dollars) per unit and the quantity x supplied. If the price is set at $65 per unit, what quantity will be supplied?

24. **(SUPPLY)** Let $p = 5 + .04x$ be the relationship between the price (in dollars) per unit and the quantity (x) supplied. If the price is set at $73 per unit, what quantity will be supplied?

25. **(SUPPLY AND COST)** Assume the supply equation is $p = 24 + .4x$ dollars.
(a) Determine the cost function.
(b) Find $C(20)$.
(c) What is the cost of the 10th unit?

26. **(SUPPLY AND COST)** What is the cost of producing 100 units if the supply equation is $p = 8 + .01x$ dollars?

(EQUILIBRIUM) In Exercises 27–32, use the given demand equation and supply equation to determine (a) the equilibrium quantity, (b) the equilibrium price, and (c) the equilibrium point. Assume p is in dollars.

27. demand: $p = 20 - .3x$; supply: $p = .1x + 8$

28. demand: $p = 74 - .08x$; supply: $p = .02x + 3$

29. demand: $p = 100 - .1x$; supply: $p = 52$

30. demand: $p = 104$; supply: $p = .5x + 14$

31. demand: $p = 47 - .2x$; supply: $p = 1 + .03x$

32. demand: $p = 22 - .04x$; supply: $p = .2x + 4$

(EQUILIBRIUM) In Exercises 33–36, use the given supply and demand functions to determine the quantity and price at which equilibrium occurs. The monetary unit is dollars.

33. $S(x) = 2x + 43; D(x) = 160 - x$

34. $S(x) = .04x + 10; D(x) = 38 - .03x$

35. $S(x) = 5 + .3x; D(x) = 29$

36. $S(x) = x + 1; D(x) = 91 - .2x$

W 37. **(EQUILIBRIUM)** Once the equilibrium quantity x is determined, then the equilibrium price can be determined from either the supply equation or the demand equation. Why doesn't it matter which of the two equations is used to determine the equilibrium price?

W 38. Is a break-even point the same as an equilibrium point? Explain.

W 39. **(FIXED COST)** Which function (C_1, C_2, or C_3) includes the largest fixed cost? Explain.

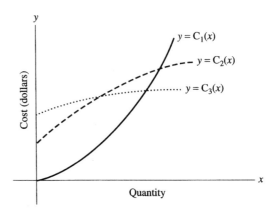

 TECHNOLOGY *EXERCISES*

Note Keep in mind that when dealing with functions in economics, the number of units (x) is never negative. Of the functions themselves, only profit might be negative for some quantity. Intervals for x and y should be chosen accordingly.

1. **(BREAK EVEN)** Assume a company's profit is given by $P(x) = x^{1.5} - 4x - 2$ hundred dollars, where x is the number of units sold. Use a graph to determine (to the nearest whole number) how many units must be sold in order to break even. Use x in $[0,30]$ and y in $[-20,20]$.

2. **(BREAK EVEN)** Graph both the revenue function $R(x) = .2x^2$ and the cost function $C(x) = .9x + 4$. Use the window $[0,20]$ for both x and y.

   (a) Determine the break-even quantity (to the nearest whole number).

   (b) Determine, to the nearest tenth, the y coordinate of the break-even point.

W 3. **(BREAK EVEN)** Graph the cost function $C(x) = 2.1 + .3x$ and the revenue function $R(x) = 1.2\sqrt{x}$. Is there anything unusual about the break-even point? What would be your recommendation to management?

4. **(PROFIT)** Suppose profit in hundreds of dollars is given by $P(x) = -x^3 + 6x^2 - 19$. Graph the function, using x in $[0,15]$ and y in $[-20,20]$. To the nearest hundred dollars, what is the largest profit attainable?

5. **(EQUILIBRIUM)** Let the demand equation be $p = .2x^2 - 8.4x + 120$ and the supply equation be $p = 3.4 + .2x^2$. Graph the functions in order to determine the equilibrium point (both coordinates to the nearest whole number).

Key Terms and Ideas

open interval
closed interval
half-open interval
quadratic formula
function
independent variable
dependent variable
domain
range
zero of a function
composition of functions
linear function
slope
y intercept

point-slope form
slope-intercept form
parallel lines
graph of a function
vertical line test
square function
quadratic functions
vertex of a parabola
square root function
cube function
reciprocal function
absolute value function
two-piece function
two-part function

piecewise function
vertical translation (optional)
reflection (optional)
cost function
revenue function
profit function
overhead
fixed cost
break-even point
demand equation
price function
supply equation
equilibrium point

Review Exercises for Chapter 1

1. Write the inequality $1 \le x < 7$ using interval notation.

2. Write the inequality $t \ge 0$ using interval notation.

3. Solve the linear inequality $4(x - 2) \le 3$ and write the answer in interval notation.

4. Solve the linear inequality $10 - 4x > 15$ and write the answer in interval notation.

Solve each quadratic equation in Exercises 5–8.

5. $2x^2 - x - 3 = 0$ **6.** $3x^2 - 14x + 8 = 0$

7. $x^2 - 5x + 2 = 0$ **8.** $x^2 + x = 3$

9. If $f(x) = \dfrac{3x^2}{1 + x}$, find $f(0)$, $f(2)$, and $f(-2)$.

W 10. Comment on the calculation of $f(-1)$, where f is the function defined in Exercise 9.

11. If $f(x) = 2\sqrt{x - 3}$, find $f(4)$, $f(7)$, and $f(8)$.

W 12. Comment on the calculation of $f(0)$, where f is the function defined in Exercise 11.

13. If $f(x) = 3x^2$, find $f(x + 1)$ and $f(x + h)$.

14. If $g(x) = x^2 - x$, find $g(x + 2)$ and $g(x + h)$.

15. If $f(x) = x^2$, find $f(x + h) - f(x)$.

16. If $g(x) = 2x^2 - 1$, find $g(x + h) - g(x)$.

In Exercises 17–20, determine the domain of each function.

17. $f(x) = \dfrac{x}{2x - 1}$ **18.** $f(x) = \dfrac{1 - x}{x}$

19. $g(x) = \sqrt{x + 9}$ **20.** $g(x) = x^3$

21. Find the zeros of $f(x) = 3x^2 - 27$.

22. Find the zeros of $g(x) = 1 - 3x$.

23. If $f(x) = x^2 - 3$ and $g(x) = x + 1$, find $(f \circ g)(x)$.

24. If $f(x) = 4x^2$ and $g(x) = 5x - 19$, find $(g \circ f)(x)$.

25. Find the slope of the line that passes through the points $(-1, 2)$ and $(1, 5)$ and sketch the graph.

26. Determine two points that lie on the line given by $y = -2x + 3$.

27. Find the slope and y intercept of the line given by $y = 5x - 1$.

28. Find the equation of the line having slope 3 and y intercept 11.

29. Determine the equation of the line having slope 6 and passing through the point $(2, -7)$.

30. What is the slope of a line that is parallel to the line $y = 7x - 2$?

31. Write the equation of the line that crosses the y axis where y is 6 and crosses the x axis where x is 2.

32. Determine the equation of the line parallel to the line $y = -2x + 5$ and passing through the point $(4, 0)$.

33. Sketch the graph of the quadratic function given by $f(x) = x^2 - 2x + 7$.

34. Sketch the graph of the quadratic function given by $y = -x^2 + 6x - 5$.

In Exercises 35–38, sketch the graph of each two-part function.

35. $f(x) = \begin{cases} 2 & x \le 0 \\ -x & x > 0 \end{cases}$ **36.** $f(x) = \begin{cases} x & x < 0 \\ x^2 & x \ge 0 \end{cases}$

37. $g(x) = \begin{cases} x & x < 1 \\ \sqrt{x} & x \ge 1 \end{cases}$ **38.** $g(x) = \begin{cases} |x| & x < 0 \\ 2x & x \ge 0 \end{cases}$

W 39. Can $(1, 6)$, $(2, 7)$, $(3, 5)$, $(3, -1)$, and $(4, 0)$ be points on the graph of a function? Explain.

W 40. *(PROFIT)* Distinguish among and explain the three different possibilities for profit P that depend on whether $R > C$, $R = C$, or $R < C$.

41. *(RENTAL CAR COST)* An executive rents a car for one day. The cost of the rental is $26 plus 30¢ per mile driven. Let x be the number of miles driven and y be the total rental car bill. Express y as a function of x, using $y = mx + b$.

42. *(PLUMBER'S BILL)* A plumber charges $30 to come to the house plus $50 per hour once there. Let x be the number of hours the plumber works and y be the total bill. Express y as a function of x, using $y = mx + b$.

43. *(BACTERIA CULTURE)* Suppose $n(t) = 300 + 12t + t^2$ gives the number of bacteria present in a lab culture at any time t, where t is in hours.

(a) How many bacteria were present at the beginning, when the culture was started?

W (b) Compute $n(5)$ and tell what the result means.

44. *(REVENUE)* Suppose the revenue from the sale of x bags of pretzels is $.75x$ dollars.

(a) What is the revenue when 110 bags are sold?

(b) What is the revenue from the sale of the last (110th) bag?

45. *(COST, REVENUE, AND PROFIT)* It costs a stereo manufacturer $C(x) = .1x^2 + 170x + 900$ dollars to produce x stereo units. The stereos can be sold for $300 each.

(a) Determine the revenue function R.

(b) Determine the profit function P.

W (c) Compute $P(5)$. Interpret the result.

(d) What is the cost of making 10 stereos?

(e) What is the cost of making the 10th stereo?

46. *(COST, REVENUE, AND PROFIT)* If flower pots can be produced at a cost of $1.25 each and sold at a price of $2 - .01x$ dollars each, determine the profit function P. Note that x is the number of flower pots.

47. *(EQUILIBRIUM)* Let the demand equation be given by $p = 25 - .1x$ and the supply equation be given by $p = 1 + .02x$. Find the equilibrium point.

W 48. *(COST, REVENUE, AND PROFIT)* Consider the cost and revenue functions graphed below. Which of the profits $P(x_1)$, $P(x_2)$, $P(x_3)$, $P(x_4)$, or $P(x_5)$ is the greatest? Explain your answer.

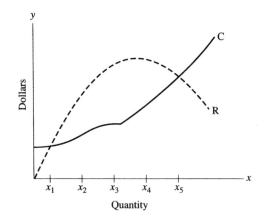

49. *(APPRECIATION)* A lakefront lot purchased 2 years ago for $30,000 is now worth $35,000. Assume the appreciation is linear.

(a) Write the equation of form $y = mt + b$ that gives the value of the lot at any time t in years.

(b) How many years from the time of purchase will it be before the land is worth $47,500?

50. *(GOLD PRICE)* Function G gives the price of an ounce of gold during a day's trading session (10 a.m. to 4 p.m.). See the accompanying figure. Here x is the time on a 24-hour clock, which means 1 p.m. = 13, 2 p.m. = 14, etc.

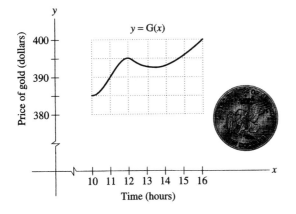

$y = G(x)$

Price of gold (dollars)

Time (hours)

(a) Determine $G(10)$.
(b) Determine x for which $G(x) = 390$.
(c) At what time did gold reach its maximum value for the day?
(d) How much did the price of gold gain or lose for the day?

51. *(PRODUCTIVITY)* Data from the Bureau of Labor Statistics shows the growth in U.S. nonfarm productivity from a 1982 base-year figure of 100% to a 1995 figure of 117%. Points of the form (year, percent) are as follows: (82, 100),

(86, 105), (89, 109), (95, 117). Using an earlier period, 1970–1981, we have points (70, 84), (73, 95), (78, 101), and (81, 102). Over which period, 1982–1995 or 1970–1981, is the productivity growth nearly linear?

52. *(FALLING APPLE)* An apple is dropped from the top of a building. Its distance from the ground t seconds after being dropped is given by

$$s(t) = 144 - 16t^2 \quad \text{feet}$$

(a) How high above the ground is the apple 2 seconds after it is dropped?
W (b) Which expression gives the height of the building— $s(0)$, $s(1)$, $s(1.5)$, or $s(3)$? Explain.
W (c) What happens at $t = 3$ seconds?

53. *(ALLIGATOR GROWTH)* Consider the following data on length (y feet) versus age (x years) for an alligator.

x	y
1	1.4
2	2.6

Assume that the relationship between length and age is linear.

(a) Obtain the function of form $y = mx + b$ that gives the relationship between length and age.
(b) When the alligator is 4 years old, how long will it be?
(c) When will the alligator be 6.8 feet long?

Chapter Projects and Essays

Many of the projects and essays lend themselves to group activity, although most can be completed by individual effort.

1. INCOME TAXES

BACKGROUND Most states tax the income of their residents. Some of these states have a *flat tax*, such as 4% of all taxable income. Other states have a *graduated tax* in which the tax rate increases as the taxable income rises. Information on the tax rates for different states is available in some almanacs and other reference books. Complete information and tax forms are available from the state treasury or revenue division in the capital of each state.

THE PROJECT Obtain the tax rates of one or more states that have a graduated tax. For each state, graph a piecewise function. Use the horizontal (*x*) axis for the taxable income amounts and the vertical (*y*) axis for the (dollar) amount of tax due. Compare the graphs of your selected state(s) with those that others in the class have done. Comment on the difference between the tax rate schedule(s) you have chosen and those that others have chosen.

2. THE NUMBER PI (π)

BACKGROUND The number π is approximately equal to 3.14. It is the ratio of the circumference of a circle to its diameter.

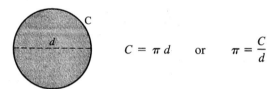

$$C = \pi d \quad \text{or} \quad \pi = \frac{C}{d}$$

The first (crude) approximation of the number that became known as π can be found in the Old Testament and in the works of the ancient Babylonians. Centuries later, Archimedes used mathematical methods to improve the approximation. Later on, further improvements were contributed by mathematicians in China, India, France, The Netherlands, England, and elsewhere.

From the time of Archimedes through the early computer era of the 1940s, there were over 100 known mathematical approximations of π. Descriptions of the methods and the resulting approximations can be found in books on the history of mathematics and in books and articles on π.

The fascination with finding many digits in the approximation of π continues even today. As one example, in Carl Sagan's best-selling novel *Contact*, a key in the communication with a civilization in deep space lies in a coded message placed in the digit pattern of π. As a second example, the computer programs written to approximate π to many digits can be used to check for errors in the computer hardware.

THE PROJECT Use reference materials of the type mentioned in "Background" to locate explanations of several approximation methods. Report on them and include the actual results that were obtained.

AN INTRODUCTION TO LIMITS

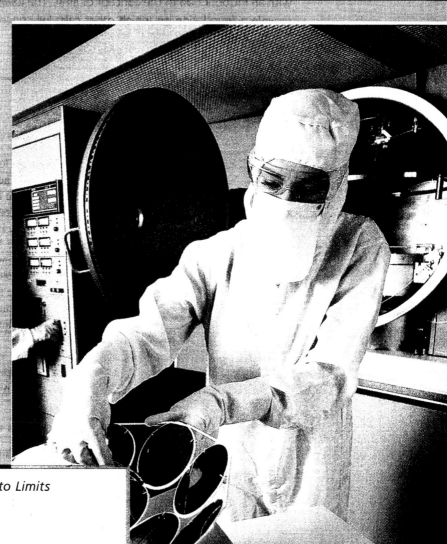

2

Technicians who check the performance of computer microchips might use the concept of a "limit." In testing the capacity of a microchip, technicians load information in small increments, edging closer and closer to the chip's breaking point. In this way, they arrive at a close approximation of its greatest storage capacity—its "limit."

We begin with some historical notes on the invention of calculus by Isaac Newton and Gottfried Wilhelm Leibniz. We then proceed with the study of calculus, beginning with an introduction to the concept of limit. The ideas about limits presented here will provide a foundation on which other calculus concepts will be built.

2.1 | *INTRODUCTION TO LIMITS*

Newton and Leibniz

Figure 1
Isaac Newton (1642–1727)

The Englishman Isaac Newton and the German Gottfried Wilhelm Leibniz are the mathematicians credited with inventing calculus. They worked independently of each other. Newton invented calculus in 1665 but took more than 20 years to publish his results, so Leibniz's development of calculus was published first. Furthermore, Leibniz's notation was considered superior to Newton's notation, and it is still used today.

Calculus-like methods had been developed before Newton and Leibniz. As problems of physics arose, solutions were found. But no one saw the pattern or underlying mathematics relating the nature of the various problems and solutions. Simon Stevin (1548–1620) used a calculus-like method to determine the force due to water pressure on a vertical dam. Johannes Kepler (1571–1630) used calculus-like methods in his investigation of the motion of planets. And there were others, including Galileo, Cavalieri, Torricelli, Fermat, Huygens, Wallis, and Barrow.

The invention of calculus had a great impact on technology as well as on the development of mathematics. Years later, calculus applications were found in a variety of nonengineering areas, including business and economics, biology, medicine, sociology, and psychology. Calculus can be used to

1. Determine the average speed at which blood flows through an artery.

2. Select the most economical dimensions for packaging.

3. Calculate how high a projectile will travel.

4. Find the production level that will maximize a company's profit.

Calculus developed as two separate branches—integral calculus and differential calculus. The original problems that led to the invention of differential calculus did not appear to resemble the problems solved by integral calculus. However, the two branches of calculus were linked together by Newton and by Leibniz in a theorem now known as the *Fundamental Theorem of Calculus.*

You will be introduced to differential calculus in Chapter 3 and to integral calculus in Chapter 6. The Fundamental Theorem is presented in Section 6.4.

Both differential calculus and integral calculus use the basic concept and notation of **limit,** as you will see in Chapters 3 and 6 and elsewhere in the text. Because of their importance, Chapter 2 is devoted to the presentation of limits.

Figure 2
Gottfried Wilhelm Leibniz
(1646–1716)

Introduction to Limits

This section offers a practical introduction to *limits*, including the background needed to understand and appreciate many of the ideas of calculus. Our approach to the subject will be intuitive.

To begin, consider the expression

$$\frac{x^2 + x - 12}{x - 3}$$

Suppose we want to know what will happen to the value of this expression as the value of x gets nearer and nearer to 3. We could study the expression by evaluating it, using x values nearer and nearer to 3. Here is such a study:

x	$\dfrac{x^2 + x - 12}{x - 3}$
2.9	6.9
2.95	6.95
2.99	6.99
2.999	6.999

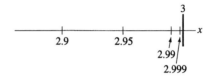

x	$\dfrac{x^2 + x - 12}{x - 3}$
3.1	7.1
3.05	7.05
3.01	7.01
3.001	7.001

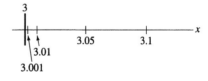

The first table shows x "approaching" 3 from the left, through values less than 3. The second table shows x approaching 3 from the right, through values greater than 3. In each instance you can see that as x gets closer to 3, the value of the expression gets closer to 7. We say

"The limit of $\dfrac{x^2 + x - 12}{x - 3}$, as x approaches 3, is 7."

In mathematical notation, we write

$$\lim_{x \to 3} \frac{x^2 + x - 12}{x - 3} = 7$$

Notice the use of an *arrow* to show what number x is approaching and the *lim* shorthand for the word "limit." Using function notation, we can say that

$$\text{if} \qquad f(x) = \frac{x^2 + x - 12}{x - 3} \qquad \text{then} \qquad \lim_{x \to 3} f(x) = 7$$

Also, $\lim_{x \to 3} f(x) = 7$ means that as x gets closer and closer to 3, $f(x)$ gets closer and closer to 7. In general,

---

Limit

For any function f,

$$\lim_{x \to a} f(x) = L$$

means that as x gets closer and closer to a, $f(x)$ gets closer and closer to L.

This definition of limit is intuitive. There is a more formal definition, one that is used in courses for mathematicians and engineers.

Note

In the example leading up to the definition of limit, we considered $\lim_{x \to 3} f(x)$ by letting x get closer and closer to 3 from both sides. We saw that the limit as x approaches 3 from the left (through values less than 3) is the same as the limit as x approaches 3 from the right (through values greater than 3). In general, *the limit exists only if the limits from both the left and the right are equal.*

Although it may be quite natural to wonder what happens when x is equal to 3 in the function we considered, that is *not* the "limit" concern. *The limit as $x \to 3$ deals with x values approaching 3 without actually being equal to 3.* The particular function and expression used here are not even defined at $x = 3$, for if 3 is substituted for x, division by zero will arise, and division by zero is not defined. Thus, we have seen that

$$\lim_{x \to 3} \frac{x^2 + x - 12}{x - 3} = 7$$

even though

$$\frac{x^2 + x - 12}{x - 3} \qquad \text{is not defined at 3.}$$

Often the expression in question *is* defined at the number the variable is approaching. Consider, for example,

$$\lim_{x \to 2} 3x$$

Two tables can be used to study this limit.

x	$3x$		x	$3x$
1.9	5.7		2.1	6.3
1.95	5.85		2.05	6.15
1.99	5.97		2.01	6.03
1.999	5.997		2.001	6.003

From the tables it appears that

$$\lim_{x \to 2} 3x = 6$$

and 6 is the number you would obtain by simply substituting 2 for x in the expression $3x$. In other words, in this example,

$$\lim_{x \to 2} 3x = 3(2) = 6$$

The example suggests that *sometimes limits can be evaluated by making the obvious substitution*. Here are two more examples.

EXAMPLE 1   Evaluate $\lim_{x \to 3} (2x + 1)$ by making the substitution for x.

SOLUTION   Using substitution, we obtain

$$\lim_{x \to 3} (2x + 1) = 2(3) + 1 = 7$$

Of course, we could make tables using x values that get closer and closer to 3. The tables would show that $2x + 1$ gets closer and closer to 7. ◆

EXAMPLE 2   **DISTANCE TRAVELED BY A TRAIN**

The distance traveled by a train that is going 60 miles per hour for t hours is $d(t) = 60t$. Make the substitution for t to evaluate

$$\lim_{t \to 3} d(t)$$

and interpret the answer.

SOLUTION
$$\lim_{t \to 3} d(t) = \lim_{t \to 3} 60t = 60 \cdot 3 = 180$$

As the time t gets closer and closer to 3 hours, the distance traveled d approaches 180 miles. ◆

It is natural to wonder when you can evaluate limits by this simple "plugging in" type of substitution and when you cannot. The answer is based on limit theorems (presented next) and continuity (the topic of the next section).

Limit Theorems

Our approach to limits has been rather informal. However, at this point a brief look at limit theorems will help you to understand the evaluation of limits. In later chapters, limit theorems will be used occasionally in the calculus operations of differentiation and integration.

Limit Theorems

If a, c, and n are real numbers, then

1. $\displaystyle\lim_{x \to a} c = c$

2. $\displaystyle\lim_{x \to a} x = a$

3. $\displaystyle\lim_{x \to a} [c \cdot f(x)] = c \cdot \lim_{x \to a} f(x)$

4. $\displaystyle\lim_{x \to a} [f(x) + g(x)] = \lim_{x \to a} f(x) + \lim_{x \to a} g(x)$

5. $\displaystyle\lim_{x \to a} [f(x) - g(x)] = \lim_{x \to a} f(x) - \lim_{x \to a} g(x)$

6. $\displaystyle\lim_{x \to a} [f(x) \cdot g(x)] = \lim_{x \to a} f(x) \cdot \lim_{x \to a} g(x)$

7. $\displaystyle\lim_{x \to a} \frac{f(x)}{g(x)} = \frac{\displaystyle\lim_{x \to a} f(x)}{\displaystyle\lim_{x \to a} g(x)}$ $\left(\displaystyle\lim_{x \to a} g(x) \neq 0\right)$

8. $\displaystyle\lim_{x \to a} [f(x)]^n = [\lim_{x \to a} f(x)]^n$

If n indicates an even root, then the limit of $f(x)$ must be nonnegative.

In words, the limit theorems say

1. The limit of a constant is that constant.

2. The limit of x as x approaches a is a.

3. The limit of a constant times a function is equal to the constant times the limit of the function.

4. The limit of a sum is equal to the sum of the limits.

5. The limit of a difference is equal to the difference of the limits.

6. The limit of a product is equal to the product of the limits.

7. The limit of a quotient is equal to the quotient of the limits (provided the denominator is nonzero).

8. The limit of the nth power of a function is the nth power of the limit of the function.

EXAMPLE 3 Use limit theorems to evaluate each limit.

(a) $\lim\limits_{x \to 3} 6$ (b) $\lim\limits_{x \to 2} (4x + 5)$ (c) $\lim\limits_{x \to 1} \sqrt{10 - x}$

SOLUTION (a) By limit theorem 1,

$$\lim_{x \to 3} 6 = 6$$

(b)
$$
\begin{aligned}
\lim_{x \to 2} (4x + 5) &= \lim_{x \to 2} 4x + \lim_{x \to 2} 5 && \text{limit theorem 4} \\
&= \lim_{x \to 2} 4 \cdot \lim_{x \to 2} x + \lim_{x \to 2} 5 && \text{limit theorem 6} \\
&= (4)(2) + 5 && \text{limit theorems 1 and 2} \\
&= 13
\end{aligned}
$$

(c)
$$
\begin{aligned}
\lim_{x \to 1} \sqrt{10 - x} &= \lim_{x \to 1} (10 - x)^{1/2} && \text{exponent notation} \\
&= [\lim_{x \to 1} (10 - x)]^{1/2} && \text{limit theorem 8} \\
&= [\lim_{x \to 1} 10 - \lim_{x \to 1} x]^{1/2} && \text{limit theorem 5} \\
&= (10 - 1)^{1/2} && \text{limit theorems 1 and 2} \\
&= 9^{1/2} = 3
\end{aligned}
$$
◆

Figure 3
Augustin Louis Cauchy
(1789–1857). Photo
courtesy of Smithsonian
Institution Libraries.

The limit theorems and Example 3 suggest that *many limits can indeed be evaluated by the "plugging in" type of substitution used in Examples 1 and 2.* But some limits cannot be evaluated in that manner. This concern is addressed in the next section, which presents the concept of continuity.

The French mathematician Augustin Louis Cauchy (1789–1857) was a leader in establishing a formal theory of limits and a rigorous treatment of calculus in general.

More recently, limits have also been applied in the study of *fractals*, a new area of geometry pioneered by Benoit Mandelbrot at IBM and Yale University. The range of applications and the availability of modern computer graphics have made fractals an area of interest to biologists, psychologists, geographers, engineers, and others.

2.1   Exercises

Find each limit in Exercises 1–14 by using limit theorems. (See Example 3.)

1. $\lim\limits_{x \to 0} (-6)$ **2.** $\lim\limits_{x \to 1} 7$

3. $\lim\limits_{x \to 4} 5x$ **4.** $\lim\limits_{x \to -3} 8x$

5. $\lim\limits_{x \to 5} (4x - 1)$ **6.** $\lim\limits_{x \to 2} (6x + 1)$

7. $\lim\limits_{t \to -3} t^2$ **8.** $\lim\limits_{u \to -1} u^4$

9. $\lim\limits_{x \to 0} \dfrac{x + 2}{9}$ **10.** $\lim\limits_{x \to 5} \dfrac{2}{3x}$

11. $\lim\limits_{x \to 8} \sqrt{x + 1}$ **12.** $\lim\limits_{x \to 16} \sqrt{4x}$

13. $\lim\limits_{x \to -1} (x^3 + x)$ **14.** $\lim\limits_{x \to 2} (1 - x^3)$

15. Determine $\lim\limits_{x \to 4} f(x)$ on the basis of the tables.

x	$f(x)$	x	$f(x)$
3.9	7.47	4.1	7.54
3.99	7.485	4.01	7.516
3.999	7.497	4.001	7.502
3.9999	7.4998	4.0001	7.5001

16. Determine $\lim\limits_{x \to 5} f(x)$ on the basis of the tables.

x	$f(x)$	x	$f(x)$
4.9	-5.8	5.1	-6.1
4.99	-5.97	5.01	-6.02
4.999	-5.991	5.001	-6.001
4.9999	-5.9998	5.0001	-6.0001

In Exercises 17–23, attempt to evaluate each limit by using the substitution approach (plugging in). If that method fails, write "cannot determine by substitution" and then proceed to *use a calculator* to create tables in order to determine the limit.

17. $\lim\limits_{x \to 2} \dfrac{x^2 - 4}{x - 2}$

18. $\lim\limits_{x \to -3} \dfrac{x^2 - 9}{x + 3}$

19. $\lim\limits_{x \to 0} \dfrac{x}{3}$

20. $\lim\limits_{x \to 0} \dfrac{7x}{2}$

21. $\lim\limits_{t \to 2} \dfrac{t^2 - 7t + 10}{t - 2}$

22. $\lim\limits_{x \to 1} \dfrac{1 - 8x}{\sqrt{x}}$

23. $\lim\limits_{t \to 3} \dfrac{t^2 - 9}{t^2 + 9}$

24. (*GEOMETRY*) The area of a circular region of radius r is $A = \pi r^2$. (See the figure.)

(a) Find $\lim\limits_{r \to 0} A$.

W (b) Explain the meaning of the limit in part (a) in light of this geometry setting.

(c) The circumference of a circle of radius r is $C = 2\pi r$. Find $\lim\limits_{r \to 0} C$.

(d) Find $\lim\limits_{r \to 0} \dfrac{C^2}{A}$.

25. (*PRICE FUNCTION*) Ordinarily, the price p of an item depends on the quantity x that is supplied or demanded. But occasionally, the price $p(x)$ is constant regardless of x. This is especially true for such consumer items as newspapers. Assume that newspapers sell for 50¢ each.
   (a) Determine the price function p. Use x for the quantity of newspapers.
   (b) Find $\lim\limits_{x \to 2000} p(x)$.

26. (*BALLOON VOLUME*) A balloon is filled with a volume V of air, and a string is tied to seal it. Suppose the string breaks, thus allowing the air to leak out. Let V be the volume of air and t the time in seconds.

   (a) Select an appropriate t value and write a limit that describes what happens to the volume of air.
W (b) Use nonmathematical words to give a written explanation of your answer to part (a).

27. (*ENDANGERED SPECIES*) An animal is considered an endangered species if its numbers are dwindling and its habitat is threatened.

Using N for the number of animals of the species and t for the time in years, write a limit that indicates that a species will become extinct in 25 years.

28. *(GEOMETRY)* Let $P(x)$ be the perimeter of the triangle shown in the figure.

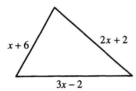

(a) Find $\lim_{x \to 7} P(x)$.

W (b) Explain the meaning of the limit in part (a) in light of this geometry setting.

29. *(NUMBER OF CHIRPS)* The number of chirps per minute made by a cricket depends on the temperature. If x is the temperature in degrees Fahrenheit, and $x \geq 40$, then the number of chirps per minute is $4x - 160$. What will be the number of chirps per minute on a cold night when the temperature approaches $40°$ Fahrenheit?

30. *(GEOMETRY)* If x represents the length of the side of a cube, then the volume of the cube is x^3. Suppose the length of each side approaches zero. What does the volume approach?

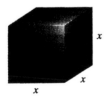

31. *(TELEPHONE CALL)* When you make a telephone call, the phone rings for 2 seconds, is quiet for 4 seconds, rings again for 2 seconds, and so on. The figure below shows the graph of the sound-level function S based on the sound from a phone call in which the caller hangs up after three rings. Here A represents the sound level in a room when the phone is quiet, and B represents the sound level when the phone is ringing.

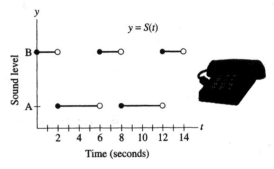

Three rings of a telephone

(a) Find $\lim_{t \to 4} S(t)$.

(b) Find $\lim_{t \to 7} S(t)$.

Consideration of a limit such as

$$\lim_{t \to 6} S(t)$$

introduces some concerns. The limit does not exist. After all, if t is approached using values less than 6 (that is, from the left), the $S(t)$ values obtained are different from those obtained using an approach through values greater than 6 (that is, from the right). These concerns are examined in the next two sections—Continuity (2.2) and One-Sided Limits (2.3).

  T̶E̶C̶H̶N̶O̶L̶O̶G̶Y̶ *E X E R C I S E S*

In the next section, graphs are used to assist in the study of limits. The graphing exercises given here can be considered a preview or a transition. If preferred, these exercises can be used instead with Section 2.2.

In Exercises 1–4, study the graph of each function in order to determine the given limit.

1. $f(x) = \dfrac{x^2 - 1}{x - 1}$ $\qquad \lim\limits_{x \to 1} f(x)$

2. $f(x) = \dfrac{3x^3 - .48x}{x - .4}$ $\qquad \lim\limits_{x \to .4} f(x)$

3. $f(x) = \dfrac{x^{2.5} - .04x^{.5}}{x^{1.5} - .2x^{.5}}$ $\qquad \lim\limits_{x \to .2} f(x)$

4. $f(x) = \dfrac{\dfrac{1}{x} - \dfrac{1}{2}}{x - 2}$ $\qquad \lim\limits_{x \to 2} f(x)$

5. Graph the function defined by

$$f(x) = (1 + x)^{1/x}$$

and zoom in as needed to determine (to one decimal place)

$$\lim_{x \to 0} (1 + x)^{1/x}$$

6. Graph the function

$$f(x) = \frac{3 - 3^x}{1 - x}$$

and zoom in repeatedly to determine (to three decimal places)

$$\lim_{x \to 1} \frac{3 - 3^x}{1 - x}$$

7. Graph the function

$$f(x) = \frac{x^2 - 4x}{\sqrt[3]{x - 4}}$$

and use the graph to determine

$$\lim_{x \to 4} \frac{x^2 - 4x}{\sqrt[3]{x - 4}}$$

Repeated zooming in will be necessary, especially since your original graph of the function will probably disguise the limit rather than reveal it.

Note   In addition to displaying graphs of functions (see Section 1.4), computer algebra systems can also evaluate limits. The limit

$$\lim_{x \to 2} (5x + 3)$$

is evaluated as follows.

Mathematica: **`Limit [5x + 3, x - > 2]`**

Maple: **`limit (5 * x + 3, x = 2);`**

If software is available, use it to evaluate the limits of Exercises 13, 17, 21, and 23.

2.2 | *CONTINUITY*

We turn to graphs in order to see why some limits cannot be found directly by substitution. To begin, let f be the function defined by $f(x) = 2x + 1$, and consider the limit of $f(x)$ as x approaches 3.

$$\lim_{x \to 3} f(x) = \lim_{x \to 3} (2x + 1) = 7$$

The graph of $y = 2x + 1$ shows that as x gets closer and closer to 3, the y values get closer and closer to 7. See Figure 4.

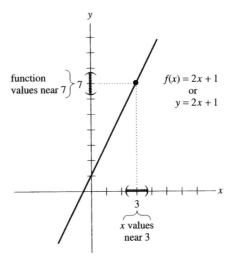

Figure 4 The function values are near 7 when the x values are near 3.

Notice that there is no break or jump in the graph of $f(x) = 2x + 1$. Functions whose graphs have no breaks, gaps, holes, or jumps in them are called **continuous functions**. If the limit of $f(x)$ as x approaches some number a is $f(a)$, then there can be no break in the graph at $x = a$. This means that when the limit of $f(x)$ as x approaches a is $f(a)$, the function is continuous at a. These observations are restated below, to provide the definition of **"function f is continuous at a."**

Function *f* Continuous at *a*

If f *is continuous at* a, then $\lim_{x \to a} f(x) = f(a)$.

If $\lim_{x \to a} f(x) = f(a)$, then f *is continuous at* a.

The definition includes three conditions that must be met for f to be continuous at a.

1. $\lim_{x \to a} f(x)$ must exist.

2. $f(a)$ must be defined.

3. The limit (in condition 1) must be equal to $f(a)$.

> **Note**
>
> A function is **continuous on an open interval** (a, b) *if it is continuous at every number in the interval. This idea will be pursued in Exercises* 44–49.

Because many of the examples and exercises of the previous section involved functions that were continuous, the limits could be determined by substituting for x the value that x was approaching. The following table serves to summarize some of those examples. Notice that in each instance the limit of $f(x)$ as x approaches a is the same as $f(a)$, which means that f is continuous at a.

function f	$\lim\limits_{x \to a} f(x)$	$f(a)$
$f(x) = 3x$	$\lim\limits_{x \to 2} 3x = 6$	$f(2) = 6$
$f(x) = 2x + 1$	$\lim\limits_{x \to 3} (2x + 1) = 7$	$f(3) = 7$
$f(x) = 15$	$\lim\limits_{x \to 2} 15 = 15$	$f(2) = 15$
$f(x) = x^3 + x$	$\lim\limits_{x \to -1} (x^3 + x) = -2$	$f(-1) = -2$
$f(x) = \dfrac{5x}{1 + x}$	$\lim\limits_{x \to 0} \dfrac{5x}{1 + x} = 0$	$f(0) = 0$

Some types of functions are continuous at every number in their domain. Limits of such functions can always be determined by the substitution approach. *Polynomial functions* are continuous at every real number. *Rational functions* are continuous at every real number, except at numbers for which the denominator is zero.

Consider the following limit:

$$\lim_{x \to 3} \frac{x^2 + x - 12}{x - 3}$$

In the previous section, an attempt to determine this limit by substituting 3 for x led to division by zero. Specifically, using 3 for x will result in 0/0, which is undefined. The function

$$f(x) = \frac{x^2 + x - 12}{x - 3}$$

is not continuous at 3 because $f(3)$ is not defined. That is precisely why we cannot evaluate this limit simply by using 3 for x in $f(x)$. However, the limit can be evaluated without using a calculator. In fact, the next example shows the use of *factoring* to determine the limit when 0/0 results from the substitution approach.

EXAMPLE 1   Find the limit.

$$\lim_{x \to 3} \frac{x^2 + x - 12}{x - 3}$$

SOLUTION   As suggested above, we begin by factoring.

$$\lim_{x \to 3} \frac{x^2 + x - 12}{x - 3} = \lim_{x \to 3} \frac{(x - 3)(x + 4)}{(x - 3)}$$

The factors $(x - 3)$ can be eliminated by division as long as x is not 3. (If x is 3, then we would be dividing by zero.) And we know that x is not 3 because the limit as $x \to 3$ indicates that x is *approaching* 3, getting closer and closer to 3, but is not actually 3. The limit can be simplified as

$$\lim_{x \to 3} \frac{(x - 3)(x + 4)}{(x - 3)} = \lim_{x \to 3} (x + 4) = 7$$

Thus, the limit equals 7.   ◆

Consider the following two ideas, which are based on the function and results of Example 1.

1. For this function, $\lim_{x \to a} f(x) \neq f(a)$. Specifically, we have $\lim_{x \to 3} f(x) \neq f(3)$, because $\lim_{x \to 3} f(x) = 7$ and $f(3)$ is not defined. Thus, this function is *not continuous* at 3. We say it is **discontinuous** at 3.

2. Because

$$\frac{x^2 + x - 12}{x - 3} \quad \text{reduces to} \quad x + 4 \quad \text{when } x \neq 3$$

the two expressions are in fact equal to each other for all values of x except 3. Hence the graph of

$$f(x) = \frac{x^2 + x - 12}{x - 3}$$

is the same as the graph of

$$f(x) = x + 4 \qquad (x \neq 3)$$

It is the graph of the line $y = x + 4$, with a point missing at $x = 3$. It is a straight line with a hole in it at $(3, 7)$. Visually, since the graph has a break (hole) in it at $x = 3$, the function is discontinuous there. See Figure 5.

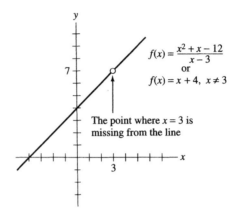

Figure 5 Function *f* is discontinous at 3

Here are three applications involving **discontinuities.**

EXAMPLE 2 *FLASH PHOTOGRAPHY*

Consider what you see when someone takes a photograph using a flash. The level of light in the room is constant. Suddenly, the flash goes off and creates more light for an instant. Then the light in the room returns immediately to the preflash level. See Figure 6 and note that the graphed function is discontinuous at t_1.

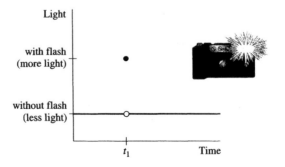

Figure 6 The flash goes off at time t_1.   ◆

EXAMPLE 3 *POSTAL RATES FOR FIRST-CLASS MAIL*

The function that describes first-class mail postage rates has discontinuities. The cost of first-class mail (1996) is 32¢ for the first ounce (or less) and then 23¢ for each additional ounce above that. The graph for up to 4 ounces is shown. (See Figure 7.)

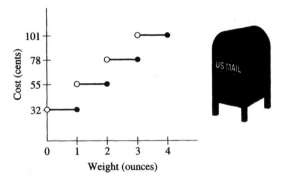

Figure 7 Postal rates for first-class mail

Notice the discontinuities at 1, 2, and 3 ounces, where the graph jumps.   ◆

> *Note*
>
> In Example 3, the discontinuities at 1, 2, and 3 are obvious from the jumps in the graph. From a limit perspective, the function is not continuous at 1, 2, and 3 because the limit does not exist. In each case, the limit when approaching from the left is different from the limit when approaching from the right. This concern will be pursued when one-sided limits are studied in the next section.

EXAMPLE 4 *ADAPTATION OF THE EYE TO DARKNESS*

Sensory psychologists have studied the adaptation of the human eye to light and dark. Adaptation begins with the cones of the eyes. After about 8 minutes the rods take over the adaptation. The graph of the adaptation function shows a discontinuity at the time ($t = 8$ minutes) when the rods take over. See Figure 8.

Once again we have a situation in which the limit does not exist (at 8) because the left-hand and right-hand limits are different.   ◆

Figure 8 Adaptation of the human eye to darkness

2.2 Exercises

Evaluate each limit in Exercises 1–10 by using the substitution approach (plugging in). Keep in mind that the method will work because each function given here is continuous at the number that x is approaching.

1. $\lim\limits_{x \to 10} (3x - 2)$

2. $\lim\limits_{x \to 4} (x^3 - 7)$ 57

3. $\lim\limits_{x \to -3} (1 - 9x + x^2)$ ~37

4. $\lim\limits_{x \to 0} (12 - x^2)$

5. $\lim\limits_{x \to 5} \dfrac{x - 3}{x + 2}$ $\frac{2}{7}$

6. $\lim\limits_{x \to 7} \dfrac{x + 6}{x - 3}$ $\frac{13}{4}$

7. $\lim\limits_{x \to 2} \dfrac{1 - x}{x^2 + 1}$ $-\frac{1}{5}$

8. $\lim\limits_{x \to 4} \dfrac{x - 1}{1 + 3x^2}$

9. $\lim\limits_{x \to -4} \sqrt{x^2 + 9}$ -16

10. $\lim\limits_{x \to 40} \sqrt{1 + 2x}$

Attempt to evaluate each limit in Exercises 11–18 by the substitution approach. If 0/0 is produced, simplify the expression by factoring and then try again.

11. $\lim\limits_{x \to 4} \dfrac{x^2 - x - 12}{x - 4}$ 0

12. $\lim\limits_{x \to 3} \dfrac{x^2 + 2x - 15}{x - 3}$

13. $\lim\limits_{x \to 0} \dfrac{x^2}{x}$

14. $\lim\limits_{x \to 5} \dfrac{x^2 + 8x + 15}{x + 3}$

15. $\lim\limits_{x \to 2} \dfrac{x - 2}{x + 3}$

16. $\lim\limits_{x \to 1} \dfrac{x - 1}{x + 1}$

17. $\lim\limits_{x \to 1} \dfrac{3x - 3}{x^2 - 1}$

18. $\lim\limits_{x \to 2} \dfrac{x^2 - 4}{2x - 4}$

Sketch a graph of each function in Exercises 19–22. Use the limit and continuity information obtained from the exercise referenced.

19. $f(x) = \dfrac{x^2 - x - 12}{x - 4}$ See Exercise 11.

20. $f(x) = \dfrac{x^2 + 2x - 15}{x - 3}$ See Exercise 12.

21. $f(x) = \dfrac{3x}{x}$

22. $f(x) = \dfrac{x^2}{x}$ See Exercise 13.

 In Exercises 23–26, each function is discontinuous at the given value of x because f is not defined there. In each case, attempt to obtain $f(x)$ for the given value of x and indicate why the attempt fails.

23. $f(x) = \sqrt{x - 4}$ at $x = 3$

24. $f(x) = \dfrac{x + 5}{x - 2}$ at $x = 2$

25. $f(x) = \dfrac{x - 1}{x + 1}$ at $x = -1$

26. $f(x) = \dfrac{x^2 + 3x - 28}{x - 4}$ at $x = 4$

In Exercises 27–30, indicate for what value of x the graphed function is discontinuous.

27.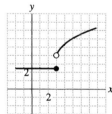

28.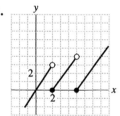

29.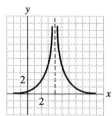

30.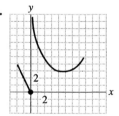

31. *(SOCIAL WORK)* A social worker begins a new job in January 1994 (1/94) and is given a specified workload. Because it is based on the number of cases assigned, the workload may be two thousand hours or more. Many of the cases will be completed during the year. Additional cases are given to the social worker at the beginning of each successive year (1/95, 1/96, and so on).

(a) From the graph, determine when the discontinuities occur.

W **(b)** Using a workload perspective, explain why these discontinuities occur.

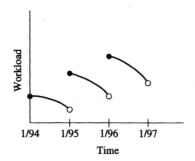

32. (BANKING) In the banking industry, a failed bank or savings and loan association is often acquired by a healthy institution. The graph below shows the assets of an acquiring institution as a function of time.

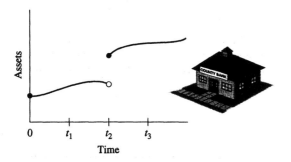

(a) When (for what value of t) does the stronger institution acquire the failed institution?

W **(b)** Explain the reason for the discontinuity at t_2 (in terms of the banking situation).

33. (POSTAL INSURANCE) The post office allows customers to insure valuable mail. The rates are as follows: 75¢ for coverage up to and including $50, $1.60 for coverage above $50 and up to and including $100, $2.40 for coverage above $100 up to and including $200, and $3.50 for coverage above $200 and up to and including $300. Sketch a graph of this function and indicate where the discontinuities are found.

34. (COMPOUND INTEREST) $1000 is invested at 8% per year compounded quarterly (that is, every three months, or four times per year). This means that the investment begins with $1000, at 3 months it becomes $1020, at 6 month it is $1040, at 9 months it is $1061, and at one year it is $1082.

Sketch a graph of this function, one that gives the amount of money at any time during the first year. Indicate where the discontinuities are to be found.

35. (LONG-DISTANCE CALL) A person-to-person phone call from Chicago to Los Angeles costs $3.50 for the first minute and 25¢ per minute after that. Sketch a graph showing the total cost of a call for all times up to 5 minutes.

36. (PLUMBER'S CHARGES) A plumber charges $40 to come to your house and $30 per half-hour (or fraction of a half-hour) of work once he arrives. Graph the function, showing the plumber's charges for times up to 3 hours.

37. (CAR RENTAL COST) Suppose a rental car costs $25 per day, with no charge for mileage. Graph the function showing the cost for as many as 5 days.

W **38.** Suppose that f is not defined at a. Does this mean that $\lim_{x \to a} f(x)$ does not exist? Explain.

W **39.** If $\lim_{x \to 2} f(x) = 5$, must $f(2)$ be equal to 5? Explain.

W **40.** Given the graph of a function, how can you tell if it is not continuous at some number such as 7?

W **41.** You are given a function f and asked to determine (without a graph) if it is continuous at 4. Explain the procedure.

W **42. (COUPON DOUBLING)** A popular supermarket practice is to double the face value of manufacturers' coupons. Under this plan a 25¢ coupon is worth 50¢, and a 40¢ coupon has a value of 80¢. Some stores, however, double the value only for coupons that have a face value of 50¢ or less. Thus, a 50¢ coupon is worth $1.00, but a 60¢ coupon is worth only 60¢. A graph of this doubling plan is shown next. (x is the face value of the coupon in cents, and y is the value the store will allow.)

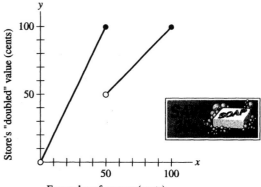

(a) Where does the function have a "jump" of discontinuity? Explain.

(b) How would you *redefine* the coupon values for $50 < x \le 100$ in order to eliminate the jump discontinuity, avoid doubling for $x > 50$, and eliminate the problem that a 60¢ coupon is worth less than a 50¢ coupon?

W **43.** **(HICCUPS)** Suppose that a person has the hiccups. Describe the appearance, and explain the discontinuities, of the graph of the sound emitted from the person as a function of time.

As noted earlier, a function is *continuous on an open interval* (a, b) if it is continuous at every number in the interval. In Exercises 44–49, examine each function and interval. Indicate whether the function is continuous on the interval and, if it is not, where in the interval it is discontinuous.

44. $f(x) = 1 - x^3$ on $(-\infty, \infty)$

45. $f(x) = x^2 + 8x + 1$ on $(-\infty, \infty)$

46. $f(x) = \dfrac{3}{x - 4}$ on $(0, 30)$

47. $f(x) = \dfrac{1}{x^2}$ on $(-3, 10)$

48. $f(x) = \sqrt{x - 1}$ on $(0, 1)$

49. $f(x) = \sqrt{x}$ on $(-\infty, 0)$

Evaluate each limit in Exercises 50–51. *Hint*: In Exercise 50, rationalize the denominator by multiplying the denominator and numerator by $\sqrt{x} + 2$. In Exercise 51, rationalize the numerator by multiplying both numerator and denominator by $\sqrt{x} + 1$.

50. $\displaystyle\lim_{x \to 4} \dfrac{x - 4}{\sqrt{x} - 2}$

51. $\displaystyle\lim_{x \to 1} \dfrac{\sqrt{x} - 1}{x - 1}$

Evaluate each limit in Exercises 52–53. You will need to simplify the complex fraction in each case.

52. $\displaystyle\lim_{x \to 4} \dfrac{\dfrac{1}{4} - \dfrac{1}{x}}{x - 4}$

53. $\displaystyle\lim_{x \to 3} \dfrac{\dfrac{1}{x} - \dfrac{1}{3}}{x - 3}$

W **54.** Describe a realistic situation that can be represented by a function having at least one discontinuity. Do not use situations presented in any of the examples or exercises in the text.

TECHNOLOGY *EXERCISES*

1. The function

$$f(x) = \frac{x^2 + 1}{x^2 - 5x + 3}$$

is discontinuous at two values of x, because f is not defined there. Graph the denominator function $y = x^2 - 5x + 3$ in order to determine (to the nearest tenth) the two numbers at which f is not continuous.

2. Repeat the procedure of Exercise 1, but use

$$f(x) = \frac{3x + 1}{x^2 + 6x - 2}$$

and the associated denominator function $y = x^2 + 6x - 2$.

3. Repeat the procedure of Exercise 1, but use

$$f(x) = \frac{5x^2}{x^3 - 2x^2 + x - 1}$$

Find (to the nearest tenth) the one number at which f is not continuous.

Graph each function in Exercises 4–7. Use x in $[-10, 10]$ and y in $[-10, 10]$. Indicate over what interval the function is discontinuous because it is not defined.

4. $f(x) = \sqrt{x^4 - 81}$ **5.** $f(x) = \sqrt{10 - 2x}$

6. $f(x) = \sqrt{3 + \dfrac{2x}{4}}$ **7.** $f(x) = \sqrt{\dfrac{92x}{x^2 + 8.3}}$

2.3 | *ONE-SIDED LIMITS*

As you know, $\lim\limits_{x \to a} f(x)$ is the value that $f(x)$ approaches as x gets closer and closer to a.

Consider then $\lim\limits_{x \to 2} f(x)$ for the function graphed in Figure 9.

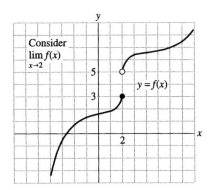

Figure 9

From the graph, you can see that as x approaches 2 from the left (that is, via numbers less than 2), $f(x)$ approaches 3. In other words, coming from the left, the closer x gets to 2, the closer $f(x)$ gets to 3. By contrast, the graph also shows that as x approaches 2 from the right (via numbers greater than 2), $f(x)$ approaches 5. The limit is different depending on the side from which x is approaching 2. This situation suggests the following:

1. The graph will have a break at $x = 2$, and thus f is discontinuous at 2.

2. $\lim\limits_{x \to 2} f(x)$ does not exist in the usual sense.

The **left-hand limit** and **right-hand limit** can be considered separately as special limits having their own notation.

$$\text{The left-hand limit:} \quad \lim_{x \to 2^-} f(x) = 3$$

$$\text{The right-hand limit:} \quad \lim_{x \to 2^+} f(x) = 5$$

The raised minus specifies "from the left." The raised plus specifies "from the right." Limits of this type are called **one-sided limits.**

EXAMPLE 1   For the function graphed in Figure 10, determine the one-sided limits $\lim_{x \to 3^-} f(x)$ and $\lim_{x \to 3^+} f(x)$.

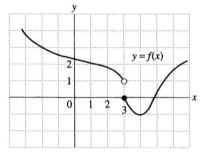

Figure 10

SOLUTION   A study of the graph yields the two limit statements

$$\lim_{x \to 3^-} f(x) = 1 \qquad \text{and} \qquad \lim_{x \to 3^+} f(x) = 0 \qquad\qquad \blacklozenge$$

APPLIED

EXAMPLE 2   **POSTAL RATES FOR FIRST CLASS MAIL**

Consider the first-class postage function graphed in Figure 11.

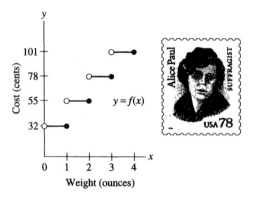

Figure 11

Determine $\lim\limits_{x \to 1} f(x)$.

SOLUTION From the graph we can see that

$$\lim_{x \to 1^-} f(x) = 32 \qquad \text{and} \qquad \lim_{x \to 1^+} f(x) = 55$$

Since the left-hand limit and the right-hand limit are different, it follows that

$$\lim_{x \to 1} f(x) \quad \text{does not exist} \qquad \blacklozenge$$

EXAMPLE 3 Determine $\lim\limits_{x \to 0} \sqrt{x}$.

SOLUTION At first glance this limit may look simple, since you could easily believe that the limit is zero. However, *the limit is not zero*. Although it is true that

$$\lim_{x \to 0^+} \sqrt{x} = 0$$

it is also true that

$$\lim_{x \to 0^-} \sqrt{x} \quad \text{does not exist}$$

Why? Because approaching from the left in this instance means using numbers less than zero (negative numbers) for x, and $\sqrt{x}$ is not defined for such numbers. *A function must be defined for all of the values of x along the approach, or else the limit does not exist.* Figure 12 shows the graph of $f(x) = \sqrt{x}$, which is defined only for $x \geq 0$.

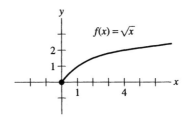

Figure 12 A function defined only for $x \geq 0$

Our conclusion:

$$\lim_{x \to 0^+} \sqrt{x} = 0 \qquad \lim_{x \to 0^-} \sqrt{x} \quad \text{does not exist} \qquad \lim_{x \to 0} \sqrt{x} \quad \text{does not exist} \qquad \blacklozenge$$

In general,

$$\lim_{x \to a} f(x) \text{ exists if both } \lim_{x \to a^-} f(x) \text{ and}$$
$$\lim_{x \to a^+} f(x) \text{ exist and are equal.}$$

In Example 1, both one-sided limits existed, but they were different. The same thing was true in Example 2. In Example 3, one of the one-sided limits failed to exist. (A look back at the first limit presented in Section 2.1 shows an instance where both one-sided limits existed and were the same.)

EXAMPLE 4   Determine $\lim\limits_{x \to 0^-} f(x)$ and $\lim\limits_{x \to 0^+} f(x)$ for the function defined by

$$f(x) = \begin{cases} x^2 & x \le 0 \\ x + 3 & x > 0 \end{cases}$$

SOLUTION   In this two-piece function, the value of $f(x)$ is computed as x^2 when $x \le 0$ but as $x + 3$ when $x > 0$. Thus,

$$\lim_{x \to 0^-} f(x) = \lim_{x \to 0^-} x^2 = 0 \qquad \lim_{x \to 0^+} f(x) = \lim_{x \to 0^+} (x + 3) = 3$$

Since the limits are different, we conclude that $\lim\limits_{x \to 0} f(x)$ does not exist.

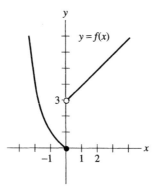

Figure 13   ◆

EXAMPLE 5   Determine $\lim\limits_{x \to 1^-} f(x)$ and $\lim\limits_{x \to 1^+} f(x)$ for the function defined by

$$f(x) = \begin{cases} 2x + 1 & x \le 1 \\ 4 - x & x > 1 \end{cases}$$

SOLUTION   Here

$$\lim_{x \to 1^-} f(x) = \lim_{x \to 1^-} (2x + 1) = 3$$

$$\lim_{x \to 1^+} f(x) = \lim_{x \to 1^+} (4 - x) = 3$$

Because the left-hand and right-hand limits are the same, 3, we conclude that

$$\lim_{x \to 1} f(x) = 3$$

Furthermore, since $f(1) = 3$, we have $\lim\limits_{x \to 1} f(x) = f(1)$. In other words, the function is continuous at 1. The graph is shown in Figure 14.

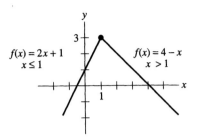

Figure 14

◆

Note

Recall that for f to be continous at a, we need

$$\lim_{x \to a} f(x) = f(a)$$

In other words, the following three conditions must be met:

1. $\lim_{x \to a} f(x)$ must exist.

2. f must be defined at a.

3. The limit (in condition 1) must be equal to $f(a)$.

In Example 5, the conditions are met at $x = 1$, so f is continuous at 1. In Example 4, $\lim_{x \to 0} f(x)$ fails to exist because the left- and right-hand limits are different. Thus, f is *not continuous at 0*, because the limit fails to exist.

2.3   Exercises

Evaluate each one-sided limit in Exercises 1–6. (*Note*: Some limits may not exist.) Be sure to refer to the proper graph in each case.

1. (a) $\lim_{x \to 2^-} f(x)$

   (b) $\lim_{x \to 2^+} f(x)$

2. (a) $\lim_{x \to 0^-} g(x)$

   (b) $\lim_{x \to 0^+} g(x)$

The graphs are at the right.

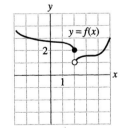

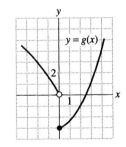

3. (a) $\lim\limits_{x \to 1^-} h(x)$

(b) $\lim\limits_{x \to 1^+} h(x)$

4. (a) $\lim\limits_{x \to 4^-} k(x)$

(b) $\lim\limits_{x \to 4^+} k(x)$

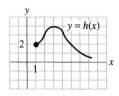

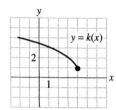

5. (a) $\lim\limits_{x \to 5^-} m(x)$

(b) $\lim\limits_{x \to 5^+} m(x)$

6. (a) $\lim\limits_{x \to 4^-} n(x)$

(b) $\lim\limits_{x \to 4^+} n(x)$

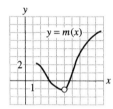

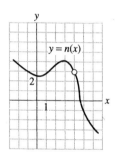

W In Exercises 7–12, explain why each limit does not exist.

7. $\lim\limits_{x \to 0^-} \sqrt{2x}$

8. $\lim\limits_{x \to 4^-} \sqrt{x - 4}$

9. $\lim\limits_{x \to 1^+} \sqrt{1 - x}$

10. $\lim\limits_{x \to 5^+} \sqrt{5 - x}$

11. $\lim\limits_{x \to 0} \sqrt{3x}$

12. $\lim\limits_{x \to 2} \sqrt{x - 2}$

Evaluate each one-sided limit in Exercises 13–16.

13. (a) $\lim\limits_{x \to 0^-} f(x)$

(b) $\lim\limits_{x \to 0^+} f(x)$

$$f(x) = \begin{cases} x + 2 & x \leq 0 \\ x - 1 & x > 0 \end{cases}$$

14. (a) $\lim\limits_{x \to 0^-} g(x)$

(b) $\lim\limits_{x \to 0^+} g(x)$

$$g(x) = \begin{cases} 3x & x \leq 0 \\ x^2 & x > 0 \end{cases}$$

15. (a) $\lim\limits_{x \to 2^-} h(x)$

(b) $\lim\limits_{x \to 2^+} h(x)$

$$h(x) = \begin{cases} 1 - x & x \leq 2 \\ x^2 - 5 & x > 2 \end{cases}$$

16. (a) $\lim\limits_{x \to 4^-} j(x)$

(b) $\lim\limits_{x \to 4^+} j(x)$

$$j(x) = \begin{cases} 5x - 1 & x < 4 \\ 4x + 3 & x \geq 4 \end{cases}$$

In Exercises 17–20, find the limit, if it exists, or indicate that it does not exist. The functions used here (f, g, h, and j) are the functions of Exercises 13–16.

17. $\lim\limits_{x \to 0} f(x)$

18. $\lim\limits_{x \to 0} g(x)$

19. $\lim\limits_{x \to 2} h(x)$

20. $\lim\limits_{x \to 4} j(x)$

21. *(POSTAL INSURANCE)* Function M (shown in the figure) gives the cost of postal insurance for coverage up to $200.

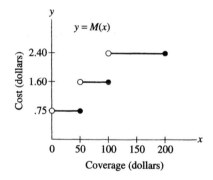

(a) Determine $M(120)$.

(b) Determine $M(100)$.

(c) Determine $\lim\limits_{x \to 50^+} M(x)$, if it exists.

(d) Determine $\lim\limits_{x \to 50^-} M(x)$, if it exists.

(e) Determine $\lim\limits_{x \to 50} M(x)$, if it exists.

(f) Is M continuous at 50?

W (g) Is M continuous at 120? Explain.

22. *(COMPUTER RENTAL COST)* A computer rental company charges $30 per week to rent a basic PC. Let $C(x)$ be the cost of renting the PC for x weeks. The graph of $y = C(x)$ for $0 \leq x \leq 4$ is shown in the figure at the top of the next page.

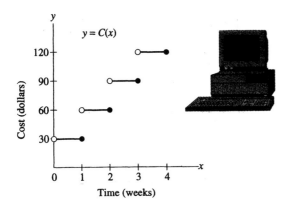

(a) Determine $\lim\limits_{x \to 2^-} C(x)$, if it exists.

(b) Determine $\lim\limits_{x \to 2^+} C(x)$, if it exists.

(c) Determine $\lim\limits_{x \to 2} C(x)$, if it exists.

W **(d)** Is C continuous at 2? Explain.

23. **(HOME LOAN RATES)** The following graph shows the interest rates offered by a lender who examines the market every 30 days for possible rate changes. The function is called H. The variable t represents the number of days since the beginning of the year.

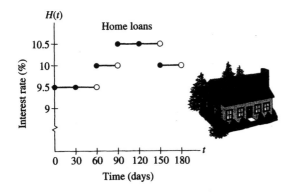

(a) Determine $H(60)$.

(b) Determine $H(100)$.

(c) Is H discontinuous at 30?

(d) Find $\lim\limits_{t \to 60^-} H(t)$.

(e) Find $\lim\limits_{t \to 60^+} H(t)$.

(f) Is H continuous at 60?

24. **(PARKING FEE)** A downtown parking lot charges \$2 for the first hour (or portion of the first hour) and then \$1 per hour (or portion of an hour). The maximum fee for a day is \$8. Let p be the function that gives the parking fee in terms of time t, where t is in hours.

(a) Sketch a graph of function p.

(b) At what values of t is p discontinuous?

(c) What is the value of $p(1/2)$?

(d) What is the value of $p(12)$?

25. **(MEDICINE)** A patient is given 600 milligrams of a medicine by injection. As a follow-up, the patient receives 200-milligram injections every 3 hours. Let $A(t)$ be the amount of medicine in the bloodstream at any time t hours. Consider the graph.

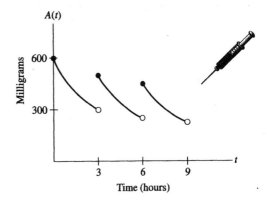

(a) Determine $\lim\limits_{t \to 3^-} A(t)$.

(b) Determine $\lim\limits_{t \to 3^+} A(t)$.

W **(c)** Explain, in terms of the application setting, why the two limits you have found are so different in value. Use nonmathematical language.

26. **(LIMITING TEMPERATURE)** The temperature of a thermometer that is x inches from a fire is given by

$$T(x) = \frac{840}{1 + .5x} \quad \text{degrees Fahrenheit}$$

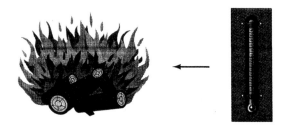

(a) Determine $\lim\limits_{x \to 0^+} T(x)$.

W **(b)** Use words to express the result of part (a).

W **(c)** Why is a one-sided limit appropriate for this application?

(d) Assume that the fire and the thermometer are outside, where the air temperature is 60°. Determine a reasonable domain for function T.

W In Exercises 27–30, explain why the given function is *continuous* at $x = a$. Be sure to determine the limit as x approaches a and the value of $f(a)$, and use them in your explanation. (You may want to read Example 5 and the note that follows it.)

27. $f(x) = \begin{cases} 3x + 2 & x \le 3 \\ 17 - 2x & x > 3 \end{cases}$ at $x = 3$

28. $f(x) = \begin{cases} 1 + x & x \le 7 \\ 4x - 20 & x > 7 \end{cases}$ at $x = 7$

29. $f(x) = \begin{cases} x^2 + 1 & x \le 5 \\ 3x & x > 5 \end{cases}$ at $x = 2$

30. $f(x) = \begin{cases} \sqrt{x} & 0 \le x \le 4 \\ x^3 & x > 4 \end{cases}$ at $x = 3$

W In Exercises 31–34, explain why the function is *not continuous* at $x = a$. (You may want to read the note that follows Example 5.)

31. $f(x) = \begin{cases} 5x + 1 & 0 \le x \le 2 \\ x + 14 & 2 < x \le 5 \end{cases}$ at $x = 2$

32. $f(x) = \begin{cases} 4 + 2x & x \le 0 \\ 9 - x & x > 0 \end{cases}$ at $x = 0$

33. $f(x) = \begin{cases} 3x + 2 & x \le 4 \\ x^2 - 3 & x > 4 \end{cases}$ at $x = 4$

34. $f(x) = \begin{cases} x^3 & -5 \le x \le -1 \\ x^2 & x > -1 \end{cases}$ at $x = -1$

W **35.** Suppose $\lim\limits_{x \to 3^-} f(x) = 5$ and $\lim\limits_{x \to 3} f(x) = 5$. Is it possible that $\lim\limits_{x \to 3^+} f(x) = 4$? Explain.

W **36.** Describe a realistic situation that can be represented by a function for which $\lim\limits_{x \to a} f(x)$ does not exist because the left- and right-hand limits are different for some number a. Do not use situations presented in any of the examples or exercises in the text.

TECHNOLOGY *EXERCISES*

In Exercises 1 and 2, graph the function to determine whether the given limit exists. If the limit exists, find it. If the limit does not exist, so indicate.

1. $f(x) = 1 + \sqrt{x^2 - 4x + 3}$

   (a) $\lim\limits_{x \to 2} f(x)$ **(b)** $\lim\limits_{x \to 3^-} f(x)$ **(c)** $\lim\limits_{x \to 3^+} f(x)$ **(d)** $\lim\limits_{x \to 3} f(x)$ **(e)** $\lim\limits_{x \to 4} f(x)$

2. $f(x) = 5 - \sqrt{8 - x^{1.5}}$

   (a) $\lim\limits_{x \to 4^-} f(x)$ **(b)** $\lim\limits_{x \to 4^+} f(x)$ **(c)** $\lim\limits_{x \to 4} f(x)$

3. Graph $f(x) = x^x$ and use repeated zooming in to determine

$$\lim_{x \to 0^+} x^x$$

Note On graphing calculators, piecewise functions such as

$$f(x) = \begin{cases} 2x & 0 < x < 5 \\ 3 & x \geq 5 \end{cases}$$

are easy to graph. This function would be entered into TI calculators as

$$Y1 = (2X)(0 < X)(X < 5) + (3)(X \geq 5)$$

If you keep the calculator in the standard **connected** mode, the calculator will draw a vertical line of connection between the two pieces of the graph. (Try this.) *To avoid this problem*, use **dot** mode. (Try this too, and compare.)

Graph each piecewise function in Exercises 4–7. Indicate whether the function appears to be continuous on the interval given for *x*. If it is not continuous, indicate for what *x* the function is discontinuous.

4. $f(x) = \begin{cases} x^2 + 1 & x \leq 1 \\ x + 2 & x > 1 \end{cases}$ 　　　　**5.** $f(x) = \begin{cases} |7.4 - 3x| & x \leq 3.5 \\ x^2 - 8.1 & x > 3.5 \end{cases}$

6. $f(x) = \begin{cases} 6x - 8 & x < 2.25 \\ 4 + \sqrt{x} & x \geq 2.25 \end{cases}$ 　　**7.** $f(x) = \begin{cases} x^2 + 1.86 & 0 < x < 1.8 \\ \sqrt{9x + 9.81} & x \geq 1.8 \end{cases}$

Note Evaluation of limits by computer algebra systems (see Section 2.1) can be extended to one-sided limits. The *Maple* command

```
limit(sqrt(x), x = 0, right);
```

will evaluate the limit

$$\lim_{x \to 0^+} \sqrt{x}$$

The corresponding *Mathematica* command is

```
Limit[Sqrt[x], x -> 0, Direction -> -1]
```

For the "Direction," use −1 to approach from the right and 1 to approach from the left.

2.4 | LIMITS AT INFINITY

Sometimes we are concerned with the behavior of a function *f* as the magnitude of the variable increases without bound (that is, the magnitude becomes infinitely large). The limits studied in such instances are called **limits at infinity** and are written as

$$\lim_{x \to \infty} f(x) \qquad \text{and} \qquad \lim_{x \to -\infty} f(x)$$

The notation $x \to \infty$ can be read "as *x* increases without bound" or "as *x* tends toward infinity." Similarly, $x \to -\infty$ is read "as *x* decreases without bound" or "as *x* tends toward minus infinity."

Consider the function $f(x) = 1/x$. The larger x becomes, the closer $1/x$ gets to zero. The table that follows illustrates this statement. The graph of $f(x) = 1/x$ also shows this—that as x becomes larger, $1/x$ gets closer to 0. See Figure 15.

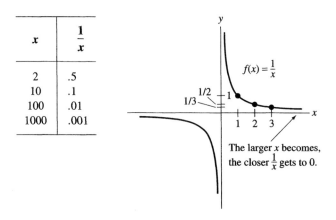

x	$\dfrac{1}{x}$
2	.5
10	.1
100	.01
1000	.001

$f(x) = \dfrac{1}{x}$

The larger x becomes, the closer $\dfrac{1}{x}$ gets to 0.

Figure 15

We say that the limit of $1/x$ as x increases without bound is 0. This is written

$$\lim_{x \to \infty} \frac{1}{x} = 0$$

In a similar manner, we can determine that

$$\lim_{x \to -\infty} \frac{1}{x} = 0$$

Note that $1/x$ is *never equal to zero*. The limits above merely describe the behavior of $1/x$ as the magnitude of x increases without bound. They describe the tendency of $1/x$ toward zero as x tends toward infinity.

Consider next the function defined by

$$f(x) = \frac{1}{x^n} \qquad n \text{ is a positive integer}$$

Compare $1/x^n$ and $1/x$, noting that the magnitude of x^n is larger than the magnitude of x when x is approaching infinity or minus infinity. It then follows that

$$\lim_{x \to \infty} \frac{1}{x^n} = 0 \qquad \text{and} \qquad \lim_{x \to -\infty} \frac{1}{x^n} = 0 \qquad (n \text{ is a positive integer})$$

If the function is $f(x) = c/x^n$, where c is a finite constant, then the limit as x increases or decreases without bound will still be zero. Consider that c/x^n is $c \cdot 1/x^n$, and $1/x^n$ will be zero in the limit, so that c/x^n will be $c \cdot 0$, or 0 in the limit. This important result is stated next.

> **Theorem for Limits at Infinity**
>
> $$\lim_{x \to \infty} \frac{c}{x^n} = 0 \qquad\qquad \lim_{x \to -\infty} \frac{c}{x^n} = 0$$
>
> c is a constant, n is a positive integer.

EXAMPLE 1   Evaluate each limit.

(a) $\lim\limits_{x \to \infty} \dfrac{1}{x^8}$ **(b)** $\lim\limits_{x \to -\infty} \dfrac{500}{x^3}$ **(c)** $\lim\limits_{x \to \infty} \dfrac{-30}{x^2}$

SOLUTION   These limits can be determined by using the Theorem for Limits at Infinity.

(a) $\lim\limits_{x \to \infty} \dfrac{1}{x^8} = 0$ **(b)** $\lim\limits_{x \to -\infty} \dfrac{500}{x^3} = 0$ **(c)** $\lim\limits_{x \to \infty} \dfrac{-30}{x^2} = 0$ ◆

EXAMPLE 2   Determine $\lim\limits_{x \to \infty} \dfrac{3x + 2}{4x + 9}$.

SOLUTION   This limit does not appear to fit the c/x^n form under consideration. However, if each term of the numerator and denominator is divided by x, the expression will consist only of constants and terms that are of the form c/x^n. Then we can apply the limit theorems (from Section 2.1), which do hold for limits at infinity.

$$\lim_{x \to \infty} \frac{3x + 2}{4x + 9} = \lim_{x \to \infty} \frac{\dfrac{3x}{x} + \dfrac{2}{x}}{\dfrac{4x}{x} + \dfrac{9}{x}} = \lim_{x \to \infty} \frac{3 + \dfrac{2}{x}}{4 + \dfrac{9}{x}} = \frac{\lim\limits_{x \to \infty} \left(3 + \dfrac{2}{x}\right)}{\lim\limits_{x \to \infty} \left(4 + \dfrac{9}{x}\right)}$$

$$= \frac{\lim\limits_{x \to \infty} 3 + \lim\limits_{x \to \infty} \dfrac{2}{x}}{\lim\limits_{x \to \infty} 4 + \lim\limits_{x \to \infty} \dfrac{9}{x}} = \frac{3 + 0}{4 + 0} = \frac{3}{4}$$

Note that in the limit, $2/x$ tends to 0 and $9/x$ tends to 0.   ◆

EXAMPLE 3   Determine $\lim\limits_{x \to -\infty} \dfrac{x^3 - 8x + 1}{5x^3 - 3x^2 - 17}$.

SOLUTION   As an extension of the approach used in Example 2, divide each term of the numerator and denominator by *the highest power of x present in the denominator*, namely x^3. The resulting expression will consist only of constants and terms of the form c/x^n—each of which is zero in the limit, according to the Theorem for Limits at Infinity. Thus,

$$\lim_{x \to -\infty} \frac{x^3 - 8x + 1}{5x^3 - 3x^2 - 17} = \lim_{x \to -\infty} \frac{1 - \dfrac{8}{x^2} + \dfrac{1}{x^3}}{5 - \dfrac{3}{x} - \dfrac{17}{x^3}} = \frac{1 - 0 + 0}{5 - 0 - 0} = \frac{1}{5}$$ ◆

Note

The idea of dividing each term by a power of x is used *only* for limits at infinity. It will not help in the evaluation of other kinds of limits.

In the next section, we will see that with limits at infinity such as those of Examples 2 and 3, if the degree of the numerator is greater than the degree of the denominator, then the limit of the entire expression as x approaches infinity or minus infinity will be infinite.

A limit at infinity such as $\lim_{x \to \infty} (1/x) = 0$ describes the behavior of the function $f(x) = 1/x$ as x tends toward infinity. The function values approach 0 as x tends toward infinity. The graph in Figure 16 shows how the curve tends toward the line $y = 0$ as x approaches infinity.

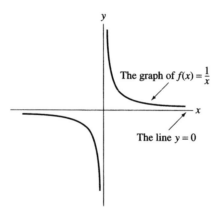

The graph of $f(x) = \frac{1}{x}$

The line $y = 0$

Figure 16

We say that the x axis (the horizontal line $y = 0$) is an *asymptote* for the graph of the function defined by $f(x) = 1/x$. In general,

---

The line $y = L$ is a **horizontal asymptote** for the graph of $y = f(x)$ if the limit at either infinity or minus infinity is the number L.

EXAMPLE 4   Determine the horizontal asymptote for the graph of $f(x) = \dfrac{3x + 2}{4x + 9}$.

SOLUTION   In Example 2, the limit of $f(x)$ as $x \to \infty$ was determined to be 3/4.

$$\lim_{x \to \infty} \frac{3x + 2}{4x + 9} = \frac{3}{4}$$

Thus, $y = 3/4$ is a horizontal asymptote for the graph of the function.

APPLIED

EXAMPLE 5   **LIMIT ON PROFIT**

Suppose that profit from the sale of x units is $P(x) = 2000 - \dfrac{300}{x}$ dollars for $x \geq 1$. Considering the limit of $P(x)$ as x increases without bound, we find that

$$\lim_{x \to \infty} P(x) = \lim_{x \to \infty} \left(2000 - \frac{300}{x} \right)$$

$$= \lim_{x \to \infty} 2000 - \lim_{x \to \infty} \frac{300}{x}$$

$$= 2000 - 0$$

$$= 2000$$

The graph of function P shows profit beginning at \$1700 for $x = 1$ unit and tending toward \$2000 as x increases without bound. (See Figure 17.) Note that the line $y = 2000$ is a horizontal asymptote.

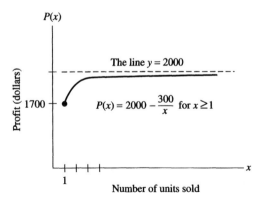

Figure 17 Profit function P ◆

English mathematician John Wallis (1616–1703) was the first to use the symbol ∞ for infinity. He was also a significant contributor to the development of integral calculus (studied in Chapter 6). As a teacher, Wallis was a pioneer in developing a system for teaching the deaf.

2.4   Exercises

In Exercises 1–4, complete the tables to determine the limits. Use a calculator.

1.

$$\lim_{x \to \infty} \frac{x + 1}{x}$$

x	$\dfrac{x + 1}{x}$
100	
1000	
10,000	
1,000,000	

2.

$$\lim_{x \to \infty} \frac{x}{1 + x^2}$$

x	$\dfrac{x}{1 + x^2}$
100	
1000	
10,000	
100,000	

3.

$$\lim_{x \to -\infty} \frac{1 + 3x}{2x}$$

x	$\dfrac{1 + 3x}{2x}$
−100	
−1000	
−10,000	
−1,000,000	

4.

$$\lim_{x \to -\infty} \frac{1 - 5x}{2x}$$

x	$\dfrac{1 - 5x}{2x}$
−100	
−1000	
−10,000	
−1,000,000	

Use the Theorem for Limits at Infinity to evaluate each limit in Exercises 5–12.

5. $\lim\limits_{x \to \infty} \dfrac{1}{x}$

6. $\lim\limits_{x \to \infty} \dfrac{1}{x^2}$

7. $\lim\limits_{x \to \infty} \dfrac{-20}{x^4}$

8. $\lim\limits_{x \to -\infty} \dfrac{170}{x^3}$

9. $\lim\limits_{x \to \infty} \dfrac{1000}{x^2}$

10. $\lim\limits_{x \to \infty} \dfrac{-1}{x^6}$

11. $\lim\limits_{x \to -\infty} \left(-\dfrac{1}{x^4} \right)$

12. $\lim\limits_{x \to \infty} \left(-\dfrac{2}{x^5} \right)$

Use the Theorem for Limits at Infinity to evaluate each limit in Exercises 13–22.

13. $\lim\limits_{x \to \infty} \dfrac{3x + 2}{5x - 4}$

14. $\lim\limits_{x \to \infty} \dfrac{7x + 1}{2x + 6}$

15. $\lim\limits_{x \to \infty} \dfrac{2x^2 + 8x + 6}{x^2 - 3x + 1}$

16. $\lim\limits_{x \to \infty} \dfrac{5x^2 - 17}{x^2 + 2}$

17. $\lim\limits_{x \to \infty} \dfrac{x^3 - 15}{2x^3 + x^2 + 1}$

18. $\lim\limits_{x \to \infty} \dfrac{5x^2 - 19}{1 + x + x^3}$

19. $\lim\limits_{x \to \infty} \dfrac{1 - x}{1 + 2x}$

20. $\lim\limits_{x \to \infty} \dfrac{1 + x^2}{1 - x^2}$

21. $\lim\limits_{x \to \infty} \dfrac{1 + 3x}{x^2 - 5x + 2}$

22. $\lim\limits_{x \to \infty} \dfrac{5x + x^2}{x - x^2}$

Determine the horizontal asymptote for the graph of each function defined in Exercises 23–30.

23. $f(x) = \dfrac{2x + 1}{x - 4}$

24. $f(x) = \dfrac{8x - 7}{2x + 3}$

25. $f(x) = \dfrac{x}{1 - x}$

26. $f(x) = \dfrac{8x}{1 + 4x}$

27. $f(x) = \dfrac{x^2 + 3}{x^3 - 1}$

28. $f(x) = \dfrac{3x^2 - 7x + 1}{x - 5x^3}$

29. $f(x) = \dfrac{x^2 - 8x + 2}{3x^2 + 6x - 5}$

30. $f(x) = \dfrac{1 - 16x^2}{2x^2 - 3}$

31. (**WITCH OF AGNESI**) The curve described by

$$y = \frac{8}{x^2 + 4}$$

is called a *witch of Agnesi*.

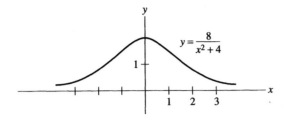

Curves of this form were studied by Italian mathematician Maria Agnesi in the 1740s. (Although the word ''witch'' was the result of a mistranslation into English, the curve is still called a witch of Agnesi.)

(a) Evaluate the limit

$$\lim_{x \to \infty} \frac{8}{x^2 + 4}$$

(b) Write the equation of the horizontal asymptote for this graph.

32. (***PAINT PRICE***) A wholesaler prices the best latex flat paint at

$$\frac{15x}{x - 1} \text{ dollars per gallon}$$

where x is the number of gallons and $x \geq 2$. The more you buy, the lower the price will be per gallon. As you buy more and more gallons, what price per gallon does the paint approach?

33. (***AVERAGE COST***) A company makes soccer balls. When x balls are made, the average cost per ball, $\overline{C}(x)$, is

$$\overline{C}(x) = \frac{1500 + 12x}{x} \text{ dollars} \qquad \text{for } x \geq 1$$

When 100 balls are made, the average cost per ball is $\overline{C}(100)$, or $27. When 1000 balls are made, the average cost per ball drops to $13.50. As more and more soccer balls are made, the average cost per ball continues to drop and tends toward a particular low average cost value. Determine that value.

34. (***PROFIT***) If the profit from the sale of x units is

$$P(x) = \frac{1400x - 250}{x} \text{ dollars} \qquad \text{for } x \geq 1$$

what is the limit of the profit as the quantity sold increases without bound?

35. (***ANIMAL HEIGHT***) Suppose that the function h defined by

$$h(t) = \frac{5t - 2}{t} \text{ feet} \qquad t \geq 1$$

gives the approximate height of a particular animal after t years. Toward what height does the adult animal tend?

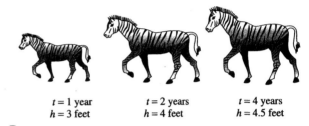

| $t = 1$ year | $t = 2$ years | $t = 4$ years |
| $h = 3$ feet | $h = 4$ feet | $h = 4.5$ feet |

36. (***TREE HEIGHT***) After t years, the height of a particular type of tree is given by

$$f(t) = \frac{20t - 15}{2t} \text{ feet} \qquad t \geq 1$$

Toward what height does the tree grow?

37. (***DRUG ABSORPTION***) The amount of a drug that remains in a person's bloodstream t hours after being injected is given by

$$f(t) = \frac{.15t}{1 + t^2}$$

(a) Find $\lim_{t \to \infty} f(t)$.

W (b) Use nonmathematical words to explain the meaning of the result obtained in part (a). Explain it in terms of the application.

W 38. In the limit statement

$$\lim_{x \to \infty} \frac{c}{x^n} = 0$$

why can't n be a *negative* integer?

39. (***WEISS' LAW***) According to Weiss' law, the intensity of electric current needed to excite muscle and nerve tissue depends on how long the current flows to the tissue. The longer the duration of the current flow, the less current is needed to excite the tissue. The relationship is given by

$$I(t) = \frac{a}{t} + b$$

where I is the current's intensity, t is the time (duration) of current flow, and a and b are constants. Determine the (theoretically) smallest possible current that would be needed to excite the tissue.

40. **(GEOMETRY)** The number of degrees d in each interior angle of a regular polygon of n sides is

$$d = \frac{180n - 360}{n}$$

For example, in an equilateral triangle ($n = 3$ sides), the number of degrees in each angle is 60, calculated from

$$d = \frac{180(3) - 360}{3} = 60$$

In a square ($n = 4$ sides), each angle is 90°. In a regular pentagon ($n = 5$ sides), each angle is 108°.

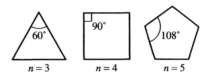

$n = 3$ $n = 4$ $n = 5$

(a) Determine the number of degrees in each interior angle of a regular hexagon ($n = 6$ sides).

(b) The number of degrees d in each interior angle of a regular polygon gets larger as n gets larger. Find the limit—that is, the number of degrees toward which the angles tend as n gets larger and larger.

W **41.** Limits at infinity are quite different from ordinary limits in which the variable x approaches a finite number a. Nevertheless, in a way they do resemble one-sided limits. Explain.

 TECHNOLOGY *EXERCISES*

1. Verify the limit

$$\lim_{x \to \infty} \left(1 + \frac{1}{x}\right)^x \approx 2.718$$

by graphing the function

$$f(x) = \left(1 + \frac{1}{x}\right)^x$$

Set the range to allow x to be very large (for example, 10,000), and then trace the graph out to the right.

2. Use the procedure of Exercise 1, except use [0,20] for y, to determine (to two decimal places) the limit

$$\lim_{x \to \infty} \left(1 + \frac{1}{x}\right)^{2.5x}$$

In Exercises 3 and 4, graph the function to determine each limit at infinity.

3. $f(x) = \dfrac{10 + x + x^3}{x^3}$

    (a) $\lim\limits_{x \to \infty} f(x)$ **(b)** $\lim\limits_{x \to -\infty} f(x)$

4. $f(x) = \dfrac{3x^2 + x}{x^2 - 4}$

    (a) $\lim\limits_{x \to \infty} f(x)$ **(b)** $\lim\limits_{x \to -\infty} f(x)$

In Exercises 5 and 6, graph the function. Then follow the graph to the right until you can determine the horizontal asymptote. (Extend the x portion of the window as needed.)

5. $f(x) = \dfrac{9}{x^2 + 1}$ **6.** $f(x) = \dfrac{-4x^2 - 7}{x^2 + 3}$

In Exercises 7–10, graph the function. Then follow the graph *to the right* until you can determine a horizontal asymptote. Next, follow the graph *to the left* to determine the other horizontal asymptote. (Extend the x portion of the window as needed.)

7. $f(x) = \dfrac{2x}{\sqrt{x^2 + 1}}$ **8.** $f(x) = \dfrac{-x}{\sqrt{1 + 4x^2}}$

9. $f(x) = \dfrac{-3x}{|1 + x|}$ **10.** $f(x) = \dfrac{2x}{|1 + 3x|}$

Note Computer algebra systems can be used to evaluate limits at infinity. The limit

$$\lim_{x \to \infty} \frac{5x + 1}{3 - 2x}$$

can be evaluated as follows.

Mathematica: `Limit[(5x + 1)/(3 - 2x), x -> Infinity]`

Maple: `limit(5 * x + 1)/(3 - 2 * x), x = infinity);`

If you have such software, use it to evaluate the limits of Exercises 15 and 21.

2.5 | INFINITE LIMITS

When considering $\lim\limits_{x \to a} f(x)$, it may happen that $f(x)$ increases without bound (that is, becomes infinite) as x approaches a. In such instances, the limit does not exist in the usual sense. However, this situation can be described by writing

$$\lim_{x \to a} f(x) = \infty$$

Such a limit is called an **infinite limit.** A study of the graph shown in Figure 18 should help you to understand this kind of limit.

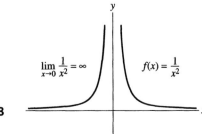

$$\lim_{x \to 0} \frac{1}{x^2} = \infty \qquad f(x) = \frac{1}{x^2}$$

Figure 18

One incidental observation that can be made from the graph is that function f is not continuous at 0, since there is a break in the graph at $x = 0$. Note that the closer x gets to 0, the larger the functional values become. The table that follows demonstrates that as x gets closer and closer to 0, $1/x^2$ gets larger and larger.

x	$\dfrac{1}{x^2}$
1	1
.5	4
.1	100
.01	10,000
.001	1,000,000

Approaching 0 from the left, the x values would be -1, $-.5$, $-.1$, $-.01$, and $-.001$. The corresponding values of $1/x^2$ would be the same as those shown in the table.

If instead function f was defined to be $f(x) = -1/x^2$, then the graph would appear as shown in Figure 19. Again the magnitude of $f(x)$ increases without bound (becomes infinite) as x approaches 0. However, this time the values of $f(x)$ are negative; the values of $f(x)$ approach $-\infty$.

$$\lim_{x \to 0} \left(-\frac{1}{x^2} \right) = -\infty$$

Next, consider the graph of $f(x) = 1/x$, which suggests two interesting one-sided limits. The graph is shown in Figure 20.

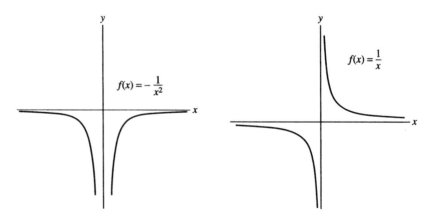

Figure 19   **Figure 20**

$$\lim_{x \to 0^+} \frac{1}{x} = \infty \qquad \lim_{x \to 0^-} \frac{1}{x} = -\infty$$

Numerically, you can interpret the limit $\lim_{x \to 0^+} (1/x) = \infty$ as follows: If the number 1 is divided by positive numbers that get closer and closer to zero, the results obtained will get larger and larger. In fact, for any positive constant c,

$$\lim_{x \to 0^+} \frac{c}{x} = \infty \qquad (c > 0)$$

If c is a negative constant, then the result will be negative:

$$\lim_{x \to 0^+} \frac{c}{x} = -\infty \qquad (c < 0)$$

Based on these two limits, we will use the notation "approach zero (+)" to indicate the behavior of the denominator x as $x \to 0^+$ for the following arithmetic.

$$\frac{\text{positive constant}}{\text{approach zero } (+)} = \infty \qquad\qquad \frac{\text{negative constant}}{\text{approach zero } (+)} = -\infty$$

EXAMPLE 1 Determine each limit. Use the ideas developed above.

(a) $\lim_{x \to 2^+} \dfrac{1}{x - 2}$ (b) $\lim_{x \to 0} \dfrac{-35}{x^2}$

SOLUTION (a) $\lim_{x \to 2^+} \dfrac{1}{x - 2} = \dfrac{\text{positive constant}}{\text{approach zero } (+)} = \infty$

When $x \to 2^+$, the x values are greater than 2; thus the expression $x - 2$ will approach zero via positive values.

(b) $\lim_{x \to 0} \dfrac{-35}{x^2} = \dfrac{\text{negative constant}}{\text{approach zero } (+)} = -\infty$

Here it does not matter whether x approaches 0 from the left or the right, because when x is squared the result will be positive in either case.   ♦

Approaching 0 from the left, rather than from the right, leads to two other cases.

$$\lim_{x \to 0^-} \frac{c}{x} = -\infty \qquad (c > 0)$$

$$\lim_{x \to 0^-} \frac{c}{x} = \infty \qquad (c < 0)$$

The corresponding notation and arithmetic are given next.

$$\frac{\text{positive constant}}{\text{approach zero } (-)} = -\infty \qquad\qquad \frac{\text{negative constant}}{\text{approach zero } (-)} = \infty$$

EXAMPLE 2   Determine each limit. Use the ideas developed above.

(a) $\displaystyle\lim_{x\to 2^-}\frac{3}{x-2}$ (b) $\displaystyle\lim_{x\to 3^-}\frac{-1}{x-3}$

SOLUTION   (a) $\displaystyle\lim_{x\to 2^-}\frac{3}{x-2}=\frac{\text{positive constant}}{\text{approach zero }(-)}=-\infty$

Note that as $x\to 2^-$, the x values are less than 2, and so the expression $x-2$ will approach 0 via negative values.

(b) $\displaystyle\lim_{x\to 3^-}\frac{-1}{x-3}=\frac{\text{negative constant}}{\text{approach zero }(-)}=\infty$ ◆

The limits studied in this section lead naturally to a discussion of vertical asymptotes. Examination of the graph of $f(x)=1/x^2$ shows that as x approaches 0, the magnitude of $f(x)$ tends toward infinity. The curve tends toward the vertical line $x=0$. See Figure 21. The line $x=0$ is a *vertical asymptote* for the graph of $f(x)=1/x^2$. In general,

Vertical Asymptotes

The line $x=a$ is a **vertical asymptote** for the graph of $y=f(x)$ if the limit of $f(x)$ as x approaches a (from either side or both sides) is ∞ or $-\infty$.

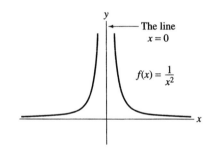

Figure 21 $x=0$ is a vertical asymptote.

Vertical asymptotes occur only when the denominator of the expression is zero. In other words, to find vertical asymptotes, determine the values of x that make the denominator zero. Then check to be sure the limit is infinite.

EXAMPLE 3   Determine the vertical asymptote for the graph of each function defined.

(a) $f(x)=\dfrac{1}{x-2}$ (b) $g(x)=\dfrac{2}{(x+1)^2}$

SOLUTION   (a) When x approaches 2, denominator $x-2$ approaches 0 and causes the expression $1/(x-2)$ to approach infinity. Thus, $x=2$ is a vertical asymptote.

(b) When x approaches -1, denominator $(x+1)^2$ approaches 0 and causes the expression $2/(x+1)^2$ to approach infinity. Thus, $x=-1$ is a vertical asymptote.   ◆

Some limits at infinity are in fact infinite limits as well. For example, it is fairly obvious that

$$\lim_{x \to \infty} 3x = \infty$$

A less obvious limit such as

$$\lim_{x \to \infty} \frac{x^2 + 5}{x + 1} = \infty$$

can be determined by using a procedure similar to that of Examples 2 and 3 of Section 2.4. In that procedure we must also use the following result:

$$\lim_{x \to \infty} cx^n = \infty \qquad c > 0, n > 0$$

EXAMPLE 4   Determine the limit.

$$\lim_{x \to \infty} \frac{4x^3 + 5}{x + 1}$$

SOLUTION   Divide each term of the numerator and denominator by the highest power of x in the denominator, namely x. The result is

$$\lim_{x \to \infty} \frac{4x^3 + 5}{x + 1} = \lim_{x \to \infty} \frac{\dfrac{4x^3}{x} + \dfrac{5}{x}}{\dfrac{x}{x} + \dfrac{1}{x}} = \lim_{x \to \infty} \frac{4x^2 + \dfrac{5}{x}}{1 + \dfrac{1}{x}}$$

As $x \to \infty$, the expressions $5/x$ and $1/x$ tend to 0 and $4x^2$ tends to ∞ (an example of cx^n as $x \to \infty$). This means that the numerator of the fraction is tending toward ∞ while the denominator tends toward 1. Thus, the limit is ∞.

$$\lim_{x \to \infty} \frac{4x^3 + 5}{x + 1} = \frac{\infty}{1} = \infty$$

◆

In general,

When the degree of the numerator is greater than the degree of the denominator, the limit at infinity will be infinite (either ∞ or $-\infty$).

2.5   Exercises

Determine each limit in Exercises 1–10.

1. $\lim\limits_{x \to 0} \dfrac{2}{x^2}$

2. $\lim\limits_{x \to 0} \dfrac{100}{x^2}$

3. $\lim\limits_{x \to 1^+} \dfrac{1}{x - 1}$

4. $\lim\limits_{x \to 2^+} \dfrac{-3}{x - 2}$

5. $\lim\limits_{x \to 3^+} \dfrac{-6}{x - 3}$

6. $\lim\limits_{x \to 4^+} \dfrac{15}{x - 4}$

7. $\lim\limits_{x \to 4^-} \dfrac{11}{x - 4}$

8. $\lim\limits_{x \to 5^-} \dfrac{2}{x - 5}$

9. $\lim\limits_{x \to 1^-} \dfrac{-3}{x - 1}$

10. $\lim\limits_{x \to 2^-} \dfrac{-2}{x - 2}$

Determine each limit in Exercises 11–18.

11. $\lim\limits_{x \to 2^+} \dfrac{5}{2 - x}$

12. $\lim\limits_{x \to 3^+} \dfrac{17}{3 - x}$

13. $\lim\limits_{x \to 1^+} \dfrac{-9}{1 - x}$

14. $\lim\limits_{x \to 2^-} \dfrac{3}{2 - x}$

15. $\lim\limits_{x \to 4^-} \dfrac{1}{4 - x}$

16. $\lim\limits_{x \to 2^+} \dfrac{-1}{2 - x}$

17. $\lim\limits_{x \to 2^-} \dfrac{-3}{2 - x}$

18. $\lim\limits_{x \to 1^-} \dfrac{-2}{1 - x}$

19. (POLLUTION CLEANUP) Suppose that the cost to remove x percent of the pollutants in a lake is given by

$$C(x) = \frac{900{,}000}{100 - x} \text{ dollars}$$

(a) Complete the table below and note the cost trend.

percent removed	cost
10	
25	
50	
80	
90	
95	
98	

W (b) According to our formula, is it theoretically possible to eliminate all of the pollutants? Explain. Include in your explanation the evaluation of the limit

$$\lim_{x \to 100^-} C(x)$$

20. (QUALITY CONTROL) An auto manufacturer wants to reduce the number of defects in the cars it produces. At present, 10% of their cars are delivered with some kind of defect. The cost to produce cars x percent of which are defective ($x < 10$) is given by

$$C(x) = \frac{800{,}000 - 5000x}{x} \text{ dollars}$$

(a) Complete the table below and note the cost trend.

percent defects	cost
8	
5	
2	
1	
1/2	

W (b) According to our formula, is it theoretically possible to produce no defective cars? Explain. Include in your explanation the evaluation of the limit

$$\lim_{x \to 0^+} C(x)$$

Determine the vertical asymptote for the graph of each function defined in Exercises 21–28.

21. $f(x) = \dfrac{4}{x - 5}$

22. $f(x) = \dfrac{1}{7 - x}$

23. $f(x) = \dfrac{2}{x^2}$

24. $f(x) = \dfrac{2}{x - 6}$

25. $f(x) = \dfrac{1}{x + 2}$

26. $f(x) = \dfrac{-1}{x^3}$

27. $f(x) = \dfrac{-3}{(x - 1)^2}$

28. $f(x) = \dfrac{2}{1 - x}$

Evaluate each limit in Exercises 29–34.

29. $\displaystyle\lim_{x\to\infty} 3x^2$

30. $\displaystyle\lim_{x\to\infty} \frac{x^5}{x^3 + 7x}$

31. $\displaystyle\lim_{x\to\infty} \frac{x^3 - 6x^2 + 3}{5x^2 + x - 1}$

32. $\displaystyle\lim_{x\to\infty} \frac{x^2 + 8x - 2}{x^4 + 6x + 1}$

33. $\displaystyle\lim_{x\to\infty} \frac{5x - 2}{7x + 1}$

34. $\displaystyle\lim_{x\to\infty} 8$

35. (*BASEBALL E.R.A*) In baseball, a pitcher's *earned run average* (E.R.A) is the average number of runs given up (that is, scored) per game while he or she is pitching. (Runs scored as a result of errors are not included, because such runs are not "earned.") A game consists of 9 innings, and an inning includes 3 outs. Thus, there are 27 outs per game for E.R.A. considerations. The function

$$A(t) = \frac{27r}{t}$$

gives the E.R.A., $A(t)$, where r is the number of earned runs and t is the number of outs.

(a) Use the function to determine the earned run average of a pitcher who has given up 3 earned runs in 6 innings.

(b) What limit would you evaluate when determining the E.R.A. of the unfortunate pitcher who has given up 3 earned runs in the first game of the season but has gotten no one out?

(c) Evaluate the limit of part (b).

W **36.** Is $x = 1$ a vertical asymptote for the graph of the following function? Explain.

$$f(x) = \frac{x^2 - x}{x^2 - 1}$$

TECHNOLOGY *EXERCISES*

In Exercises 1–3, study the graph of the function in order to determine whether the required limit is finite, ∞, or $-\infty$. (If finite, determine the number.)

1. $f(x) = \dfrac{x^3 - 3x + 4}{1 - x}$

    (a) $\displaystyle\lim_{x\to 1^+} f(x)$ **(b)** $\displaystyle\lim_{x\to 1^-} f(x)$

2. $f(x) = \dfrac{x^2}{x^2 - 9}$

    (a) $\displaystyle\lim_{x\to 3^+} f(x)$ **(b)** $\displaystyle\lim_{x\to 3^-} f(x)$ **(c)** $\displaystyle\lim_{x\to -3^+} f(x)$ **(d)** $\displaystyle\lim_{x\to -3^-} f(x)$

3. $f(x) = \dfrac{x^2 - x}{x^2 + 3x - 4}$

    (a) $\displaystyle\lim_{x\to 1^+} f(x)$ **(b)** $\displaystyle\lim_{x\to 1^-} f(x)$ **(c)** $\displaystyle\lim_{x\to -4^+} f(x)$ **(d)** $\displaystyle\lim_{x\to -4^-} f(x)$

Note Be aware of a potential problem when graphing functions that have vertical asymptotes. Depending on the function and the ranges used, a graphing calculator may show a vertical line that is not part of the function. You can see this by graphing

$$f(x) = \frac{1}{x + 1} \qquad\qquad \text{This note is continued on the next page.}$$

98

using the standard ranges of $[-10, 10]$ and the standard "connected" mode. One way to eliminate the problem is to use "dot" mode. Another way is to change the ranges to $[-5, 5]$. (Try it.)

In Exercises 4–7, look at the graph of the function in order to determine the vertical asymptote of the function. Once you have found the general location of the asymptote, narrow the interval for x considerably. Answers should contain approximations to the nearest tenth.

4. $f(x) = \dfrac{1.4x + 5}{2.5x + 4}$

5. $f(x) = \dfrac{x^3}{x^4 - 64x}$

6. $f(x) = \dfrac{x^2}{x^4 - 15.625x}$

7. $f(x) = \dfrac{12}{1.38x - \sqrt{5x}}$

Note *Maple* and *Mathematica* can determine infinite limits. The commands are the same as those mentioned in Sections 2.1, 2.3, and 2.4. If you have access to such software, try Exercises 5, 7, 13, and 15.

Key Terms and Ideas

limit

continuity

continuous

discontinuous

discontinuity

left-hand limit

right-hand limit

one-sided limits

limits at infinity

horizontal asymptotes

infinite limits

vertical asymptotes

Review Exercises for Chapter 2

In Exercises 1–8, evaluate each limit.

1. $\lim\limits_{x \to 4} x^{-3}$

2. $\lim\limits_{n \to 3} \sqrt{n^2 + 16}$

3. $\lim\limits_{x \to 6} \dfrac{\sqrt{37 - 2x}}{x + 7}$

4. $\lim\limits_{m \to 2} \pi$

5. $\lim\limits_{x \to 5} \dfrac{x^2 - 25}{2x - 10}$

6. $\lim\limits_{x \to 2} \sqrt{\dfrac{5x^2}{x + 2}}$

7. $\lim\limits_{x \to 7} \dfrac{14 - 2x}{7x}$

8. $\lim\limits_{x \to 0} \dfrac{x^3}{x^2}$

Evaluate each one-sided limit in Exercises 9–12.

9. $\lim\limits_{x \to 1^-} f(x)$

10. $\lim\limits_{x \to 1^+} f(x)$

$f(x) = \begin{cases} 4x & x \le 1 \\ 2x + 1 & x > 1 \end{cases}$

11. $\lim\limits_{x \to 0^-} g(x)$

12. $\lim\limits_{x \to 0^+} g(x)$

$g(x) = \begin{cases} 3x & x < 0 \\ \sqrt{x + 1} & x \ge 0 \end{cases}$

In Exercises 13–16, evaluate each limit at infinity.

13. $\lim\limits_{x \to \infty} \dfrac{5x - 19}{7x + 2}$

14. $\lim\limits_{x \to \infty} \dfrac{30}{1 + x^{10}}$

15. $\displaystyle\lim_{x\to\infty}\frac{3x^2}{x^3-x^2+x}$ **16.** $\displaystyle\lim_{x\to\infty}\frac{5+x^2}{5+x^3}$

Determine each limit in Exercises 17–20.

17. $\displaystyle\lim_{x\to5^-}\frac{2}{x-5}$ **18.** $\displaystyle\lim_{x\to5^+}\frac{2}{x-5}$

19. $\displaystyle\lim_{x\to0^+}\frac{3}{2x^5}$ **20.** $\displaystyle\lim_{x\to3^-}\frac{-4}{x-3}$

In Exercises 21–24, determine the limit, if it exists.

21. $\displaystyle\lim_{x\to2}f(x)$ **22.** $\displaystyle\lim_{x\to4}f(x)$

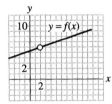   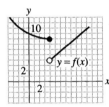

23. $\displaystyle\lim_{x\to2}g(x)$ **24.** $\displaystyle\lim_{x\to5}g(x)$

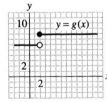   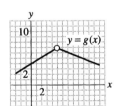

25. Answer the questions on the basis of the graph of f shown in the figure below.
  (a) Is f continuous at 0?
  (b) Is f continuous at -3?
  (c) Does $\displaystyle\lim_{x\to2}f(x)$ exist?
  (d) Is f continuous at 2?
  (e) Does $\displaystyle\lim_{x\to6}f(x)$ exist?
  (f) Is f continuous at 6?
  (g) Does $\displaystyle\lim_{x\to4}f(x)$ exist?
  (h) Is f continuous at 4?

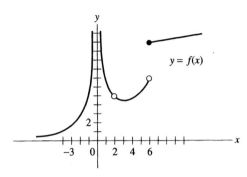

26. Answer the questions on the basis of the graph of g shown in the figure below.
  (a) Does $\displaystyle\lim_{x\to0}g(x)$ exist?
  (b) Is g continuous at 0?
  (c) Does $\displaystyle\lim_{x\to2}g(x)$ exist?
  (d) Is g continuous at 2?
  (e) Does $\displaystyle\lim_{x\to5}g(x)$ exist?
  (f) Is g continuous at 5?
  (g) Is g continuous at 1?
  (h) Is g continuous at 10?

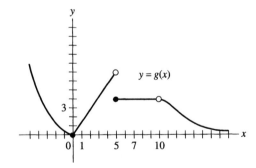

27. **(PSYCHOLOGY EXPERIMENT)** A psychologist studies the time required to complete a devised task. He finds that as people gain experience, they complete the task in less time; in fact,

$$T(n) = 4 + \frac{6}{n}$$

where n is the number of times they perform the task and T is the time (in minutes) it takes them to complete the task. Based on the formula and your knowledge of limits, what is the (theoretically) shortest time needed to complete the task?

28. **(PRICE TENDENCY)** The price of oak chairs being supplied to a wholesaler is given by

$$p = \frac{40}{x} + 120 \quad \text{dollars}$$

where p is the price per chair and x is the number of chairs supplied. Toward what amount is the price tending as the number of chairs supplied increases?

29. **(COMPOUND INTEREST)** If $8800 is invested at 8% annual interest compounded n times a year for 1 year, the total amount accumulated at the end of the year will be

$$7800 \left(1 + \frac{.08}{n} \right)^n \quad \text{dollars}$$

Complete the table below to help you determine the total amount accumulated, if the interest is compounded an "infinite" number of times. In other words, find

$$\lim_{n \to \infty} \left[\$7800 \left(1 + \frac{.08}{n} \right)^n \right]$$

n	$\$7800 \left(1 + \dfrac{.08}{n} \right)^n$
12	
365	
1000	
10,000	
100,000	

30. **(CAR RENTAL COST)** A car rental company charges $30 for the first day and $25 per day for additional days. There are no other charges. Let x be the number of days for which the car is rented.

(a) Graph the function (call it C) for $0 < x < 4$.

W (b) Is C continuous at 2? Explain.

W (c) Is C continuous at 2.5? Explain.

W (d) Determine $\lim_{x \to 3} C(x)$. Comment.

(e) Compare $\lim_{x \to 1^-} C(x)$ and $\lim_{x \to 1^+} C(x)$.

31. **(AVERAGE COST)** A new business spends $2300 in fixed costs. Its product, a disposable camera, costs $7 each to produce.

(a) Determine the total cost $C(x)$ of producing x cameras.

(b) Determine the average cost per camera, $\overline{C}(x)$, which is $C(x)/x$.

(c) What is the limit of the average cost per camera as the number of cameras produced increases without bound?

32. **(NUMBER OF PETS)** Let $n(t)$ be the number of pets living in your home at any time t in years. At the beginning, you have a dog. A year later you adopt a stray cat, which will be good company for the dog. Six months later, the cat has three kittens. Six months after that, you give away two of the kittens. No change in the number of pets occurs in the next year.

(a) Sketch a graph of $y = n(t)$ over the interval $[0,3]$.

(b) At what values of t in the interval $(0,3)$ is the function n discontinuous?

33. **(C.O.D. FEES)** The following table gives U.S.P.S. fees for C.O.D.

amount due (x)	C.O.D. fee (y)
$50 or less	$3.50
$50.01–$100	$4.50
$100.01–$200	$5.50
$200.01–$300	$6.50

Evaluate each limit, if it exists.

(a) $\lim_{x \to 50^+} y$

(b) $\lim_{x \to 100^-} y$

(c) $\lim_{x \to 200} y$

34. **(INSECTICIDE)** An ant trap is used to eliminate an ant colony. The number of ants living t hours after the trap is put out is given by

$$n(t) = \begin{cases} 2040 - 5t & 0 \le t < 24 \\ 2880 - 40t & 24 \le t \le 72 \end{cases}$$

(a) How many ants were originally in the colony?

(b) How many ants are left after 72 hours?

W (c) Is the function continuous at $t = 24$ hours? Explain.

35. **(FEVER REDUCTION)** A woman with a temperature of 103.7°F is given medicine that will reduce her temperature. The medicine takes one hour before it begins to work, and after that (that is, for $t \ge 1$), her temperature at t hours will be

$$B(t) = 103.7 - \frac{5.1t - 4.5}{t} \quad \text{degrees}$$

(a) What is her temperature at $t = 1$ hour, 3 hours, and 10 hours?

(b) Eventually, to what temperature is her body reduced?

36. Consider the graph of $y = f(x)$ shown next.

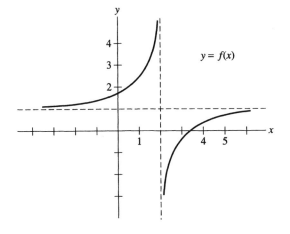

(a) Write the two limits at infinity that can be determined from the graph.

(b) Write the two infinite limits that can be determined from the graph.

W 37. If you could view the graph of

$$f(x) = \frac{x^2 + 7x - 8}{x - 1}$$

would the function appear to be continuous at $x = 1$? Explain.

W 38. If you could view the graph of

$$f(x) = \frac{x^2 - 4x - 12}{x - 6}$$

would there be a point $(6, f(6))$ on the graph? Explain.

W 39. If function f is continuous at $x = a$, is it necessarily true that the limit of $f(x)$ as x approaches a exists? Explain.

W 40. If the limit of $f(x)$ as x approaches a exists, is it necessarily true that function f is continuous at $x = a$? Explain. Use examples as needed.

Chapter Projects and Essays

Many of the projects and essays lend themselves to group activity, although most can be completed by individual effort.

1. MARIA AGNESI

BACKGROUND In Exercise 31 of Section 2.4, you saw an example of a curve called a "witch of Agnesi." Maria Agnesi was a brilliant and well-educated woman. Her accomplishments are fascinating: at age nine, for instance, she published a defense of higher education for women!

Maria Agnesi (1718–1799)

THE PROJECT   Locate books or articles on the history of mathematics or the life of Maria Agnesi. Select information about her and discuss, *among other things,*

(a) An explanation of the mistranslation that led to the name ''witch'' of Agnesi for the curves she studied.

(b) The general equation for all curves that are witches of Agnesi. (The function used in Exercise 31 of Section 2.4 is merely one specific example.)

(c) A brief description of any book or books she wrote that seem related to this calculus course.

2. CALCULUS IN HISTORY

BACKGROUND   Newton and Leibniz worked on the invention of calculus in the mid- and late seventeenth century. You can gain some perspective on their accomplishments by considering nonmathematical development at that time.

THE PROJECT   Write an essay about what was happening in other fields while calculus was being developed. Depending on your interests and on the depth of your research, consider including material that responds to any or all of the following questions.

(a) What was happening politically in North America, Western Europe, Africa, Asia, and South America? Were there any wars?

(b) What discoveries and progress was being made in science and medicine?

(c) Who were the prominent artists and composers and what were their creations?

(d) Who were the leading writers and poets and what were their works?

3. LIMIT APPLICATIONS

BACKGROUND   This chapter has presented the basic concepts of limits and continuity.

THE PROJECT   Prepare a paper on a modern application of the concepts of this chapter. Include at least one of the following concepts: discontinuities, limits at infinity, infinite limits. Your reference sources can include journals, books, faculty members, and fellow students.

Each of the five statements that follow suggests a limit at infinity. You can pursue one of them or merely consider them as examples.

(a) There are long-term effects of stress on the human species.

(b) Some long-term economic trends can be predicted.

(c) A national debt can ultimately bankrupt a country.

(d) An endangered species can eventually become extinct.

(e) There will not always be life on earth.

3

DERIVATIVES

The speed of divers when they hit the water helps determine whether or not they achieve the sought-after "rip"—or splashless—entry. This diver is executing a reverse tuck from a three-meter springboard. Because gravity pulls objects downward at a fixed rate per second, mathematically-minded onlookers might use the first derivative to calculate the diver's velocity at any point between her maximum height and her final splashdown.

*T*he study of limits provided new directions and applications. Familiar algebra and graphs were used in ways that you probably had not anticipated.

As we continue the presentation of calculus, the opportunity will arise to use limits in the study of an operation called differentiation. You will see how limits occur in the basic definitions and throughout the development of this key calculus topic. Limits will be combined with the familiar idea of slope of a straight line. This will set the stage for defining differentiation and developing basic rules for carrying it out. A variety of applications will be included, all based on various interpretations of the differentiation process.

3.1 | *INTRODUCTION TO THE DERIVATIVE*

Calculus and the mathematics beyond it have a broad appeal. Many people who are well known outside of mathematics have studied calculus and obtained degrees in mathematics, including Harry Blackmun, U.S. Supreme Court justice; David Dinkins, former mayor of New York City; Art Garfunkel, popular singer; Ira Glasser, Executive Director of the ACLU; David Robinson, NBA all-star center; Carl Rowan, journalist and commentator; and Virginia Wade, Wimbledon tennis champion.

Before proceeding to a formal introduction to the derivative, we consider some background information on the nature of the derivative. Simply stated, *the derivative is a rate of change*. Three examples are given next to offer some preliminary insight into the notion of rate of change.

1. Consider an outbreak of the flu. A function specifies the number of people sick with flu at any particular time. The derivative of the function indicates the *rate* at which illness due to flu is spreading at any particular time.

2. Suppose that a function gives the average cost per unit of producing x units. The derivative of the function yields information about when the average cost per unit is increasing and when it is decreasing.

3. A function may describe the motion of a rocket, giving the distance traveled for any time t. The derivative of this function is the rate of change of distance with respect to time—the velocity. From the derivative we can determine the velocity at any instant desired.

The slope of a straight line can be considered a rate of change. It is the rate of change of y with respect to x.

$$\text{slope } (m) = \frac{\Delta y}{\Delta x}$$

The slope of a line is a number that specifies the change in y compared with the change in x in going from point to point on the line. For any particular line, the slope is constant for the entire line. See Figure 1.

But what happens when the function under consideration is not linear? In order to consider the rate of change in such instances, we might choose to extend the notion of slope to curves other than straight lines. Consider, for example, the graph of the function f defined by $f(x) = x^2$, shown in Figure 2.

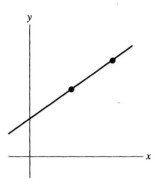

Figure 1 A linear function (straight line); constant slope and constant rate of change

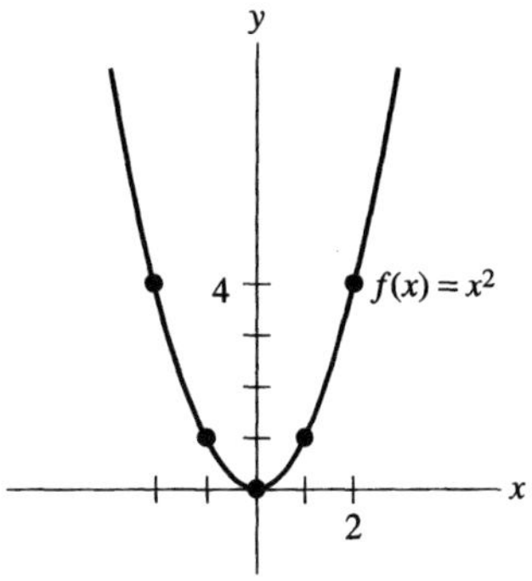

Figure 2

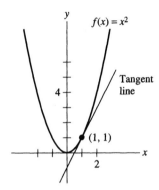

Figure 3
The tangent line at (1, 1)

How do we talk about the slope of a curve that is not a straight line? *The slope of a curve at any point is considered to be the slope of the line tangent to (that is, touching) the curve at that point. Such a line has the same steepness as the curve at that point.* For example, the slope of the parabola $f(x) = x^2$ at (1, 1) is the slope of the line tangent to the curve at (1, 1). See Figure 3.

The slope of a straight line can be determined from two points on that line by computing the change in the y coordinates (Δy) and the change in the x coordinates (Δx). The slope is

$$m = \frac{\Delta y}{\Delta x}$$

Proceeding in a similar fashion for a curve, we can begin our search for the slope of the tangent line by using two points on the curve. Let $(x, f(x))$ be any point through which we want the tangent line. To obtain a second point on the curve, add to the x coordinate the nonzero amount Δx. This means that the x coordinate of the second point is $x + \Delta x$, and the second point itself is $(x + \Delta x, f(x + \Delta x))$. The two points and the line through them are shown in Figure 4.

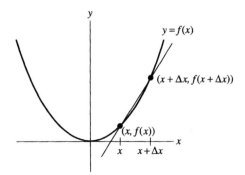

Figure 4

A true tangent line to the graph of $y = f(x)$ at $(x, f(x))$ would touch the curve at only one point, namely at $(x, f(x))$. Yet the line in our drawing passes through the curve at *two* points. Such a line is called a *secant line*. Using the notation m_{sec} to mean "the slope of the secant line," we have

$$m_{\text{sec}} = \frac{\Delta y}{\Delta x} = \frac{f(x + \Delta x) - f(x)}{(x + \Delta x) - x}$$

which simplifies to

$$m_{\text{sec}} = \frac{f(x + \Delta x) - f(x)}{\Delta x}$$

Notice from the drawing in Figure 5 that as Δx gets smaller, the secant line comes closer and closer to being the tangent line. As Δx approaches 0, the secant line approaches the tangent line.

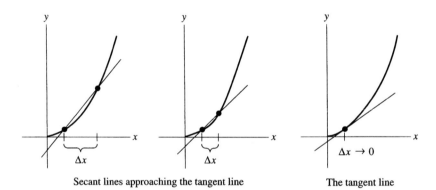

Secant lines approaching the tangent line   The tangent line

Figure 5

This means that the slope of the tangent line is the limit of the slope of the secant line as Δx approaches 0. Using the notation m_{tan} to mean "the slope of the tangent line," we make the following definition:

Slope of the Tangent Line

The **slope of the tangent line** to the graph of f at any point $(x, f(x))$ is

$$m_{\text{tan}} = \lim_{\Delta x \to 0} \frac{f(x + \Delta x) - f(x)}{\Delta x}$$

provided this limit exists.

The **tangent line** to the graph of f at any point $(x, f(x))$ can now be defined; it is the line through the point $(x, f(x))$ and having slope

$$m = \lim_{\Delta x \to 0} \frac{f(x + \Delta x) - f(x)}{\Delta x}$$

EXAMPLE 1 Determine the slope of the line tangent to the graph of $f(x) = x^2$ at any point $(x, f(x))$.

SOLUTION Using the definition, with $f(x) = x^2$, we have

$$
\begin{aligned}
m_{\text{tan}} &= \lim_{\Delta x \to 0} \frac{f(x + \Delta x) - f(x)}{\Delta x} \\
&= \lim_{\Delta x \to 0} \frac{(x + \Delta x)^2 - x^2}{\Delta x} \\
&= \lim_{\Delta x \to 0} \frac{x^2 + 2x(\Delta x) + (\Delta x)^2 - x^2}{\Delta x} \\
&= \lim_{\Delta x \to 0} \frac{2x(\Delta x) + (\Delta x)^2}{\Delta x} \\
&= \lim_{\Delta x \to 0} \frac{\Delta x(2x + \Delta x)}{\Delta x} \qquad \text{factoring } \Delta x \text{ out} \\
&\qquad\qquad\qquad\qquad\qquad \text{of the numerator}
\end{aligned}
$$

The factors of Δx in the numerator and denominator can be eliminated by division, because $\Delta x \neq 0$.

$$m_{tan} = \lim_{\Delta x \to 0} (2x + \Delta x)$$

Finally, taking the limit as $\Delta x \to 0$, we obtain

$$m_{tan} = 2x$$

Thus, the slope of the line tangent to the graph of $f(x) = x^2$ at any point $(x, f(x))$ is $2x$. Specifically, the slope of the tangent line at $(1, 1)$ is $2(1)$, or 2. The slope of the tangent line at $(-2, 4)$ is $2(-2)$, or -4. See Figure 6.

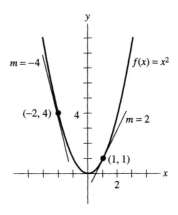

Figure 6 Slopes of tangent lines to the graph of $y = x^2$ ◆

Later in this chapter, as well as in Chapter 4, you will see that the limit

$$\lim_{\Delta x \to 0} \frac{f(x + \Delta x) - f(x)}{\Delta x}$$

has many applications. In view of this, it is given a special name and notation. It is called the **derivative** of the function.

Derivative

The *derivative* of function f with respect to x is the function f' defined by

$$f'(x) = \lim_{\Delta x \to 0} \frac{f(x + \Delta x) - f(x)}{\Delta x}$$

provided this limit exists.

The *domain* of f' consists of all x for which this limit exists. When the derivative exists, the function is said to be **differentiable.** The process of obtaining the derivative is called **differentiation.** To **differentiate** a function means to determine its derivative.

A variety of notations are used to indicate the derivative.

Notations for the Derivative

$f'(x)$	read as "f prime of x"
y'	read as "y prime"
$\dfrac{dy}{dx}$	read as "the derivative of y with respect to x" or as "dee y dee x"
$\dfrac{d}{dx} f(x)$	read as "the derivative of $f(x)$ with respect to x" or as "dee f dee x"
$D_x y$	read as "the derivative of y with respect to x"
$D_x f(x)$	read as "the derivative of $f(x)$ with respect to x"

The third notation listed, dy/dx, is the original notation of Leibniz.

Keep in mind that in working with functions of x, we are differentiating *with respect to x*. With functions of t, we would be differentiating with respect to t and the notation would be $f'(t)$, dy/dt, etc. If we had $y = f(u)$, then the differentiation would be with respect to u and the notation would be $f'(u)$, dy/du, etc. (Examples using letters other than x will appear throughout the text, beginning in the next section.)

As a final note on notation, consider that

$$\frac{f(x + \Delta x) - f(x)}{\Delta x} = \frac{\Delta y}{\Delta x}$$

which means that the derivative can also be considered as follows:

$$\frac{dy}{dx} = \lim_{\Delta x \to 0} \frac{\Delta y}{\Delta x} \qquad \text{provided the limit exists.}$$

The *dy/dx* notation is popular and will be used extensively.

Note

Δx is one number. Think of it as a single symbol. It is important to keep in mind that Δx *does not mean* Δ times x.

EXAMPLE 2 Let $f(x) = x^3$. Find the derivative.

SOLUTION Using the definition of the derivative, we have

$$f'(x) = \lim_{\Delta x \to 0} \frac{f(x + \Delta x) - f(x)}{\Delta x}$$

$$= \lim_{\Delta x \to 0} \frac{(x + \Delta x)^3 - x^3}{\Delta x}$$

$$= \lim_{\Delta x \to 0} \frac{x^3 + 3x^2(\Delta x) + 3x(\Delta x)^2 + (\Delta x)^3 - x^3}{\Delta x}$$

$$= \lim_{\Delta x \to 0} \frac{3x^2(\Delta x) + 3x(\Delta x)^2 + (\Delta x)^3}{\Delta x}$$

$$= \lim_{\Delta x \to 0} \frac{\Delta x\,[3x^2 + 3x(\Delta x) + (\Delta x)^2]}{\Delta x}$$

$$= \lim_{\Delta x \to 0} [3x^2 + 3x(\Delta x) + (\Delta x)^2]$$

$$= 3x^2$$

We see that if $f(x) = x^3$, then $f'(x) = 3x^2$.   ♦

Note

We have been using Δx to show the change in the independent variable x and to display the connection among the slope, the derivative, and the notation for derivatives. Other uses for Δx appear throughout the remainder of this chapter.

1. In Section 3.3, the Δx notation will smooth the transition from average rate of change to instantaneous rate of change.

2. The discussion of marginal analysis (Section 3.4) is clarified by using the Δx notation.

3. The chain rule (Section 3.6) can be seen intuitively using the "delta" notation.

4. In order to define differentials (Section 3.10), Δx notation must be used along with the slopes of the secant line and the tangent line.

Some people prefer to replace Δx by the letter h when calculating the derivative from the definition. The next example offers a comparison. Your instructor may indicate a preference for Δx or for h.

EXAMPLE 3 (a) Determine $f'(x)$ if $f(x) = x^2 - 5x + 1$. Use the Δx notation.

(b) Determine $f'(x)$ if $f(x) = x^2 - 5x + 1$. Use h instead of Δx.

SOLUTION (a) Using the definition of derivative, we have

$$f'(x) = \lim_{\Delta x \to 0} \frac{f(x + \Delta x) - f(x)}{\Delta x}$$

To continue, obtain $f(x + \Delta x)$ by replacing *every* x by $x + \Delta x$.

$$f'(x) = \lim_{\Delta x \to 0} \frac{[(x + \Delta x)^2 - 5(x + \Delta x) + 1] - (x^2 - 5x + 1)}{\Delta x}$$

$$= \lim_{\Delta x \to 0} \frac{x^2 + 2x(\Delta x) + (\Delta x)^2 - 5x - 5(\Delta x) + 1 - (x^2 - 5x + 1)}{\Delta x}$$

$$= \lim_{\Delta x \to 0} \frac{2x(\Delta x) + (\Delta x)^2 - 5(\Delta x)}{\Delta x}$$

$$= \lim_{\Delta x \to 0} \frac{\Delta x(2x + \Delta x - 5)}{\Delta x}$$

$$= \lim_{\Delta x \to 0} (2x + \Delta x - 5)$$

$$= 2x - 5$$

Using d/dx to mean "the derivative with respect to x of," we can write

$$\frac{d}{dx}(x^2 - 5x + 1) = 2x - 5$$

(b) Using the definition of derivative, with h instead of Δx, we have

$$f'(x) = \lim_{h \to 0} \frac{f(x + h) - f(x)}{h}$$

To continue, obtain $f(x + h)$ by replacing *every* x by $x + h$.

$$f'(x) = \lim_{h \to 0} \frac{[(x + h)^2 - 5(x + h) + 1] - (x^2 - 5x + 1)}{h}$$

$$= \lim_{h \to 0} \frac{(x^2 + 2xh + h^2 - 5x - 5h + 1) - (x^2 - 5x + 1)}{h}$$

$$= \lim_{h \to 0} \frac{2xh + h^2 - 5h}{h}$$

$$= \lim_{h \to 0} \frac{h(2x + h - 5)}{h}$$

$$= \lim_{h \to 0} (2x + h - 5)$$

$$= 2x - 5 \qquad \text{the same result as in part (a)} \qquad \blacklozenge$$

EXAMPLE 4   Find $f'(x)$ if $f(x) = \dfrac{1}{x}$.

SOLUTION   Using the definition of the derivative, we have

$$f'(x) = \lim_{\Delta x \to 0} \frac{f(x + \Delta x) - f(x)}{\Delta x}$$

$$= \lim_{\Delta x \to 0} \frac{\dfrac{1}{x + \Delta x} - \dfrac{1}{x}}{\Delta x}$$

Because the expression is a complex fraction involving denominators $x + \Delta x$ and x, multiply all three terms of the complex fraction by the common denominator $(x + \Delta x)(x)$. This will change the complex fraction to an ordinary fraction and make it easier to work with.

$$f'(x) = \lim_{\Delta x \to 0} \frac{\dfrac{1}{x + \Delta x} \cdot (x + \Delta x)(x) - \dfrac{1}{x} \cdot (x + \Delta x)(x)}{\Delta x (x + \Delta x)(x)}$$

$$= \lim_{\Delta x \to 0} \frac{x - (x + \Delta x)}{(\Delta x)(x + \Delta x)(x)}$$

$$= \lim_{\Delta x \to 0} \frac{-\Delta x}{(\Delta x)(x + \Delta x)(x)}$$

$$= \lim_{\Delta x \to 0} \frac{-1}{(x + \Delta x)(x)} \qquad \begin{array}{l} \text{dividing out } \Delta x \text{ factors in} \\ \text{numerator and denominator} \end{array}$$

$$f'(x) = \frac{-1}{(x)(x)} = \frac{-1}{x^2} \qquad \text{since } \Delta x \to 0$$

In conclusion,

$$\frac{d}{dx}\left(\frac{1}{x}\right) = -\frac{1}{x^2}$$

This result can also be expressed using negative exponents, as

$$\frac{d}{dx}(x^{-1}) = -1 \cdot x^{-2}$$

This latter form will be used in the next section to obtain an important generalization. $\blacklozenge$

In the next section we will begin to develop some rules that will make it much easier to determine derivatives of functions. Nevertheless, use of the definition of the derivative will remain important, because we will need it whenever new types of functions arise. This will happen when we study exponential functions, logarithmic functions, and trigonometric functions, among others.

As a final note, consider this theorem.

If a function f is differentiable at $x = a$, then it is continuous at $x = a$.

After all, if f is differentiable at a, then a tangent line can be drawn to the graph at $(a, f(a))$. This means there can be no break (discontinuity) at $(a, f(a))$, and therefore f must be continuous at a. (See Figure 7.)

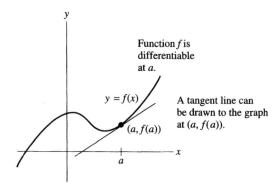

Figure 7 If f is differentiable at a, then it is continuous at a.

In Section 4.1 we will examine some graphs that lead to the following conclusion: *If function f is continuous at $x = a$, it is not necessarily differentiable at $x = a$.*

3.1   Exercises

For each function given in Exercises 1–18, use the *definition* of the derivative to obtain $f'(x)$.

1. $f(x) = 5x + 1$

2. $f(x) = 3x - 4$

3. $f(x) = x^2 + 3$

4. $f(x) = x^2 - 8$

5. $f(x) = x^2 - 4x + 2$

6. $f(x) = x^2 + 3x - 7$

7. $f(x) = 3x^2 + 7x$

8. $f(x) = 2x^2 - 5x$

9. $f(x) = 6$

10. $f(x) = 2$

11. $f(x) = x^3 + 2$

12. $f(x) = x^3 - 1$

13. $f(x) = x^3 + x^2 + x$

14. $f(x) = x^3 - 4x^2 + 2$

15. $f(x) = \dfrac{2}{x}$

16. $f(x) = \dfrac{1}{x^2}$

17. $f(x) = x^4$

18. $f(x) = x^5$

In Exercises 19–22, find the slope of the line tangent to the graph of the function f at any point $(x, f(x))$. Then find the slope at the specific point given.

19. $f(x) = x^2 + 6x$; the point $(2, 16)$

20. $f(x) = x^2 - 3x + 5$; the point $(4, 9)$

21. $f(x) = x^3 - 9$; the point $(4, 55)$

22. $f(x) = \dfrac{1}{x}$; the point $(1/2, 2)$

23. Determine the equation of the tangent line mentioned in Exercise 19.

24. Determine the equation of the tangent line mentioned in Exercise 22.

W **25.** Explain why we can use division to eliminate the Δx in

$$\lim_{\Delta x \to 0} \frac{\Delta x(2x + \Delta x)}{\Delta x} = \lim_{\Delta x \to 0} (2x + \Delta x)$$

After all, division by zero is not defined. Isn't this division by zero?

26. Considering that the derivative dy/dx can be defined as the limit of $\Delta y/\Delta x$ as $\Delta x \to 0$, give the notation for the derivatives defined here.

(a) $\displaystyle\lim_{\Delta x \to 0} \frac{\Delta u}{\Delta x}$ **(b)** $\displaystyle\lim_{\Delta t \to 0} \frac{\Delta v}{\Delta t}$

27. (a) At which x value (a, b, c, or d) does $f'(x)$ have the smallest value? Consider that the derivative is the slope of the tangent line.

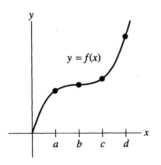

W **(b)** Explain your choice.

W **28.** Consider the functions f and g graphed next.

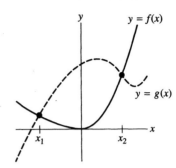

(a) Which function has the larger derivative at x_1? Explain.

(b) Which function has the larger derivative at x_2? Explain.

W **29.** Consider the graph of function f, a semicircle that is centered at the origin, has a radius of 2, and is defined for all x on the open interval $(-2, 2)$. Describe the graph of a function g such that $g'(x) = f'(x)$ for all x on $(-2, 2)$ and $g(0) = 3$.

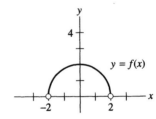

30. Graph $y = x^2 - x - 2$ and $y = -x^2 + 2x$. Study the graphs to determine which function has the larger derivative at $x = 1$.

![Technology icon] **TECHNOLOGY** *EXERCISES*

1. From the graph of the function

$$f(x) = \frac{18}{x^2 - 2x + 4}$$

determine whether the slope of the tangent line would be positive, negative, or zero at the points given below.

(a) $(-2, 1.5)$ **(b)** $(1, 6)$ **(c)** $(0, 4.5)$ **(d)** $(2, 4.5)$

2. Graph $y = x^2 + 5x + 1$ and $y = -5.25$. Does the line appear to be tangent to the curve?

3. Graph $y = 1 - 3x^2 - x^3$ and $y = 2x - 1$. Does the line appear to be tangent to the curve?

4. Graph $y = 3 - x^4$ and $y = -4x + 6$. Does the line appear to be tangent to the curve?

5. Graph $f(x) = -x^3 + 3x^2 + 5$ and estimate, to the nearest integer, the x coordinate of each point at which the tangent line is horizontal. (Zoom in as needed.)

6. Graph $f(x) = 2x^3 + 3x^2 - 12x - 5$ and estimate, to the nearest integer, the x coordinate of each point at which the tangent line is horizontal. You will find that in order to include enough of the graph, the window for y must be larger than $[-10, 10]$.

7. Graph $f(x) = -x^2 + 10x - 17$ and $g(x) = 2\sqrt{x + 1}$. Study the graphs to determine which function has the larger derivative at $x = 3$.

8. Graph $f(x) = .5x^2 + 2$ and $g(x) = \sqrt{x^2 + 1}$. Study the graphs to determine which function has the larger derivative at $x = 4$.

9. Consider the function $f(x) = x^2 + 4x - 1$. Obtain f'. Then graph both f and f' together.

   (a) From the graph of f, what is the nature of the slope of the curve to the left of $x = -2$?

   (b) From the graph of f', what is the nature of the f' values to the left of $x = -2$?

W   **(c)** Account for the relationship between the answers to part (a) and part (b).

   (d) Redo parts (a) through (c) for f and f' to the right of $x = -2$.

W **10.** Consider the function $f(x) = 2x + 1$. Obtain f'. Then graph f and f' together. Relating the graph of f' to the function f, explain why the graph of f' is a horizontal line.

Note   Computer algebra systems can graph a function *and* the line tangent to it at any specific point. The x coordinate of the point must be indicated. The slope of the tangent line is determined as the derivative of the function. The tangent line itself must be defined using the point-slope formula for the equation of a straight line.

3.2   BASIC RULES FOR DIFFERENTIATION

As a beginning, we have obtained derivatives of functions by using the definition of the derivative, namely,

$$f'(x) = \lim_{\Delta x \to 0} \frac{f(x + \Delta x) - f(x)}{\Delta x}$$

Because using the definition of the derivative can be a lengthy and difficult procedure, rules that simplify differentiation have been developed. This section presents some of these rules.

    Functions such as $f(x) = 2$ and $f(x) = -5$ are called *constant functions* because they have the same value for every x. The graph of any constant function $f(x) = c$ is a horizontal straight line. The slope of any such line is zero, which means that the derivative $f'(x)$ is zero. Thus, the derivative of a constant is zero. See Figure 8.

The Derivative of a Constant Is Zero

$$\frac{d}{dx}(c) = 0 \qquad c \text{ is a constant}$$

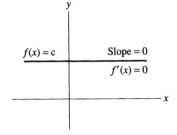

Figure 8

EXAMPLE 1 Here are four examples of the rule that the derivative of a constant is zero.

SOLUTION (a) $\dfrac{d}{dx}(15) = 0$ (b) If $f(t) = 1$, then $f'(t) = 0$.

(c) $\dfrac{d}{dx}(-6) = 0$ (d) If $y = \sqrt{3}$, then $\dfrac{dy}{dx} = 0$.   ◆

In the first section we obtained the following results, which are restated below to make the pattern more obvious.

$$\frac{d}{dx}(x^2) = 2x^1 \qquad \frac{d}{dx}(x^3) = 3x^2 \qquad \frac{d}{dx}(x^{-1}) = -1x^{-2}$$

These derivatives are examples of the **power rule** for derivatives of powers of x.

Power Rule

$$\frac{d}{dx}(x^n) = nx^{n-1}$$

where n is a real number.

The power rule will be proved formally at the end of Section 5.4.

Here are some examples that demonstrate the use of the power rule to differentiate functions we have not previously differentiated.

EXAMPLE 2 Find the derivative of $y = x^5$.

SOLUTION By the power rule,

$$\frac{dy}{dx} = \frac{d}{dx}(x^5) = 5x^4$$ ◆

EXAMPLE 3   If $y = \sqrt{x}$, determine dy/dx.

SOLUTION   In order to apply the power rule, we need a *numerical exponent* representation for $\sqrt{x}$, so we write $\sqrt{x}$ as $x^{1/2}$. Now

$$y = x^{1/2} \qquad \text{and} \qquad \frac{dy}{dx} = \frac{1}{2}x^{-1/2} = \frac{1}{2x^{1/2}} = \frac{1}{2\sqrt{x}} \qquad \blacklozenge$$

EXAMPLE 4   Obtain the derivative of $f(t) = \dfrac{1}{t^2}$.

SOLUTION   In order to apply the power rule, rewrite $1/t^2$ as t^{-2}. Now the expression is indeed a power of t. As originally given, the expression was 1 *divided by* a power of t. Continuing,

$$f(t) = t^{-2} \qquad \text{leads to} \qquad f'(t) = -2t^{-3} = \frac{-2}{t^3} = -\frac{2}{t^3} \qquad \blacklozenge$$

The next rule specifies how to find the derivative of a constant times a function, when the derivative of the function is known.

$$\frac{d}{dx}[c \cdot f(x)] = c \cdot \frac{d}{dx} f(x)$$

where c is a constant.

In words, *the derivative of a constant times a function is that constant times the derivative of the function*. Here is an opportunity to see some "formal" mathematics. Proof of this derivative rule follows readily from the definition of the derivative, as shown next.

$$\frac{d}{dx}[c \cdot f(x)] = \lim_{\Delta x \to 0} \frac{c \cdot f(x + \Delta x) - c \cdot f(x)}{\Delta x}$$

$$= \lim_{\Delta x \to 0} \frac{c\,[f(x + \Delta x) - f(x)]}{\Delta x}$$

$$= \lim_{\Delta x \to 0} c \cdot \frac{f(x + \Delta x) - f(x)}{\Delta x}$$

$$= c \cdot \lim_{\Delta x \to 0} \frac{f(x + \Delta x) - f(x)}{\Delta x}$$

$$= c \cdot \frac{d}{dx} f(x)$$

The rule says, in effect, that a constant can be moved out in front of the differentiation.

EXAMPLE 5   Find $\dfrac{dy}{dx}$.   **(a)** $y = 4x^6$ **(b)** $y = \dfrac{x^3}{5}$

SOLUTION   **(a)** $\dfrac{dy}{dx} = \dfrac{d}{dx}(4x^6) = 4 \cdot \dfrac{d}{dx}(x^6) = 4 \cdot 6x^5 = 24x^5$

(b) $\dfrac{dy}{dx} = \dfrac{d}{dx}\left(\dfrac{x^3}{5}\right) = \dfrac{d}{dx}\left(\dfrac{1}{5}x^3\right) = \dfrac{1}{5}\cdot\dfrac{d}{dx}(x^3) = \dfrac{1}{5}\cdot 3x^2 = \dfrac{3x^2}{5}$ ◆

Perhaps you can see the shortcut in differentiating expressions such as those of the previous example—that is, expressions of the form cx^n.

$$\frac{d}{dx}(cx^n) = n\cdot cx^{n-1}$$

Thus, for example,

$$\frac{d}{dx}(8x^4) = 4\cdot 8x^3 = 32x^3$$

$$\frac{d}{dt}(3t^9) = 9\cdot 3t^8 = 27t^8$$

Another special case is worth noting here. Since $y = cx$ is the equation of a straight line with slope c, it follows that

$$\frac{d}{dx}(cx) = c$$

This result can also be seen as a special case of the derivative of cx^n, as shown next.

$$\frac{d}{dx}(cx) = \frac{d}{dx}(cx^1) = 1\cdot cx^0 = 1\cdot c\cdot 1 = c$$

Here are some examples of this special case.

$$\frac{d}{dx}(5x) = 5 \qquad \frac{d}{dx}(x) = 1$$

$$\frac{d}{dx}(\pi x) = \pi \qquad \frac{d}{dt}(9t) = 9$$

The next rule will enable us to combine the separate rules already developed.

Sum and Difference Rules

$$\frac{d}{dx}[f(x) + g(x)] = \frac{d}{dx}f(x) + \frac{d}{dx}g(x)$$

$$\frac{d}{dx}[f(x) - g(x)] = \frac{d}{dx}f(x) - \frac{d}{dx}g(x)$$

In words, *the derivative of a sum is the sum of the derivatives*, and *the derivative of a difference is the difference of the derivatives*. A sum or difference can be differentiated term by term. If you do not feel intuitively that this rule is true, then consider the following proof, which uses the definition of the derivative.

$$\frac{d}{dx}[f(x) + g(x)] = \lim_{\Delta x \to 0} \frac{[f(x + \Delta x) + g(x + \Delta x)] - [f(x) + g(x)]}{\Delta x}$$

$$= \lim_{\Delta x \to 0} \frac{[f(x + \Delta x) - f(x)] + [g(x + \Delta x) - g(x)]}{\Delta x}$$

$$= \lim_{\Delta x \to 0} \left[\frac{f(x + \Delta x) - f(x)}{\Delta x} + \frac{g(x + \Delta x) - g(x)}{\Delta x} \right]$$

$$= \lim_{\Delta x \to 0} \frac{f(x + \Delta x) - f(x)}{\Delta x} + \lim_{\Delta x \to 0} \frac{g(x + \Delta x) - g(x)}{\Delta x}$$

$$= \frac{d}{dx} f(x) + \frac{d}{dx} g(x)$$

EXAMPLE 6 Differentiate $y = x^{10} + 3x$.

SOLUTION The differentiation will make use of the sum rule.

$$\frac{dy}{dx} = \frac{d}{dx}(x^{10} + 3x)$$

$$= \frac{d}{dx}(x^{10}) + \frac{d}{dx}(3x) \qquad \text{by the sum rule}$$

$$= 10x^9 + 3 \qquad \text{after differentiating} \qquad \blacklozenge$$

The sum rule can be extended to sums of three or four or more functions, as demonstrated in the next example.

EXAMPLE 7 Determine the derivative of $y = x^3 + 4x^2 - 7x + 1$.

SOLUTION

$$\frac{dy}{dx} = \frac{d}{dx}(x^3 + 4x^2 - 7x + 1) \qquad \text{step 1}$$

$$= \frac{d}{dx}(x^3 + 4x^2) + \frac{d}{dx}(-7x + 1) \qquad \text{step 2}$$

$$= \frac{d}{dx}(x^3) + \frac{d}{dx}(4x^2) + \frac{d}{dx}(-7x) + \frac{d}{dx}(1) \qquad \text{step 3}$$

$$= 3x^2 + 8x - 7$$

Step 2 (above) was included to show you why the sum rule can be extended to more than two terms. In the future, go directly from step 1 to step 3. $\blacklozenge$

EXAMPLE 8 (a) Find the slope of the line tangent to the graph of $y = x^2 + 5x - 3$ at the point $(3, 21)$.

(b) Find the equation of the tangent line mentioned in part (a).

SOLUTION (a) Since the slope of the tangent line is the derivative, we will obtain dy/dx.

$$m_{\tan} = \frac{dy}{dx} = 2x + 5$$

At $(3, 21)$, $m_{\tan} = 2(3) + 5 = 11$; the slope of the tangent line is 11.

(b) The line we seek has the form $y = mx + b$. Since slope m is 11,

$$y = 11x + b$$

Because the line passes through the point $(3, 21)$, it follows that $x = 3$ and $y = 21$ must satisfy the equation of the line. We have then

$$21 = 11(3) + b$$
$$21 = 33 + b$$
$$b = -12$$

The equation of the tangent line is $y = 11x - 12$ ◆

EXAMPLE 9 Given $f(x) = x^2 + 4\sqrt{x}$, determine $f'(1)$.

SOLUTION We seek a specific value of the derivative function f'. First obtain $f'(x)$. Then evalute f' at $x = 1$.

$$f(x) = x^2 + 4\sqrt{x} = x^2 + 4x^{1/2}$$

So

$$f'(x) = 2x + \frac{1}{2} \cdot 4x^{-1/2} = 2x + \frac{2}{\sqrt{x}}$$

Substituting 1 for x in the derivative yields

$$f'(1) = 2(1) + \frac{2}{\sqrt{1}} = 4$$ ◆

3.2 Exercises

Determine the derivative of each function defined in Exercises 1–20. Do not leave negative exponents in answers. Also, recall that $\sqrt[n]{x} = x^{1/n}$.

1. $f(x) = x^4$

2. $f(x) = x^{80}$

3. $f(x) = x^{-2}$

4. $y = x^{-10}$

5. $g(x) = 16$

6. $g(x) = -8$

7. $y = x^{3/2}$

8. $y = x^{2/3}$

9. $y = x^{-2/3}$

10. $y = x^{-3/2}$

11. $f(x) = \frac{1}{x^5}$

12. $f(t) = \frac{1}{t^{11}}$

13. $y = \sqrt[3]{x}$

14. $y = \sqrt[4]{x}$

15. $f(x) = 30\sqrt{x}$

16. $f(x) = 10\sqrt[3]{x}$

17. $y = \frac{x^4}{4}$

18. $f(x) = \frac{x^5}{3}$

19. $y = \frac{10}{\sqrt{t}}$

20. $f(x) = \pi$

In Exercises 21–26, obtain each derivative.

21. $D_x(1 - x^3)$

22. $D_x(x^2 + 3x - 1)$

23. $\dfrac{d}{dx}\left(\dfrac{1}{x} + \sqrt{2}\right)$

24. $\dfrac{d}{dx}\left(5 - \dfrac{4}{x}\right)$

25. $D_x(\sqrt{x} - 2)$

26. $D_x(5 + \sqrt[3]{x})$

Find dy/dx in Exercises 27–32.

27. $y = x^2 - 5x + 19$

28. $y = x^3 + 6x - 3$

29. $y = x^{3/2} + 4x^2$

30. $y = x^{4/3} - 16x^2$

31. $y = \dfrac{2}{\sqrt{x}} - 3 + \pi^2$

32. $y = 1 - \dfrac{6}{\sqrt[3]{x}}$

Find $D_x y$ in Exercises 33–36.

33. $y = 1 - x^4 + 3x^6$

34. $y = 2x^{10} + 5x^9 + 13x^5$

35. $y = 1 - x^{-5}$

36. $y = x^{-3} + 4$

Find $f'(x)$ in Exercises 37–42.

37. $f(x) = x^3 - 6x^2 + 4x - 1$

38. $f(x) = x^7 + 5x^4 - 16x$

39. $f(x) = 8x^{7/4} + 6x^{5/3} - 9$

40. $f(x) = 12x^{5/3} + 3x^{4/3}$

41. $f(x) = 3\sqrt{x} + 5x^2$

42. $f(x) = \dfrac{4}{x} - 2x - 5$

Determine each of the derivatives specified in Exercises 43–48.

43. $f'(3)$ when $f(x) = x^2 + 8x + 4$

44. $f'(1)$ when $f(x) = 5x^2 - 16x + 2$

45. $f'(-1)$ when $f(x) = 4x^3 - 7x^2 + 8x - 12$

46. $f'(-2)$ when $f(x) = \dfrac{5}{x^2}$

47. $f'(9)$ when $f(x) = 1 + \sqrt{x}$

48. $f'(8)$ when $f(x) = 6\sqrt[3]{x}$

In Exercises 49–54, find the slope of the line tangent to the graph of the given function at the given point.

49. $y = x^2 + 3x + 4$ at $(-1, 2)$

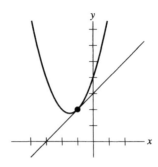

50. $y = x^2 - 5x + 12$ at $(4, 8)$

51. $y = 1 - x^3$ at $(-2, 9)$

52. $y = x^4$ at $(-2, 16)$

53. $y = 8\sqrt{x}$ at $(4, 16)$

54. $y = \sqrt[3]{x}$ at $(1, 1)$

55. Determine the equation of the tangent line mentioned in Exercise 52.

56. Determine the equation of the tangent line mentioned in Exercise 53.

57. Use the *definition* of the derivative to prove that if $f(x) = c$, then $f'(x) = 0$.

58. Use the *definition* of the derivative to prove that

$$\frac{d}{dx}[f(x) - g(x)] = \frac{d}{dx}f(x) - \frac{d}{dx}g(x)$$

W 59. Consider the function $f(x) = 1/x$. In view of the *definition* of the derivative, explain why $f'(x)$ does not exist when $x = 0$.

W 60. Complete the sentence. For any function f, if f is not defined at a, then f'_____.

W 61. When finding a specific value of a derivative, such as $f'(3)$ or $f'(1)$, we differentiate the function first *and then* substitute the 3 or the 1 for x. Why don't we substitute the 3 or the 1 at the beginning and then differentiate the function?

W 62. Suppose $f'(x) = g'(x)$. Does this necessarily mean that $f(x) = g(x)$? Explain.

63. Answer each question on the basis of the graphs of f and g shown in the figure on the next page. You will need to use the fact that the derivative of a function is the slope of the tangent line.

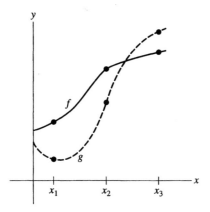

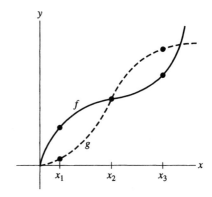

(a) Which is greater, $f'(x_1)$ or $g'(x_1)$?
(b) Which is greater, $f'(x_2)$ or $g'(x_2)$?
(c) Which is greater, $f'(x_3)$ or $g'(x_3)$?

(a) Which is greater, $f'(x_1)$ or $g'(x_1)$?
(b) Which is greater, $f'(x_2)$ or $g'(x_2)$?
(c) Which is greater, $f'(x_3)$ or $g'(x_3)$?

64. Answer each question on the basis of the graphs of f and g shown in the next figure.

W 65. The limit below can be determined by using algebraic simplification and the like. It can also be evaluated "instantly" by noting the *meaning* of the limit. Find the limit and comment.

$$\lim_{\Delta x \to 0} \frac{[(x + \Delta x)^2 + 7] - [x^2 + 7]}{\Delta x}$$

TECHNOLOGY *EXERCISES*

1. Graph $f(x) = x^3 - 2x^2 - 3x$ and study the graph to determine which is larger, $f'(2)$ or $f'(3)$.

2. Graph $f(x) = x^4 + 3x^3 - 5x^2 - 3x + 4$ and study the graph to determine which is larger, $f'(-2)$ or $f'(-1)$.

3. Graph the two functions

$$f(x) = x^2 - 6x + 1 \qquad g(x) = -x^2 - 4x$$

Study the graphs to determine which is larger, $f'(5)$ or $g'(-2)$.

4. Graph the two functions

$$f(x) = \frac{6x}{x^2 + 1} \qquad g(x) = \frac{9}{x^2 + 1}$$

Study the graphs to determine which is larger, $f'(2)$ or $g'(2)$.

5. Graph

$$f(x) = \frac{8}{x^2 - 6x + 10}$$

and estimate, to the nearest integer, the value of x for which $f'(x) = 0$.

6. Graph

$$f(x) = \frac{3x^2 - 12x - 6}{x^2 - 4x - 5}$$

and estimate, to the nearest integer, the value of x for which $f'(x) = 0$.

7. Graph $f(x) = x^3 - 3x^2 + 1$ and $g(x) = x^3 - 3x^2 + 3$ using x in $[-2, 4]$ and y in $[-6, 6]$.

  (a) Point for point, how do the slopes of the tangent lines to f compare with those to g?
  (b) Use the rules for differentiation to determine the derivative of each function and then compare the derivatives.
  W **(c)** In a sentence or two, link the results of parts (a) and (b).

3.3 | *RATES OF CHANGE*

Applications that follow from interpreting the derivative as a rate of change are presented next. Additional rate-of-change applications will be given in Sections 3.7, 3.9, and 4.3 and elsewhere in the text.

To set the stage for the rate-of-change interpretation, we begin with three examples of **average rate of change.**

APPLIED

EXAMPLE 1 *AVERAGE SPEED*

If Juwan walks 7 miles in 2 hours, what is his average speed?

SOLUTION We shall use the letter s to represent *distance*, not speed. This is a common convention in mathematics.

Average speed is defined to be the change in distance Δs divided by the change in time Δt.

$$\text{average speed} = \frac{\Delta s}{\Delta t}$$

In this instance,

$$\frac{\Delta s}{\Delta t} = \frac{7 \text{ miles}}{2 \text{ hours}} = 3.5 \text{ miles per hour}$$

His average speed is 3.5 miles per hour. ◆

EXAMPLE 2   ***AVERAGE CHANGE IN AMTRAK'S REVENUE***

From 1986 to 1991, Amtrak's annual revenue increased from from \$861,000,000 to \$1,359,000,000. What was the average change in revenue per year during this time?

SOLUTION   The average change in revenue per year is the change in revenue ΔR divided by the change in years Δt.

$$\frac{\Delta R}{\Delta t} = \frac{1,359,000,000 - 861,000,000}{1991 - 1986} = \frac{\$498,000,000}{5 \text{ years}} = \$99,600,000 \text{ per year}$$

As you can see, from 1986 to 1991, Amtrak's annual revenue increased at the average rate of \$99,600,000 per year. ◆

The ''average rate of change'' concept suggested in Examples 1 and 2 can be applied to a function $y = f(x)$, as shown in the next example.

EXAMPLE 3   What is the average rate of change of $y = x^2$ from $x = 1$ to $x = 5$?

SOLUTION   The average rate of change is the change in y divided by the change in x, namely

$$\frac{\Delta y}{\Delta x} = \frac{(5)^2 - (1)^2}{5 - 1} = \frac{25 - 1}{4} = \frac{24}{4} = 6$$

◆

The $\Delta y/\Delta x$ in Example 3 should remind you of slope. The slope of a line is an example of a rate of change—the rate of change of y with respect to x. A slope of 3 means that the rate of change of y with respect to x is 3; that is, there is a 3-unit change in y for each 1-unit change in x.

For $y = f(x)$, the derivative

$$f'(x) = \lim_{\Delta x \to 0} \frac{\Delta y}{\Delta x}$$

gives the slope of the tangent line at any point (x, y). So it can also be said that $f'(x)$ or dy/dx gives the rate of change of y with respect to x at any *point* (x, y). It is the *rate of change at a particular value of* x, rather than an average rate of change over an interval. Consequently, the derivative is considered to be the **instantaneous rate of change** of y with respect to x.

If $y = f(x)$, then dy/dx is the *instantaneous rate of change* of y with respect to x, or the instantaneous rate of change of $f(x)$ with respect to x.

> *Note*
>
> The instantaneous rate of change is often called simply the **rate of change**.

EXAMPLE 4   VELOCITY OF A FALLING OBJECT

A ball dropped from the top of a cliff will fall such that the distance it has traveled after *t* seconds is

$$s(t) = -16t^2 \text{ feet}$$

(a) What is the *average* velocity for the first 3 seconds?

(b) How fast is the ball traveling at 3 seconds?

SOLUTION   **(a)** Just as in Example 1, the *average* speed is $\Delta s/\Delta t$. Here it is the average speed between $t = 0$ and $t = 3$.

$$\frac{\Delta s}{\Delta t} = \frac{s(3) - s(0)}{3 - 0} = \frac{[-16(3)^2] - [-16(0)^2]}{3} = \frac{-144}{3} = -48$$

The average speed is 48 feet per second. The *minus* indicates that the ball is traveling in a *downward* direction. The *velocity* (which includes speed and direction) is -48 feet per second. If the ball were traveling upward, then the velocity would be positive.

(b) The velocity at 3 seconds is an *instantaneous* velocity. It is the velocity at a specific time, when $t = 3$. So we need to evaluate ds/dt at $t = 3$. Since $s = -16t^2$,

$$v = \frac{ds}{dt} = -32t \text{ feet per second}$$

At $t = 3$,

$$\frac{ds}{dt} = -32(3) = -96 \text{ feet per second}$$

The ball is traveling 96 feet per second (downward) after 3 seconds.   ◆

For future reference, we shall note here that **instantaneous velocity** is defined as the rate of change of distance with respect to time.

> ### Instantaneous Velocity
>
> $$v = \frac{ds}{dt}$$
>
> v = velocity, s = distance, t = time

EXAMPLE 5   Let $y = 5x^3 - x^2 + 8x + 1$. Determine the rate of change of y with respect to x when x is 4.

SOLUTION   The rate of change of y with respect to x is dy/dx, and we are given that $y = 5x^3 - x^2 + 8x + 1$. It follows that

$$\frac{dy}{dx} = 15x^2 - 2x + 8$$

Specifically, when $x = 4$,

$$\frac{dy}{dx} = 15(4)^2 - 2(4) + 8 = 240$$

Thus, when $x = 4$, the rate of change of y with respect to x is 240.   ◆

APPLIED

EXAMPLE 6   ***VELOCITY OF A RACING CAR***

The driver of an experimental racing car begins a test run. During the first 6 seconds, the distance s (in feet) of the car from the starting point is

$$s = 14t^2 - \frac{1}{3}t^3 \qquad 0 \le t \le 6$$

where t is the number of seconds the car has been moving. (See Figure 9.) What is the velocity of the car after 4 seconds have passed?

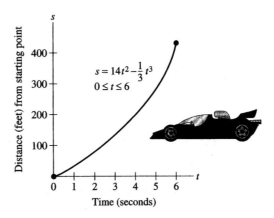

Figure 9

SOLUTION The velocity at any particular time is the value of ds/dt at that time. Thus we seek ds/dt for $t = 4$. From

$$s = 14t^2 - \frac{1}{3}t^3$$

we determine that

$$v = \frac{ds}{dt} = 28t - t^2$$

Specifically, for $t = 4$,

$$v = \frac{ds}{dt} = 28(4) - (4)^2 = 96$$

We conclude that the velocity of the car after 4 seconds is 96 feet per second (which, by the way, is approximately 65 miles per hour). ◆

EXAMPLE 7 **CITY GOVERNMENT EXPENDITURES**

Figure 10 shows the city government expenditures during the administrations of three mayors, each of whom promised to reduce expenditures.

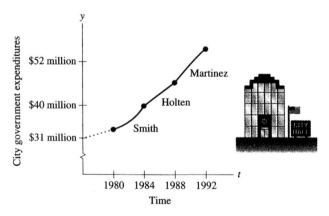

Figure 10

(a) Did any of the three mayors actually reduce expenditures?

(b) Which mayor can claim to have reduced the *rate* of government expenditure?

SOLUTION **(a)** The y coordinate represents expenditures. From the graph you can see that the y coordinate (expenditures) increased throughout each mayor's term. We conclude that none of the mayors reduced expenditures.

(b) The *rate* of government expenditures is the derivative, dy/dt—the slope of the curve. By following the curve from before 1980, we can see that the slope of the curve (that is, the rate of expenditure) increased during Smith's term. When Holten took over in 1984, the rate of expenditure was very high. (Note the steep slope at the end of Smith's term.) The rate of expenditure during Holten's term is considerably less than it was when she took office in 1984. (The slope of her portion of the curve is much less than that of Mayor Smith.) When Martinez took over in 1988, the rate of expenditure increased again (as displayed by the increased slope of the curve).

We conclude that only Holten can claim that as mayor she reduced the rate of government expenditures. ◆

Note on Marginal Analysis

It seems natural to apply the "instantaneous rate of change" concept to functions that describe cost, revenue, and profit. This application, called *marginal analysis*, is a particularly important business application, one that deserves full attention when studied. Consequently, it will be presented separately and unhurriedly in the next section.

3.3 | EXERCISES

Determine the *average rate of change* that is requested in Exercises 1–8.

1. **(COIN APPRECIATION)** According to *Coin World*, the value of uncirculated Indian head nickels increased by 18% from August 1994 to August 1995. What was the average rate of increase per month during this period?

2. **(INVENTORY)** At the end of November, an automobile manufacturer's inventory consisted of 160,000 cars. At the end of March, the inventory consisted of 220,000 cars. What was the average rate of increase in inventory per month during this period?

3. **(POPULATION DECLINE)** In 1980 the population of Buffalo, New York, was 355,000. In 1990 it was 328,000. What was the average rate of decrease in the population per year between 1980 and 1990?

4. **(CORPORATE PROFIT)** In 6 years a corporation's annual profit increased from $10,000 to $130,600. What was the average rate of increase in profit per year during this 6-year period?

5. **(STOCK MARKET)** The Dow Jones Industrial Average gained 162 points over the last 3 days. What was the average rate of gain per day?

6. **(DIETING)** David has been dieting for 15 months and has lost 24 pounds. What is his average weight loss per month?

7. **(FALLING OBJECT)** A ball is dropped from the top of a 400-foot-tall buildling and falls such that its distance from the ground at t seconds is $s = -16t^2 + 400$ feet. What is the average velocity of the ball for the first 4 seconds?

8. **(DIVING HAWK)** Assume that a hawk dives from a height of 300 feet and that its distance from the ground at t seconds is $s = 300 - 16t^2$ feet. What is the hawk's average velocity during the first 4 seconds?

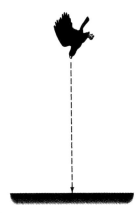

9. Let $y = x^2 - 6x + 2$. Determine the rate of change of y with respect to x when x is 4.

10. Let $f(x) = 1 - x^2 + x^3$. Determine the rate of change of $f(x)$ with respect to x when x is 10.

11. Let $f(t) = 4.2\sqrt{t} - 3$. Determine the rate of change of $f(t)$ with respect to t when t is 15, approximating the result to the nearest hundredth.

12. *(ROCKET VELOCITY)* A toy rocket is shot straight up from the ground and travels so that its distance from the ground after t seconds is $s = 200t - 16t^2$ feet. What is the velocity of the rocket after 2 seconds have passed?

13. *(FALLING OBJECT)* A brick comes loose from near the top of a building and falls such that its distance s (in feet) from the street (after t seconds) is given by $s = 150 - 16t^2$. How fast is the brick falling after 3 seconds have passed?

14. *(VELOCITY OF A CAR)* A racing car begins a short test run and travels according to $s = 8t^2 + \frac{1}{3}t^3$, where s is the distance traveled in feet and t is the time in seconds. What is the velocity of the car after 3 seconds have passed?

15. *(BACTERIA GROWTH)* Two bacteria cultures are used to test the relative effect of two different growth inhibitors. The number of bacteria n in the cultures after t hours is given by

$$n = 1000 + 100t + 20t^2 \quad \text{(inhibitor A used)}$$
$$n = 1000 + 200t - 10t^2 \quad \text{(inhibitor B used)}$$

Compare the rates of growth of the two cultures after 5 hours and after 10 hours.

16. *(BACTERIA GROWTH)* A colony of 1000 bacteria is introduced to a growth-inhibiting environment and grows according to the formula

$$n = 1000 + 20t + t^2$$

where n is the number of bacteria present at any time t (t is measured in hours).
   (a) According to the formula, how many bacteria are present at the beginning?
   (b) What is the rate of growth of the bacteria at any time t?
   (c) What is the rate of growth after 3 hours?
   (d) How many bacteria are present after 3 hours?

17. *(FLU OUTBREAK)* Suppose that when a flu outbreak strikes, the number of people n that are sick with flu at a particular time t (within a month of the outbreak) is given by $n = 100t^2 - 2t^3$. Time t is the number of days after the start of the outbreak.
   (a) How many people will be sick with flu after 20 days?
   (b) At what rate is illness due to flu increasing after 20 days?

18. *(SALES)* Suppose that in June a chain of stores had combined daily sales of ice cream cones given by

$$s = -.01x^2 + .48x + 50$$

where s is the number of hundreds of ice cream cones sold and x is the day of the month.
   (a) How many ice cream cones were sold by the chain on June 3?
   (b) At what rate were sales changing on June 10?
   (c) At what rate were sales changing on June 28?
   (d) On what day was the rate of change of sales equal to 10 cones per day?

19. *(EYE PUPIL SIZE)* The intensity of light that enters the eye depends on the radius of the pupil. As the pupil increases in size, the amount of light entering the eye increases. Specifically, $I = kr^2$, where I is the intensity of light, r is the radius of the pupil, and k is some constant. Determine the (instantaneous) rate of change of intensity with respect to radius.

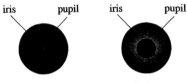

iris   pupil   iris   pupil

More light enters   Less light enters

20. Given $L = 12/\sqrt{t}$, find the rate of change of L with respect to t when $t = 4$.

21. *(FACTORY PRODUCTION)* In t hours of a day's operation, a factory produces $48t - t^2$ automobile tires $(0 \le t \le 12)$.
  (a) At what rate is the factory producing tires 4 hours into the day's operation?
  (b) When will the factory be producing tires at the rate of 36 per hour?

22. *(VOLUME)* The volume V of a spherical balloon with radius r is $V = \frac{4}{3}\pi r^3$. As air is blown into the balloon, both the radius and the volume of the balloon increase. Determine the rate of change of the volume with respect to the radius when the radius is 10 centimeters.

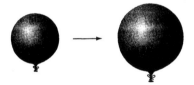

23. *(AREA)* Determine the rate of change of the area A of a circle with respect to its radius r. The area of a circle is $A = \pi r^2$.

24. *(TEMPERATURE)* Determine the rate of change of temperature in degrees Fahrenheit (F) with respect to the temperature in degrees Celsius (C). The relationship between F and C is $F = 1.8C + 32$.

25. *(RISING BALLOON)* A weather balloon is released and rises vertically according to

$$s(t) = t^2 + t + 4 \qquad 0 \le t \le 15$$

where s is its distance (in feet) from the ground after t seconds.
  (a) Find the velocity of the balloon after 1 second and after 5 seconds.

(b) When is the balloon 24 feet above the ground?
(c) How fast is the balloon traveling when it is 24 feet above the ground?
(d) When is the velocity of the balloon equal to 23 feet per second?

26. *(GROWTH OF YEAST CULTURE)* Consider the rate of change in the number of yeast cells growing in a culture (see the figure). Three times are marked in the illustration: t_1, t_2, and t_3. The function is called n.

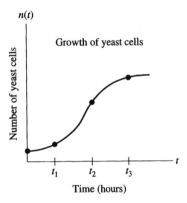

(a) At which of the three times (t_1, t_2, t_3) is the rate of growth the greatest?
(b) At which of the three times (t_1, t_2, t_3) is the rate of growth the least?
(c) True or false: $n(t_3) > n(t_1)$?
(d) True or false: $n'(t_1) > n'(t_2)$?
(e) True or false: $n'(t_3) < n'(t_2)$?

W 27. *(GROSS DOMESTIC PRODUCT)* The figure below shows the graphs of two estimates of future GDP growth.

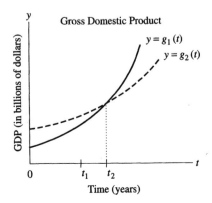

(a) Which function (g_1 or g_2) shows the greater rate of increase of GDP at time t_1? Explain.

(b) Consider the rates of increase of GDP at time t_2. Are the rates of increase the same for both g_1 and g_2? Explain.

28. *(LEARNING/RECALL)* Psychologists have found that previous learning interferes with recall. The more groups of items people are required to learn, the smaller the percentage that they can recall. A graph of three recall functions $r_1, r_2,$ and r_3 is shown in the figure. Here t is time and y is the percentage of items recalled. Function r_3 includes the most groups: r_1 includes the least.

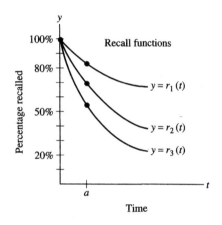

Time

(a) Consider $r_1(a)$, $r_2(a)$, and $r_3(a)$. Which is the largest and which is the smallest?

(b) Consider the absolute value of $r_1{}'(a)$, $r_2{}'(a)$, and $r_3{}'(a)$. Which is the largest and which is the smallest?

29. *(BICYCLE TRIP)* A boy leaves home and rides his bicycle to a movie theatre. On the graph shown next, time (t) is measured in minutes and distance from home (s) is measured in miles.

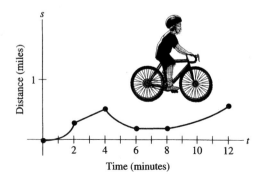

Time (minutes)

(a) When and for how long did the boy stop to talk with a friend?

(b) Approximately when is he going fastest?

(c) When is his speed constant?

(d) When did he turn around and head back to a mailbox to mail some letters?

W 30. *(SERVING DINNER)* In preparing to serve dinner, a family removes baked potatoes from the hot oven and cold drinks from the refrigerator. Let $p(x)$ be the temperature of the potatoes x minutes after being removed from the oven, and let $d(x)$ be the temperature of the drinks x minutes after being removed from the refrigerator. Write a sentence of explanation (interpretation) for each of these mathematical statements.

(a) $p(0) > d(0)$ **(b)** $p(5) < p(0)$
(c) $d(5) > d(0)$ **(d)** $p'(4) < 0$
(e) $d'(4) > 0$

W 31. *(SNOWFALL)* Suppose that $s(x)$ is the number of inches of snow that falls in x hours. Use nonmathematical words to answer the following questions.

(a) What is the meaning of the statement $s(6) = 14$?

(b) What is the meaning of the following expression: $s(4) - s(3)$?

(c) What is the meaning of the statement $s'(2) = 3$?

(d) What is the meaning of the following statement: $s'(4) > s'(3)$?

W 32. *(ACCELERATION)* Some of the following limits represent *acceleration*, the instantaneous rate of change of velocity with respect to time. Here $v = v(t)$ is velocity as a function of time t. Select the limits (below) that do indeed represent acceleration, and explain why.

(a) $\lim\limits_{\Delta t \to 0} \dfrac{v(t + \Delta t) - v(t)}{\Delta t}$ **(b)** $\lim\limits_{\Delta t \to 0} \dfrac{\Delta v}{\Delta t}$

(c) $\lim\limits_{\Delta t \to 0} \dfrac{v(t) + \Delta t}{\Delta t}$ **(d)** $\lim\limits_{\Delta t \to 0} \dfrac{v}{t}$

W 33. Compare the instantaneous rate of change and the average rate of change for a linear function such as $f(x) = 10x + 25$.

W 34. Compare the instantaneous rate of change and the average rate of change for a constant function such as $f(x) = 50$.

TECHNOLOGY *EXERCISES*

1. **(MOVING BALL)** A ball is shot upward from the ground and travels so that its distance s (in feet) from the ground after t seconds is

$$s(t) = -16t^2 + 75t \qquad t \geq 0$$

Graph the distance function. Use the window $[0, 10]$ for x and $[0, 100]$ for y.
   (a) Estimate, to the nearest tenth of a second, when the velocity of the ball will be zero.
      (*Hint*: The derivative is both the slope of the tangent line and the velocity.)
   (b) Estimate, to the nearest foot, the maximum height that the ball will reach.

2. Graph

$$y = \frac{-10.3x}{.5x^2 + 1}$$

Is the rate of change of y with respect to x greater at $x = 3$ or at $x = 5$?

3. **(GROSS DOMESTIC PRODUCT)** Suppose that two estimates of future GDP are given by $y = 2(1.3)^x$ and $y = .25x^2 + 2$, where x is the time in years and y is the GDP in billions of dollars. Begin by graphing the functions for x in $[0, 5]$ and y in $[0, 10]$.

   (a) Which estimate anticipates the greater rate of growth in GDP during the first year?
   (b) Which estimate anticipates the greater rate of growth in GDP during the fifth year?

4. **(BACTERIA GROWTH)** Suppose the numbers of bacteria in two different inhibited growth cultures are given by

$$y = 300 + 1.5x + .1x^2 \qquad 0 \leq x \leq 24$$
$$y = 200 + x + .5x^2 \qquad 0 \leq x \leq 24$$

where x is the time in hours. Begin by graphing the functions for x in the interval $[0, 24]$ and y in the interval $[0, 1000]$. Next, from the graph determine which culture is growing at a faster rate at $x = 14$ hours.

3.4 | *MARGINAL ANALYSIS*

The managers of a manufacturing operation are naturally concerned about the total cost of maintaining a particular level of production. In other words, they want to know the cost $C(x)$ of producing x units. Furthermore, when a particular level of production is being maintained, it is important to know the cost of producing one additional unit. For example, if they are already making 100 TV sets, what will it cost to make one more—the 101st TV? Such information assists management in making decisions about production.

   The rate-of-change interpretation of the derivative leads to a calculus application here. If $C(x)$ is the total cost of producing x units, then $C'(x)$ is the rate of change of the total cost and gives the *approximate* cost of producing one additional unit. $C'(x)$ is called the **marginal cost**.

Marginal Cost

$C(x)$ = the total cost of producing x units

$C'(x)$ = *marginal cost*, the approximate cost
of producing the next unit

Ordinarily, $C'(x)$ is a good approximation of the exact cost of producing one more unit, the $(x + 1)$st unit. In other words, $C'(x) \approx C(x + 1) - C(x)$. Consider that the exact cost of one more unit is $\Delta C / \Delta x$ with $\Delta x = 1$ and the marginal cost is dC/dx. The two values are equal when C is a linear function; otherwise dC/dx only approximates $\Delta C / \Delta x$. (Graphically, dC/dx is the slope of the tangent line, whereas $\Delta C / \Delta x$ is the slope of the secant line.) Consider that

$$C(x + 1) - C(x) = \frac{C(x + 1) - C(x)}{1} \approx \lim_{\Delta x \to 0} \frac{C(x + \Delta x) - C(x)}{\Delta x} = C'(x)$$

because $\Delta x \to 0$ is approximated by $\Delta x = 1$.

In this section, you will see that the marginal cost function and other marginal functions are relatively easy to obtain and use.

EXAMPLE 1   MARGINAL COST

Suppose the cost of producing x units is $C(x) = 100 + 30x - x^2$ dollars (for $0 \le x \le 12$). Determine the marginal cost when $x = 9$.

SOLUTION   The marginal cost is

$$C'(x) = 30 - 2x$$

For $x = 9$, we have

$$C'(9) = 30 - 2(9) = 12$$

The marginal cost when $x = 9$ is \$12. This means that after 9 units have been produced, the cost of producing the next unit (the tenth unit) will be *approximately* \$12.

By the way, the *exact* cost of producing the tenth unit can be computed as $C(10) - C(9)$, a method used in Chapter 1.

$$C(10) - C(9) = [100 + 30(10) - (10)^2] - [100 + 30(9) - (9)^2]$$
$$= 300 - 289$$
$$= \$11$$

Figure 11 shows a graph of the marginal cost $C'(x)$ and the exact cost of the next unit for x between 0 and 11 units.

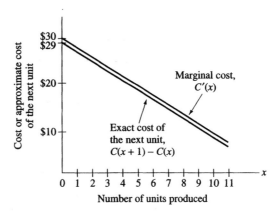

Figure 11 Comparison of marginal cost and exact cost for the cost function of Example 1   ◆

Note

It is natural to wonder why we would want the approximate cost of the tenth unit when the exact cost is relatively easy to determine. The answer to this question will emerge as we study various applications, beginning later in this section with a relationship involving marginal cost, marginal revenue, and marginal profit. In a later chapter, you will learn how to use the marginal cost function to construct the cost function C.

APPLIED

EXAMPLE 2   **MARGINAL COST**

A furniture manufacturer determines that the marginal cost for making tables is always increasing. The company decides to stop table production when that marginal cost reaches $110. Assuming the cost function for tables is

$$C(x) = .01x^2 + 80x + 100$$

how many tables will the company make before it halts table production?

SOLUTION   Since the cost is given as $C(x) = .01x^2 + 80x + 100$, it follows that the marginal cost $C'(x)$ is

$$C'(x) = .02x + 80$$

The marginal cost will be $110 when $C'(x)$ is 110, so solve

$$110 = .02x + 80$$

The result is $x = 1500$. Thus, they will make 1500 tables.   ◆

Marginal revenue and **marginal profit** are defined in much the same manner as marginal cost.

Marginal Revenue

$R(x) =$ the total revenue from the sale of x units

$R'(x) = $ *marginal revenue*, the approximate revenue from the sale of the next unit

---

Marginal Profit

$P(x) = R(x) - C(x)$, the total profit from the production and sale of x units

$P'(x) = R'(x) - C'(x)$, *marginal profit*, the approximate profit from the production and sale of the next unit

---

Economists sometimes use the notations MC for marginal cost, MR for marginal revenue, and MP for marginal profit.

$MC(x) = C'(x) = $ marginal cost

$MR(x) = R'(x) = $ marginal revenue

$MP(x) = P'(x) = $ marginal profit

APPLIED

EXAMPLE 3   *MARGINAL COST, MARGINAL REVENUE, AND MARGINAL PROFIT*

The cost of producing x deep-tread radial tires is $C(x) = 4000 + 70x - .01x^2$ dollars, and the revenue from the sale of x tires is $R(x) = 105x - .02x^2$ dollars.

(a) Determine marginal cost.

(b) Determine marginal revenue.

(c) Determine MR(50) and tell what it means.

(d) Determine marginal profit.

(e) For what value of x is the marginal cost equal to the marginal revenue, and what is the marginal profit in that instance?

SOLUTION   **(a)** $MC(x) = C'(x) = 70 - .02x$. The marginal cost is $70 - .02x$ dollars.

(b) $MR(x) = R'(x) = 105 - .04x$. The marginal revenue is $105 - .04x$ dollars.

(c) From $MR(x) = 105 - .04x$, it follows that

$$MR(50) = 105 - .04(50) = \$103$$

This means that once 50 tires have been sold, the revenue to be obtained from the sale of the next tire (the 51st) is approximately $103.

(d) $P(x) = R(x) - C(x)$

$$= (105x - .02x^2) - (4000 + 70x - .01x^2)$$

$$= -.01x^2 + 35x - 4000$$

Differentiating yields

$$MP(x) = P'(x) = -.02x + 35$$

The marginal profit is $-.02x + 35$ dollars.

(e) Marginal cost is $70 - .02x$ and marginal revenue is $105 - .04x$. They are equal when $x = 1750$, as shown next.

$$70 - .02x = 105 - .04x$$

$$.02x = 35$$

$$x = 1750$$

The marginal profit is then $P'(1750) = -.02(1750) + 35 = 0$. Thus, the marginal profit is zero when $x = 1750$ tires. This should not be particularly surprising, because $P'(x) = R'(x) - C'(x)$ and $R'(x) - C'(x) = 0$ when marginal cost and marginal revenue are equal. ◆

Note

The opportunity to graph these marginal revenue functions is provided in the Technology Exercises at the end of this section.

The last result of Example 3 is worth noting for future reference.

> Marginal profit is zero when marginal revenue equals marginal cost.

If marginal revenue and marginal cost are equal, then the revenue from the sale of the next item is the same as the cost of producing that next item. Consequently, there is no profit on the next item, which means that the marginal profit is zero.

3.4 Exercises

(MARGINAL COST) Determine the marginal cost function in Exercises 1–6.

1. $C(x) = 50 - .1x^2$ **2.** $C(x) = 80 - .2x^2$

3. $C(x) = 1000 + 150x - x^2$ $C'(x) = -.4x$

4. $C(x) = 500 + 40x - x^2$

5. $C(x) = 90x + .02x^2$

6. $C(x) = 120x + .03x^2$

7. (MARGINAL COST) Suppose the cost of producing x units is given by $C(x) = 150 + 40x - x^2$ dollars, for $0 \le x \le 16$.
 (a) Determine the marginal cost when $x = 10$ units.
 (b) Determine the exact cost of the 11th unit.
 W (c) What is the meaning of MC(10)?

8. (MARGINAL COST) Suppose the cost of producing x units is given by $C(x) = 200 + 15x - .5x^2$ dollars, for $0 \le x \le 12$.
 (a) Determine the marginal cost when $x = 7$ units.
 (b) Determine the exact cost of the 8th unit.
 W (c) What is the meaning of MC(7)?

9. (LIMITING PRODUCTION) A furniture manufacturer plans to stop production of oak chairs if and when the marginal cost reaches $70. If the cost function is given as $C(x) = .5x^2 + 50x + 90$ dollars, how many chairs will the manufacturer produce?

10. (LIMITING PRODUCTION) A small clothing manufacturer will stop producing hats if and when the marginal cost reaches $31. If the cost of making x hats is given as $C(x) = .5x^2 + 5x + 120$ dollars, how many hats will this manufacturer produce?

11. (LIMITING PRODUCTION) Redo Exercise 10 assuming that the cost function is $C(x) = x^2 + 3x + 75$.

(MARGINAL REVENUE) Find the marginal revenue function in Exercises 12–15.

12. $R(x) = 20x + .1x^2$ **13.** $R(x) = 50x + .2x^2$

14. $R(x) = .002x^2 + .4x$ **15.** $R(x) = .001x^2 + .7x$

16. (MARGINAL REVENUE) Revenue from the sale of x liter bottles of cola is $R(x) = .70x + .001x^2$ dollars.

 (a) Determine the revenue from the sale of 1 bottle, 2 bottles, and 10 bottles.
 (b) Find the marginal revenue.
 W (c) Determine MR(10) and tell what it means.

17. (MARGINAL REVENUE) Let the revenue from the sale of x compact disc players be $R(x) = 400x - .01x^2$ dollars, for $0 \le x \le 20,000$.
 (a) Find the revenue from the sale of 1 player, 10 players, and 100 players.
 (b) Determine the marginal revenue.
 W (c) Determine MR(1000) and tell what it means.

(MARGINAL PROFIT) Determine the marginal profit function in Exercises 18–21.

18. $P(x) = .01x^2 + 5x - 100$

19. $P(x) = .02x^2 + 9x - 72$

20. $P(x) = 50x - .03x^2$ **21.** $P(x) = 40x - .01x^2$

22. (PROFIT AND LOSS) A compact disc (CD) maker says the company's profit on the manufacture and sale of x CDs is $P(x) = .02x^2 + 10x - 300$ dollars.
 (a) What is the company's total profit on 50 units?
 (b) How much money does the company lose if it makes and sells only 10 units?
 (c) Determine the marginal profit function.

23. (PROFIT AND LOSS) A potato chip maker says that the company's profit on the manufacture and sale of x 8-ounce bags of chips ($0 \le x \le 500$) is given by $P(x) = .0005x^2 + x - 160$ dollars.
 (a) Determine the total profit on 200 bags.
 (b) How much will the company lose if it makes and sells only 50 bags?
 (c) Find the marginal profit function.

(MARGINAL PROFIT) In Exercises 24–27, determine the marginal profit that corresponds to the given revenue and cost functions.

24. $R(x) = 150x - .02x^2$; $C(x) = 200 + 15x - .01x^2$

25. $R(x) = 95x - .01x^2$; $C(x) = 140 + 10x - .02x^2$

26. $R(x) = 100x + .01x^2$; $C(x) = 140 + 90x + .01x^2$

27. $R(x) = 80x + .001x^2$; $C(x) = 210 + 70x + .001x^2$

(MARGINAL REVENUE/MARGINAL COST) In Exercises 28–31, determine the number of units x for which marginal revenue is equal to marginal cost.

28. $R(x) = 55x - .03x^2; C(x) = 250 + 30x - .02x^2$

29. $R(x) = 300x - .02x^2; C(x) = 100x$

30. $R(x) = 240x - .02x^2; C(x) = 210x$

31. $R(x) = 150x + .01x^2; C(x) = 120x + .03x^2$

(MARGINAL PROFIT) In Exercises 32–35, determine the number of units x for which marginal profit is zero.

32. $R(x) = 100x - .02x^2; C(x) = 200 + 50x - .01x^2$

33. $R(x) = 80x - .01x^2; C(x) = 130 + 90x - .02x^2$

34. $R(x) = 5x + .002x^2; C(x) = 12x + .001x^2$

35. $R(x) = 7x + .001x^2; C(x) = 5x + .003x^2$

36. **(MARGINAL PROFIT)** A manufacturer of telephones determines that the cost of producing x telephones is $C(x) = 500 + 15x - .01x^2$ dollars and the revenue received from the sale of x telephones is $R(x) = 75x - .02x^2$ dollars.
 (a) Determine the marginal profit function.
 (b) What production level results in a marginal profit of zero?

37. **(MARGINAL PROFIT)** A tire manufacturer has found that the cost of making x tires is given by the function $C(x) = 240 + 64x - .02x^2$ dollars and the revenue received from the sale of x tires is $R(x) = 90x - .03x^2$ dollars.
 (a) Find the marginal profit function.
 (b) What production level results in a marginal profit of zero?

38. **(MARGINAL PROFIT)** A manufacturer of knives can make x knives at a cost of $8 - .01x$ dollars *per knife*. If x knives can be sold for a total of $20x - .04x^2$ dollars, determine the marginal profit when the number of knives manufactured and sold is 50.

39. **(MARGINAL PROFIT)** A bicycle manufacturer estimates that it can price its bicycles at $p = 140 - .02x$ dollars each, where x is the number sold. The cost of producing x bicycles is $900 + 80x - .01x^2$ dollars. Determine the marginal profit when 20 bicycles are made.

40. **(MARGINAL PROFIT)** Suppose each tennis racquet costs $15 to make. If x racquets can be sold at $70 - .03x$ dollars each, find the marginal profit function.

41. **(MARGINAL PROFIT)** It will cost a small manufacturer $600 - .02x$ dollars each to make x stereo units. The price at which each unit can be sold is given by $p = 1000 - .04x$ dollars.
 (a) Determine the marginal revenue function.
 (b) Determine the marginal profit when $x = 150$.
 (c) Find the exact profit on the 151st unit.

42. **(MARGINAL PROFIT)** A company plans to produce x units of its product. The fixed costs of production are $300. The variable costs are $20 per unit produced. The relationship between the number of units sold x and the price per unit is given by the demand equation $x = 5000 - 100p$.
 (a) Determine the revenue function R by using $R(x) = xp$.
 (b) Determine the marginal cost function.
 (c) Determine the marginal profit function.

W 43. **(INCOME TAX)** Consider the following tax schedule. (i) If your taxable income is $0–$7999, there is no tax due. (ii) If your taxable income is $8000–$19,999, the tax due is 16% of taxable income. (iii) If your taxable income is $20,000 or more, the tax due is $3200 + 26% of the taxable income above $20,000. Explain why the tax rates 16% and 26% in this setting are sometimes called "marginal" rates. (The accompanying figure shows a graph of tax due as a function of taxable income.)

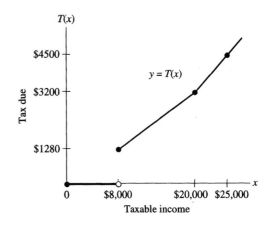

44. **(MARGINAL COST)** In this exercise, we'll investigate the following statement. *When the cost function C is linear, the marginal cost $C'(x)$ is the same as the exact cost of producing the next unit.* Consider the general linear cost function $C(x) = mx + b$. Compute the exact cost of the tenth item, namely $C(10) - C(9)$. Then compute $C'(9)$. Both will have the same value. The computations can be repeated for the fifth unit or the eighth unit or any other unit, and the result will be the same, as you can see once you have done the calculations for the tenth unit.

W 45. *(MARGINAL COST)* Consider the cost function graphed next. Is marginal cost greater at x_1 or at x_2? Explain.

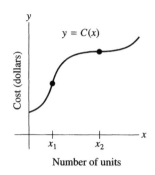

TECHNOLOGY *EXERCISES*

1. *(MARGINAL COST)* Graph the cost function using x in $[0, 90]$ and y in $[0, 200]$.

$$C(x) = 43 + 5.2x - .1x^2 \qquad x \geq 0$$

Find, to the nearest unit, the number of units (x) for which marginal cost is zero.

2. *(MARGINAL PROFIT)* Graph the profit function, adjusting windows as needed.

$$P(x) = 8.5x - .2x^2 \qquad x \geq 0$$

Determine, to the nearest unit, the number of units (x) for which marginal profit is zero.

3. *(MARGINAL PROFIT)* Graph the profit function

$$P(x) = x^3 - 52x^2 + 700x - 1200 \qquad 0 \leq x \leq 22$$

Keep in mind that $P(x)$ values are very large.
(a) Is marginal profit positive, negative, or zero at $x = 6$ units?
(b) Is marginal profit positive, negative, or zero at $x = 14$ units?

4. *(MARGINAL COST)* Given the cost function

$$C(x) = 700 + .2x^2 - .01x^3 \qquad 0 \leq x \leq 12$$

obtain the marginal cost function and graph it.
(a) Is marginal cost increasing or decreasing at $x = 5$ units?
(b) Is marginal cost increasing or decreasing at $x = 11$ units?

W 5. *(MARGINAL REVENUE)* Graph the revenue function

$$R(x) = .05x^3 - 1.05x^2 + 7.35x - 2.15$$

Use x in $[1, 20]$ and y in $[0, 50]$. Is the marginal revenue greater at $x = 3$ units or at $x = 14$ units? Explain.

6. **(MARGINAL CONCEPTS)** This exercise is a follow-up to Example 3.

   (a) Graph the functions $MC(x) = 70 - .02x$ and $MR(x) = 105 - .04x$ to determine the quantity x for which $MC = MR$. For windows, use x in $[0, 2500]$ and y in $[0, 150]$. Zoom in as needed.

   (b) From the graph, determine the marginal cost and marginal revenue for which $MC = MR$.

   (c) Graph $MP(x) = -.02x + 35$ to determine x for which $MP = 0$. Use x in $[0, 2000]$ and y in $[0, 50]$.

3.5 | *THE PRODUCT AND QUOTIENT RULES*

The rules for finding the derivative of a product and the derivative of a quotient are not as simple or as straightforward as the rules developed and used in Section 3.2. In view of this, we introduce a notation that will simplify the appearance of the rules and make them easier to apply.

If a function is to be considered as the product or quotient of two functions, we will call the two functions u and v. This means we will have

$$u \cdot v \qquad \text{product of two functions; } u = \text{first, } v = \text{second}$$

$$\frac{u}{v} \qquad \text{quotient of two functions; } u = \text{numerator, } v = \text{denominator}$$

The derivative of a product is *not* the product of the derivatives. To see this, consider $y = x^3$. Clearly $dy/dx = 3x^2$. If we consider x^3 as the product $x^2 \cdot x$, then the product of the derivatives is $2x \cdot 1$, or $2x$, which is incorrect.

> *Note*
>
> The derivative of a product is *not* the product of the derivatives.

The product rule is stated at the top of the next page.

Since it is far from obvious that the product rule is true in general, we will use the definition of the derivative to prove the product rule.

Product Rule

If $u = u(x)$ and $v = v(x)$ are differentiable functions, then

$$\frac{d}{dx}(u \cdot v) = u \cdot v' + v \cdot u'$$

or

$$\frac{d}{dx}(u \cdot v) = u \cdot \frac{dv}{dx} + v \cdot \frac{du}{dx}$$

The derivative of the product of two functions is the first times the derivative of the second *plus* the second times the derivative of the first.

PROOF Using the definition of the derivative, we can begin with

$$\frac{d}{dx}[u(x)v(x)] = \lim_{\Delta x \to 0} \frac{u(x + \Delta x)v(x + \Delta x) - u(x)v(x)}{\Delta x}$$

At this point we must do something to make the numerator look more like an expression that will eventually lead to $uv' + vu'$. Specifically, we will add "zero" to the numerator. But zero will be chosen in the useful form

$$-u(x)v(x + \Delta x) + u(x)v(x + \Delta x)$$

The reason for this choice will become apparent as the proof progresses. As a result of our adding this form of zero to the numerator, the limit that represents the derivative of product $u(x)v(x)$ becomes

$$\lim_{\Delta x \to 0} \frac{u(x + \Delta x)v(x + \Delta x) - u(x)v(x + \Delta x) + u(x)v(x + \Delta x) - u(x)v(x)}{\Delta x}$$

The quotient can be split into two quotients and then into two limits, as we anticipate a limit that will yield vu' and a limit that will yield uv'.

$$\lim_{\Delta x \to 0} \frac{u(x + \Delta x)v(x + \Delta x) - u(x)v(x + \Delta x)}{\Delta x} + \lim_{\Delta x \to 0} \frac{u(x)v(x + \Delta x) - u(x)v(x)}{\Delta x}$$

Next, $v(x + \Delta x)$ can be factored out of the first numerator, and $u(x)$ can be factored out of the second numerator. The result is

$$\lim_{\Delta x \to 0} \frac{[u(x + \Delta x) - u(x)]v(x + \Delta x)}{\Delta x} + \lim_{\Delta x \to 0} \frac{u(x)[v(x + \Delta x) - v(x)]}{\Delta x}$$

Perhaps you can see in the first limit the part that will become $u'(x)$ and in the second limit the part that will become $v'(x)$. We proceed in that direction by using the limit theorem that says, "the limit of the product is the product of the limits." The result:

$$\lim_{\Delta x \to 0} \frac{u(x + \Delta x) - u(x)}{\Delta x} \cdot \lim_{\Delta x \to 0} v(x + \Delta x) + \lim_{\Delta x \to 0} u(x) \cdot \lim_{\Delta x \to 0} \frac{v(x + \Delta x) - v(x)}{\Delta x}$$

The first limit above is the derivative of $u(x)$, namely $u'(x)$. The second limit is simply $v(x)$. The third limit is $u(x)$. The fourth limit is $v'(x)$. Thus, we have

$$\frac{d}{dx}[u(x)v(x)] = u'(x)v(x) + u(x)v'(x) = u(x)v'(x) + v(x)u'(x)$$

The latter form is written with the $u(x)v'(x)$ term first.

EXAMPLE 1   Find $f'(x)$ for $f(x) = (3x + 5)(x^2 - 7x)$. Use the product rule.

SOLUTION   Function f is clearly a product. The factors are $u = 3x + 5$ and $v = x^2 - 7x$. Using the product rule yields

$$f'(x) = (3x + 5) \cdot \frac{d}{dx} (x^2 - 7x) + (x^2 - 7x) \cdot \frac{d}{dx} (3x + 5)$$

$$= (3x + 5)(2x - 7) + (x^2 - 7x)(3)$$

$$= 6x^2 - 21x + 10x - 35 + 3x^2 - 21x \qquad \text{after multiplying}$$

$$= 9x^2 - 32x - 35 \qquad \text{after combining like terms} \qquad \blacklozenge$$

In this instance, it is natural to ask why we don't just multiply out the original expression *before* differentiating. Then the sum rule could be used, which seems simpler. Actually, you could do that, and indeed it may even be simpler. However, in the next section there will be products that are difficult to multiply out, such as $(4x + 1)^3(x^2 - 3)^5$. The idea in this section is to learn the product rule by using it now. Then, when you really need it, you will know it.

EXAMPLE 2   Find the derivative of $y = (2x + 1)\left(1 - \dfrac{1}{x}\right)$. Use the product rule.

SOLUTION   Before using the product rule, rewrite $1/x$ as x^{-1} to prepare for the differentiation process.

$$\frac{dy}{dx} = \frac{d}{dx}[(2x + 1)(1 - x^{-1})]$$

$$= (2x + 1) \cdot \frac{d}{dx} (1 - x^{-1}) + (1 - x^{-1}) \cdot \frac{d}{dx} (2x + 1)$$

$$= (2x + 1)(x^{-2}) + (1 - x^{-1})(2)$$

$$= (2x + 1)\left(\frac{1}{x^2}\right) + \left(1 - \frac{1}{x}\right)(2)$$

$$= \frac{2x + 1}{x^2} + 2 - \frac{2}{x}$$

All three terms can be combined by using the common denominator x^2.

$$\frac{dy}{dx} = \frac{2x + 1}{x^2} + \frac{2x^2}{x^2} - \frac{2x}{x^2} = \frac{2x^2 + 1}{x^2} \qquad \blacklozenge$$

Next we consider the quotient rule. The derivative of a quotient is *not* the quotient of the derivatives. To see this, consider $y = x^3$. Clearly, $dy/dx = 3x^2$. If we consider x^3 as the quotient x^4/x, then the quotient of the derivatives is $4x^3/1$, or $4x^3$, which is incorrect.

Here then is the quotient rule. The proof is similar to the proof of the product rule and is suggested as an exercise with hint. (See Exercise 48.)

Quotient Rule

If $u = u(x)$ and $v = v(x)$ are differentiable functions and $v(x) \neq 0$, then

$$\frac{d}{dx}\left(\frac{u}{v}\right) = \frac{v \cdot u' - u \cdot v'}{v^2}$$

or

$$\frac{d}{dx}\left(\frac{u}{v}\right) = \frac{v \cdot \dfrac{du}{dx} - u \cdot \dfrac{dv}{dx}}{v^2}$$

The derivative of a quotient of two functions is the denominator times the derivative of the numerator *minus* the numerator times the derivative of the denominator—all divided by the denominator squared.

Note

The derivative of a quotient is *not* the quotient of the derivatives.

EXAMPLE 3 Find the derivative of $f(x) = \dfrac{5x - 1}{1 + 2x}$.

SOLUTION The function is clearly a quotient. The numerator (u) is $5x - 1$. The denominator (v) is $1 + 2x$.

$$f'(x) = \frac{(1 + 2x) \cdot \dfrac{d}{dx}(5x - 1) - (5x - 1) \cdot \dfrac{d}{dx}(1 + 2x)}{(1 + 2x)^2}$$

$$= \frac{(1 + 2x)(5) - (5x - 1)(2)}{(1 + 2x)^2}$$

$$= \frac{5 + 10x - 10x + 2}{(1 + 2x)^2} = \frac{7}{(1 + 2x)^2} \qquad ◆$$

Note

1. It is better *not* to consider an expression such as $\frac{x^2}{9}$ to be a quotient. Instead, consider that

$$\frac{x^2}{9} = \frac{1}{9}x^2$$

and thus

$$\frac{d}{dx}\left(\frac{x^2}{9}\right) = \frac{d}{dx}\left(\frac{1}{9}x^2\right) = 2 \cdot \frac{1}{9}x = \frac{2}{9}x \quad \text{or} \quad \frac{2x}{9}$$

Of course, the expression $\frac{x^2}{9}$ could be considered to be a quotient, and the quotient rule could be used, but the differentiation and simplification are more complicated. (See Exercise 49.)

2. Consider that

$$\frac{1}{x^2} \qquad \text{should be rewritten as} \qquad x^{-2}$$

so that the power rule can be used. The original expression should *not* be considered a quotient.

EXAMPLE 4   Find the derivative of $f(x) = \dfrac{3x^2 - 4x}{x^2 + 7x + 1}.$

SOLUTION   The function f is a quotient, with the numerator u being $3x^2 - 4x$ and the denominator v being $x^2 + 7x + 1$.

$$f'(x) = \frac{(x^2 + 7x + 1)(6x - 4) - (3x^2 - 4x)(2x + 7)}{(x^2 + 7x + 1)^2}$$

$$= \frac{6x^3 - 4x^2 + 42x^2 - 28x + 6x - 4 - (6x^3 + 21x^2 - 8x^2 - 28x)}{(x^2 + 7x + 1)^2}$$

$$= \frac{6x^3 + 38x^2 - 22x - 4 - (6x^3 + 13x^2 - 28x)}{(x^2 + 7x + 1)^2}$$

$$= \frac{25x^2 + 6x - 4}{(x^2 + 7x + 1)^2} \qquad ◆$$

3.5   Exercises

Use the product rule to determine the derivative of each function in Exercises 1–14.

1. $y = (x + 1)(x - 2)$

2. $y = (x - 7)(x + 4)$

3. $f(x) = (5x - 3)(2x + 1)$

4. $f(x) = (3x - 5)(4x - 2)$

5. $y = (t^2 + 6)(1 + t^2)$

6. $y = (t^3 - 1)(t^2 + 3)$

7. $f(x) = (4x - 3)x^3$

8. $y = (3 + x^2)x^4$

9. $y = (4x + 1)\left(1 + \dfrac{1}{x}\right)$

10. $y = (1 + 2x)\left(2 + \dfrac{1}{x}\right)$

11. $y = (x^3 + 2)(1 - x)$

12. $y = (x^2 + 5)(1 - 2x)$

13. $y = (1 - x^3)(1 + x^2)$

14. $y = (1 - x^4)(1 + x^3)$

Use the quotient rule to determine the derivative of each function in Exercises 15–26.

15. $y = \dfrac{x}{1 + x}$

16. $y = \dfrac{x - 2}{4x + 1}$

17. $f(x) = \dfrac{2x}{3x + 1}$

18. $f(x) = \dfrac{x^2}{2x - 1}$

19. $f(t) = \dfrac{1 - t}{t - 1}$

20. $f(t) = \dfrac{t - 3}{3 - t}$

21. $s(t) = \dfrac{4t^2 + t}{1 + 3t}$

22. $s(t) = \dfrac{t^2 + t + 1}{t + 1}$

23. $y = \dfrac{x^2 + 5x - 3}{x + 4}$

24. $f(x) = \dfrac{x^2 - 7x + 1}{x - 2}$

25. $y = \dfrac{4 + 2x}{x^{3/2}}$

26. $y = \dfrac{6x - 2}{x^{5/2}}$

Use appropriate rules to determine the derivative of each function in Exercises 27–34.

27. $y = 1 - x - \dfrac{1}{x^3}$

28. $y = \dfrac{1 + x}{1 - x}$

29. $f(x) = \dfrac{1}{x} + 7x - \dfrac{x^2}{3}$

30. $f(t) = \dfrac{t}{7} + 10\sqrt{t} - 19$

31. $f(t) = (t^2 - 8)(t^3 + 1)$

32. $y = x^2(1 - 10x)$

33. $s = \dfrac{t^2 + 3t + 5}{1 - t}$

34. $y = 9x^2 - 6x + 14$

In Exercises 35–38, use the product rule or quotient rule to find the slope of the line tangent to the graph of the function at the given point. Then compare your result visually with the given graph—as a rough check.

35. $f(x) = (x^2 - 4)(1 + 2x)$ at $(-1, 3)$

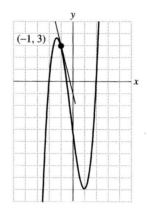

36. $f(x) = x^2(1 + 3x^2)$ at $(1, 4)$

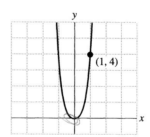

37. $y = \dfrac{x^2 - 4}{x + 8}$ at $(4, 1)$

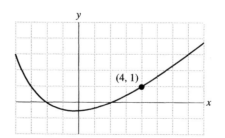

38. $y = \dfrac{x - 2}{x^2 + 3x + 4}$ at $(-2, -2)$

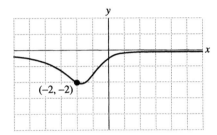

$(-2, -2)$

In Exercises 39–42, determine the rate of change of y with respect to x for the given value of x.

39. $y = \dfrac{x^2 + 3}{x + 1}$ when $x = 1$

40. $y = \dfrac{x + 4}{x - 1}$ when $x = 2$

41. $y = (1 - x)(1 - x^2)$ when $x = 2$

42. $y = (1 + 3x)(1 - x)$ when $x = 3$

43. (VELOCITY) An inventor has created a space toy that travels so that after t seconds its distance in inches from a starting point is

$$s = \frac{4t^2 + 6}{t + 1} \qquad 1 \leq t \leq 30$$

What is the velocity of the toy at 9 seconds?

44. (MARGINAL COST) Find the marginal cost function that corresponds to the cost function

$$C(x) = \frac{100 + 80x + x^2 + x^3}{x + 2}$$

45. (PROFIT) A company's profit (in dollars) from the sale of x VCRs is approximately

$$P(x) = \frac{10x^2 - 50x}{x + 1} \qquad x \geq 1$$

(a) If the company sells only 1 VCR, what is the profit? Any comment?
(b) If it sells 5 VCRs, what is the profit?
(c) What is the profit on the sale of 10 VCRs?
(d) Determine the marginal profit function.

46. (MARGINAL REVENUE) Suppose that revenue comes from two sources. One source: the sale of x gallons of sealant at $18 per gallon. The other source: x boxes of blocks at $x/(x - 1)$ dollars each (and $x \geq 2$).
(a) Determine the revenue function R.
(b) Find the marginal revenue function.

47. (POLLUTION REDUCTION) The pollution in a lake is being reduced over a 5-year period. The amount of pollutants (in pounds) is given by

$$A = 110 - \frac{90t}{t + 1} \qquad 0 \leq t \leq 5$$

where t is the time in years.
(a) Determine the amount of pollution in the lake at the beginning, after 2 years, and after 5 years.
(b) Determine the rate at which the pollution in the lake is changing at $t = 2$ years.
W (c) What is the meaning of the *sign* obtained in part (b)?

48. *Quotient Rule.* Use the definition of the derivative to prove the quotient rule.

$$\frac{d}{dx}\left[\frac{u(x)}{v(x)}\right] = \frac{v(x)u'(x) - u(x)v'(x)}{[v(x)]^2}$$

Hint: Once you have applied the definition of the derivative to the function $u(x)/v(x)$, it will be necessary to follow the lead of the proof of the product rule. Insertion of an appropriate form of zero is needed. Your choice should be based on what must be added in order to create the desired numerator, $v(x)u'(x) - u(x)v'(x)$.

49. Near the end of the section, we recommended avoiding the use of the quotient rule in finding the derivative of $x^2/9$. Now, use the quotient rule to determine the derivative of $x^2/9$. You will see that it is indeed more complicated this way.

W 50. Explain how the derivative of

$$y = \frac{x^2 + 1}{x}$$

can be obtained easily without using the quotient rule or the product rule.

W 51. Explain why it is better to write $1/x^2$ as x^{-2} to prepare for differentiation. Why not just use the quotient rule to differentiate $f(x) = 1/x^2$?

TECHNOLOGY *EXERCISES*

1. Graph the function defined by

$$f(x) = \frac{x + 5}{x + 2}$$

Determine whether the slope of the tangent line is positive, negative, or zero at the given value of x.

(a) $x = 4$ (b) $x = -1$ (c) $x = -3$

2. Graph the function defined by

$$f(x) = \frac{10x}{x^2 + 2}$$

Determine whether the slope of the tangent line is positive, negative, or zero at the given value of x.

(a) $x = 3$ (b) $x = -3$ (c) $x = 9$

Note Because the screen of a graphing calculator is wider than it is high, the standard range setting (and most zoom settings) allow more space per unit on the x axis than on the y axis. This means, for example, that the slopes of lines will appear to have smaller magnitudes than they do. You can remedy this distortion by using **Zoom Square.** As an example, graph $y = 3x + 1$ using the window $[-10, 10]$ for x and y. Then use zoom square and notice the change.

3. Use the product rule to find the slope of the line tangent to the graph of $f(x) = 2x(x^2 - 1)$ at the point $(1, 0)$. Then graph the function and compare your result visually with the graph as a rough check.

4. Use the quotient rule to find the slope of the line tangent to the graph of

$$f(x) = \frac{2x + 3}{x - 4}$$

at the point $(2, -3.5)$. Then graph the function and compare your result visually with the graph as a rough check.

3.6 | *THE CHAIN RULE*

We already have a rule for obtaining derivatives of powers of x, namely

$$\frac{d}{dx} x^n = nx^{n-1}$$

For example,

$$\frac{d}{dx} x^8 = 8x^7$$

But we do not yet have a rule for obtaining derivatives of powers of *functions of x*. This means that we cannot yet easily differentiate expressions such as

$$(x^2 + 1)^8 \qquad \text{or} \qquad (2x - 3)^8$$

The rule we have is for differentiating powers of x, not powers of $x^2 + 1$, or powers of $2x - 3$, or powers of other functions of x.

In the presentation that follows we will be using $u(x)$, or "u" for short, as the name of the expression (such as $x^2 + 1$ or $2x - 3$) that is raised to a power. This means that we need a rule for obtaining dy/dx when $y = f(u)$. To begin, we return to the definition of the derivative.

$$\frac{dy}{dx} = \lim_{\Delta x \to 0} \frac{\Delta y}{\Delta x}$$

Consider that since u is a function of x, a change in x (called Δx) creates a change in u (called Δu). If we multiply $\Delta y/\Delta x$ by 1 in the form of $\Delta u/\Delta u$, we have

$$\frac{dy}{dx} = \lim_{\Delta x \to 0} \left(\frac{\Delta y}{\Delta x} \cdot \frac{\Delta u}{\Delta u} \right) = \lim_{\Delta x \to 0} \left(\frac{\Delta y}{\Delta u} \cdot \frac{\Delta u}{\Delta x} \right) = \left(\lim_{\Delta x \to 0} \frac{\Delta y}{\Delta u} \right) \left(\lim_{\Delta x \to 0} \frac{\Delta u}{\Delta x} \right)$$

As $\Delta x \to 0$, Δu also approaches zero, so we can change the notation $\Delta x \to 0$ to $\Delta u \to 0$ in the limit of $\Delta y/\Delta u$. Then we have

$$\frac{dy}{dx} = \lim_{\Delta u \to 0} \frac{\Delta y}{\Delta u} \cdot \lim_{\Delta x \to 0} \frac{\Delta u}{\Delta x}$$

Each limit on the right side of the equation is a derivative. The first is dy/du; the second is du/dx. Thus, we now have the result

$$\frac{dy}{dx} = \frac{dy}{du} \cdot \frac{du}{dx}$$

This important result is known as the **chain rule.**

Chain Rule

If y is a function of u and u is a function of x, then y is a function of x, and

$$\frac{dy}{dx} = \frac{dy}{du} \cdot \frac{du}{dx}$$

Our "proof" or development of this rule assumed that whenever $\Delta x \neq 0$, then $\Delta u \neq 0$ also. However, it is possible that for some function u, $\Delta u = 0$ even though $\Delta x \neq 0$. In such a case we cannot introduce $\Delta u/\Delta u$, because division by zero is not defined. A more elaborate formal proof is required in that case.

Considering the derivative as a rate of change leads to another way of seeing what is happening in the chain rule. Suppose that $dy/du = 5$ and $du/dx = 3$. This means that the rate of change of y with respect to u is 5 and the rate of change of u with respect to x is 3. In other words, y is changing 5 times as fast as u, and u is changing 3 times as fast as x. It follows that y is changing 15 times as fast as x. In other words, $dy/dx = 5 \cdot 3 = 15$. This result is an example of the chain rule,

$$\frac{dy}{dx} = \frac{dy}{du} \cdot \frac{du}{dx}$$

EXAMPLE 1   Use the chain rule to differentiate $y = (x^2 + 1)^8$.

SOLUTION $y = (x^2 + 1)^8$ can be considered $y = (u)^8$, where $u = x^2 + 1$. Using

$$\frac{dy}{dx} = \frac{dy}{du} \cdot \frac{du}{dx}$$

with $y = u^8$ and $u = x^2 + 1$, we have $dy/du = 8u^7$ and $du/dx = 2x$. Thus,

$$\frac{dy}{dx} = \frac{dy}{du} \cdot \frac{du}{dx}$$

$$= 8u^7 \cdot 2x$$

Next, replacing u by $x^2 + 1$ produces the final result, one expressed in terms of x (that is, without u in it).

$$\frac{dy}{dx} = 8(x^2 + 1)^7 \cdot 2x = 16x(x^2 + 1)^7 \qquad \blacklozenge$$

Alternatively, the chain rule can be stated using composition of functions.

$$[f(g(x))]' = f'(g(x)) \cdot g'(x)$$

Note

In practice, the chain rule is often applied rather mechanically, without actually substituting u into the written work. If you examine the function and the derivative obtained in the preceding example, you will be able to see how this can be done.

Function: $y = (x^2 + 1)^8$

Derivative: $\dfrac{dy}{dx} = 8(x^2 + 1)^7 \cdot 2x$

The $8(x^2 + 1)^7$ portion of the derivative comes from the power rule. The factor $2x$ is the derivative of the function $x^2 + 1$ that was raised to the power.

Here are two more examples that show the use of the chain rule without actually substituting u into the written work.

$$\frac{d}{dx}(7x+2)^{10} = 10(7x+2)^9 \cdot 7 = 70(7x+2)^9$$

$$\frac{d}{dx}(1-x^4)^{3/2} = \frac{3}{2}(1-x^4)^{1/2} \cdot (-4x^3) = -6x^3(1-x^4)^{1/2}$$

These chain rule applications are all examples of the **general power rule.**

General Power Rule

If u is a differentiable function of x and n is a real number, then

$$\frac{d}{dx}u^n = nu^{n-1} \cdot \frac{du}{dx}$$

In function notation, the general power rule appears as follows for $f(x) = [u(x)]^n$:

$$f'(x) = n[u(x)]^{n-1} \cdot u'(x)$$

EXAMPLE 2   Determine the derivative of $y = \sqrt{x^2 + 4x - 1}$.

SOLUTION   First, change the radical form of the square root to the numerical exponent 1/2.

$$y = (x^2 + 4x - 1)^{1/2}$$

Next, apply the general power rule.

$$\frac{dy}{dx} = \frac{1}{2}(x^2 + 4x - 1)^{-1/2}(2x + 4)$$

The calculus is now complete; however, we should simplify the result.

$$\frac{dy}{dx} = \frac{1}{2}(2x + 4)(x^2 + 4x - 1)^{-1/2}$$

$$= (x + 2)(x^2 + 4x - 1)^{-1/2}$$

$$= \frac{x + 2}{(x^2 + 4x - 1)^{1/2}} \qquad \text{or} \qquad \frac{x + 2}{\sqrt{x^2 + 4x - 1}}$$

Either of these last two forms is mathematically correct and simplified. Here the example *began* with a radical, so it would seem fitting that the final form also have a radical.   ◆

EXAMPLE 3   Find the derivative of $f(x) = \dfrac{1}{(x^2 + 5)^3}$

SOLUTION   Although the quotient rule could be used here, it is simpler to rewrite the expression by using a negative exponent. Then the general power rule applies.

$$f(x) = \frac{1}{(x^2 + 5)^3} = (x^2 + 5)^{-3}$$

Now, by the general power rule,

$$f'(x) = -3(x^2 + 5)^{-4}(2x) = \frac{-6x}{(x^2 + 5)^4}$$

If you use the quotient rule instead, you will see it is more difficult. (See Exercise 48.) ◆

EXAMPLE 4   Differentiate $f(x) = \dfrac{(2x + 1)^5}{3x + 1}$.

SOLUTION   Using the quotient rule, we obtain as a first step

$$f'(x) = \frac{(3x + 1) \cdot \dfrac{d}{dx} (2x + 1)^5 - (2x + 1)^5 \cdot \dfrac{d}{dx} (3x + 1)}{(3x + 1)^2}$$

Next, keeping in mind that the general power rule applies when differentiating $(2x + 1)^5$, we obtain

$$f'(x) = \frac{(3x + 1) \cdot 5(2x + 1)^4 \cdot 2 - (2x + 1)^5 \cdot 3}{(3x + 1)^2}$$

This expression can be simplified by factoring $(2x + 1)^4$ from each term of the numerator.

$$f'(x) = \frac{(2x + 1)^4 [(3x + 1) \cdot 5 \cdot 2 - (2x + 1) \cdot 3]}{(3x + 1)^2}$$

$$= \frac{(2x + 1)^4 (30x + 10 - 6x - 3)}{(3x + 1)^2}$$

$$= \frac{(2x + 1)^4 (24x + 7)}{(3x + 1)^2} \qquad\qquad ◆$$

EXAMPLE 5   Find dy/dx when $y = (4x + 1)^3(x^2 - 3)^5$.

SOLUTION   Using the product rule, we obtain as a first step

$$\frac{dy}{dx} = (4x + 1)^3 \cdot \frac{d}{dx} (x^2 - 3)^5 + (x^2 - 3)^5 \cdot \frac{d}{dx} (4x + 1)^3$$

Next, keeping in mind that the general power rule applies when differentiating $(x^2 - 3)^5$ and $(4x + 1)^3$, we have

$$\frac{dy}{dx} = (4x + 1)^3 \cdot 5(x^2 - 3)^4 \cdot 2x + (x^2 - 3)^5 \cdot 3(4x + 1)^2 \cdot 4$$

At this point we can factor out $(4x + 1)^2$, $(x^2 - 3)^4$, and 2.

$$\frac{dy}{dx} = 2(4x + 1)^2 (x^2 - 3)^4 [(4x + 1) \cdot 5 \cdot x + (x^2 - 3) \cdot 3 \cdot 2]$$

$$= 2(4x + 1)^2 (x^2 - 3)^4 (20x^2 + 5x + 6x^2 - 18)$$

$$= 2(4x + 1)^2 (x^2 - 3)^4 (26x^2 + 5x - 18) \qquad\qquad ◆$$

3.6 Exercises

Simplify all derivatives in the exercises of this section.

Differentiate each function in Exercises 1–16.

1. $y = (x^2 + 3)^5$

2. $y = (x^2 + 1)^4$

3. $y = (3x)^5$

4. $y = (2x)^7$

5. $y = (3x + 4)^{1/3}$

6. $y = (9x)^{1/3}$

7. $s = (1 - t^4)^{-6}$

8. $s = (t^3 + 2)^{-10}$

9. $y = \sqrt{4x + 1}$

10. $y = \sqrt{10x - 7}$

11. $f(x) = (x^4 + x^2 + 1)^4$

12. $f(x) = (x^2 + 7x - 2)^5$

13. $f(t) = \dfrac{1}{(t^2 + 1)^6}$

14. $f(t) = \sqrt{1 - t}$

15. $y = \dfrac{1}{\sqrt{6x + 5}}$

16. $y = 3 + \sqrt{1 - 2t^2}$

Determine the derivative in Exercises 17–34.

17. $y = x^2(5x - 2)^4$

18. $y = x^3(3x + 4)^6$

19. $y = (x + 3)(2x + 1)^3$

20. $y = (2x + 1)^4 (x^2 + 3)$

21. $y = (x^2 + 1)^4 (x - 2)$

22. $y = (3x - 1)(1 - x^2)^3$

23. $y = (5x - 2)^2 (x^2 + 7)^3$

24. $y = (3x + 1)^3 (1 + 2x)^2$

25. $y = (2t + 3)^4 (t - 7)^3$

26. $y = (1 + 4t)^3 (t^2 + 3)^4$

27. $y = \dfrac{(x + 4)^3}{x + 1}$

28. $y = \dfrac{(x - 1)^5}{x + 2}$

29. $y = \dfrac{(2t + 3)^4}{t - 2}$

30. $y = \dfrac{(4t + 1)^6}{t - 3}$

31. $y = (2x - 5)(2x + 1)^{3/2}$

32. $y = (6x - 1)^{4/3}(x^2 + 3)$

33. $y = 2x\sqrt{2x + 1}$

34. $y = x^2\sqrt{4x + 1}$

Find dy/dx in Exercises 35–38.

35. $y = \left(\dfrac{x - 1}{x + 1}\right)^4$

36. $y = \left(\dfrac{x^2 + 1}{x + 1}\right)^3$

37. $y = \sqrt{\dfrac{2x + 1}{x - 1}}$

38. $y = \sqrt{\dfrac{1 - 2x}{1 + x}}$

In Exercises 39–42, differentiate in order to find the slope of the line tangent to the graph of the function at the given point. Then compare your result visually with the graph, as a rough check.

39. $f(x) = (x^2 - 3x + 1)^4$ at $(2, 1)$

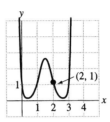

40. $f(x) = 3x(x^2 - 1)^3$ at $(0, 0)$

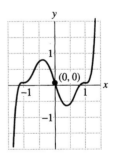

41. $y = \sqrt{4x + 1}$ at $(2, 3)$

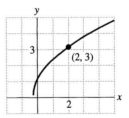

42. $y = \dfrac{4}{(1 + x^2)^2}$ at $(-1, 1)$

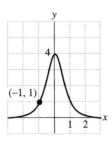

In Exercises 43–44, determine the rate of change of y with respect to x at the given value of x.

43. $y = \sqrt[3]{6x - 4}$ when $x = 2$

44. $y = (10x + 1)^{-1}$ when $x = 0$

45. **(MARGINAL PROFIT)** An upstart insurance company has determined that its profit from the sale of x "units" of auto insurance is approximately P dollars, where

$$P(x) = 100(x^2 - 1)^{1/2} \qquad \text{for } x \geq 2$$

Determine the marginal profit function.

46. **(SPEED)** A windup toy car rolls around, returns to its starting point, and then stops. Its distance s from the starting point at any time t during its 10-second run is

$$s = \frac{2}{9}(10 - t)^2 t^{3/2}$$

where s is in centimeters and t is in seconds. What is the speed of the car after 1 second has passed?

 47. **(POLLUTANT CONCENTRATION)** A factory has dumped pollutants into a river that passes next to it. The relative concentration is considered to be 100% at the spot where the pollutants enter the river. The relative concentration then decreases until the pollutants virtually disappear about 21.54 miles downstream. The *percent* of relative concentration (p) is given by

$$p = \sqrt{10,000 - x^3}$$

where x is the distance in miles downstream from the factory ($0 \leq x \leq 21.54$).

(a) Using the function given, determine the relative concentration of pollutants at distances of 0 miles, 10 miles, and 20 miles from the factory. Use a calculator.

(b) Determine the rate of change of this relative concentration at 0 miles, 10 miles, and 20 miles from the factory. Use a calculator.

48. Use the quotient rule to find $f'(x)$ for the function f defined in Example 3.

W 49. Explain why we need the chain rule. Include two functions such as $y = x^3$ and $y = (x^2 + 1)^3$ in your explanation. Be sure to focus on *why* the differentiation of the two functions is different rather than on *how* it is different.

W 50. **(FOOD CHAIN)** Consider a food chain in which algae are eaten by small fish and the small fish are eaten by large fish. Let y be the number of large fish, u be the number of small fish, and x be the number of algae.

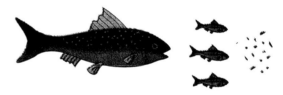

(a) Explain the meaning of dy/dx, dy/du, and du/dx in this setting.

(b) Translate the chain rule

$$\frac{dy}{dx} = \frac{dy}{du} \cdot \frac{du}{dx}$$

into words that describe this setting.

Determine dy/dx in Exercises 51–53.

51. $y = (x + 1)^2(2x - 3)^5(x^2 + 1)^8$

52. $y = \dfrac{(1 + x)^3(2x + 3)^4}{5x - 1}$

53. $y = \dfrac{(x^2 + 3)^5(x + 1)^2}{2x + 7}$

TECHNOLOGY *EXERCISES*

1. Graph function f and determine whether $f'(20)$ is positive or negative.

$$f(x) = (x^2 + 1)^{1/2}(x - 1)^{3/4}$$

2. Graph the function defined by

$$f(x) = \sqrt{\frac{x + 6}{x + 2}}$$

Is $f'(0) > f'(1)$?

3. Graph $y = x^2 - x\sqrt{2x + 1}$.

(a) Find a positive value of x for which $y' > 0$.

(b) Find a value of x for which $y' = 0$.

(c) Find a positive value of x for which $y' < 0$.

4. Consider the function

$$y = \frac{4.9x + 3}{\sqrt{8x^2 + 19}}$$

Is the slope of the tangent line positive, negative, or zero at $x = 0$?

5. Consider $f(x) = (x^2 + 4.6x + 7.1)^3$.

(a) Use the chain rule to obtain $f'(x)$.
(b) Graph $f'(x)$ and determine, to the nearest tenth, the value of x for which $f'(x) = 0$.

6. Consider $f(x) = \sqrt{2x^2 - 12.8x + 24.9}$.

(a) Use the chain rule to obtain $f'(x)$.
(b) Graph $f'(x)$ and determine, to the nearest tenth, the value of x for which $f'(x) = 0$.

7. Use calculus to find the slope of the line tangent to the graph of $f(x) = \sqrt{x^2 + 3}$ at the point $(1, 2)$. Then graph the function. Using Zoom In and Zoom Square, compare your result visually with the graph, as a rough check.

> **Note** Computer algebra systems can perform symbolic differentiation of functions. The derivative of $x^5 + 1$ with respect to x can be obtained as follows.
>
> Mathematica: `D[x^5 + 1, x]`
>
>   Maple: `diff(x^5 + 1, x);`
>
> If you have access to such software, try using it to do Exercises 33 and 35.

3.7 | *HIGHER-ORDER DERIVATIVES*

We proceed next to find the derivative of the derivative of a function. The "second derivative," as it is called, will be used here in applications involving acceleration of a moving object and rate of change of marginal cost and marginal revenue. In Chapter 4 the second derivative will be used to aid in curve sketching. Other uses of the second derivative and higher-order derivatives appear in the study of differential equations and infinite series.

To begin, consider the function defined by

$$f(x) = x^5 + 3x^4 - x^2 + 9x - 22$$

Differentiation yields

$$f'(x) = 5x^4 + 12x^3 - 2x + 9$$

Since f' is itself a function that can be differentiated, we will differentiate it. The result is called the **second derivative** and is denoted by f''. Here

$$f''(x) = 20x^3 + 36x^2 - 2$$

Similarly, the derivative of f'' is the **third derivative** and is denoted f'''. Here

$$f'''(x) = 60x^2 + 72x$$

The fourth derivative is denoted by $f^{(4)}$, the fifth derivative by $f^{(5)}$, and so on.

Since the second derivative is the derivative of the first derivative, in dy/dx notation the second derivative appears as

$$\frac{d}{dx}\left(\frac{dy}{dx}\right)$$

which is abbreviated to

$$\frac{d^2y}{dx^2}$$

Next is a summary table showing notations used to denote various derivatives.

Derivative Notations

first derivative	y'	f'	$\frac{dy}{dx}$	$D_x y$
second derivative	y''	f''	$\frac{d^2y}{dx^2}$	$D_x^2 y$
third derivative	y'''	f'''	$\frac{d^3y}{dx^3}$	$D_x^3 y$
fourth derivative	$y^{(4)}$	$f^{(4)}$	$\frac{d^4y}{dx^4}$	$D_x^4 y$
nth derivative	$y^{(n)}$	$f^{(n)}$	$\frac{d^ny}{dx^n}$	$D_x^n y$

EXAMPLE 1   If $y = 8x^{3/2}$, determine y''.

SOLUTION
$$y = 8x^{3/2}$$
$$y' = \frac{3}{2} \cdot 8x^{1/2} = 12x^{1/2}$$
$$y'' = \frac{1}{2} \cdot 12x^{-1/2} = 6x^{-1/2} = \frac{6}{x^{1/2}} \quad \text{or} \quad \frac{6}{\sqrt{x}} \qquad \blacklozenge$$

EXAMPLE 2   Let $f(x) = x^2 + 7x - 1$. Find $f^{(5)}(x)$.

SOLUTION
$$f(x) = x^2 + 7x - 1$$
$$f'(x) = 2x + 7$$
$$f''(x) = 2$$
$$f'''(x) = 0$$
$$f^{(4)}(x) = 0$$
$$f^{(5)}(x) = 0$$

Notice that for $f(x) = x^2 + 7x - 1$, all derivatives from f''' on are equal to zero. $\blacklozenge$

EXAMPLE 3   Let $f(x) = x^4 - 4x^2 + x - 2$. Find $f''(1)$.

SOLUTION $f''(1)$ is the second derivative evaluated at $x = 1$. First determine $f''(x)$. Then let $x = 1$ in $f''(x)$.
$$f(x) = x^4 - 4x^2 + x - 2$$
$$f'(x) = 4x^3 - 8x + 1$$
$$f''(x) = 12x^2 - 8$$

Now
$$f''(1) = 12(1)^2 - 8 = 4 \qquad \blacklozenge$$

Recall from Section 3.3 that the derivative of a function can be interpreted as the instantaneous rate of change of the function with respect to the variable. f' is the (instantaneous) rate of change of f with respect to x. It follows that

> *The second derivative of a function is the* (instantaneous) *rate of change of the first derivative* with respect to the variable.

Thus, f'' is the rate of change of f' with respect to x.

EXAMPLE 4 **RATE OF CHANGE OF MARGINAL COST**

A manufacturer of stands for computers finds that the cost of producing x stands is $C(x) = 800 + 50x - .04x^2$ dollars. Determine the rate of change of the marginal cost when 35 stands are produced.

SOLUTION Since $C(x) = 800 + 50x - .04x^2$, the marginal cost $C'(x)$ is given by

$$C'(x) = 50 - .08x$$

The rate of change of the marginal cost is the derivative of the marginal cost—that is, $C''(x)$.

$$C''(x) = -.08$$

The function C'' gives the rate of change of marginal cost for any level of production x. In this example, $C''(x)$ is constant: $C''(x) = -.08$ for all x. Specifically, $C''(35) = -.08$. Thus, the rate of change of the marginal cost when 35 stands are produced is $-.08$ dollars per stand per stand. In other words, marginal cost is decreasing (which accounts for the *minus*) at the rate of 8¢ per stand per stand.   ◆

Acceleration a is the instantaneous rate of change of velocity v with respect to time t. That is,

$$a = \frac{dv}{dt}$$

Using s for distance and the fact that $v = ds/dt$, we can obtain the alternative form

$$a = \frac{dv}{dt} = \frac{d}{dt}\left(\frac{ds}{dt}\right) = \frac{d^2s}{dt^2} \qquad \boxed{a = \frac{dv}{dt} = \frac{d^2s}{dt^2}}$$

EXAMPLE 5 **ACCELERATION OF A FALLING OBJECT**

In Example 4 of Section 3.3, a ball is dropped and travels such that the distance it has traveled after t seconds is $s = -16t^2$ feet. Find the acceleration of the ball at any time t.

SOLUTION From $s = -16t^2$, we obtain

$$v = \frac{ds}{dt} = -32t$$

$$a = \frac{dv}{dt} = -32$$

The acceleration of the ball is -32 feet per second per second. The minus sign specifies that the direction of the acceleration is downward, toward the ground. This acceleration is due to the constant pull of gravity on the ball, which is why the acceleration is a constant. ◆

3.7 Exercises

Determine the specified derivative for each function in Exercises 1–8.

1. Find $f''(x)$ for $f(x) = x^4 - 10x^2$.

2. Find $f''(x)$ for $f(x) = 1 - 3x + x^2 + 10x^3$.

3. Find y''' for $y = x^3 - 7x^2 + 100x + 1$.

4. Find y''' for $y = x^{1/2}$.

5. Find $f^{(4)}(x)$ for $f(x) = x^4$.

6. Find $f^{(4)}(x)$ for $f(x) = x^5$.

7. Find $D_x^3 y$ for $y = x^{5/3}$.

8. Find $D_x^3 y$ for $y = 1 - x^{3/2}$.

Find y'' for each function in Exercises 9–12.

9. $y = 9x$

10. $y = 1 - 2x$

11. $y = \dfrac{x}{1 + x}$

12. $y = \dfrac{1 - x}{1 + x}$

Find $d^2 y/dx^2$ for each function in Exercises 13–14.

13. $y = (3x - 1)^5$

14. $y = (1 - 2x)^6$

In Exercises 15–18, determine the specified derivative.

15. $s = -16t^2 + 96t + 108$; find $d^2 s/dt^2$

16. $s = \dfrac{3}{t - 1}$; find s''

17. $y = \dfrac{10}{t^4}$; find $d^2 y/dt^2$

18. $C(x) = 100 - .03x^2$; find $C''(x)$

Determine $f''(4)$ for each function in Exercises 19–24.

19. $f(x) = x^3 - 5x^2 + x - 3$

20. $f(x) = x^3 + 2x^2 - 10x + 16$

21. $f(x) = \dfrac{1}{x}$

22. $f(x) = \dfrac{1}{x^2}$

23. $f(x) = 10\sqrt{x}$

24. $f(x) = \dfrac{1}{\sqrt{x}}$

In Exercises 25–28, determine the indicated rate of change.

25. The rate of change of $f'(x)$ when $f(x) = x^3 - 7x^2$

26. The rate of change of $g'(x)$ when $g(x) = 5 - \dfrac{12}{x^2}$

27. The rate of change of $f'(t)$ when $f(t) = \sqrt{8t}$ and $t = 2$

28. The rate of change of dy/dx for $y = \dfrac{1 + x}{x}$ when $x = 1$

(COST/MARGINAL COST) For each cost function in Exercises 29–30, determine the rate of change of the marginal cost when 10 items are produced.

29. $C(x) = 300 + 40x - .06x^2$

30. $C(x) = 500 + 30x - .03x^2$

(REVENUE/MARGINAL REVENUE) For each revenue function in Exercises 31–32, determine the rate at which marginal revenue is changing when 20 items are sold.

31. $R(x) = 20x - \dfrac{20}{x}$

32. $R(x) = 30x + \dfrac{40}{x}$

33. **(ACCELERATION)** A ball is thrown straight up from the ground and travels such that its distance from the ground at any time t is $s = -16t^2 + 80t$ feet. Find its acceleration at any time t.

34. **(ACCELERATION)** What will be the acceleration of the ball mentioned in Exercise 33 if the distance function is $s = -16t^2 + 200t$?

35. **(VELOCITY/ACCELERATION)** A ball travels on a hilly path according to

$$s = t^2 - 2t + \frac{4}{t} \qquad t \ge 1$$

s is its distance in feet from the beginning point, and t is the number of seconds it has been rolling.

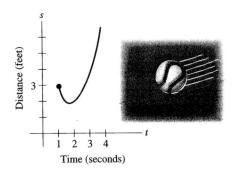

(a) Determine a formula for the speed of the ball at any time t.
(b) Determine the magnitude of its acceleration at any time t.
(c) Determine the magnitude of its acceleration when $t = 1$.
(d) Determine the magnitude of its acceleration at 2 seconds.

36. **(VELOCITY/ACCELERATION)** Redo Exercise 35 using

$$s = t^2 - 3t - \frac{8}{t} \qquad t \ge 1$$

Determine the second derivative of each function given in Exercises 37–40.

37. $f(x) = \dfrac{x^3 + 1}{x^2 + 1}$

38. $f(x) = \dfrac{1 + x^2}{1 - x^2}$

39. $y = 5x \sqrt{1 + x^2}$

40. $y = x(3x + 1)^6$

41. **(VELOCITY/ACCELERATION)** A ball thrown upward from the surface of the moon will go higher and take longer to return than a ball thrown upward from the surface of the earth, assuming the same initial velocity. The ball on the moon travels according to

$$s = -2.65t^2 + 106t$$

where s is the distance from the surface (in feet) and t is time (in seconds).
(a) Determine the velocity at any time t.
(b) Determine the acceleration at any time t.
W (c) Does your answer to part (b) seem consistent with the statement that the ball will go higher and take longer to return than it would on earth? Explain.
(d) How long does it take the ball to reach the ground?

42. Consider the third derivative of y with respect to x as an instantaneous rate of change, and fill in the blanks. d^3y/dx^3 is the instantaneous rate of change of _____ with respect to _____ .

W 43. **(PROFIT)** Explain the meaning of $P''(x)$ if $P(x)$ is a profit function.

44. For the quadratic polynomial function $f(x) = x^2$, we find that $f'''(x) = 0$. For $g(x) = x^{-2}$, we find that $g'''(x) \ne 0$.
(a) Verify the two statements.
W (b) For $g(x) = x^{-2}$, how many more derivatives (beyond g''') must we obtain before the resulting function will be zero (as it was with f)? Explain.

W 45. What is the meaning or interpretation of the following limit?

$$\lim_{\Delta x \to 0} \frac{f'(x + \Delta x) - f'(x)}{\Delta x}$$

W 46. Let $f(x) = x^9 + 7x^4 + 18x + 3$.
(a) In words, describe the graph of $y = f^{(9)}(x)$.
(b) How does the graph of $y = f^{(9)}(x)$ differ from the graph of $y = f^{(10)}(x)$?

W 47. Consider $f(x) = (2x + 1)^4$ and $g(x) = (x^2 + 1)^4$. Which second derivative is more difficult to determine, $f''(x)$ or $g''(x)$? Explain.

 TECHNOLOGY *EXERCISES*

1. Use the graph of $f'(x) = .2x\sqrt{x^2 - 9}$ to determine whether $f''(x)$ is positive, negative, zero, or undefined at the given value of x.

(a) $x = 4.2$ (b) $x = 1.7$ (c) $x = -5.1$

2. **(MARGINAL PROFIT)** Graph the marginal profit function

$$MP(x) = 8.03\sqrt{x} - 1.1x$$

and use the graph to determine whether the rate of change of marginal profit is positive or negative for the given number of units sold (x).

(a) x between 5 and 9 units   (b) x between 24 and 30 units

3. Consider $f(x) = 6x^3 + 40x^2 + 81x + 29$.

(a) Obtain $f'(x)$ and $f''(x)$.
(b) Graph f'' and determine the values of x for which $f''(x) > 0$.

4. Consider $f(x) = 2x^4 + x^3 - 8x^2 + 9x + 114$.

(a) Obtain $f'(x)$ and $f''(x)$.
(b) Graph f'' and determine the values of x for which $f''(x) > 0$.

Note   Computer algebra systems can find higher-order derivatives by using a modified differentiation command that includes a 2 for second derivatives, a 3 for third derivatives, and so on. In *Mathematica*,

```
D[x ^ 5, {x, 2}]
```

will produce the second derivative of x^5 with respect to x. In *Maple*, the command is

```
diff (x ^ 5, x$2);
```

If you have access to such a system, use it to do Exercises 13, 19, and 37.

3.8   IMPLICIT DIFFERENTIATION

Up until now, every function of x that we have differentiated has been given in an explicit manner, such as

$$y = x^2 + 3x - 2 \qquad\qquad f(x) = \sqrt{x^3 - 6}$$

In other words, the variable y has been written explicitly in terms of the other variable x. Always y, or $f(x)$, has been on one side of the equation and the expression in x has been on the other side.

But it can happen that the function to be differentiated is not presented this way. For example, the two equations

$$3xy - 2 = 0 \qquad\qquad y^3 - x^2 + xy = 3$$

provide relationships between x and y in which y is not given explicitly as a function of x.

When x and y appear together on the same side of the equation, as they do in these examples, the equation is said to define an *implicit function*. A relationship between x and y is implied, but it is not given explicitly, as it was in the two functions noted at the very beginning of this section.

The equation $3xy - 2 = 0$ can be readily manipulated to give y explicitly in terms of x. The steps are shown next.

$$3xy - 2 = 0$$
$$3xy = 2$$
$$y = \frac{2}{3x}$$

By contrast, the equation $y^3 - x^2 + xy = 3$ cannot be so readily manipulated.

While there is nothing "wrong" with having equations in which y is given implicitly as a function of x, the procedure for determining dy/dx is different in such cases. The process used to determine the derivative is called **implicit differentiation,** and it uses the chain rule in a very interesting way. Recall the general power rule, with u being a function of x:

$$\frac{d}{dx} u^n = n \cdot u^{n-1} \cdot \frac{du}{dx}$$

In a setting such as $y^3 - x^2 + xy = 3$, y can be considered a function of x, just as u is a function of x in the general power rule stated above. This means we can differentiate y^3 by using the general power rule, with u changed to y.

$$\frac{d}{dx} y^n = n \cdot y^{n-1} \cdot \frac{dy}{dx}$$

Specifically,

$$\frac{d}{dx} y^3 = 3y^2 \cdot \frac{dy}{dx}$$

Similarly, xy can be differentiated by using the product rule.

$$\frac{d}{dx} (xy) = x \cdot \frac{d}{dx} (y) + y \cdot \frac{d}{dx} (x)$$
$$= x \cdot \frac{dy}{dx} + y \cdot 1$$
$$= x \frac{dy}{dx} + y$$

Now we will combine all of these ideas in an example that shows how to determine the derivative dy/dx for an equation such as $y^3 - x^2 + xy = 3$, in which y is given implicitly as a function of x.

EXAMPLE 1   Determine dy/dx if $y^3 - x^2 + xy = 3$.

SOLUTION   Because $y^3 - x^2 + xy$ is equal to 3, it follows that the derivative of $y^3 - x^2 + xy$ is equal to the derivative of 3. That is, from

$$y^3 - x^2 + xy = 3$$

we obtain

$$\frac{d}{dx}(y^3 - x^2 + xy) = \frac{d}{dx}(3)$$

or

$$\frac{d}{dx}(y^3) - \frac{d}{dx}(x^2) + \frac{d}{dx}(xy) = \frac{d}{dx}(3)$$

In work done just before this example, we determined that

$$\frac{d}{dx}y^3 = 3y^2 \frac{dy}{dx} \qquad \text{and} \qquad \frac{d}{dx}(xy) = x\frac{dy}{dx} + y$$

Also, we can see readily that

$$\frac{d}{dx}x^2 = 2x \qquad \text{and} \qquad \frac{d}{dx}(3) = 0$$

Putting all of this together yields

$$3y^2 \frac{dy}{dx} - 2x + x\frac{dy}{dx} + y = 0$$

At this point the "calculus" is finished. We need only do some algebraic manipulation to solve for dy/dx. Begin by adding $2x$ and $-y$ to both sides of the equation. This will leave only dy/dx terms on the left side.

$$3y^2 \frac{dy}{dx} + x\frac{dy}{dx} = 2x - y$$

Next, factor out dy/dx.

$$(3y^2 + x)\frac{dy}{dx} = 2x - y$$

Finally, divide by $3y^2 + x$. The result is the desired derivative, dy/dx.

$$\frac{dy}{dx} = \frac{2x - y}{3y^2 + x} \qquad\qquad \blacklozenge$$

Implicit differentiation is not a difficult concept, but it is surely different from what you are used to doing. Here is another example.

EXAMPLE 2   Find dy/dx if $xy^4 + y - 2y^{3/2} = x^3 - 6$.

SOLUTION Begin by indicating the term-by-term differentiation. From

$$xy^4 + y - 2y^{3/2} = x^3 - 6$$

we obtain

$$\frac{d}{dx}(xy^4) + \frac{d}{dx}(y) - \frac{d}{dx}(2y^{3/2}) = \frac{d}{dx}(x^3) - \frac{d}{dx}(6)$$

Differentiate, keeping in mind that xy^4 is a product.

$$x \cdot 4y^3 \cdot \frac{dy}{dx} + y^4 \cdot 1 + \frac{dy}{dx} - 3y^{1/2} \cdot \frac{dy}{dx} = 3x^2 - 0$$

$$4xy^3 \frac{dy}{dx} + y^4 + \frac{dy}{dx} - 3y^{1/2}\frac{dy}{dx} = 3x^2$$

Add $-y^4$ to both sides to isolate the dy/dx terms.

$$4xy^3 \frac{dy}{dx} + \frac{dy}{dx} - 3y^{1/2}\frac{dy}{dx} = 3x^2 - y^4$$

Factor out dy/dx.

$$(4xy^3 - 3y^{1/2} + 1)\frac{dy}{dx} = 3x^2 - y^4$$

Finally, divide both sides by the coefficient of dy/dx.

$$\frac{dy}{dx} = \frac{3x^2 - y^4}{4xy^3 - 3\sqrt{y} + 1}$$

The procedure for determining dy/dx by implicit differentiation is summarized next.

Implicit Differentiation

If the equation contains x and y,

1. Differentiate both sides (all terms) of the equation with respect to x.

2. Collect all terms containing dy/dx on one side and all other terms on the other side.

3. Factor out dy/dx from all terms that contain it.

4. Solve for dy/dx by dividing both sides by the coefficient of dy/dx.

EXAMPLE 3 Find the slope of the tangent line to the ellipse given by $3x^2 + y^2 = 12$ at the point $(1, 3)$. See Figure 12.

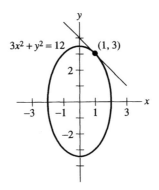

Figure 12 The tangent line at (1, 3)

SOLUTION The slope of the tangent line is given by dy/dx, so we must find dy/dx and evaluate it at (1, 3). From

$$3x^2 + y^2 = 12$$

we obtain

$$\frac{d}{dx}(3x^2) + \frac{d}{dx}(y^2) = \frac{d}{dx}(12)$$

$$6x + 2y\frac{dy}{dx} = 0$$

$$2y\frac{dy}{dx} = -6x$$

$$\frac{dy}{dx} = \frac{-6x}{2y} = -\frac{3x}{y}$$

At (1, 3), we have

$$\frac{dy}{dx} = \frac{-3(1)}{(3)} = -1$$

Thus, the slope of the tangent line to the ellipse at (1, 3) is -1. ◆

In the next section, the concept of implicit differentiation will be applied to situations involving rates of change.

3.8   Exercises

Obtain dy/dx by implicit differentiation in Exercises 1–18.

1. $x^2 + y^2 = 3$

2. $3x^2 + 2y^2 = 6$

3. $y^3 - x^2 = 6x$

4. $x^4 - y^2 = 2x - 5$

5. $x^3 + y^3 = 9$

6. $y^5 = x^4 + 6$

7. $y^2 = x^2 + 7x - 4$ **8.** $y^2 = x^3 - 10x^2$

9. $x^2 + y^2 - y^3 - x = 0$

10. $y^4 - x^3 + y^2 - 10 = 0$

11. $2x^{3/2} + 2y^{3/2} = 15$ **12.** $3x^{4/3} + 3y^{4/3} = 1$

13. $x^2y^2 - x - 3y = 0$ **14.** $x^2y^2 - 2x + 7y = 0$

15. $xy^3 + 5y = 3x$ **16.** $xy^2 + x = 4y$

17. $8xy + x = 9$ **18.** $7xy + y = 2$

In Exercises 19–22, use implicit differentiation to determine dy/dx. Then find the *slope* of the tangent line to the curve at the specified point.

19. $x^2 + y^3 - y = 7$ at $(1, 2)$

20. $x^3 + y^2 + x = 19$ at $(2, 3)$

21. $10xy + x + 45 = 0$ at $(5, -1)$

22. $y - 3xy = 22$ at $(4, -2)$

23. Determine the equation of the line tangent to the circle $x^2 + y^2 = 25$ at the point $(3, 4)$. See the accompanying figure.

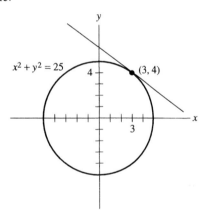

24. Determine the equation of the line tangent to the ellipse $x^2 + 4y^2 = 25$ at the point $(3, -2)$.

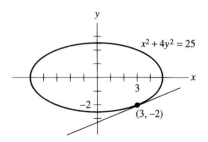

25. The graph of $9y^2 = 6x^3 - x^4$ is called a *piriform*, or pear-shaped curve.
  (a) Determine dy/dx.
  (b) Determine the x coordinate where the tangent lines to the graph are horizontal.
  In the Technology Exercises, you will have a chance to produce the graph of this equation.

26. The graph of $x^4 = 4x^2 + 4y^2$ is called a *kampyle of Eudoxus*. Obtain dy/dx. (In the Technology Exercises, you will have an opportunity to produce the graph of this equation.)

27. The graph of $x^{2/3} + y^{2/3} = 5$ is a curve called an *astroid*.

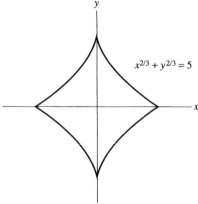

  (a) Verify that $(8, 1)$ and $(-1, 8)$ are points on the curve.
  (b) Obtain dy/dx.
  (c) Find the slope of the tangent line to the curve at $(8, 1)$.
  (d) Find the slope of the tangent line to the curve at $(-1, 8)$.

28. The graph of $x^3 + y^3 - 6xy = 0$ is a curve called a *folium*.

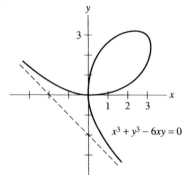

(a) Verify that $(3, 3)$ is a point on the curve.
(b) Obtain dy/dx.
(c) Find the slope of the tangent line to the curve at $(3, 3)$.

Obtain dy/dx by implicit differentiation in Exercises 29–32.

29. $(y - 3)^3 = (x + 5)^2$ **30.** $x + y = \sqrt{2x + 3y}$

31. $x^2 (y^2 - 1) = x + y$ **32.** $(x + 3)^2(y + 1)^2 = 7$

33. Answer "yes" or "no" to whether implicit differentiation should be used to determine dy/dx in each of the four equations given.

(a) $y = x^3 + x$ **(b)** $x^3y = 1 + xy^2$
(c) $y = x^2 - 3xy^2$ **(d)** $x^2 - 9x = y$

W **34.** Explain your answer to Exercise 33(c).

W **35.** Explain your answer to Exercise 33(d).

 # TECHNOLOGY *EXERCISES*

1. Graph the circle given by the equation

$$x^2 + y^2 = 25$$

Begin by manipulating the equation into $y = \pm\sqrt{25 - x^2}$ and graphing the two functions $y = \sqrt{25 - x^2}$ and $y = -\sqrt{25 - x^2}$. Then use implicit differentiation on the equation $x^2 + y^2 = 25$ to obtain the slope of the tangent line to the circle. Next, obtain the equation of the tangent line at the point $(-3, 4)$. Finally, graph the tangent line together with the circle. (The equation of the tangent line is given in the answer section.) Use Zoom Square to give the circle its proper shape.

2. In order to graph the piriform of Exercise 25, consider it as

$$y = \pm\sqrt{6x^3 - x^4}/3$$

and graph the two functions

$$f(x) = +\sqrt{6x^3 - x^4}/3 \qquad \text{top}$$

and

$$g(x) = -\sqrt{6x^3 - x^4}/3 \qquad \text{bottom}$$

As you will see, the graph is indeed pear-shaped. Next, verify that the tangent lines are horizontal at the x value obtained in Exercise 25 (b).

3. In order to graph the kampyle of Eudoxus (introduced in Exercise 26), consider it as

$$y = \pm\sqrt{x^4 - 4x^2}/2$$

and graph the two functions

$$f(x) = +\sqrt{x^4 - 4x^2}/2$$

and

$$g(x) = -\sqrt{x^4 - 4x^2}/2$$

4. Consider the equation

$$\pm\sqrt{y} \pm\sqrt{x} = 2$$

which can be separated into the two equations

$$\pm\sqrt{y} = 2 - \sqrt{x} \qquad \text{and} \qquad \pm\sqrt{y} = 2 + \sqrt{x}$$

(a) Show that the two separated equations can be written as

$$y = 4 + x - 4\sqrt{x} \qquad \text{and} \qquad y = 4 + x + 4\sqrt{x}$$

Graph them using the window [0, 20] for both x and y. Then, use Zoom Square.

W (b) Add a third graph, that of $y = x$, to your graphs from part (a). Describe the (visual) relationship of $y = x$ to the other two graphed equations.

Note The *Mathematica* command

```
ImplicitPlot[x^2 + 4y^2 = = 16, {x, -5, 5}]
```

will graph $x^2 + 4y^2 = 16$ for x in the interval $[-5, 5]$. In *Maple*, the command is

```
implicitplot(x^2 + 4 * y^2 = 16, x = -5..5, y = -5..5);
```

If you have access to software that can graph implicit functions, try it on Exercises 27 and 28.

3.9 | *RELATED RATES*

The concept of implicit differentiation can be applied to situations involving rates of change. In most of our applications there will be two variables, and each of them will be a function of some third variable. For example, the variables may be x and y, and each of them may be a function of time t. As we shall see, differentiating such an equation with respect to t will introduce a relationship between dx/dt and dy/dt. In other words, we will have a relationship between rates of change—**related rates.**

We begin with a preliminary example in order to provide some orientation.

EXAMPLE 1 Suppose that x and y are functions of t and that $x^3 + 5x^2 - 2y = 19$. Differentiate this equation with respect to t.

SOLUTION As a beginning, we have

$$\frac{d}{dt}(x^3 + 5x^2 - 2y) = \frac{d}{dt}(19)$$

$$\frac{d}{dt}(x^3) + \frac{d}{dt}(5x^2) - \frac{d}{dt}(2y) = \frac{d}{dt}(19)$$

To complete the differentiation, we must obtain the four derivatives suggested in this last equation. And they are as follows:

$$\frac{d}{dt}(19) = 0 \qquad \text{The derivative of a constant is zero.}$$

$$\frac{d}{dt}(2y) = 2 \cdot \frac{d}{dt}(y) = 2\frac{dy}{dt}$$

$$\frac{d}{dt}(5x^2) = 10x \cdot \frac{d}{dt}(x) = 10x\frac{dx}{dt}$$

$$\frac{d}{dt}(x^3) = 3x^2 \cdot \frac{dx}{dt} \qquad \text{using the general power rule}$$

Putting all this together, we see that differentiation yields the equation

$$3x^2\frac{dx}{dt} + 10x\frac{dx}{dt} - 2\frac{dy}{dt} = 0 \qquad\qquad\qquad\qquad ◆$$

The next examples offer applications in which related rates arise naturally.

EXAMPLE 2   *JAPANESE BEETLE INFESTATION*

A Japanese beetle infestation is spreading from the center of a small rural town. (See Figure 13.) The beetles fly off in all directions, so the region they cover is circular.

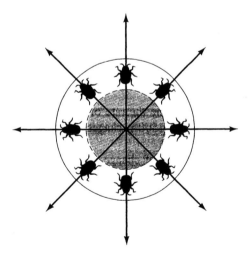

Figure 13 Spread of a beetle infestation

The radius of the circular region of infestation is increasing at the rate of 1.5 miles per year. Determine the rate of change of the area of infestation when the radius is 4 miles.

SOLUTION   The area of the circular region of infestation is given by

$$A = \pi r^2$$

where r is the radius of the circle. We want to determine the rate of change of area A with respect to time t. This means we want the derivative of A with respect to t, dA/dt. We are given the rate of change of the radius r with respect to time t; that is, we know from the statement of the problem that dr/dt is 1.5. In view of all this, and realizing that both A and r are functions of time t, we differentiate $A = \pi r^2$ with respect to t.

$$\frac{d}{dt}(A) = \frac{d}{dt}(\pi r^2) = \pi \frac{d}{dt}(r^2) = \pi \cdot 2r \frac{dr}{dt}$$

That is,

$$\frac{dA}{dt} = 2\pi r \frac{dr}{dt}$$

We are seeking dA/dt when $r = 4$, and we already know that dr/dt is 1.5. Putting these known values into our equation for dA/dt produces

$$\frac{dA}{dt} = 2\pi(4)(1.5) = 12\pi \quad \text{square miles per year}$$

Using 3.14 as an approximation for π, we can determine that 12π is approximately 38. This means that the area of infestation is increasing at the rate of approximately 38 square miles per year when the radius is 4 miles. ◆

EXAMPLE 3   **INCREASING PRODUCTION LEVEL**

APPLIED

A manufacturer of tennis balls decides to increase production at the rate of 30 packages per day (time t will be in days). Total revenue from the sale of all x packages produced is

$$R = 2.14x - .0001x^2 \quad \text{dollars}$$

Determine the rate of change of revenue with respect to time when the daily production level is 1500 packages.

SOLUTION   The rate of change of revenue with respect to time is dR/dt, which can be obtained by differentiating

$$R = 2.14x - .0001x^2$$

with respect to t. (Such differentiation is reasonable because both revenue R and quantity x are functions of time t.) The derivative is

$$\frac{dR}{dt} = 2.14 \frac{dx}{dt} - .0002x \frac{dx}{dt}$$

A daily production level of 1500 means that $x = 1500$. Production increasing at the rate of 30 packages per day means that $dx/dt = 30$. Using 1500 for x and 30 for dx/dt yields

$$\frac{dR}{dt} = 2.14\ (30) - .0002\ (1500)(30) = 55.20$$

The manufacturer's revenue is increasing at the rate of \$55.20 per day. ◆

APPLIED

EXAMPLE 4   *KITE FLYING*

A kite is flying 150 feet high, where the wind causes it to move horizontally at the rate of 5 feet per second. In order to maintain the kite at a height of 150 feet, the person must allow more string to be let out. (See Figure 14.) At what rate is the string being let out when the length of the string already out is 250 feet?

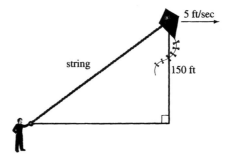

Figure 14 Flying a kite

SOLUTION   We will use x for the length of the horizontal side of the right triangle and z for the length of the hypotenuse. (If the vertical side were not a constant 150 feet, we would use y to represent its length.) See Figure 15. As the kite moves horizontally, both x and z increase. See Figure 16.

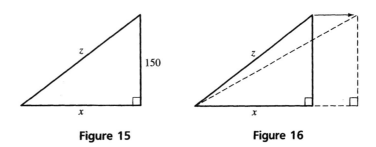

Figure 15   **Figure 16**

The rate of change of x is dx/dt, and it is given as 5 feet per second. The rate of change of z is dz/dt and is not yet known. In fact, dz/dt is the rate at which the string is being let out; it is the rate we seek. If we can find a relationship between x and z, then we can differentiate it and thus introduce dx/dt and dz/dt. We would then have an equation from which we could determine the value of dz/dt.

The **Pythagorean theorem** offers a relationship between the hypotenuse of a right triangle and the other two sides. See the drawing and statement at the top of the next page.

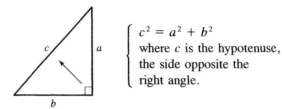

$$\begin{cases} c^2 = a^2 + b^2 \\ \text{where } c \text{ is the hypotenuse,} \\ \text{the side opposite the} \\ \text{right angle.} \end{cases}$$

Using the Pythagorean theorem and Figure 15, we can establish a relationship between x and z, namely

$$z^2 = x^2 + 150^2$$
$$z^2 = x^2 + 22,500$$

Differentiating with respect to t yields

$$2z\frac{dz}{dt} = 2x\frac{dx}{dt}$$

From the statement of the problem, we know that $dx/dt = 5$ and the string length is $z = 250$. The value of x can be determined from the right triangle by using the Pythagorean theorem. (See Figure 17.)

$$250^2 = x^2 + 150^2$$
$$x^2 = 250^2 - 150^2$$
$$x^2 = 40,000$$
$$x = \sqrt{40,000}$$
$$x = 200$$

Figure 17

Now, return to the equation containing dz/dt and dx/dt and substitute 200 for x, as well as 250 for z and 5 for dx/dt. The result:

$$2(250)\left(\frac{dz}{dt}\right) = 2(200)(5)$$
$$\frac{dz}{dt} = \frac{2(200)(5)}{2(250)} = 4$$

The string is being let out at the rate of 4 feet per second when its length is 250 feet. ◆

When you encounter related-rates problems, you may want to use the procedure suggested next.

Steps for Solving Related-Rates Problems

1. Make a drawing of the situation, if possible.

2. Use letters to represent the variables involved in the situation—say x, y, etc.

3. Identify all rates of change given and those to be determined. Use calculus notation dx/dt, dy/dt, etc., to represent them.

4. Determine an equation that both (a) involves the variables of step 2 *and* (b) will involve the derivatives of step 3, when differentiated.

5. Differentiate (by implicit differentiation) the equation of step 4.

6. Substitute all known values into the differentiated equation. (The original equation of step 4 may be needed to calculate an unknown value.)

7. Use algebraic manipulation, if necessary, to solve for the desired unknown rate or quantity.

3.9   Exercises

1. **(GYPSY MOTH INFESTATION)** A gypsy moth infestation is spreading from the center of a small rural town. The radius of the circular region of infestation is increasing at the rate of .75 mile per year. Determine the rate of change of the area of infestation when the radius is 3 miles.

2. **(POND RIPPLE)** A boy walking on a bridge across a pond stops in the middle. He then drops a rock into the water, causing a circular ripple. If the ripple moves away from the center in such a way that its radius is increasing at the rate of 2.5 feet per second, determine how fast the area within the ripple is changing when the radius is 9 feet.

3. **(OIL SPILL)** Suppose an oil spill has taken the form of a circular region and its area is increasing at the rate of 100 square meters per hour. At what rate is the radius of the region increasing when the radius is 200 meters?

4. **(MELTING ICE)** A large cube of ice is melting in such a way that the length s of a side is decreasing at the rate of 2 centimeters per minute. Find the rate of decrease in volume when each side is 100 centimeters. (Use $V = s^3$.)

5. **(TUMOR GROWTH)** If a tumor is approximately spherical in shape, its volume is approximately

$$V = \frac{4}{3}\pi r^3$$

The radius r of a tumor growing in an animal is increasing at a rate of 1.25 millimeters per month. Determine how fast the volume of the tumor is increasing when the radius is 10 millimeters.

6. **(TUMOR REMISSION)** Refer to Exercise 5. Suppose the animal is in remission and the radius of the tumor is decreasing at the rate of 1.5 millimeters per month. How fast is the volume of the tumor decreasing when its radius is 12 millimeters?

7. (INFLATING A BALLOON) Consider a spherical balloon $\left(V = \frac{4}{3}\pi r^3\right)$ that is being inflated by helium at the rate of 4 cubic feet per minute. At what rate is the radius increasing when the radius is 2 feet?

8. (INFLATING A BALLOON) A child is blowing air into a spherical balloon. The radius of the balloon is increasing at the rate of 2 centimeters per second. What is the rate of change of the volume of the balloon when its radius is 3 centimeters?

9. (INCREASING AREA) The length of each side of a square is increasing at the rate of 3 millimeters per second. Determine the rate of increase of the area when the sides are each 24 millimeters.

10. (SPINNING A WEB) Assume that a spider is spinning a circular web, and suppose that the radius of the web is changing at the rate of 8 millimeters per hour.
  (a) Find the rate at which the area of the web is increasing when the radius is 50 millimeters.
  (b) Find the rate at which the circumference ($C = 2\pi r$) is increasing when the radius is 50 millimeters.

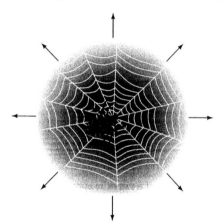

11. (MANUFACTURING) A manufacturer of baseball bats decides to increase production at the rate of 50 bats per day. The total cost of producing x bats is

$$C = 8x + 350 \quad \text{dollars}$$

Find the rate of change of cost with respect to time.

12. (MANUFACTURING) A calculator manufacturer will be increasing production at the rate of 400 calculators per week. Total revenue from the sale of all x calculators produced is

$$R = 18x - .0002x^2 \quad \text{dollars}$$

Determine the rate of change of revenue with respect to time when the weekly production level is 8000 calculators.

13. On the basis of the table provided, write an equation that expresses the most apparent relationship between dy/dt and dx/dt.

$\dfrac{dx}{dt}$	$\dfrac{dy}{dt}$
-3	6
5	-10
10	-20
12	-24

14. Both v and w are functions of t. Use the graph that follows to help you establish an equation that contains both the rate of change of w with respect to t and the rate of change of v with respect to t.

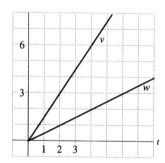

15. (BOTTLE PRODUCTION) A bottle producer is increasing its production at the rate of 250 bottles per week. The selling price p per bottle is given by the weekly demand function

$$p = 12 - .00015x \quad \text{cents}$$

where x is the number of bottles produced and sold.
  (a) Determine the weekly revenue function R.
  (b) Find the rate of change of revenue with respect to time when the weekly production level is 10,000 bottles.

16. (PRODUCTION) A company is increasing production of its product at the rate of 20 units per day. The selling price p per unit is given by the daily demand function

$$p = 340 - .003x \quad \text{dollars}$$

where x is the number of units produced and sold. Determine the rate of change of revenue with respect to time when the daily production level is 3000 units.

17. **(SLIDING LADDER)** A 30-foot ladder is leaning against a building. Suppose the ladder is sliding down the wall in such a way that the bottom of the ladder is moving away from the wall at the rate of 2 feet per second. At what rate is the top of the ladder sliding down the wall when the top of the ladder is 24 feet above the ground?

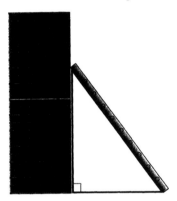

18. **(SLIDING LADDER)** A 20-foot ladder is leaning against a building. Suppose the ladder is sliding down the wall in such a way that the top of the ladder is moving down the wall at the rate of 1.5 feet per second. At what rate is the bottom of the ladder moving away from the wall when it is 16 feet from the wall?

19. **(SAND PILE FORMATION)** Sand poured at the rate of 8 cubic feet per minute is forming a pile in the shape of a cone (see the figure).

(a) The volume of a cone is $V = \frac{1}{3}\pi r^2 h$, where r is the radius of the base and h is the height. Suppose the height is always the same as the radius in this instance ($h = r$). Make a substitution into the volume equation

to produce V as a function of r (that is, with no h in the equation).

(b) Use the assumption and the result of part (a) to determine how fast the radius of the base is increasing when the pile is 10 feet high.

20. **(RESERVOIR FILLING)** Water runs into a conical reservoir at the rate of 7 cubic feet per minute (see figure). The radius of the water's surface is always half the height of the water.

$$V = \frac{1}{3}\pi r^2 h$$

How fast is the water level rising when the water is 2 feet deep?

21. **(MOVING DOT)** A dot moves along the curve $y = \sqrt{x^3 + 17}$. When the dot is at $(2, 5)$, x is increasing at the rate of 10 units per second. How fast is y changing then?

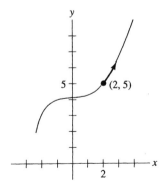

22. **(AIRPLANE FLIGHT)** An airplane is flying at a height of 5 miles and traveling at a speed of 400 miles per hour toward Denver. When its distance (z in the figure) from Denver is 13 miles, how fast is it approaching Denver? (See the figure on the next page.)

is thus described by $x^2 + y^2 = 100$. Assume that when cars are at the point $(8, 6)$, their x (east-west) coordinate is changing at the rate of -33 miles per hour. How fast is their y (north-south) coordinate changing? (See the figure.)

23. **(ROCKET LAUNCH)** A rocket is launched straight up. There is an observation station 7 miles from the launch site. At what rate is the distance between the rocket and the station increasing when the rocket is 24 miles high and traveling at 2000 miles per hour?

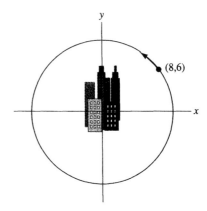

25. **(BEETLE INFESTATION)** Consider Example 2, the beetle infestation.
    (a) What are the two related rates—in symbols?
    W (b) What are the two related rates—in words?
    (c) What equation shows how the two rates of change are related?

26. **(PRICE AND QUANTITY)** Consider a commodity for which price p (in dollars) and quantity x are related by the equation $8p + 5x + xp = 75$. Assuming that both p and x are functions of time t (in days), determine the rate of change of price when $p = \$6$, $x = 3$ units, and $dx/dt = 2$ units per day.

24. **(AUTO TRAVEL)** A city is surrounded by a circular interstate highway with a radius of 10 miles. The path cars travel on it

---

3.10 DIFFERENTIALS

The derivative, dy/dx, has been defined as

$$\frac{dy}{dx} = \lim_{\Delta x \to 0} \frac{\Delta y}{\Delta x}$$

Because dy/dx is the slope of the tangent line and $\Delta y/\Delta x$ is the slope of the secant line, it follows that *for small values of* Δx,

$$\frac{dy}{dx} \approx \frac{\Delta y}{\Delta x}$$

This idea of approximation can be pursued by separating the notation dy/dx into two parts, dy and dx, called **differentials**. Before actually stating the definition of the differentials dy and dx, let us first see some justification.

By considering dy and dx to be separable quantities, we can rewrite

$$\frac{dy}{dx} = f'(x)$$

as

$$dy = f'(x)\, dx$$

The secant and tangent lines to the graph of $y = f(x)$ are shown in Figure 18.

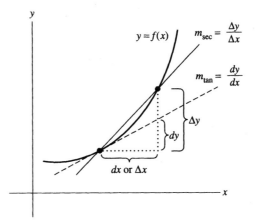

Figure 18 The secant and tangent lines to the graph of a function

The drawing shows that $dy \approx \Delta y$ and suggests that $dx = \Delta x$. We use this geometric justification to define dx. Here then are the definitions of dy and dx.

Differentials

Let $y = f(x)$ be a function whose derivative exists. Then

$$dx = \Delta x$$
$$dy = f'(x)\, dx$$
$$(dy = f'(x)\, \Delta x)$$

It is understood that dx is a small, nonzero real number.

The remainder of the section offers you an opportunity to become familiar with differential notation and to see the use of differentials to obtain approximations. The notation of differentials will be used extensively in our study of integration (Chapter 6).

EXAMPLE 1   Let $y = x^2$. Determine dy.

SOLUTION   *One approach*: From $y = f(x) = x^2$, we readily obtain

$$f'(x) = 2x$$

Since

$$dy = f'(x)\, dx$$

we have

$$dy = 2x\, dx$$

Another approach: The derivative is

$$\frac{dy}{dx} = 2x$$

Because dy and dx can be considered separate quantities, we can multiply both sides of this equation by dx. The result is

$$dy = 2x\, dx \qquad\qquad \blacklozenge$$

EXAMPLE 2   Find dy if $y = (x^2 - 7)^4$.

SOLUTION   Differentiating $y = (x^2 - 7)^4$ yields

$$\frac{dy}{dx} = 4(x^2 - 7)^3 \cdot 2x$$

$$\frac{dy}{dx} = 8x(x^2 - 7)^3$$

Finally,

$$dy = 8x(x^2 - 7)^3\, dx \qquad\qquad \blacklozenge$$

Because $dy \approx \Delta y$, the differential dy gives an approximation to the change in y (that is, Δy) corresponding to a small change in x.

EXAMPLE 3   Let $f(x) = 4x^2 - 9$.

(a) Use differentials to find dy (the approximate change in y) when x changes from 6 to 6.01.

(b) Determine the exact change in y (that is, Δy) when x changes from 6 to 6.01.

SOLUTION   **(a)** First, obtain the derivative.

$$f'(x) = 8x$$

Then, using

$$dy = f'(x)\, dx$$

we have

$$dy = 8x\, dx$$

The x value begins at 6 and changes to 6.01. This means that $x = 6$ and $dx = .01$. Thus,

$$dy = 8(6)(.01) = .48$$

The change in y is approximately .48.

(b) The exact change, Δy, is $f(6.01) - f(6)$.

$$f(6.01) - f(6) = [4(6.01)^2 - 9] - [4(6)^2 - 9]$$
$$= 135.4804 - 135$$
$$= .4804$$

Notice that differentials provide a good, quick approximation—.48 versus .4804. ◆

EXAMPLE 4   **REVENUE ASSOCIATED WITH ADVERTISING**

The revenue of many businesses is affected by advertising. For a local department store, the function defined below (for $0 \le x \le 40$) gives the revenue in *thousands* of dollars that is associated with an expenditure of x *hundred* dollars on advertising.

$$R(x) = -.25x^2 + 20x + 100$$

If the amount being spent on advertising now stands at \$1500, use differentials to determine the approximate increase in revenue associated with a \$100 increase in advertising.

SOLUTION   The approximate increase in revenue will be the value of dR for $x = 15$ and $dx = 1$. (An x value of 15 represents \$1500 and $dx = 1$ represents \$100.)

$$\frac{dR}{dx} = -.5x + 20$$

$$dR = (-.5x + 20)\,dx = [-.5(15) + 20]\,(1) = 12.5$$

Thus, the approximate increase in revenue associated with a \$100 increase in advertising is \$12,500.

Exercise 23 asks you to show that the exact increase in revenue is \$12,250.   ◆

3.10   Exercises

In Exercises 1–8, determine dy.

7. $y = (1 - 9x)^4$ **8.** $y = (5 - x^2)^3$

1. $y = x^3$ **2.** $y = x^4$

In Exercises 9–14, determine dy for the given values of x and dx. (It is understood that $y = f(x)$.)

3. $y = x^2 + 5x - 1$ **4.** $y = x^3 + 7x^2 + 5$

5. $y = (x^2 - 3)^5$ **6.** $y = (5x + 2)^4$ **9.** $f(x) = 5x^2$; $x = 4, dx = .02$

10. $f(x) = x^2 - 7x; \quad x = 3, dx = .01$

11. $f(x) = \sqrt{x^2 + 9}; \quad x = 4, dx = .01$

12. $f(x) = \sqrt{3x}; \quad x = 12, dx = .03$

13. $f(x) = \dfrac{2x}{x + 1}; \quad x = 3, dx = .001$

14. $f(x) = \dfrac{x}{x - 1}; \quad x = 2, dx = .002$

In Exercises 15–20, use differentials to approximate the change in y corresponding to the given change in x. (It is understood that $y = f(x)$.)

15. $f(x) = 3x^2 + 1; \quad x$ changes from 5 to 5.01

16. $f(x) = x^3 - 7; \quad x$ changes from 4 to 4.02

17. $f(x) = 2x - 5\sqrt{x}; \quad x$ changes from 9 to 9.015

18. $f(x) = x + \sqrt{x}; \quad x$ changes from 16 to 16.01

19. $f(x) = x - \dfrac{20}{x}; \quad x$ changes from 4 to 3.98

20. $f(x) = \dfrac{5x}{x + 1}; \quad x$ changes from 3 to 2.99

21. **(ADVERTISING)** Redo Example 4 assuming that the amount now spent on advertising stands at $2300 and a $150 increase is planned.

22. **(REVENUE)** Determine the *exact* increase in revenue for the situation described in Exercise 21.

23. **(REVENUE)** Show that the *exact* increase in revenue for the situation described in Example 4 is $12,250.

24. **(ADVERTISING)** Suppose the revenue in thousands of dollars associated with an expenditure of x hundred dollars on advertising is

$$R(x) = -.5x^2 + 18x + 70 \qquad 0 \le x \le 18$$

Use differentials to determine the approximate decrease in revenue associated with cutting the advertising expenditure from $1100 to $1000.

25. **(DEMAND)** Consider the demand equation given by $p = 20 - .4\sqrt{x}$, where x is the quantity demanded and p is the price per unit. Use differentials to approximate the change in price that would cause the quantity demanded to increase from 100 to 101 units.

26. **(SUPPLY)** Consider the supply equation given by $p = 6 + .01\sqrt{x + 25}$, where x is the quantity supplied and p is the price per unit. Use differentials to approximate the change in price that would cause the quantity supplied to increase from 144 to 145.

27. **(BACTERIA GROWTH)** After t hours, the number of bacteria in a laboratory culture is given by

$$n = 6t^2 + 200$$

Use differentials to approximate the change in the number of bacteria when t changes from 5 hours to 5 hours and 3 minutes.

28. **(YEAST CULTURE GROWTH)** After t hours, the number of yeast cells (n) in a culture is $n = 6t^2 + 2t + 150$. Use differentials to approximate the change in the number of yeast cells when the time changes from 4 hours to 4 hours and 6 minutes.

29. **(COST CUTTING)** A fast food restaurant serves soft drinks in a cylindrical cup that has a radius of 1.5 inches. The volume of soft drink that this cup can hold (using $V = \pi r^2 h$ with $r = 1.5$) is $V = 2.25\pi h$ cubic inches. Ordinarily, the restaurant fills the cup to a height of 8 inches. Suppose that  instead the restaurant decides to fill the cup to a height of only $7\frac{1}{2}$ inches. Use differentials to approximate the number of cubic inches of soft drink the restaurant saves on each serving.

30. **(LEAKING SAND)** Leaking sand forms a conical pile in which the height is always twice the radius ($h = 2r$). Consider the moment at which the radius is 9 centimeters. Use differentials to determine the approximate change in the volume when the radius changes by .1 centimeter.

$$V = \frac{1}{3}\pi r^2 h$$

W **31.** You have seen the use of differentials to find dy, an approximation to Δy. Are differentials used this way because the exact change Δy cannot be determined? Explain.

W **32.** Consider the two graphs given next. In which case will dy provide the better approximation of Δy? Explain.

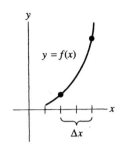
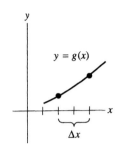

Key Terms and Ideas

slope of the tangent line
tangent line
derivative
differentiable
differentiation
differentiate
rules for differentiation
power rule
sum rule

difference rule
average rate of change
instantaneous rate of change
instantaneous velocity
marginal cost
marginal revenue
marginal profit
product rule
quotient rule

chain rule
general power rule
second derivative
acceleration
implicit differentiation
related rates
Pythagorean theorem
differentials

Review Exercises for Chapter 3

In Exercises 1–16, find the derivative of each function.

1. $f(x) = 2\pi$

2. $f(t) = 20t$

3. $f(x) = \dfrac{x^7}{7}$

4. $f(x) = \dfrac{2x^7}{5}$

5. $f(t) = \dfrac{1}{4\sqrt{t}}$

6. $f(x) = \dfrac{1}{6\sqrt[3]{x}}$

7. $y = 6x^{2/3} - 14x$

8. $y = 15 - 9x^{1/3}$

9. $y = 1 + x^{-1}$

10. $y = 17 - x^{-2}$

11. $y = \dfrac{1}{x} - \dfrac{x^9}{7}$

12. $y = \dfrac{5}{x^2} - \dfrac{x^4}{3}$

13. $y = \dfrac{3}{\sqrt[3]{x}}$

14. $y = 15 - \dfrac{4}{\sqrt{x}}$

15. $f(x) = x^{5/3} + 14$

16. $f(x) = x^{8/5} + 19$

Differentiate each function in Exercises 17–22.

17. $y = (8x)^{1/2}$

18. $y = (1 + 4x)^{1/2}$

19. $f(t) = \sqrt[3]{1 + t^2}$

20. $g(t) = 1 + \sqrt{t^2 + 1}$

21. $y = \dfrac{1}{\sqrt[3]{1 + x^3}}$

22. $y = \dfrac{1}{(x^3 - 2)^4}$

In Exercises 23–26, determine dy/dx.

23. $y = \dfrac{(2x - 1)^4}{x^2 + 4}$

24. $y = \dfrac{(7x + 1)^3}{x^2 + 1}$

25. $y = (x^2 + 7)^3(x - 5)^4$

26. $y = (2x - 3)^4(3x + 1)^2$

In Exercises 27–28, determine the slope of the line that is tangent to the graph of the given function at the particular point indicated.

27. $y = \sqrt{1 + 3x^2}$ at $(1, 2)$

28. $y = x(x^2 + 1)^2$ at $(-2, -50)$

In Exercises 29–30, find y''.

29. $y = \dfrac{2x}{x + 3}$ **30.** $y = x(x^2 + 1)^5$

In Exercises 31–32, use implicit differentiation to find dy/dx.

31. $xy^4 + x^2 - y = 1$ **32.** $y^2 - 3xy + 4y = 0$

In Exercises 33–34, use differentials to approximate the change in y corresponding to the given change in x. (It is understood that $y = f(x)$.)

33. $f(x) = x + 7\sqrt{x}$; x changes from 4 to 4.01

34. $f(x) = \dfrac{3x}{x + 4}$; x changes from 3 to 3.02

35. *(RATE OF CHANGE)* Determine the rate of change of $f(t) = (t^2 + 5)^3$ with respect to t when $t = 2$.

36. *(VELOCITY)* A ball is dropped from the top of a tall building and falls such that its distance s (in feet) from the ground after t seconds is $s = 200 - 16t^2$. How fast is the ball falling at 2 seconds?

37. *(HEATED METAL)* Let $T(x) = -2x^2 + 60x + 70$ be the temperature (in degrees Fahrenheit) of a metal bar when it is in a furnace for x seconds. Find the rate of change of the temperature of the bar at $x = 3$ seconds.

W 38. *(INSECT POPULATION GROWTH)* Suppose a local insect population is growing according to the graph shown next. Let n be the number of insects, and let t be the time. At which time (t_1, t_2, t_3, or t_4) is the rate of growth greatest? Explain.

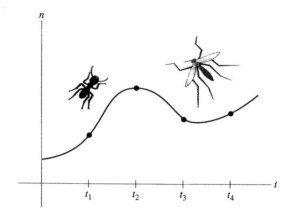

39. *(MARGINAL COST)* Let the cost of producing x units be $C(x) = 400 + 35x - .01x^2$ dollars.
   (a) Determine the marginal cost when x is 10.
   (b) Determine the exact cost of producing the 11th unit.
   (c) Find the rate of change of the marginal cost.

40. *(MARGINAL PROFIT)* If $MR(x) = 140 - .04x$ and $MC(x) = 12 - .02x$, for what value of x is marginal profit zero?

41. *(MARGINAL PROFIT)* If $R(x) = 6x + .002x^2$ and $C(x) = 150 + 10x + .001x^2$, determine the marginal profit function.

42. *(MARGINAL PROFIT)* If $C(x) = 300 + 40x - .01x^2$ and $R(x) = 70x - .02x^2$, determine the rate of change of marginal profit.

43. *(MARGINAL COST)* The cost to manufacture x tables is $C(x) = x^2 + 80x + 150$. At what production level does the marginal cost equal \$150?

44. *(CIRCLE)* The radius of a circle is increasing at the rate of 2 centimeters per second.
   (a) Find the rate of change of the circumference when the radius is 6 centimeters. ($C = 2\pi r$)
   (b) Find the rate of change of the area when the radius is 6 centimeters. ($A = \pi r^2$)

45. *(LEMNISCATE)* The graph of $(x^2 + y^2)^2 - 4xy = 0$ is a figure-eight-shaped curve called a *lemniscate*. (See the figure on the next page.)
   (a) Verify that $(-1, -1)$ is a point on the curve.
   (b) Use implicit differentiation to determine dy/dx.

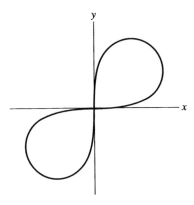

(c) Determine the slope of the tangent line to the curve at the point $(-1, -1)$.

W 46. *(MARGINAL REVENUE)* Explain in words the meaning of "The marginal revenue is $86."

47. *(TUMOR GROWTH)* Use differentials to approximate the change in volume of a sphere-shaped tumor $(V = \frac{4}{3}\pi r^3)$ when its radius increases from 1 to 1.1 centimeters.

W 48. Consider the two derivatives $f'(2)$ and $[f(2)]'$. One of these derivatives has a specific value regardless of the definition of function f. The value of the other derivative depends on the function. Explain. (If helpful, use $f(x) = x^2 + 1$ and $f(x) = x^3 + 5$ to assist you.)

49. *(FALLING OBJECT)* The Gateway arch in St. Louis is 630 feet high. If a piece came loose at the top, it would fall according to

$$s(t) = 630 - 16t^2$$

where t is the time in seconds and $s(t)$ is the distance of the object from the ground at t seconds.

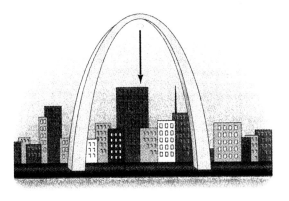

(a) When will the piece reach the ground?
(b) With what velocity will the piece strike the ground?

50. *(FLU OUTBREAK)* Suppose that when a flu outbreak strikes a community, the number of people n that are sick with flu t days after the outbreak is given by

$$n = 48t - 2t^2 \qquad 0 \le t \le 30$$

(a) When is the flu spreading at the rate of 12 people per day?
(b) How many people have the flu when it is spreading at the rate of 12 people per day?

51. *(HELICOPTER TAKEOFF)* A helicopter rises vertically at the rate of 10 feet per second. There is a marker (M in the figure) 80 feet from where the helicopter lifts off. At what rate is the distance between the helicopter and the marker changing when the helicopter is 192 feet high?

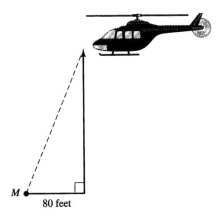

M •
80 feet

52. *(LEAKING WATER)* A cylindrical can with radius 6 inches and height 20 inches is completely filled with water. Suddenly, it is punctured at the bottom, after which water pours out at the rate of 12 cubic inches per second. How fast is the water level falling?

$$V = \pi r^2 h$$

53. (MELTING SNOW) Assume that a spherical snowball $(V = \frac{4}{3}\pi r^3)$ melts in such a way as to remain spherical. If the radius is decreasing at the rate of 1 centimeter per hour, at what rate is the volume decreasing when the radius is 3 centimeters?

W 54. (FALCON RETURNS) The American peregrine falcon was removed from the endangered species list in 1995, after a 30-year recovery from near extinction by DDT. A pere- grine can swoop down on its prey at a speed of 200 miles per hour.

(a) Write a calculus equation that states that the bird's speed is 200 miles per hour.

(b) In part (a), you used two variables. Indicate what each of them represents, including the units of measure.

55. Assume that x and y are functions of t. If $y = 4.3x^2$ and $dx/dt = 5.7$ when $x = 12.8$, determine dy/dt.

56. Consider $f(x) = \sqrt{x}$. Obtain f', f'', f''', and $f^{(4)}$. Then answer the questions on the basis of the evolving pattern.

W (a) Is $f^{(50)}(x)$ positive or negative? Explain.

(b) The constant in the denominator of $f^{(4)}(x)$ is 16. What is the constant in the denominator of $f^{(12)}(x)$?

(c) What is the power of x in $f^{(31)}(x)$?

(d) What is the constant in the numerator of $f^{(9)}(x)$?

Chapter Projects and Essays

Many of the projects and essays lend themselves to group activity, although most can be completed by individual effort.

1. MARGINAL COST

BACKGROUND   The idea of marginal cost was introduced in Section 3.4 as a special application of a rate of change. The marginal cost concept is widely used in economics.

THE PROJECT   Consult an introductory economics textbook to investigate several of the following applications of marginal cost. Describe your findings in a written paper.

(a) The relationship of marginal cost to various average costs, such as *average variable cost*, *average total cost*, and *average fixed cost*.

(b) The relationship between marginal cost and *marginal product*.

(c) The nature of the marginal cost involved in reducing an *externality* such as industrial pollution.

(d) The role of marginal costs in *benefit-cost analysis*.

(e) The nature of an *increasing-cost industry* and its effect on marginal costs.

(f) The relationship between marginal cost and *short-run supply*.

2. RATES OF CHANGE

BACKGROUND   In Section 3.3 you were introduced to the derivative as the (instantaneous) rate of change. A few examples of rate-of-change applications are given in the table below.

Application	Rate of change of	With respect to
velocity	distance	time
inflating balloon	volume	radius
snowfall	height of snow	time
culture growth	number of cells	time

THE PROJECT

(a) Get together with a few of your classmates for a brainstorming session in order to create your own table of rate-of-change applications *not given in the book*. Keep in mind that such applications are everywhere. Here is one new application to start you out.

Application	Rate of change of	With respect to
tanning	skin color	time

(b) Create another rate-of-change table by looking for applications in newspapers and magazines. Think about the rate-of-change concept as you read.

(c) Construct a rate-of-change problem based on one of your applications.

ADDITIONAL APPLICATIONS OF THE DERIVATIVE

For many homeowners, the rustic setting around Banff National Park in Canada makes this real estate desirable. Accordingly, developers must plan their building strategy with care. If they clutter the view with too many condominiums, they risk disenchanting potential buyers. How many condos should wise developers build to maximize revenues? Calculus plays a role in settling these and other economic questions.

Applications of calculus to business, science, and industry are widespread. Our examples and exercises have been chosen to provide a feeling for how the derivative can be used to solve real problems when the situation can be represented by or approximated by a function.

Given a few intuitive guidelines, you will be able to look at the graph of a function and see where the function is increasing, where it is decreasing, where it is maximum, and where it is minimum. This means that you will be able to "read" the graph of a profit function to see where profit is increasing, where it is decreasing, and how to obtain the maximum profit. You will be able to look at the graph of a temperature function and see when a metal is being heated or cooled. Learning how to interpret graphs will be an important experience, one filled with practical applications. A study of how derivatives apply to graphs will also enable you to make many of the same determinations without the benefit of a graph.

4.1 | *INCREASING AND DECREASING, GRAPHS, AND CRITICAL NUMBERS*

A function is said to be **increasing** when its graph rises as it goes from left to right. A function is **decreasing** when its graph falls as it goes from left to right. See Figure 1.

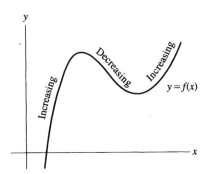

Figure 1 A graph with increasing and decreasing portions

The increasing/decreasing concept can be associated with the slope of the tangent line. After all, the slope of the tangent line to a curve will be positive when the curve is rising and negative when it is falling. See Figure 2.

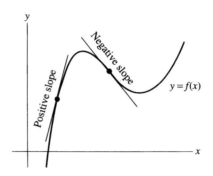

Figure 2 The slope of the tangent line

Since $f'(x)$ is the slope of the tangent line, it follows that if $f'(x) > 0$, then function f is increasing, and if $f'(x) < 0$, then f is decreasing.

Increasing/Decreasing

1. *At a point* (at which f is defined)

   (a) If $f'(a) > 0$, then f is increasing at $x = a$.

   (b) If $f'(a) < 0$, then f is decreasing at $x = a$.

2. *On an interval* (on which f is defined)

   (a) If $f'(x) > 0$ for all x in an interval, then f is increasing on the interval.

   (b) If $f'(x) < 0$ for all x in an interval, then f is decreasing on the interval.

EXAMPLE 1   Consider the function defined by $f(x) = x^2 - 8x + 7$. Where is f increasing and where is it decreasing?

SOLUTION   The derivative of $f(x) = x^2 - 8x + 7$ is $f'(x) = 2x - 8$. Thus, $f(x)$ is increasing when $2x - 8 > 0$—that is, when $x > 4$. It can also be said that $f(x)$ is increasing when x is in the interval $(4, \infty)$. Similarly, $f(x)$ is decreasing when $2x - 8 < 0$—that is, when $x < 4$. We can also say that $f(x)$ is decreasing when x is in the interval $(-\infty, 4)$. Figure 3 shows a graph of f. Note that it is decreasing for $x < 4$ and increasing for $x > 4$.   ♦

Although the increasing/decreasing idea was derived by studying graphs, applications of the increasing/decreasing concept extend far beyond graphs. The next four examples offer such applications.

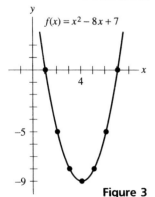

Figure 3

APPLIED

EXAMPLE 2 *HEATING AND COOLING*

Let $T(x) = -3x^2 + 60x + 70$ be the temperature after x seconds of a metal tray undergoing a chemical finishing process. Determine when the metal is cooling.

SOLUTION The metal is cooling when the temperature $T(x)$ is decreasing. Because a function is decreasing when its derivative is less than zero, $T(x)$ is decreasing when $T'(x) < 0$. From

$$T(x) = -3x^2 + 60x + 70$$

we obtain

$$T'(x) = -6x + 60$$

$T'(x)$ is less than zero when $-6x + 60$ is less than zero. Solving the inequality $-6x + 60 < 0$ leads to

$$x > 10$$

We conclude that the metal is cooling after 10 seconds. (It is heated during the first 10 seconds and cooled after that. Notice that $T'(x) > 0$ for $x < 10$ shows heating for the first 10 seconds.) ♦

APPLIED

EXAMPLE 3 *GLUCOSE TOLERANCE TEST*

A glucose tolerance test is used to determine whether a person is diabetic. If a certain amount of glucose is eaten or drunk, a normal person's blood sugar will rise somewhat, then fall back to a normal range within 2 hours. A diabetic's blood sugar will start high and continue to get higher throughout the 2-hour interval. See Figure 4.

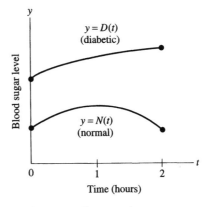

Figure 4 Glucose tolerance test

(a) For what values of t in [0, 2] is $D'(t) > 0$?

(b) For what values of t in [0, 2] is $N'(t) > 0$?

(c) Is $N'(t) > D'(t)$ on [1, 2]? Explain.

SOLUTION   (a) $D'(t)$ is the slope of the curve given by $y = D(t)$. The slope is positive throughout the interval [0, 2]. Thus, $D'(t) > 0$ for all t in the interval [0, 2]. The function D is increasing throughout the interval.

(b) $N'(t)$ is the slope of the curve given by $y = N(t)$. From the graph, it appears that the slope is positive throughout the interval [0, 1]. (We can't be sure just where the slope becomes negative, but it looks like it changes from positive to negative at about $t = 1$.) Thus, $N'(t) > 0$ for all t in the interval [0, 1]. The function is increasing there.

(c) No, $N'(t)$ is not greater than $D'(t)$ on [1, 2]. The graph of N has a negative slope on [1, 2], whereas the graph of D has a positive slope on [1, 2]. Thus, $N'(t) < D'(t)$ on [1, 2]. ◆

APPLIED

EXAMPLE 4   *TELEPHONE MANUFACTURER'S PROFIT*

Suppose that $P(x) = -.01x^2 + 60x - 500$ is the profit from the manufacture and sale of x telephones. Is profit increasing or decreasing when 100 phones have been sold?

SOLUTION   The derivative is

$$P'(x) = -.02x + 60$$

When $x = 100$, we have

$$P'(100) = -.02(100) + 60 = 58$$

Thus, $P'(100) > 0$, which means that profit is increasing when 100 phones have been sold. ◆

APPLIED

EXAMPLE 5   *PROFIT, MARGINAL REVENUE, AND MARGINAL COST*

Show that profit $P(x)$ is increasing when marginal revenue is greater than marginal cost.

SOLUTION   Begin with profit expressed as revenue minus cost.

$$P(x) = R(x) - C(x)$$

Differentiating will introduce marginal revenue $R'(x)$ and marginal cost $C'(x)$.

$$P'(x) = R'(x) - C'(x)$$

The idea that "marginal revenue is greater than marginal cost" translates into $R'(x) > C'(x)$. Adding $- C'(x)$ to both sides of this inequality leads to the inequality $R'(x) - C'(x) > 0$. Because $P'(x)$ is the same as $R'(x) - C'(x)$, we have, by substitution,

$P'(x) > 0$. And $P'(x) > 0$ means that $P(x)$ is increasing. Thus, we have shown that profit is increasing when marginal revenue is greater than marginal cost.

For another perspective, note that if marginal revenue exceeds marginal cost, then the revenue generated by the sale of the next unit will be more than the cost of making the next unit. As a result, there will be a (positive) profit on the production and sale of the next unit. Thus, marginal profit is positive when marginal revenue is greater than marginal cost. ◆

Assuming that the graph of a function is continuous at the point where the function changes from increasing to decreasing, that point is called a **relative maximum point.** This concept is illustrated in the two graphs of Figure 5. Similarly, if the graph is continuous at the point where a function changes from decreasing to increasing, that point is called a **relative minimum point.** This idea is illustrated in the two graphs of Figure 6.

Pepperdine University professor Arthur Laffer has been chief economist for the Office of Management and Budget as well as a member of the President's Economic Policy Advisory Board. Dr. Laffer is most famous for the graph that bears his name — the *Laffer Curve*.

A graph of the Laffer Curve shows the amount of tax revenue as a function of the tax rate. As the tax rate increases from 0%, tax revenue will increase from $0 until it reaches a maximum amount. Tax revenue will then decrease if the tax rate is raised any further. The reasoning behind this is that higher tax rates discourage consumer earning and spending as well as business investment.

Maximizing revenue is but one of the optimization applications we investigate in this chapter.

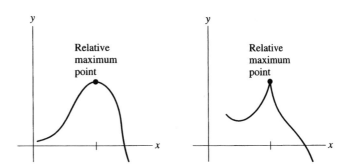

Figure 5 Relative maximum points

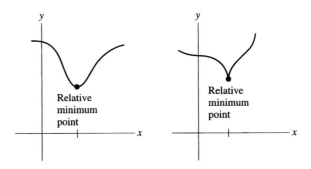

Figure 6 Relative minimum points

The points are called *relative* maximum or minimum points because they are the highest or lowest points compared with other points "nearby." There may be higher or lower points elsewhere on the graph, however. Figure 7 shows a graph with a relative maximum point and higher points elsewhere, away from the relative maximum point.

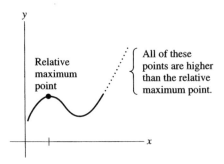

Figure 7

The graph will be "rounded" at the relative maximum or minimum point if $f'(x) = 0$ there. The slope of the tangent line is zero at such points. The tangent line is horizontal. See Figure 8. *The graph will be "pointed" at the relative maximum or minimum point when $f'(x)$ is not defined there*. The slope of the tangent line is undefined at such points. The tangent line either is vertical or else does not exist. See Figure 9. Exercise 71 offers an

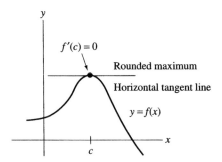

Figure 8 A "rounded" relative maximum

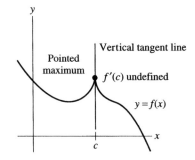

Figure 9 A "pointed" relative maximum

opportunity to consider an example of a function with a pointed relative maximum where the tangent line does not exist. Both Exercise 71 and the graph shown in Figure 9 suggest the following result.

If function f is continuous at $x = a$,
it is not necessarily differentiable at $x = a$.

The derivative will fail to exist where there is a vertical tangent (slope undefined) or where there is a sharp corner (as in Exercise 71) or abrupt turn in the graph.

In order to sketch graphs of functions and to solve various applied problems, it will be very helpful to be able to determine relative maximum and relative minimum points. This means you will be looking for x such that $f'(x) = 0$ or $f'(x)$ is undefined. Consequently, the following definition will be useful.

Critical Number

Suppose f is defined at some real number c; that is, $f(c)$ exists. If $f'(c) = 0$ or $f'(c)$ is undefined, then c is called a **critical number** of function f.

The critical numbers are the candidates (the only *possible* numbers) that can lead to relative maximum and relative minimum points. Only when $f'(x)$ is zero or undefined can the graph of the function have a relative maximum or minimum point. (Recall that if $f'(x) > 0$, the graph is increasing, and if $f'(x) < 0$, it is decreasing. The graph cannot have a relative maximum or minimum point where it is increasing or decreasing.)

EXAMPLE 6 Determine the critical numbers of $f(x) = x^3 + 3x^2 - 24x + 17$.

SOLUTION The function is defined for every real number x. The derivative of the function is $f'(x) = 3x^2 + 6x - 24$, and it is never undefined. But $f'(x)$ may be zero. Consider $f'(x) = 0$.

$$3x^2 + 6x - 24 = 0$$
$$x^2 + 2x - 8 = 0 \qquad \text{dividing by 3}$$
$$(x + 4)(x - 2) = 0 \qquad \text{factoring}$$
$$x = -4, \quad x = 2$$

Thus, $f'(x) = 0$ when $x = -4$ or $x = 2$. The numbers -4 and 2 are the critical numbers of the function $f(x) = x^3 + 3x^2 - 24x + 17$. ◆

Note

If the quadratic expression of Example 6 could not be factored, then the quadratic formula would have been needed to solve the equation.

> *Note*
>
> If the roots of the quadratic equation had contained the square root of a negative number, then there would have been no critical numbers derived from the equation. All of the functions here are functions of real numbers, and the square root of a negative number is not a real number.

EXAMPLE 7   Find the critical numbers of $f(x) = \sqrt[3]{x}$.

SOLUTION   From

$$f(x) = \sqrt[3]{x} = x^{1/3}$$

we obtain

$$f'(x) = \frac{1}{3}x^{-2/3} = \frac{1}{3x^{2/3}}$$

The derivative is not defined at 0, because the denominator of $f'(x)$ is 0 when $x = 0$. Yet function f is defined at 0. Thus, 0 is a critical number of the function. Considering $f'(x) = 0$ for other possible critical numbers, we see that $f'(x)$ always has 1 as the numerator and thus can never be zero.

$$\frac{1}{3x^{2/3}} \quad \text{can never be zero}$$

We conclude that there are no additional critical numbers. This means that 0 is the only critical number of f.   ◆

> *Note*
>
> Keep in mind that a fractional expression is equal to zero only when the numerator is zero and the denominator is not zero.
>
> $$\frac{\textbf{zero}}{\textbf{nonzero}} = \textbf{zero}$$

EXAMPLE 8   Determine the critical numbers of the function defined by

$$f(x) = \frac{x^2}{x - 3}$$

SOLUTION   Upon differentiating, we obtain

$$f'(x) = \frac{(x - 3)(2x) - x^2(1)}{(x - 3)^2} = \frac{2x^2 - 6x - x^2}{(x - 3)^2}$$

or

$$f'(x) = \frac{x^2 - 6x}{(x - 3)^2}$$

For critical numbers, note that $f'(x) = 0$ when the numerator $x^2 - 6x$ is zero.

$$x^2 - 6x = 0$$
$$(x)(x - 6) = 0$$
$$x = 0, \quad x = 6$$

We now have $f'(0) = 0$ and $f'(6) = 0$, *and* the original function f is defined at 0 and at 6. This means that 0 and 6 are critical numbers of the function.

We must also consider where $f'(x)$ is undefined. A quick look at the derivative

$$f'(x) = \frac{x^2 - 6x}{(x - 3)^2}$$

shows that $f'(x)$ is undefined when $x = 3$, because division by zero would be implied then, and division by zero is not defined. *However*, the original function f is also undefined at 3, so the number 3 cannot be a critical number.

The only critical numbers of the function are 0 and 6. ◆

In the next section we will have a test for determining whether a critical number is associated with a relative maximum point, a relative minimum point, or neither.

4.1 Exercises

In Exercises 1–6, study each graph to determine the intervals on which the function f is increasing and the intervals on which it is decreasing. Use inequality or interval notation.

1.
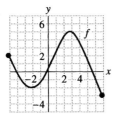

2.
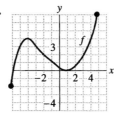

3.
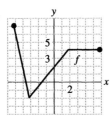

4.
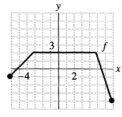

5.
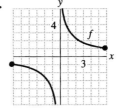

6.
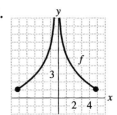

Determine where each function in Exercises 7–14 is increasing and where it is decreasing. Write your answers in inequality notation.

7. $f(x) = x^2 - 6x + 19$ **8.** $f(x) = x^2 - 14x + 100$

9. $f(x) = 1 - 4x^2$ **10.** $f(x) = 5x^2 + 42$

11. $m(x) = 10x - x^2$ **12.** $m(x) = 12x - 3x^2$

13. $f(x) = 50 + 6x - .02x^2$

14. $f(x) = 200 + 30x - .01x^2$

Determine where each function in Exercises 15–22 is increasing and where it is decreasing. Write your answers in inequality notation.

15. $f(x) = \dfrac{1}{x}$ *Hint:* $x^2 > 0$ for $x > 0$ and for $x < 0$.

16. $f(x) = \dfrac{1}{x^2}$ **17.** $f(x) = x^{3/2}$

18. $f(x) = \sqrt[3]{x}$ **19.** $f(x) = \sqrt{x}$

20. $f(x) = \dfrac{x-1}{x}$ **21.** $f(x) = \dfrac{x+1}{x}$

22. $f(x) = x^3 - 12x + 1$

23. (*COOLING*) Let $T(x) = -2x^2 + 64x + 65$ be the temperature after x seconds of a plate undergoing a finishing process. When is the plate cooling?

24. (*HEATING*) When is the plate used in Exercise 23 being heated?

25. (*ROCKET LAUNCH*) A rocket is launched vertically so that its distance from the ground at t seconds is

$$s(t) = -16t^2 + 800t \qquad \text{feet}$$

(a) When is the rocket rising?
(b) When does the rocket strike the ground? In other words, when is $s(t)$ equal to zero?
(c) When is the rocket falling?

26. (*ROCKET LAUNCH*) Redo Exercise 25 assuming that the distance from the ground is given instead by

$$s(t) = -16t^2 + 448t$$

27. (*COST*) Suppose it costs $C(x) = 36x - .02x^2$ dollars for a company to produce a total of x TV antennas $(0 \le x \le 1200)$. When is the total cost increasing?

28. (*REVENUE*) Let $R(x) = 8x + .03x^2$ dollars be the revenue from the sale of x calculators. Show that the revenue is always increasing.

Determine whether each function defined in Exercises 29–32 is increasing or decreasing at the given point.

29. $f(x) = x^2 - 7x + 50$ at $(1, 44)$

30. $f(x) = x^3 - 8x$ at $(3, 3)$

31. $f(x) = 10 - \dfrac{1}{x}$ at $(-1, 11)$

32. $f(x) = \sqrt{1-x}$ at $(-3, 2)$

33. (*AVERAGE COST*) Since $C(x)$ is the total cost of x units, the average cost per unit is $C(x)$ divided by x.

$$\overline{C}(x) = \frac{C(x)}{x} = \text{average cost per unit}$$

(a) For the cost function in Exercise 27, determine the average cost function $\overline{C}(x)$.
(b) For what values of x is the average cost decreasing?

34. (*PROFIT*) Use the approach of Example 5 to show that profit is decreasing when marginal revenue is less than marginal cost.

35. (*REVENUE*) If revenue from the sale of x units is $80x - .01x^2$ dollars, is revenue increasing or decreasing when 600 units have been sold?

36. (*PROFIT*) Let $P(x) = 1500 - \dfrac{1200}{x}$ dollars for the sale of x units.
(a) Is $P(x)$ increasing or decreasing for $x \ge 1$?
(b) Make a table showing x and $P(x)$ values for $x = 1, 2, 3, 4, 10, 100,$ and 1200.
(c) Use limits to determine the number of dollars toward which profit tends as the number of units sold gets greater and greater.

W 37. (*BEHAVIOR MODIFICATION*) Psychologists have determined that behavior modification is a better approach to dieting than is crash dieting (see the figure).

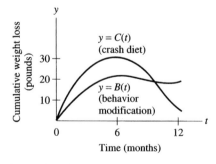

Comparison of crash dieting and behavior modification

(a) Is $B(t) > C(t)$ on $[0, 6]$? Explain.
(b) Is $B'(t) > C'(t)$ on $[0, 6]$? Explain.
(c) On the basis of the graph, explain why behavior modification is considered better than the crash diet approach.

W 38. (*CRIME STUDY*) A sociologist has gathered data showing the number of crimes reported each month of the year in a northern U.S. city. To get a better picture, she plotted the 12 points and then passed a curve $y = c(t)$ through them. Answer the following questions on the basis of her graph (shown below).
(a) Is $c'(t)$ positive, negative, or zero on $[3, 6]$? Interpret your answer from a crime perspective.
(b) Is $c'(t) < 0$ on $[9, 12]$? What does this mean in terms of crime?

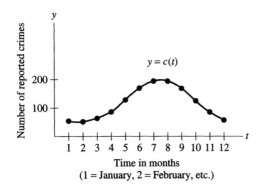

Crime in a northern U.S. city

39. (*INFLATION*) The prices of goods and services rise during periods of inflation. Consider the graph shown here.

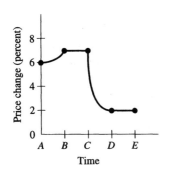

(a) Indicate whether the rate of *inflation* increased, decreased, or stayed the same during each of the following periods.
 (i) From A to B   (ii) From B to C
 (iii) From C to D
(b) Indicate whether *prices* increased, decreased, or stayed the same during each of the following periods.
 (i) From A to B   (ii) From B to C
 (iii) From C to D

W 40. (*PLANT PROPOGATION*) A popular method of plant propogation is to cut off a stem and place it in water. Because the leaves supply nutrients, the number of roots formed increases with the number of leaves left on the cutting.

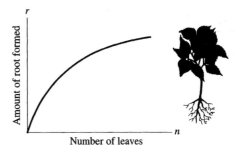

If r is the amount of root formed and n is the number of leaves left on the stem, is dr/dn positive, negative, or zero? Explain.

Determine the critical numbers of each function given in Exercises 41–52.

41. $f(x) = x^2 - 16x$ **42.** $f(x) = x^2 - 7x + 3$

43. $f(x) = 5x^2 + 3x - 2$ **44.** $f(x) = 5x^2$

45. $f(x) = x^3 - 2$ **46.** $f(x) = 1 - x^4$

47. $f(x) = x^3 + x^2 - 5x$ **48.** $f(x) = x^3 - 27x$

49. $f(x) = x^3 - 6x + 1$ **50.** $f(x) = x^3 - 15x - 7$

51. $f(x) = x^3 + 6x^2 + 3x + 1$

52. $f(x) = x^3 + \frac{1}{2}x^2 - x + 19$

Determine the critical numbers of each function given in Exercises 53–64.

53. $f(x) = x^{1/3} + 6$ **54.** $f(x) = 6x^{2/3}$

55. $f(x) = \dfrac{1}{\sqrt{x}}$ **56.** $f(x) = x^{-1/4}$

57. $f(x) = x^3 + 3x^2 - 15x - 9$

58. $f(x) = x^3 - 3x^2 - 18x + 7$

59. $f(x) = \dfrac{1}{x}$ **60.** $f(x) = \dfrac{1}{x^2}$

61. $f(x) = \dfrac{x^2}{x - 1}$ **62.** $f(x) = \dfrac{x + 2}{x^2 + 5}$

63. $f(x) = (3x - 1)(2x + 3)^5$

64. $f(x) = (2x + 1)(x + 5)^3$

Determine where each function given in Exercises 65–68 is increasing and where it is decreasing.

65. $f(x) = \sqrt{x^2 + 5}$ **66.** $f(x) = x\sqrt{2x + 1}$

67. $f(x) = x^4 + 4x^3 - 7$ **68.** $f(x) = x^3 - 3x^2 + 3x$

Determine the critical numbers of each function in Exercises 69–70.

69. $f(x) = x^4 + 8x^3 + 4x^2 + 15$

70. $f(x) = x\sqrt{4x + 5}$

71. The tangent line to the graph of f (see the figure) does not exist at $x = 3$.

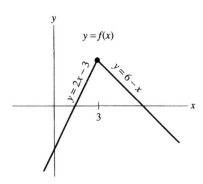

(a) Find the slope of the tangent line to the left of 3.
(b) Find the slope of the tangent line to the right of 3.
(c) What is the slope of the tangent line at 3?

72. Consider the function graphed in the next figure. Deter-

mine whether the function is (i) continuous and (ii) differentiable at each value of x (a, b, c, d, e).

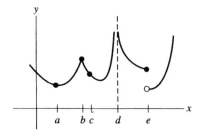

73. Consider the function graphed in the figure below. Determine whether the function is (i) continuous and (ii) differentiable at each value of x (a, b, c, d, e).

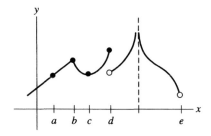

W **74.** If $f'(2)$ is undefined, is 2 then a critical number of f? Explain.

W **75.** If $f'(3) = 0$, is 3 a critical number of f? Explain.

W **76.** There are functions that have no critical numbers. If you were testing a function f, how would you conclude that it has no critical numbers? Explain.

W **77.** Explain in words how you would proceed to determine the critical numbers of a function g.

W **78.** Is it possible for $f(x)$ to be negative at some x in an interval on which f is increasing? Explain.

W **79.** Explain why critical numbers are the only possible numbers that can lead to relative maximum or relative minimum points. Explain why x values for which $f'(x) > 0$ or $f'(x) < 0$ cannot lead to relative maximum or relative minimum points.

80. Consider the graphs of $f(x) = x^2 + 4x + 4$ and $f'(x) = 2x + 4$, shown next.

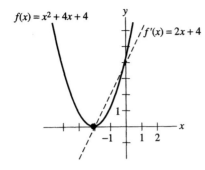

$f(x) = x^2 + 4x + 4$

$f'(x) = 2x + 4$

(a) For what values of x is f decreasing?

(b) For what values of x is the graph of f' below the x axis?

W (c) Explain the connection between the results of parts (a) and (b) and the nature of the derivative where a function is decreasing.

W (d) Redo parts (a) through (c), this time considering where f is increasing, where the graph of f' is above the x axis, and the connection.

W 81. In Example 5, we obtained the result

$$P'(x) = R'(x) - C'(x)$$

State in words the derivative rule that enables us to obtain this result from the equation

$$P(x) = R(x) - C(x)$$

~~TECHNOLOGY~~ *EXERCISES*

1. Graph the given function to determine where it is increasing and where it is decreasing.

$$f(x) = \frac{20}{x^2 + 4}$$

2. Graph the given function to determine where it is increasing and where it is decreasing.

$$f(x) = \frac{x^2}{16 - x^2}$$

3. Graph $f(x) = -x^3 + 3x^2 + 1$ to determine where the function is increasing and where it is decreasing.

4. For $f(x) = x^3 - 3x^2 + 20$, obtain $f'(x)$. Then graph $f'(x)$ to determine where f is increasing and where it is decreasing.

5. For $f(x) = 15 - 6x^{2/3}$, obtain $f'(x)$. Then graph $f'(x)$ to determine where f is increasing and where it is decreasing.

6. Consider $f(x) = x^3 + 3.75x^2 - 4.5x - 1.5$. Graph the function f and its derivative f' using x in $[-5, 5]$ and y in $[-10, 20]$.

    (a) For what values of x is f increasing?

    (b) For what values of x is f' greater than zero?

    (c) For what values of x is f decreasing?

    (d) For what values of x is f' less than zero?

In Exercises 7–10, determine the derivative of each function f. Then graph the derivative in order to estimate, to the nearest tenth, the critical numbers of the original function f. (Keep in mind that for polynomial functions, the critical numbers are the x values for which $f'(x) = 0$.)

7. $f(x) = x^3 - 8x^2 + 6x + 1$ **8.** $f(x) = x^3 - 7x^2 + 5x - 14$

9. $f(x) = .2x^3 - .1x^2 - 1.8x$ **10.** $f(x) = 1.1x^4 - x^2 - 1.5$

11. Consider $f(x) = 2x^{2/3}$.

   (a) Use calculus to show that $f'(0)$ is not defined.

   W (b) Graph f and explain, using the graph and tangent lines, why $f'(0)$ is not defined. To get the entire graph (both quadrants), you may need to split the exponent 2/3 and key in either $2(x^2)^{1/3}$ or $2(x^{1/3})^2$. Use windows $[-2, 2]$ for x and $[-1, 3]$ for y.

12. Graph $f(x) = \sqrt[4]{25x^2 - 60x + 36}$. Then estimate, to the nearest tenth, the value of x for which f' is undefined.

4.2 | RELATIVE EXTREMA AND CURVE SKETCHING

Some important ideas about relative maximum and relative minimum points were suggested in the previous section. These ideas are organized here and presented as two rules. Together, the rules are known as the **first derivative test**. Briefly, the ideas are

1. A relative maximum point of f occurs at $(c, f(c))$ if the function changes from increasing to decreasing there.

2. A relative minimum point of f occurs at $(c, f(c))$ if the function changes from decreasing to increasing there.

First Derivative Test

1. Let c be a critical number of f and let f be continuous on an interval containing c. Then $(c, f(c))$ is a *relative maximum point* provided that $f'(x) > 0$ in an interval to the left of c and $f'(x) < 0$ in an interval to the right of c.

2. Let c be a critical number of f and let f be continuous on an interval containing c. Then $(c, f(c))$ is a *relative minimum point* provided that $f'(x) < 0$ in an interval to the left of c and $f'(x) > 0$ in an interval to the right of c.

> **Note**
>
> In practice, a critical number is tested by evaluating the derivative at an x value on each side of the critical number (one x value less than c and one x value greater than c). *Be careful that the interval that includes the x values you select does not include any other critical numbers.*

> **Note**
>
> Not every critical number is associated with a relative maximum or relative minimum. *The derivative can be zero or undefined without there being a relative maximum or relative minimum.* This fact will be illustrated in Example 3.

The expression **relative extremum** of f is often used to refer to either a relative maximum or a relative minimum value of f. The **relative extrema** (plural) of a function include all relative maxima and all relative minima. A point associated with a relative extremum is called a **relative extreme point.**

EXAMPLE 1   Determine all relative extreme points (if any) of the function and sketch a graph.

$$f(x) = x^3 - 3x^2 + 1$$

SOLUTION   We seek all relative maximum points and all relative minimum points of the function. Begin by obtaining the derivative,

$$f'(x) = 3x^2 - 6x$$

Since this particular derivative can never be undefined, the only critical numbers will be x for which $f'(x) = 0$. To find them, solve $3x^2 - 6x = 0$.

$$3x^2 - 6x = 0$$
$$(3x)(x - 2) = 0$$
$$x = 0, \quad x = 2$$

Thus, the critical numbers of f are 0 and 2. Next, apply the first derivative test to the critical numbers. Beginning with 0, evaluate the derivative at an x value on each side of critical number 0. We have decided to evaluate the derivative at -1 and 1. (We were careful not to choose 2 or any number to the right of 2, because 2 is also a critical number.)

$$
\begin{array}{ll}
f'(-1) = +9 & \quad f'+++++ \quad f'----- \\
f'(0) = 0 & \quad \underline{f \text{ increasing} \mid f \text{ decreasing}} \\
f'(1) = -3 & \qquad\qquad x = 0
\end{array}
$$

Since $f'(x)$ is positive (f increasing) to the left of critical number 0 and negative (f decreasing) to the right, the point $(0, f(0))$ must be a relative maximum point.

Next, apply the first derivative test to critical number 2. Test $f'(x)$ at 1 and 3. (Keep in mind that you cannot use 0 or any number to the left of 0, because 0 is also a critical number.)

$$f'(1) = -3 \qquad\qquad f'----- \quad f'+++++$$
$$f'(2) = 0 \qquad\qquad\qquad f \text{ decreasing } \Big| \; f \text{ increasing}$$
$$f'(3) = \;\; +9 \qquad\qquad \overline{ x = 2 }$$

Since $f'(x)$ is negative (f decreasing) to the left of critical number 2 and positive (f increasing) to the right, the point $(2, f(2))$ is a relative minimum point.

We now return to the original function, $f(x) = x^3 - 3x^2 + 1$, to find the y coordinate of each relative extreme point. Substitute 0 for x to determine that $(0, f(0))$ is in fact $(0, 1)$. Also, substitute 2 for x to determine that $(2, f(2))$ is $(2, -3)$. Thus, $(0, 1)$ is a relative maximum point and $(2, -3)$ is a relative minimum point. The graph will be rounded (rather than pointed) at these relative extreme points because the derivative is equal to zero there. Using this information, we find that the graph thus far appears as shown in Figure 10.

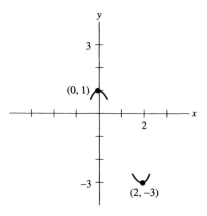

Figure 10

We should now determine a few more points in order to complete the sketch. Examining the graph thus far reveals that good choices for x would be 1, 3, and -1. These x values are integers, and they are close to the critical numbers 0 and 2. (If more points are needed after that, you might let x be 4 and -2.) Using 1, 3, and -1 for x yields

x	$f(x)$
1	-1
3	1
-1	-3

After these three points are plotted, the graph appears as shown in Figure 11.

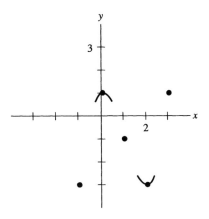

Figure 11

Connecting the points produces a reasonable sketch. See Figure 12.

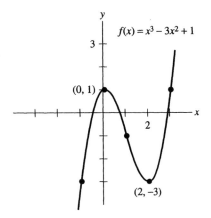

Figure 12 The completed sketch ◆

EXAMPLE 2 Determine all relative maximum and relative minimum points and sketch a graph.

$$f(x) = x^{2/3} + 1$$

SOLUTION Begin by obtaining the derivative.

$$f'(x) = \frac{2}{3}x^{-1/3} = \frac{2}{3\sqrt[3]{x}}$$

Clearly $f'(x)$ is never zero (since the numerator, 2, is never zero). But $f'(x)$ is *undefined* when $x = 0$. And since f is defined at 0, this means that 0 is a critical number of the function. The first derivative test, shown next, indicates that f has a relative minimum at $x = 0$.

$$f'(-1) = -\frac{2}{3} \qquad\qquad f'----- \quad f'+++++$$

$$f'(0) = \text{undefined} \qquad f \text{ decreasing} \mid f \text{ increasing}$$

$$f'(1) = +\frac{2}{3} \qquad\qquad \rule{3cm}{0.4pt}$$

$$x = 0$$

When $x = 0$, $y = f(0) = 1$. Thus, the point $(0, 1)$ is a relative minimum point. The graph will be pointed (rather than rounded) at the relative minimum point $(0, 1)$ because the derivative is undefined there. See Figure 13.

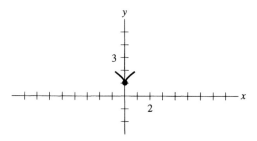

Figure 13

In order to complete the sketch, obtain a few additional points. Considering that the function involves the cube root of x, perfect cubes such as ± 1 and ± 8 would be good choices for x. (Of course, with a calculator at hand, numbers such as ± 3, ± 4, and ± 5 would be all right, too.)

x	y
1	2
−1	2
8	5
−8	5

The graph is shown in Figure 14.

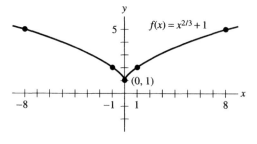

Figure 14 The completed sketch

EXAMPLE 3   Study the two functions given next for extreme points.

(a) $f(x) = x^3 + 2$ **(b)** $f(x) = x^{1/3}$

SOLUTION   **(a)** For $f(x) = x^3 + 2$, the derivative is $f'(x) = 3x^2$. Clearly $f'(x) = 3x^2$ is equal to zero when $x = 0$. Since f is defined when $x = 0$, it means that 0 is a critical number (the only critical number of this function). The first derivative test is shown next.

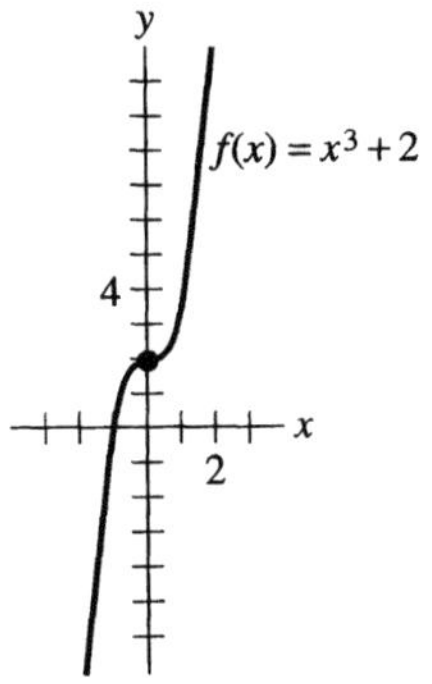

$$f'(-1) = +3 \qquad f'+++++ \quad f'+++++$$
$$f'(0) = 0 \qquad f \text{ increasing} \mid f \text{ increasing}$$
$$f'(1) = +3 \qquad \overline{}$$
$$x = 0$$

Because there is no change in the sign of the derivative, there is no relative maximum or minimum point at $(0, f(0))$. The graph of f is shown in Figure 15.

(b) In Example 7 of Section 4.1, we had $f(x) = x^{1/3}$ and $f'(x) = \dfrac{1}{3x^{2/3}}$. It was shown then that the only critical number is 0. We now apply the first derivative test to 0.

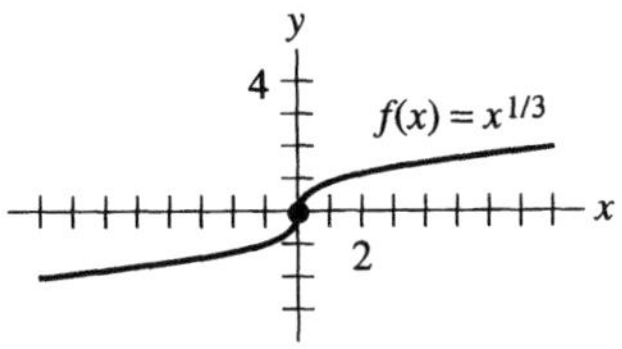

$$f'(-1) = +\frac{1}{3} \qquad f'+++++ \quad f'+++++$$
$$f'(0) = \text{undefined} \qquad f \text{ increasing} \mid f \text{ increasing}$$
$$f'(1) = +\frac{1}{3} \qquad \overline{}$$
$$x = 0$$

Because there is no change in the sign of the derivative, there is no relative extremum. The graph of f is shown in Figure 16.   ◆

Figure 15

$f(x) = x^3 + 2$

Figure 16

$f(x) = x^{1/3}$

Consider next a graphical example showing all four possibilities for the derivative of a function—positive, negative, zero, and undefined.

EXAMPLE 4   Consider the graph of f given in Figure 17.

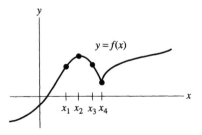

$y = f(x)$

$x_1 \; x_2 \; x_3 \; x_4$

Figure 17

Since at x_1 the function is increasing, it follows that $f'(x_1) > 0$. At x_2 the slope of the tangent line is zero, so $f'(x_2) = 0$. At x_3 the function is decreasing, so $f'(x_3) < 0$. The pointed relative minimum at x_4 means that $f'(x_4)$ does not exist.   ◆

French mathematician Pierre de Fermat preceded Newton in the use of tangent lines to study the graphs of functions (1629). He devised a form that resembles our definition of the derivative, and he used it to determine the relative maximum and relative minimum points of a curve. He then applied his theory to solve geometry and physics problems of the day. We too will apply this theory (in Section 4.5) to solve a variety of maximum/minimum applied problems.

Maximizing tax revenues was the concern of economist Arthur Laffer in the late 1970s when he proposed the Laffer Curve. He reasoned that as the tax rate increases from 0%, the tax revenue also increases. But at some point, the tax rate will be so high as to have a negative effect on the economy and cause tax revenues to decline for that or higher tax rates.

Pierre de Fermat (1601–1665)

4.2   Exercises

Find all relative maximum and minimum points of each function in Exercises 1–10. *Do not sketch graphs.*

1. $f(x) = 15 + 6x - x^2$ **2.** $f(x) = 50 - 8x - x^2$

3. $f(x) = x^2 - 20x$ **4.** $f(x) = x^2 - 9x$

5. $f(x) = x^3 - 3x - 2$ **6.** $f(x) = x^3 - 75x + 14$

7. $f(x) = x^3 - 6x^2$ **8.** $f(x) = x^3 - 27x^2$

9. $f(x) = 2x^3 + 3x^2 - 36x + 5$

10. $f(x) = 2x^3 - 12x^2 - 72x + 100$

Obtain all relative extreme points and sketch the graph of each function in Exercises 11–26.

11. $f(x) = x^2 - 8x + 9$ **12.** $f(x) = x^2 - 6x + 10$

13. $f(x) = -2x^2 + 4x - 1$ **14.** $f(x) = -2x^2 + 8x - 3$

15. $f(x) = x^3 - 3x + 5$ **16.** $f(x) = x^3 - 12x + 2$

17. $f(x) = -x^3 - 3x^2 + 7$ **18.** $f(x) = -x^3 - 6x^2 + 18$

19. $f(x) = 2x^3 - 3x^2 - 12x + 8$

20. $f(x) = 2x^3 + 3x^2 - 12x - 5$

21. $f(x) = 6x^{2/3}$ **22.** $f(x) = 3x^{2/3} + 1$

23. $f(x) = 1 - 3x^{2/3}$ **24.** $f(x) = 5 - 6x^{2/3}$

25. $f(x) = (x - 3)^{2/3}$ **26.** $f(x) = (x + 1)^{2/3}$

In Exercises 27–40, determine all relative maximum and relative minimum points of the function, if any. *Do not sketch the graph of the function.*

27. $f(x) = x^3 + 6x - 19$ **28.** $f(x) = 5x^3 + 2x + 4$

29. $f(x) = 10 - 3x^{2/3}$ **30.** $f(x) = x^{2/3} + 5$

31. $f(x) = x^3$ **32.** $f(x) = 1 - 4x^3$

33. $f(x) = \dfrac{1}{x}$ **34.** $f(x) = \dfrac{1}{x^2}$

35. $f(x) = (2x + 1)(x + 3)^4$

36. $f(x) = (3x - 7)(x + 1)^3$

37. $f(x) = 3x^{4/3}$ **38.** $f(x) = 4x - 3x^{4/3}$

39. $f(x) = 3x^4 + 4x^3 - 36x^2 + 19$

40. $f(x) = 2x^4 - 10x^3 + 9x^2 - 4$

41. (*MARGINAL COST*) Given the cost function

$$C(x) = x^3 - 6x^2 + 12x + 1 \qquad x \geq 0$$

obtain the marginal cost function. Then sketch the graph of the marginal cost function.

42. (*MARGINAL PROFIT*) Given the profit function

$$P(x) = 3x + \frac{6}{5}x^{5/3} \qquad x \geq 0$$

obtain the marginal profit function. Then sketch the graph of the marginal profit function.

For each graph in Exercises 43–44, determine whether $f'(x_1), f'(x_2), f'(x_3)$, and $f'(x_4)$ are positive, negative, zero, or undefined. (See Example 4.)

43.

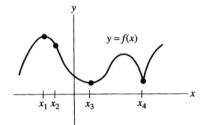

44.

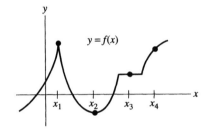

Find all relative extreme points and sketch the graph of each function in Exercises 45–47.

45. $f(x) = 4x^2 - 8x^4$　　　**46.** $f(x) = x^{5/3} - \dfrac{5}{2}x^{2/3} - 1$

47. $f(x) = 3x^{2/3} - x$

48. Consider the two graphs given next. Which one (A or B) is the graph of a function f, and which one is the graph of its derivative?

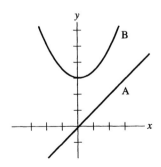

49. (WALKING DOG) A dog walks for 10 minutes along a street that runs north and south. Consider north to be the positive direction and south to be the negative direction. Time t is measured in minutes. Velocity v is measured in miles per hour. The dog's velocity is given by the graph.

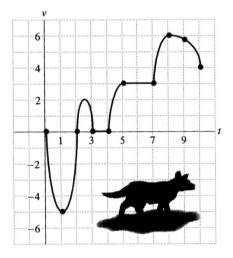

(a) When did the dog change the direction in which it was walking?

(b) When and for how long did the dog stop to be petted?

(c) While heading north, what maximum speed did the dog attain?

W (d) Describe the dog's activity between minutes 5 and 7.

W 50. The *note* after the statement of the *first derivative test* says "Be careful that the interval . . . does not include any other critical numbers." Explain and justify this note.

W 51. What is the difference between *a relative maximum function value* and *a relative maximum point*?

W 52. Suppose there is a function with exactly one critical number (call it c). Explain how you would use the first derivative test to determine whether the critical number is associated with a relative maximum, a relative minimum, or neither.

W 53. From the graph of the derivative f' (see the next figure), we can see that the corresponding function f has a relative maximum at $(2, f(2))$. Explain.

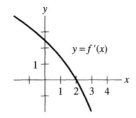

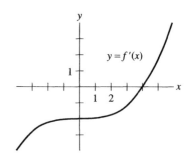

 54. From the graph of the derivative f' (see the next figure), what conclusion can be made about the function f at $x = 4$? Explain.

55. Refer to Example 3.

    (a) What word describes the tangent line to the graph of $f(x) = x^3 + 2$ at $(0, 2)$?

    (b) What word describes the tangent line to the graph of $f(x) = x^{1/3}$ at $(0, 0)$?

TECHNOLOGY EXERCISES

1. Graph $f(x) = x^4 + 4x^3 + 6x^2 + 4x - 2$ and estimate, to the nearest integer, the coordinates of all relative maximum and relative minimum points.

2. Graph $f(x) = -x^3 - 3x^2 + 6$ and estimate, to the nearest integer, the coordinates of all relative maximum and relative minimum points.

3. Graph $f(x) = x^3 - 6x^2 + 6x + 7$ and estimate, to the nearest tenth, the coordinates of all relative maximum and relative minimum points.

4. Graph $f(x) = .2x^3 + x^2 - 3x + 5$ and estimate, to the nearest tenth, the coordinates of all relative maximum and relative minimum points.

5. From the graph of $f'(x) = 3x^2 - 6x - 9$, estimate, to the nearest integer, the x coordinate of each relative extreme point of function f. Indicate whether the x is associated with a relative maximum or a relative minimum.

6. What can you conclude about the relative extreme points of f when you examine the graph of $f'(x) = 3x^2 + 12x + 12$?

7. Graph $f(x) = x^2 - 4x$ and its derivative.

    (a) What is the x coordinate of the minimum point of f?

    (b) Notice that the graph of f' crosses the x axis at the x coordinate of the minimum point of f. Is that just luck, or would you expect it to happen every time? Explain.

8. Consider $f(x) = 10 + 6x - x^2$. Determine $f'(x)$ and graph it.

    (a) For what number c is $f'(x) = 0$?

    (b) Is $f'(x)$ positive or negative for $x < c$?

(c) Is $f'(x)$ positive or negative for $x > c$?

(d) What is your conclusion about the point $(c, f(c))$ for the c value determined in part (a)?

9. Repeat the procedure of Exercise 8 using $f(x) = x^2 - 8x + 2$.

In Exercises 10–11, use the concepts developed in Exercises 7–9 to obtain the x coordinate of all relative maximum and minimum points of each function. Approximate your answers to the nearest tenth.

10. $f(x) = x^3 - 7x^2 + 3x - 4$ **11.** $f(x) = \dfrac{5x}{2x^2 + 1}$

4.3   CONCAVITY, THE SECOND DERIVATIVE TEST, AND CURVE SKETCHING

Another useful graphing concept is that of **concavity.** Although concavity can also be applied to rate-of-change situations, for now our consideration will be purely graphical. To begin, consider the graph of f shown in Figure 18.

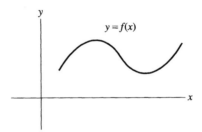

Figure 18

Visually, the graph can be split into two parts.

The graph on the left is described as being **concave down.** Casually speaking, if it were filled with water, the water would spill out because it is upside down. The graph on the right is described as **concave up,** and it would hold water.

Concave down   Concave up

In some cases, you may feel a need to imagine the graph extended in order to determine the concavity.

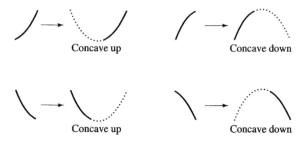

A more technical way of distinguishing concave up from concave down is as follows. A curve is *concave up* on an interval if it lies above its tangent line at every point of the interval. Similarly, a curve is *concave down* on an interval if it lies below its tangent line at every point of the interval. The drawings shown in Figure 19 serve to illustrate this concept.

Figure 19 Concavity and the tangent line

EXAMPLE 1   Where is the graph in Figure 20 concave up, and where is it concave down?

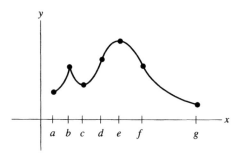

Figure 20

SOLUTION   Proceeding from left to right, we see that the graph is concave up over the intervals (a, b) and (b, d). It is then concave down over the interval (d, f) and concave up over the interval (f, g). ♦

When the graph of $y = f(x)$ is concave down, f' is a decreasing function. This can be seen in Figure 21. Look at the left portion of the graph. Notice the slopes of the tangent lines (that is, $f'(x)$) going from large positive values, to small positive values, to zero, and then negative. Accordingly, f' is a decreasing function on the interval being considered, which means that f'' is negative, because f'' is the rate of change of f'.

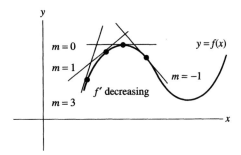

Figure 21 Concave down

A similar argument, made using the right portion of the graph, will show that f'' is positive when the graph is concave up. This study of concavity can be organized into a useful rule.

Test for Concavity

The graph of f is

1. *Concave down* where $f''(x) < 0$.

2. *Concave up* where $f''(x) > 0$.

EXAMPLE 2 Determine where the graph of $f(x) = x^3 - 3x^2 + 1$ is concave down and where it is concave up.

SOLUTION We begin by obtaining $f'(x)$ and $f''(x)$.

$$f'(x) = 3x^2 - 6x \qquad f''(x) = 6x - 6$$

The graph of f is concave down where $f''(x) < 0$—that is, where $6x - 6 < 0$. We can solve this inequality as

$$6x - 6 < 0$$
$$6x < 6$$
$$x < 1$$

Thus, f is concave down for $x < 1$.

The graph of f is concave up where $f''(x) > 0$—that is, where $6x - 6 > 0$. And $6x - 6 > 0$ when $x > 1$. Thus, f is concave up for $x > 1$.

The following chart displays our result: f is concave down when $x < 1$ and concave up when $x > 1$.

$$f'' - - - - - \qquad f'' + + + + +$$

concave down | concave up

$$x = 1$$

◆

Example 2 shows a function whose graph is concave down for $x < 1$ and concave up for $x > 1$. This means that at $x = 1$, the concavity changes from downward to upward. The point $(1, -1)$, where the concavity changes, is given a special name.

Point of Inflection

Any point at which the graph of a continuous function changes concavity is called a **point of inflection**.

Thus, $(1, -1)$ is a point of inflection of the graph of $f(x) = x^3 - 3x^2 + 1$. A graph of this function is shown in Figure 22.

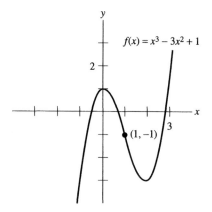

Figure 22 $(1, -1)$ is a point of inflection

In general, *once you have determined the concavity of a graph, it is an easy matter to obtain points of inflection.* For example, with $f(x) = x^3 - 3x^2 + 1$, it was determined that the graph is concave down for $x < 1$ and concave up for $x > 1$. It follows that there is a point of inflection at $x = 1$, since the function is continuous there.

It is interesting to observe that since $f''(x) < 0$ when the graph is concave down and $f''(x) > 0$ when the graph is concave up, it follows that at a point of inflection $f''(x) = 0$ or else $f''(x)$ does not exist. (After all, if f'' isn't negative or positive, then it must be zero or undefined.) However, this *does not mean* that there is necessarily a point of inflection at $(x, f(x))$ just because $f''(x) = 0$ or just because $f''(x)$ does not exist. There must also be a change of concavity at the point. Figure 23 illustrates that f'' can be zero or fail to exist at a relative minimum or relative maximum point.

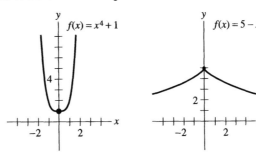

Here $f''(0) = 0$, yet $(0, 1)$ is a relative minimum, not a point of inflection

Here $f''(0)$ does not exist, yet $(0, 5)$ is a relative maximum, not a point of inflection

Figure 23

The study of concavity suggests a new test for relative maximum and relative minimum, a test that uses the second derivative. Because $f''(x) < 0$ when the graph is concave down, it follows that if $f''(c) < 0$ for the critical number c, then $(c, f(c))$ is at the "top" of a concave-down region and is therefore a relative maximum point. Similarly, because $f''(x) > 0$ where the graph is concave up, it follows that if $f''(c) > 0$ for the critical number c, then $(c, f(c))$ is at the "bottom" of a concave-up region and is therefore a relative minimum point. See Figure 24.

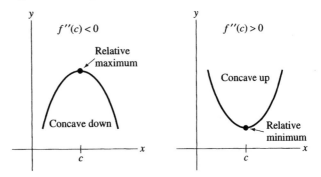

Figure 24 The second derivative and concavity in reference to relative extrema

Thus, we have the **second derivative test** for relative extrema, as stated next.

Second Derivative Test

Assuming c is a critical number of f,

1. If $f''(c) < 0$, then $(c, f(c))$ is a relative maximum point.

2. If $f''(c) > 0$, then $(c, f(c))$ is a relative minimum point.

Note: If $f''(c) = 0$ or if $f''(c)$ is undefined, you can draw no conclusion from this test. You must use the first derivative test instead.

EXAMPLE 3   Determine the relative maximum and relative minimum points, if any, of the function defined by $f(x) = x^3 - 6x^2 + 9x + 4$. Use the second derivative test.

SOLUTION   From $f(x) = x^3 - 6x^2 + 9x + 4$, we obtain the derivative

$$f'(x) = 3x^2 - 12x + 9$$

The critical numbers are x such that $f'(x) = 0$. We proceed accordingly.

$$3x^2 - 12x + 9 = 0$$
$$3(x^2 - 4x + 3) = 0$$
$$3(x - 3)(x - 1) = 0$$
$$x = 3, \quad x = 1$$

The critical numbers are 3 and 1. To use the second derivative test, obtain $f''(x) = 6x - 12$. Then evaluate f'' at 3 and at 1.

$$f''(3) = 6(3) - 12 = +6$$

Since $f''(3) > 0$, the point $(3, 4)$ is a relative minimum point. Similarly,

$$f''(1) = 6(1) - 12 = -6$$

Since $f''(1) < 0$, the point $(1, 8)$ is a relative maximum point.   ◆

EXAMPLE 4   Continue Example 3 to find the one point of inflection of the function $f(x) = x^3 - 6x^2 + 9x + 4$.

SOLUTION   We have $f(x) = x^3 - 6x^2 + 9x + 4$ and $f''(x) = 6x - 12$. The graph is concave up wherever $f''(x) > 0$—that is, whenever $6x - 12 > 0$. Thus, the graph is concave up when $x > 2$. The graph is concave down wherever $f''(x) < 0$—that is, whenever $6x - 12 < 0$. Thus, the graph is concave down when $x < 2$.

Because the graph is concave up for $x > 2$ and concave down for $x < 2$, the concavity changes at $x = 2$. Thus, $(2, 6)$ is a point of inflection, the only point of inflection of this function.   ◆

EXAMPLE 5   Continue Examples 3 and 4 to sketch the graph of $f(x) = x^3 - 6x^2 + 9x + 4$.

SOLUTION From Examples 3 and 4, we know that function f has

1. A relative maximum at $(1, 8)$

2. A relative minimum at $(3, 4)$

3. A point of inflection at $(2, 6)$

An easy point to obtain for the graph is the y intercept (that is, the point where $x = 0$). Using 0 for x in $f(x) = x^3 - 6x^2 + 9x + 4$ yields the point $(0, 4)$.

Although a few additional points are often needed in order to obtain a good sketch, here we find that once we plot the four points we know, plus the point $(4, 8)$, which can be readily determined, a nice curve can be passed through them. (See Figure 25.)

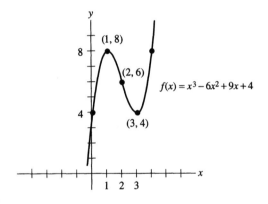

Figure 25

The curve is rounded (rather than pointed) at the relative maximum and relative minimum points because the derivative is zero there (rather than undefined). ◆

You may wish to organize your approach to **sketching graphs** of functions, especially since so many aspects of graphs have been presented. Here, then, is a straightforward, 8-step approach based on the techniques presented in the chapter.

Steps in Sketching the Graph of Function *f*

1. Determine $f'(x)$ and $f''(x)$.

2. Use $f'(x)$ to find all critical numbers.

3. Apply the second derivative test to critical numbers in order to determine relative extrema. If the test fails, use the first derivative test.

4. Determine the y coordinates of all relative maximum and relative minimum points. *(continued)*

5. Show the graph at relative extreme points as rounded (if $f'(c) = 0$) or pointed (if $f'(c)$ does not exist).

6. Determine where the graph is concave up and where it is concave down.

7. Determine points of inflection.

8. Determine one or more additional points as needed and complete the sketch.

EXAMPLE 6   Sketch the graph of $f(x) = 6x^{2/3} - 4x$.

SOLUTION   Here are the key results and information, plus the graph. You may want to do the step-by-step work to verify these results.

$$f(x) = 6x^{2/3} - 4x \qquad f'(x) = \frac{4}{x^{1/3}} - 4 \qquad f''(x) = -\frac{4}{3x^{4/3}}$$

To obtain critical numbers, first consider $f'(x) = 0$.

$$\frac{4}{x^{1/3}} - 4 = 0$$

$$\frac{4}{x^{1/3}} = 4$$

$$4 = 4x^{1/3}$$

$$x^{1/3} = 1$$

$$x = 1$$

Also consider when f' is undefined, which happens when $x = 0$. And because f is defined at 0, the number 0 is a critical number.

critical numbers: 0, 1

The second derivative test fails to tell anything when $x = 0$ is used. But the first derivative test shows that $(0, \ f(0))$ is a relative minimum point. Be careful when using the first derivative test here. You can use -1 to test $f'(x)$ to the left of 0, but you cannot use 1 on the right, because 1 is the other critical number. You might want to use 1/8 instead; 1/8 has a cube root that is easily determined without a calculator.

The second derivative test shows that $x = 1$ is associated with a relative maximum. Thus, $(1, \ f(1))$ is a relative maximum point.

relative minimum point: $(0, 0)$

relative maximum point: $(1, 2)$

The curve is pointed at $(0, 0)$ because $f'(x)$ is undefined at 0. The curve is rounded at $(1, 2)$ because $f'(x) = 0$ at 1.

In testing for concavity, we find that $f''(x)$ is negative whether x is negative or positive, because $x^{4/3}$ is positive for positive or negative values of x. Thus, the curve is always concave down. And since the concavity does not change, there can be no point of inflection.

Two other points on the graph are $(-1, 10)$ and $(8, -8)$. The graph is shown in Figure 26.

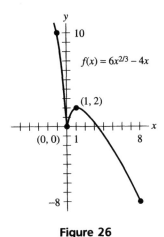

Figure 26 ◆

EXAMPLE 7 SOCIAL WORK/CELL DIVISION

Compare the *nature* of the increases shown in the two situations given next.
(a) a social worker's caseload (Figure 27)
(b) cell volume during cell division (Figure 28).

SOLUTION (a) The graph of a social worker's caseload as a function of time shows an increasing function. Furthermore, if you were to draw tangent lines to the curve, you would see that the slopes of those tangent lines increase as they go from left to right. This means that there is an increase in the *rate* at which the social worker's caseload is increasing.

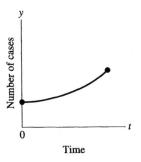

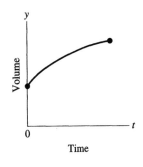

Figure 27 A social worker's caseload as a function of time

Figure 28 The volume of a cell during cell division (before it splits into two cells)

Consider too that the curve is concave up, which means that $y'' > 0$. Interpreting y'' as the rate of change of y' or the rate of change of the slope of the curve, we see that because $y'' > 0$, *the graph is increasing at an increasing rate*. This means that the social worker's caseload is increasing at an increasing rate.

(b) The graph of cell volume during cell division as a function of time shows an increasing function. If you were to draw tangent lines to the curve, you would see that the slopes of the tangent lines decrease as they go from left to right. This means that there is a decrease in the *rate* at which the cell volume is increasing.

You can also consider that the curve is concave down, which means $y'' < 0$. Interpreting y'' as the rate of change of y' or the rate of change of the slope of the curve, we see that because $y'' < 0$, *the graph is increasing at a decreasing rate*. This means that the cell's volume is increasing at a decreasing rate.   ◆

4.3   Exercises

For each graph in Exercises 1–4, indicate where the graph is concave up and where it is concave down. Use interval notation.

1.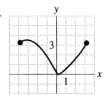

2.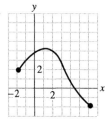

3.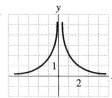

4.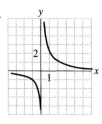

Determine where the graph of each function in Exercises 5–14 is concave up and where it is concave down. Use interval notation.

5. $f(x) = x^2 - 20x + 13$

6. $f(x) = -x^2 + 10x - 1$

7. $f(x) = x^3$

8. $f(x) = 7 - x^3$

9. $f(x) = x^3 + 3x^2 + 3x + 1$

10. $f(x) = x^3 - 3x^2 + 3x - 1$

11. $f(x) = -2x^3 + 3x^2 + 12x - 11$

12. $f(x) = -x^3 + 3x^2 + 24x + 5$

13. $f(x) = \dfrac{x+1}{x}$

14. $f(x) = 3x - \dfrac{1}{x}$

Determine all relative maximum and relative minimum points, if any, for the functions defined in Exercises 15–28. Use the second derivative test when possible.

15. $f(x) = x^3 + 3x^2 + 5$

16. $f(x) = x^3 - 6x^2 - 1$

17. $f(x) = x^3 - 48x + 2$

18. $f(x) = x^3 - 300x + 50$

19. $f(x) = -x^3 - 3x^2 + 24x + 7$

20. $f(x) = 2 + 3x^2 - x^3$

21. $f(x) = 2x^3 - 15x^2$

22. $f(x) = 23 - 6x^3$

23. $f(x) = x^{1/3}$

24. $f(x) = 2x^{1/3} + 5$

25. $f(x) = 2x^4 + 5$

26. $f(x) = 12x^{2/3} - 4x$

27. $f(x) = 3x^4 - 2x^3 - 3x^2 + 5$

28. $f(x) = x^4 + 4x^3 - 8x^2 + 17$

Each function defined in Exercises 29–36 has *one* point of inflection. Find it.

29. $f(x) = x^3 - 4$ **30.** $f(x) = x^3 + 2$

31. $f(x) = x^3 + 6x^2 + 12x + 12$

32. $f(x) = x^3 - 9x^2 + 27x - 17$

33. $f(x) = x^3 - 3x^2 + 4$

34. $f(x) = x^3 + 3x^2 - 24x + 1$

35. $f(x) = 2x^3 - 3x^2 + 12x - 2$

36. $f(x) = 2x^3 - 39x^2 + 240x + 5$

Sketch the graph of each function defined in Exercises 37–52 by using the methods developed in the chapter.

37. $f(x) = x^3 - 3x^2 + 5$ **38.** $f(x) = x^3 + 3x^2 - 5$

39. $f(x) = x^3 - 3x^2 + 3x - 1$

40. $f(x) = x^3 + 6x^2 + 12x + 8$

41. $f(x) = 1 - 3x^2 - x^3$ **42.** $f(x) = -x^3 + 12x + 1$

43. $f(x) = -x^3 + 3x^2 + 5$ **44.** $f(x) = -x^3 + 6x^2 - 19$

45. $f(x) = x^{1/3} + 1$ **46.** $f(x) = 2 + 6x^{1/3}$

47. $f(x) = 3 + x^{2/3}$ **48.** $f(x) = 1 - 3x^{2/3}$

49. $f(x) = 2x - 3x^{2/3}$ **50.** $f(x) = 12x^{2/3} - 4x - 7$

51. $f(x) = 3x^{4/3}$ **52.** $f(x) = 5 - 6x^{4/3}$

Sketch the graph of each function defined in Exercises 53–56 by using the methods developed in the chapter.

53. $f(x) = x^3 + 2$ **54.** $f(x) = 1 - x^3$

55. $f(x) = 3 - x^4$ **56.** $f(x) = x^5$

In Exercises 57–62, sketch the graph of a function f that has all of the properties given.

57. The relative maximum is at $(0, 3)$, and $f'(0) = 0$. The relative minimum is at $(2, -1)$, and $f'(2)$ is undefined. $(7, 4)$ is the only point of inflection. $(-5, 0)$ and $(3, 1)$ are other points on the graph. The domain of f is all the real numbers.

58. The relative minimum is at $(3, -2)$, and $f'(3) = 0$. The relative maximum is at $(5, 2)$, and $f'(5)$ is undefined. There is no point of inflection. $(0, 4)$ and $(6, -1)$ are other points on the graph. The domain of f is all the real numbers.

59. $f'(1) = 0$, $f(1) = 8$, and $f''(1) < 0$. $f'(5) = 0, f(5) = 0$, and $f''(5) > 0$. $(3, 4)$ is the only point of inflection. $(0, 7)$ and $(8, 11)$ are other points on the graph. The domain is all $x \geq 0$.

60. $f'(4) = 0$, $f(4) = 5$, and $f''(4) > 0$. $f'(11) = 0$, $f(11) = 8$, and $f''(11) < 0$. $(8, 6)$ is the only point of inflection. $(0, 9)$ and $(14, 0)$ are other points on the graph. The domain is all $x \geq 0$.

61. $f'(4)$ is undefined, $f(4) = 1$, $f'(x) < 0$ for $x < 4$, and $f'(x) > 0$ for $x > 4$. $(2, 5)$ and $(7, 4)$ are points of inflection. $(0, 10)$ and $(10, 6)$ are other points on the graph. The domain is all the real numbers.

62. $f'(9)$ is undefined, $f(9) = 7$, $f'(x) > 0$ for $x < 9$ and $f'(x) < 0$ for $x > 9$. $(5, 2)$ and $(11, 5)$ are points of inflection. $(0, 0)$ and $(14, 0)$ are other points on the graph. The domain is all the real numbers.

63. In Example 2 of Section 4.2 we sketched the graph of $f(x) = x^{2/3} + 1$ without knowing anything about its concavity. Since then we have studied concavity. Obtain $f''(x)$ and show that the graph is indeed concave down everywhere, as pictured in Example 2.

W 64. In Example 6 the second derivative test fails when $x = 0$. Explain why you really should have known, in advance of performing the test, that it would fail.

W 65. You have studied relative extrema and points of inflection. What seems unusual about the points $(a, f(a))$ and $(b, g(b))$ in the graphs shown here?

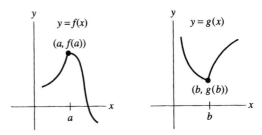

66. Sketch the graph of a continuous function that has a relative maximum and a relative minimum, but no point of inflection.

67. Refer to the graph shown on the next page and determine the value of each expression. Answers should be one of the following: positive, negative, or zero.
    (a) $f'(6)$ **(b)** $f'(10)$ **(c)** $f'(7)$
    (d) $f''(7)$ **(e)** $f'(9)$ **(f)** $f''(9)$
    (g) $f'(5)$ **(h)** $f''(5)$

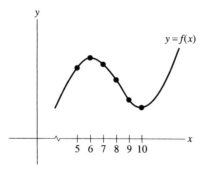

68. Refer to the graph shown below and determine the value of each expression. Answers should be one of the following: positive, negative, zero, or undefined.

(a) $f'(7)$ (b) $f''(7)$ (c) $f'(8)$

(d) $f''(8)$ (e) $f'(9)$ (f) $f''(9)$

(g) $f'(10)$ (h) $f'(11)$ (i) $f''(11)$

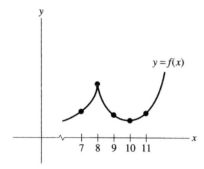

69. Is it safe to assume that a graph has a point of inflection wherever $f''(x) = 0$? Explain.

70. How do you explain the fact that the function $f(x) = x^2 - 8x + 50$ has no point of inflection?

71. The function defined by $f(x) = \dfrac{x+1}{x}$ is concave up when $x > 0$ and concave down when $x < 0$, yet there is no point of inflection at $x = 0$. Why not?

72. Is it possible for $(x_1, f(x_1))$ to be a point of inflection of f even though $f''(x_1) \neq 0$? Explain. (*Hint*: Consider $f(x) = x^{1/3}$.)

73. If the graph of f is concave up, is f' increasing or decreasing? Explain.

74. (*DANCING BEES*) German zoologist Karl von Frisch won a Nobel Prize for his study of communication among honeybees. A bee returning to the hive dances for the other bees in a way that indicates the distance of the food source from the hive. For distances between 100 meters and 4000 meters, the number of turns made within 15 seconds specifies the distance. Here is von Frisch's data, where x is the distance from the food source and n is the number of turns made by the bee.

x	n
100	9
200	7
500	6
1000	4.5
2000	3.5
2500	3
4000	2.5

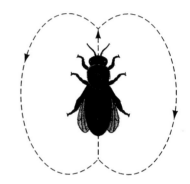

(a) Plot the seven data points of the form (x, n). Then pass a smooth curve through them.

(b) Is dn/dx positive, negative, or zero at the data points? Explain.

(c) Is d^2n/dx^2 positive, negative, or zero at the data points? Explain.

75. (*AIDS EPIDEMIC*) The number of AIDS cases n was small at first but then increased quickly at an increasing rate. Consider n as a function of time t.

(a) What is the concavity of the graph of n as a function of t?

(b) What is the nature of $n''(t)$?

76. (*SALARY CHANGES*) If faculty salaries S have been rising at a decreasing rate over a period of time t, what is the concavity of the graph of $y = S(t)$?

77. (*POPULATION*) If population P has been rising at an increasing rate over a period of time t, what is the concavity of the graph of $y = P(t)$?

78. (*ESTROGEN LEVEL*) The graph in the next figure shows a woman's estrogen level throughout a 28-day cycle. After reaching a minimum about 3 days into the cycle, the estrogen level climbs toward a maximum that occurs about 14 days into the cycle. Compare the type of increase in estrogen level during days 3 through 11 (where the curve is concave up) with the type of increase during days 11 through 14 (where the curve is concave down).

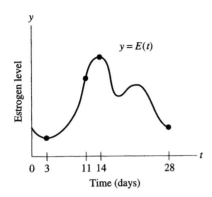

Time (days)

W 79. (REVENUE) Shown below is the graph of two revenue functions, R_1 and R_2. For which revenue function is marginal revenue a decreasing function? Explain.

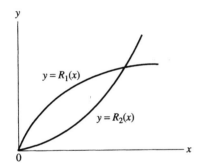

Revenue as a function of
the number of units sold

80. Consider a function that has one relative maximum point and one relative minimum point. The relative maximum is at $(0, 7)$ and the relative minimum is at $(8, -2)$.
 (a) Draw the graph of such a function, assuming it has *one* point of inflection between the maximum and the minimum.
 (b) Draw the graph assuming the function has *no* point of inflection.
 (c) Draw the graph assuming that it has *two* points of inflection between the maximum and the minimum.

81. Let

$$f'(x) = \frac{1 - x^2}{(x^2 + 1)^2}$$

and

$$f''(x) = \frac{2x(x^2 - 3)}{(x^2 + 1)^3}$$

For what value of x, if any, does the function f have a relative minimum?

82. In Chapter 1, it was claimed that the x coordinate of the vertex (maximum or minimum point) of the parabola given by $f(x) = ax^2 + bx + c$ is

$$x = -\frac{b}{2a}$$

Use calculus to verify this and show that it is a maximum when $a < 0$ and a minimum when $a > 0$.

In Exercises 83–92, use the methods of this chapter and your knowledge of asymptotes (from Chapter 2) to graph each function.

83. $f(x) = \dfrac{12}{x^2 + 3}$

84. $f(x) = \dfrac{6}{x^2 + 6}$

85. $f(x) = \dfrac{2x^2}{x^2 + 1}$

86. $f(x) = \dfrac{4x^2}{1 + x^2}$

87. $f(x) = \dfrac{x + 1}{x}$

88. $f(x) = \dfrac{1 + 2x}{x}$

89. $f(x) = \dfrac{x^2}{x^2 - 9}$

90. $f(x) = \dfrac{x^2}{4 - x^2}$

91. $f(x) = \dfrac{x}{x^2 - 4}$

92. $f(x) = \dfrac{x}{x^2 - 9}$

W 93. (NEW-CAR PRICES) If the rate of inflation associated with new-car prices is decreasing, which *one* of the following statements is correct? Explain and justify your choice.
 (i) New-car prices are decreasing.
 (ii) New-car prices are increasing.
 (iii) New-car prices are not changing.

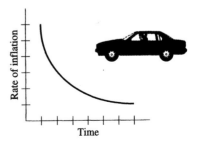

Time

W 94. (*MARGINAL COST*) For the cost function shown here, compare the behavior of *marginal cost* to the left and right of $x = 800$ units. Explain the significance of the point of inflection of such a cost curve.

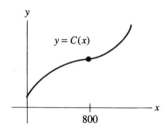

 TECHNOLOGY *EXERCISES*

1. Graph $f(x) = x^3 + 9x^2 + 27x + 29$ to determine where it is concave up and where it is concave down.

2. Graph the function to determine where it is concave up and where it is concave down.

$$f(x) = \frac{.4x^2}{x^2 - 25}$$

3. Graph $f(x) = x^3 - 5x^2 + 7x - 4$ and estimate the x coordinate of the point of inflection. Your estimate should be within .2 of the exact value.

4. Graph $f(x) = 6 - 1.5x^2 - .2x^3$ and estimate the coordinates of the point of inflection (each to the nearest integer).

In Exercises 5–8, examine the graph of each function to determine how many points of inflection it has (none, one, or two).

5. $f(x) = x^3 - 3x^2 + 3x + 1$ **6.** $f(x) = x^4 - 8x^3 + 24x^2 - 32x + 17$

7. $f(x) = x^4 - x^3 - 4x^2 + 4x + 3$ **8.** $f(x) = .3x^4 + x^3 - 4x^2 + x + 1$

9. Sketch the graph of

$$f(x) = 2 + \sqrt[3]{x - 3}$$

For ranges, use x in $[0, 8]$ and y in $[-2, 8]$. Indicate whether each of the following is positive, negative, zero, or undefined.

(a) $f''(5)$ (b) $f''(2)$ (c) $f'(3)$ (d) $f'(4)$ (e) $f'(1)$

10. Sketch the graph of

$$f(x) = x^4 - 3x^3 + x + 8$$

For ranges, use x in $[-2, 4]$ and y in $[0, 12]$. Indicate whether each of the following is positive, negative, zero, or undefined.

(a) $f'(2)$ (b) $f'(3)$ (c) $f''(2)$ (d) $f''(3)$ (e) $f'(0)$

11. Given $f(x) = x^3 - 9x^2 + 10x + 14$, obtain f'' and graph it to determine where f is concave up, where f is concave down, and for what x value f has a point of inflection.

12. Graph $f''(x) = x^3 - 9x^2 + 24x - 20$ and determine the x coordinate of each point of inflection of the function f.

13. Consider $y = 15.8 - 12.5x^2 + 1.25x^4$. Determine, to the nearest tenth, the value of x for which the rate of change of y with respect to x is a relative maximum.

4.4 | ABSOLUTE EXTREMA

Before we turn our attention to applied problems involving maxima and minima, it is appropriate to present the idea of absolute extrema. The *absolute maximum* value of a function is the largest possible value of the function. The absolute maximum value of a particular function may or may not be the same as the relative maximum value. Consider the function graphed in Figure 29, defined for x in the interval [2, 8]. The relative maximum value of the function is 5, but the absolute maximum value of the function is 9. Consider next the function graphed in Figure 30, defined for x in the interval [−3, 6]. The relative maximum value of the function is 4, and this is also the absolute maximum value of the function.

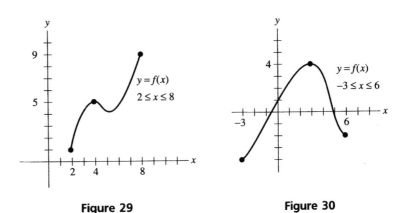

Figure 29   Figure 30

Similar drawings and reasoning can be used to present the *absolute minimum* versus relative minimum. We conclude that for continuous functions defined on a closed interval $[a, b]$:

1. The **absolute maximum** function value occurs either where there is a relative maximum or at an endpoint of the interval.

2. The **absolute minimum** function value occurs either where there is a relative minimum or at an endpoint of the interval.

Finding Absolute Extrema

Every function f that is continuous on a closed interval $[a, b]$ will have an absolute maximum and an absolute minimum on the interval. To find the absolute extrema,

1. Find all critical numbers of f that are in the interval (a, b).

2. Evaluate f at each critical number and also compute $f(a)$ and $f(b)$.

3. The largest value computed in step 2 is the *absolute maximum*. The smallest value that is computed in step 2 is the *absolute minimum*.

EXAMPLE 1   Determine the absolute extrema of $f(x) = x^2 + 4$ on the interval $[-2, 7]$.

SOLUTION   The only critical number is 0, from $f'(x) = 2x = 0$ when $x = 0$. Considering f at 0 and at the endpoints -2 and 7 of the interval, we have the following table.

x	$f(x)$
0	4
-2	8
7	53

From the table it is clear that the absolute maximum value of f is 53, which occurs at the endpoint where $x = 7$. The absolute minimum is 4, which occurs at the critical number 0.   ◆

4.4   Exercises

For each function graphed in Exercises 1–6, determine all relative maximum and relative minimum function values, if any. Also determine the absolute maximum and absolute minimum function values, if any.

1.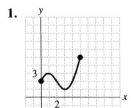

2.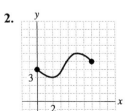

3.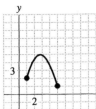

4.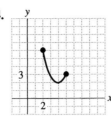

5.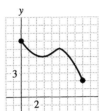

6.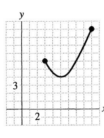

For each function in Exercises 7–20, determine the absolute extrema on the given interval.

7. $f(x) = x^2 + 5$ on $[-1, 8]$

8. $f(x) = 1 - x^2$ on $[-3, 7]$

9. $f(x) = -2x^2 + 8x - 17$ on $[0, 6]$

10. $f(x) = 3x^2 - 6x + 5$ on $[0, 4]$

11. $f(x) = x^3 - 6x^2$ on $[-1, 10]$

12. $f(x) = x^3 + 3x^2 - 9x + 2$ on $[-10, 3]$

13. $f(x) = 2x^3 - 3x^2 - 36x + 4$ on $[-5, 10]$

14. $f(x) = x^3 - 3x - 1$ on $[-5, 5]$

15. $f(x) = -x^3 + 6x^2 - 50$ on $[-1, 2]$

16. $f(x) = x^3 - 12x^2 + 3$ on $[1, 10]$

17. $f(x) = x^3 + 3x^2 + 5$ on $[0, 5]$

18. $f(x) = 2x^3 + 12x^2 - 17$ on $[-1, 1]$

19. $f(x) = x^3 - 15x^2 + 72x + 1$ on $[-4, 3]$

20. $f(x) = x^3 + 9x^2 + 24x + 7$ on $[0, 9]$

W 21. To determine the absolute extrema of a function on a closed interval, we evaluate the function at the endpoints of the interval and at the critical numbers within the interval. Why do we *omit* testing the critical numbers for relative maxima and relative minima?

22. *(PRIME RATE)* The graph of prime rates charged by banks from 1982 to 1992 (see the figure) is based on data from the Bureau of Economic Analysis. What were the absolute maximum and absolute minimum rates on the interval, and when did they occur?

Prime Rate 1982-1992

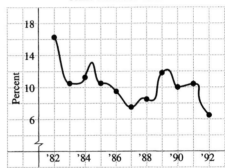

 TECHNOLOGY *EXERCISES*

1. Study the graph of $f(x) = 6 - .2x^2 + 3x^{.5}$ to estimate, to the nearest tenth, the absolute maximum value of the function on the interval $[1, 7]$.

2. Study the graph of $f(x) = -x^3 + 1.7x^2 + 3.2$ to estimate, to the nearest tenth, the absolute maximum value of the function on the specified intervals.

    (a) $[-1, 3]$ **(b)** $[0, 4]$

3. Study the graph of $f(x) = x^3 - 3.4x^2 + 4$ to estimate, to the nearest tenth, the absolute minimum value of the function on the specified intervals.

    (a) $[0, 4]$ **(b)** $[-1.5, 4.5]$

4. Obtain the graph of $f(x) = 2x - \sqrt{1 + x^3}$.

   (a) Estimate, to the nearest tenth, the absolute minimum value of the function on the interval $[-1, 6]$.

   (b) Estimate, to the nearest tenth, the absolute maximum value of the function on the interval $[-1, 6]$.

5. Obtain the graph of $f(x) = x\sqrt{16 - x^2}$.

   (a) Determine the interval over which this function is defined.

   (b) Find, to the nearest tenth, the coordinates of the absolute maximum point.

   (c) Find, to the nearest tenth, the coordinates of the absolute minimum point.

W **6.** Graph the function

$$f(x) = \frac{x^2}{2x - 7}$$

on the closed interval $[-5, 6]$. Does f have an absolute maximum or absolute minimum on the interval? Explain.

4.5 | *ADDITIONAL APPLICATIONS, APPLIED MAXIMUM / MINIMUM*

The concepts studied in this chapter can also be used to solve nongraphing problems. A variety of such applications are presented in this section.

The ideas given in Section 4.4 (absolute extrema) should serve to caution you. As we begin now to solve applied maximum and minimum problems using the techniques presented earlier in the chapter, we will be finding *relative* maximum and minimum values. Yet, the problems will always ask for *the* largest or smallest value. The application requires us to find the *absolute* maximum or minimum. The only way to be sure that the relative maximum or minimum obtained is indeed the absolute maximum or minimum is to check the endpoints of the interval on which the function is defined. Once you see the problem statements, it will become apparent that determining the interval on which the function is defined is not always a simple matter. For the applied problems in this section, the relative extrema are also the absolute extrema. Nevertheless, some of the examples will explain how to be sure that the relative extremum obtained is indeed the absolute extremum.

EXAMPLE 1   M*AXIMIZING A PRODUCER'S PROFIT*

A manufacturer of telephones determines that the profit from producing and selling x telephones is $P(x) = -.01x^2 + 60x - 500$ dollars.

(a) How many telephones should be produced in order to maximize profit?

(b) What is the maximum profit possible?

SOLUTION **(a)** To determine x for which $P(x)$ is maximum, begin by obtaining all critical numbers of the function. The derivative is

$$P'(x) = -.02x + 60$$

which is defined for all real numbers. This means that we need only consider $P'(x) = 0$ in order to find the critical numbers. Thus

$$-.02x + 60 = 0$$
$$x = 3000$$

The conclusion is that in order to maximize profit, the company should produce 3000 telephones. *However*, before rushing to this conclusion, you really should check to be sure that $x = 3000$ leads to a maximum rather than a minimum. The second derivative test works nicely here. [We have $P''(x) = -.02$, so $P''(3000) = -.02 < 0$. Thus, $P(3000)$ is a maximum.]

(b) The maximum profit is the value of $P(x)$ when $x = 3000$.

$$P(3000) = -.01(3000)^2 + 60(3000) - 500 = 89{,}500$$

The maximum profit is $89,500.

Note that the graph of the (quadratic) profit function is a parabola, which means that the relative maximum profit is also the absolute maximum profit. ◆

EXAMPLE 2 **FLIGHT OF A ROCKET**

A rocket is launched vertically such that its distance s (in feet) from the ground at any time t (in seconds) is given by

$$s(t) = -16t^2 + 640t$$

How high will the rocket travel before falling back down to the ground?

SOLUTION We seek to maximize s, because s is the height of the rocket. To begin, obtain s' and determine all critical numbers of the function s.

$$s' = -32t + 640$$

Since s' is always defined, consider $s' = 0$ for critical numbers.

$$-32t + 640 = 0$$
$$t = 20$$

We conclude that 20 is the only critical number of s. The second derivative ($s'' = -32$) is negative for $t = 20$. (Actually, s'' is negative for all values of t.) Thus, s will have a relative maximum value at 20, and the maximum value of s is $s(20)$, which is computed next.

$$s(20) = -16(20)^2 + 640(20) = -16(400) + 12{,}800 = -6400 + 12{,}800 = 6400$$

The rocket will travel to a maximum height of 6400 feet. ◆

Note

In Chapter 6, you will learn how to derive formulas of the type used in Example 2.

In Examples 1 and 2, the function to be maximized was given in the statement of the problem. But when the function is not given directly, you must establish it. Here then are guidelines to use when solving such applied problems.

Steps for Solving Maximum/Minimum Problems

1. Read the problem carefully.

2. If possible, draw a picture.

3. Determine the constants and variables. Label parts of the drawing.

4. Establish an equation containing the variable to be maximized or minimized.

5. If the equation does not give the variable to be maximized or minimized as a function of *one* variable, then you must make a substitution in order to obtain a function of just one variable.

6. Now that the function is established, proceed to obtain critical numbers and so on—as was done in Examples 1 and 2.

EXAMPLE 3   *CONSTRUCTING A PATIO*

A family plans to fence in a rectangular patio area behind their house. (See Figure 31.) They have 120 feet of fence to use. What should be the dimensions of the rectangular region if they want to make the patio area enclosed as large as possible?

Figure 31

SOLUTION   Let x be the width of the rectangular patio. (See Figure 32.)

Figure 32

Since there is 120 feet of fence, the *length* of the rectangle must be $120 - 2x$. The *area* of the patio is computed as length times width, so we have the following area A:

$$A(x) = (120 - 2x)(x)$$
$$A(x) = 120x - 2x^2$$

Differentiating yields

$$A'(x) = 120 - 4x$$

For critical numbers, determine x such that $A'(x) = 0$.

$$120 - 4x = 0$$
$$x = 30$$

(It is left for you to verify that $x = 30$ is associated with a maximum.) The length is $120 - 2x = 120 - 2(30) = 60$. Thus, the patio area will be largest when the width is 30 feet and the length is 60 feet.

Because the area function is quadratic and its graph is a parabola, the relative maximum obtained is also the absolute maximum. *Another approach*, one that can be used whether or not the function is quadratic, is to consider the interval over which function A is defined. Because x is the width of the rectangle, we insist that $x \geq 0$. Also, because there is only 120 feet of fence and there must be two widths of fence used, it follows that $x \leq 60$. Thus A is defined for x in the interval $[0, 60]$. Testing the value of A at the endpoints of this interval yields $A(0) = 0$ and $A(60) = 0$. Since $A(30) = 1800$, it follows that $x = 30$ leads to an *absolute* maximum value of A.   ◆

APPLIED

EXAMPLE 4   **MAXIMIZING A MANUFACTURER'S PROFIT**

A manufacturer can sell x headphones at a price of $140 - .01x$ dollars *each*. It costs $40x + 15,000$ dollars to produce *all x of them*. How many headphones should the manufacturer produce in order to maximize profit?

SOLUTION   The profit function P should be obtained and then maximized. Recall that $P(x) = R(x) - C(x)$; profit equals revenue minus cost. Because the revenue from the sale of *each* headphone is $140 - .01x$ dollars, the revenue $R(x)$ from the sale of x headphones can be obtained by multiplying this revenue per unit by x, the number of units. Thus,

$$R(x) = (140 - .01x)(x) \quad \text{dollars}$$
$$R(x) = 140x - .01x^2 \quad \text{dollars} \qquad \text{after simplifying}$$

The cost of producing x units is given in the statement of the problem; that is,

$$C(x) = 40x + 15{,}000 \qquad \text{dollars}$$

Using $P(x) = R(x) - C(x)$, we can now obtain the profit function.

$$P(x) = (140x - .01x^2) - (40x + 15{,}000)$$

$$P(x) = -.01x^2 + 100x - 15{,}000 \qquad \text{after simplifying}$$

In order to find x for which $P(x)$ will be maximum, obtain $P'(x)$ and set it equal to zero to determine the critical number(s).

$$P'(x) = -.02x + 100$$

$$0 = -.02x + 100$$

$$x = 5000$$

The second derivative is $P''(x) = -.02$, which is always less than zero. This means that $P(5000)$ is indeed a relative *maximum* value. Thus, *5000 units should be produced in order to maximize profit.* (If desired, we could continue and find the maximum profit, $P(5000)$, which is \$235,000.)   ◆

As an alternative approach to finding maximum profit, we will show that

---

Profit is maximized when marginal revenue R' is equal to marginal cost C', provided that $R'' < C''$.

To verify this result, consider that

$$P(x) = R(x) - C(x)$$

$$P'(x) = R'(x) - C'(x) \qquad \text{after differentiating}$$

For maximum $P(x)$, consider $P'(x) = 0$, which is the same as $R'(x) - C'(x) = 0$.

$$R'(x) - C'(x) = 0$$

which leads to

$$R'(x) = C'(x)$$

Thus, $P'(x) = 0$ when marginal revenue equals marginal cost. According to the second derivative test, $P(x)$ is maximum if $P''(x) < 0$. From

$$P'(x) = R'(x) - C'(x)$$

we can obtain

$$P''(x) = R''(x) - C''(x)$$

Now $P''(x) < 0$ becomes

$$R''(x) - C''(x) < 0$$

or

$$R''(x) < C''(x)$$

We can use this result to solve the problem of Example 4. Consider

$$R'(x) = C'(x)$$

or

$$140 - .02x = 40$$

The solution, as before, is $x = 5000$. Note that $R''(x) = -.02$ and $C''(x) = 0$. Thus, $R''(5000) < C''(5000)$, as required for a maximum.

APPLIED

EXAMPLE 5 **MINIMIZING THE COST OF MATERIALS**

A manufacturer of storage bins plans to produce some open-top rectangular boxes with square bases. The volume of each box is to be 100 cubic feet. Material for the base costs $8 per square foot, and material for the sides costs $5 per square foot. Determine the dimensions of the box that will minimize the cost of materials.

SOLUTION Suppose we let x be the width of the bin. Because the base is square, the length must also be x. No information is given about the height, so we will use h to represent it. A drawing of the storage bin is shown in Figure 33.

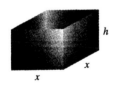

Figure 33
The storage bin
(open-top box)

The area of the base is $x \cdot x$, or x^2, square feet. Thus, at $8 per square foot, the cost of the material for the base is $8 \cdot x^2$ or $8x^2$ dollars. The area of each side is xh, so the area of the four sides is $4xh$. Since the cost of material for the sides is $5 per square foot, the cost of the material for all four sides is $5 \cdot 4xh$ or $20xh$ dollars. Thus, the total cost C of all the materials for a bin is

$$C = 8x^2 + 20xh \quad \text{dollars}$$

Unfortunately, C is a function of two variables, x and h. In order to proceed to differentiation, we must eliminate one of the variables. The variable h can be eliminated by obtaining a relationship between x and h. This can be done by considering that the volume of a box is computed as length times width times height. Here the length and width are both x and the height is h. So we have

$$V = x \cdot x \cdot h$$
$$V = x^2h$$

The problem says the volume is 100 cubic feet. Thus, we have

$$100 = x^2h$$

This equation can be manipulated into the form

$$h = \frac{100}{x^2}$$

and then $100/x^2$ can be substituted for h in the cost function

$$C = 8x^2 + 20xh$$

to produce

$$C = 8x^2 + 20x \cdot \frac{100}{x^2}$$

$$C = 8x^2 + \frac{2000}{x} \qquad \text{after simplifying}$$

Now we can differentiate and proceed toward a solution.

$$C' = 16x - \frac{2000}{x^2}$$

In search of critical numbers, consider $C' = 0$.

$$16x - \frac{2000}{x^2} = 0$$

$$16x = \frac{2000}{x^2}$$

Multiplying both sides of the equation by x^2 (to eliminate the fraction) yields

$$16x^3 = 2000$$

After dividing both sides by 16, the result is

$$x^3 = 125$$
$$x = 5$$

The value of h can now be found from $h = 100/x^2$.

$$h = \frac{100}{x^2} = \frac{100}{25} = 4$$

We conclude that the base should be made 5 feet by 5 feet and the height should be 4 feet in order to minimize cost.

To verify that C does indeed have a relative *minimum* at $x = 5$, note that

$$C''(x) = 16 + \frac{4000}{x^3}$$

and $C''(5) > 0$. Thus, by the second derivative test, C has a relative minimum at 5.   ◆

Given next are geometric formulas that you will need to use in some of the exercises that follow. The letters used in the formulas are A (area), P (perimeter), C (circumference),

V (volume), S (surface area), r (radius), l (length), w (width), h (height), and π (the irrational number "pi"—approximately 3.14).

1. *Rectangle*

$$A = lw$$
$$P = 2l + 2w$$

2. *Circle*

$$C = 2\pi r$$
$$A = \pi r^2$$

3. *Rectangular solid*

$$V = lwh$$
$$S = 2lw + 2lh + 2wh$$

4. *Cylinder*

$$V = \pi r^2 h$$
$$S = 2\pi r h \qquad \text{curved side } only$$
$$S = \pi r^2 \qquad \text{top or bottom } only$$

4.5   Exercises

1. **(HEATING METAL)** In Example 2 of Section 4.1, the function $T(x) = -3x^2 + 60x + 70$ indicated the temperature after x seconds of a metal tray undergoing a chemical finishing process. What is the hottest the metal gets during the process? (The temperature is in degrees Fahrenheit.)

2. **(ROCKET LAUNCH)** A rocket is launched vertically such that its distance s (in feet) from the ground at any time t (in seconds) is given by

$$s(t) = -16t^2 + 960t$$

   (a) When will the rocket reach its greatest height?
   (b) How high will the rocket travel before falling back down to the ground?

3. **(THROWING A BALL)** A tennis ball thrown straight up is $-16t^2 + 96t + 7$ feet above the ground after t seconds. How high will the ball go?

4. **(LEAPING PORPOISE)** The center of gravity of a leaping porpoise describes a parabola. Suppose a particular porpoise follows a path such that its height (in feet) above the water is given by $y = 3x - \frac{1}{4}x^2$. How high does this porpoise leap?

5. *(PROFIT)* Suppose that a manufacturer's profit on x items is $P(x) = 1300x - x^2$ dollars.
(a) How many items should be manufactured in order to maximize profit?
(b) What is that maximum profit?

6. *(REVENUE)* The revenue a company obtains from the sale of x items is $R(x) = 160 + 380x - 2x^2$ dollars. How many items must be sold to maximize revenue? Find the maximum revenue.

7. *(PRICE)* A manufacturer can supply x items at a price of $4x^2 - 200x + 2850$ dollars per item. How many items should be ordered from this manufacturer in order to minimize the price per item?

8. *(PROFIT)* A disgruntled employee determines that the company's profit on the production of x *hundred* units is $P(x) = 100x^2 - 1000x + 3000$ dollars. He plans to "get even with the company" by suggesting that it produce the number of items that he knows will minimize their profit. How many units will he recommend that the company produce?

9. *(MEDICINE CONCENTRATION)* When a pill such as aspirin or antihistamine is swallowed, the concentration of the medicine in the bloodstream begins at zero and increases toward a maximum concentration. The concentration then declines until there is none of the medicine present. Suppose the concentration K of a particular medicine t hours after being swallowed is

$$K = \frac{.03t}{1 + t^2}$$

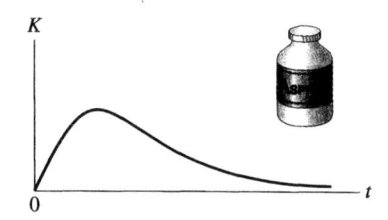

When is the concentration highest?

10. *(PATIO CONSTRUCTION)* Redo Example 3 assuming that the family has 200 feet of fence to use.

11. The sum of two positive numbers is 100. If their product is a maximum, what are the two numbers? (*Hint*: Let one number be x. What expression represents the other number?)

12. Determine two positive numbers whose product is 100 and whose sum is a minimum.

13. *(FENCING)* A farmer has 1600 feet of fencing to make a rectangular pen for his hogs. What should be the dimensions of the pen if he wants the largest area?

14. *(FENCING)* Determine the dimensions of the largest rectangular area that can be enclosed by 2000 meters of fence.

15. *(FENCING)* What is the smallest amount of fencing that can be used to enclose a rectangular garden having an area of 900 square feet?

16. *(FENCING)* A builder decides to fence in a rectangular area of 800 square feet behind his warehouse, using the wall of the building as one of the four sides (see the figure). What is the least amount of fencing necessary for the other three sides?

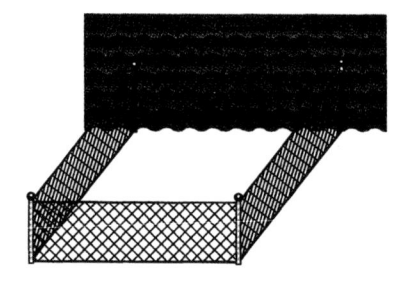

17. *(STORAGE FACILITY)* A storage company wants to create a storage facility by walling in a rectangular region containing 1728 square feet. It will also use walls to subdivide the region into five storage compartments (see the figure).

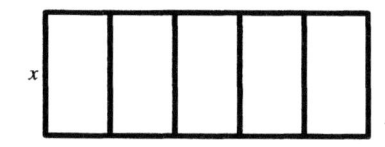

What should be the width (x) and length of the storage facility in order to use the least amount of material for the walls?

18. *(BOX SURFACE)* Determine the dimensions of a closed rectangular box with a square base if the volume must be 1000 cubic centimeters and the area of the outside surface is to be as small as possible.

19. *(BOX SURFACE)* An open rectangular box (that is, a box with no top) with a capacity of 36,000 cubic inches is needed. If the box must be twice as long as it is wide, what dimensions would require the least material?

20. (BOX SURFACE) Redo Exercise 19 assuming that the box will have a top. Approximate each dimension to the nearest tenth of an inch.

21. (FOLD-UP BOX) A square piece of cardboard 40 centimeters by 40 centimeters is used to make an open box as shown in the figure. A small square is cut from each corner of the cardboard, and then the sides are folded up. Determine the size of the cut (x in the figure) that will lead to the box of greatest volume. (*Note*: At some point it may appear that there are *two* answers, but only one of them will make sense given the size of the cardboard.)

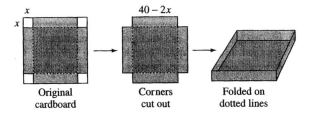

Original cardboard   Corners cut out   Folded on dotted lines

22. (FOLD-UP BOX) Redo Exercise 21 using a rectangular piece of cardboard 15 inches by 8 inches.

23. (GUTTER CONSTRUCTION) A builder plans to construct a gutter from a long sheet of metal by making two folds of equal size (see the figure). The folds are made to create perpendicular sides.

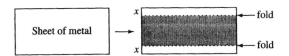

Sheet of metal

The metal is 28 centimeters wide and 500 centimeters long. How much (x) should be turned up for each side in order for the gutter to hold the most water?

24. (CYLINDRICAL CAN) A metal can is to be made in the form of a right circular cylinder that will contain 16π cubic inches. What radius of the can will require the least amount of metal (see the figure)? Note that there are three parts—a circular top, a circular bottom, and the curved side.

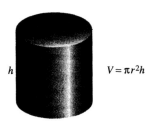

$V = \pi r^2 h$

25. (VELOCITY) If $s(t) = 35t + 9t^2 - t^3$ gives distance s in meters as a function of time t in seconds, determine the maximum velocity.

26. (MARGINAL COST) Consider the cost function

$$C(x) = 950 + 1000x + 30x^2 - x^3 \quad \text{dollars}$$

Determine the maximum marginal cost.

27. (PAPER SIZE) Determine the dimensions of the smallest size (that is, smallest area) rectangular piece of paper that satisfies all of the following conditions.
  (a) You can print 50 square inches of material on it (the shaded area in the figure).
  (b) There will be 2-inch margins on the top and bottom.
  (c) There will be 1-inch margins on the sides.

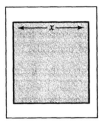

28. (LAND AREA) A corporation plans to locate its headquarters in a new rectangular one-story building to be constructed. They need 30,000 square feet of floor space. In addition, they would like to have a walkway 15 feet wide at the front and back of the building and a grass area 20 feet wide on the other two sides. Determine the length and width of the lot of smallest area that can be used. (Neglect the thickness of the walls.)

29. (FRUIT PRODUCTION) Julia wants to have a small but productive orchard. Experienced farmers have told her that if she plants 20 trees, she will get 24 bushels of fruit from each tree. But every additional tree she plants will cause crowding and result in an orchard-wide drop in yield of 1 bushel per tree. How many trees should she plant to get the greatest amount of fruit?

30. (TICKET SALES) Concert promoters estimate that they can sell 1200 tickets at $20 each. For every $1 the ticket price is lowered, they can sell 100 additional tickets.
(a) What ticket price maximizes the revenue?
(b) What is the maximum revenue?

31. (FENCING) A gardener wishes to fence in a rectangular area of 1728 square feet. She also wants to insert a fence that will divide the area into two rectangular subareas. The drawing shows that some fencing costs $4 per foot and some costs $2 per foot. Find the dimensions that will minimize the cost of the fencing.

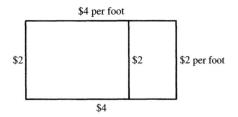

32. (STORAGE TANK) A rectangular open storage tank made with a square base is to have a volume of 768 cubic feet. Material for the base costs $6 per square foot, and that for the sides costs $2 per square foot. What dimensions will minimize the cost of materials?

33. (WINDOW AREA) Part of the side of a house is made in the shape of a 12-foot-high parabolic arch. The equation $y = 12 - x^2$ describes the arch. (x and y are in feet.) Determine the dimensions of the rectangular window of largest area that can be placed under the arch (see the figure).

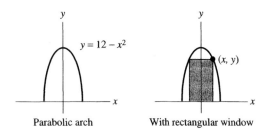

Parabolic arch   With rectangular window

Hint: Express the area of the window in terms of x and y. Then make a substitution that will leave the area as a function of x alone (that is, without y).

34. (RECTANGULAR AREA) Determine the dimensions of the rectangle of largest area that can be inscribed in a right triangle with base 10 centimeters and height 20 centimeters. *Hint*: See the figure. Use the two unlabeled points (dots) to determine the equation of the line through those points. Then use an approach similar to that suggested in the hint of Exercise 33.

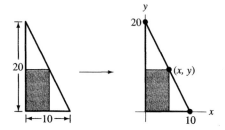

35. (PROFIT) Using the fact that profit is maximized when marginal revenue equals marginal cost (provided that $R'' < C''$), determine the number of units x that should be produced in order to maximize profit.
(a) Revenue: $R(x) = 80x - .02x^2$
     Cost: $C(x) = 130 + 74x - .01x^2$
(b) Revenue: $R(x) = 7x + .001x^2$
     Cost: $C(x) = 5x + .003x^2$

36. (PROFIT) Repeat Exercise 35, using
Revenue: $R(x) = 120x - .03x^2$
Cost: $C(x) = 250 + 30x - .02x^2$

37. (PROFIT) A manufacturer can sell x calculators at a price of $35 - .01x$ dollars *each*. It costs the manufacturer $14x + 10,000$ dollars to produce *all x of them*.
(a) How many calculators should the manufacturer make in order to maximize profit?
(b) What should be the price of each calculator in order to maximize profit?

38. (PROFIT) A manufacturer can sell x chess sets at a price of $42 - .02x$ dollars *each*. It costs $15x + 500$ dollars to produce *all x of them*.
(a) How many chess sets should the manufacturer produce in order to maximize profit?
(b) What should be the price of each chess set in order to maximize profit?

39. (AVERAGE COST) Given the cost function

$$C(x) = 192 + 7x + .03x^2$$

determine the number of units x that should be made in order to minimize the average cost per item, where

$$\overline{C} = \frac{C(x)}{x} \qquad \text{average cost}$$

40. (PROFIT) Suppose that you work for a corporation and the manager shows you the corporation's profit function $P(x) = 2000x - 8x^2$ dollars, where x is the number of units produced and sold. The manager thinks the company should try to sell 150 units, because the profit from the sale of 150 units is $120,000. What would be your advice to the manager?

41. (PROFIT) (See the figure below.) As you know, profit is maximum when marginal revenue equals marginal cost. You also know that the derivative can be interpreted as the slope of the tangent line. Combine these two ideas in order to determine the value of x (a, b, c, d, e, or f) for which profit is maximum.

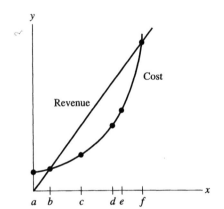

W 42. In Example 5, is 0 a critical number? After all, $C'(0)$ is undefined. Explain.

43. (TICKET WHOLESALING) An airline is selling tickets wholesale to a travel club. If the managers price the tickets at $140 each, they know they can sell 100 of them. They believe that for every $1 the ticket price is lowered, they can sell 2 more tickets.
  (a) What should be their ticket price in order to maximize revenue?
  (b) How many tickets will they sell in order to maximize revenue?
  (c) Determine the maximum revenue.

W 44. (FOLLOW-UP) Based on the statement of Exercise 43, the answer obtained in part (c) is indeed the maximum reve-

nue. However, the maximum revenue is only $4050 more than the revenue from selling 100 tickets at $140 each. Thus the airline is, in effect, selling the extra 90 tickets at only $45 each. (You can check the arithmetic.)
  (a) Give a scenario in which selling the extra 90 tickets at $45 each is a good decision.
  (b) Give a scenario in which selling the extra 90 tickets at $45 each is a bad decision.

45. (CLEARING THE LUNGS) When a person coughs to clear the lungs, pressure causes the radius of the trachea (windpipe) to decrease. According to Poiseuille's law, the rate A at which air flows through a trachea of radius b is

$$A = k(br^4 - r^5)$$

where k is a constant and r is the radius, which varies as the trachea contracts during coughing. Determine the radius that results in maximum air flow when clearing the lungs.

46. (TRIANGULAR AREA) Consider the right triangle shown. Determine how large x should be in order to maximize the area of the triangle. ($A = \frac{1}{2}bh$, b = base, h = height.)

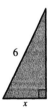

47. (COMBINED AREA) A wire 50 centimeters long is cut into two pieces. One piece (call its length x) will be bent to form a square. The other piece (of length $50 - x$) will be bent to form a circle. How much wire should be used for the square if the total area (square *plus* circle) is to be the smallest possible?

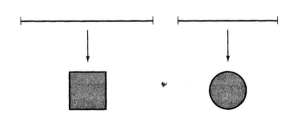

48. (*LAFFER CURVE*) The following Laffer-Curve function gives the amount of tax revenue received, $R(x)$, as a function of the tax rate.

$$R(x) = \frac{400x - 4x^2}{8 + x} \quad \text{billion dollars}$$

where x is the tax rate (expressed as a percent). According to this function, what tax rate, to the nearest tenth of a percent, will yield the maximum revenue?

 ## TECHNOLOGY *EXERCISES*

1. (*HEATING*) A metal pipe is heated in a furnace and then cooled. The entire process takes 33 minutes. The temperature of the pipe is

$$T(x) = -1.5x^2 + 50x + 70 \quad °F$$

where x is the number of minutes.

(a) Use the graph of function T to determine the maximum temperature, to the nearest degree, that the pipe reaches during the process.

(b) When, to the nearest minute, is the temperature of the pipe 350°F?

(c) When is the temperature of the pipe above 350°F?

2. (*PROFIT*) The weekly profit that a small company makes from the sale of x items is

$$P(x) = -2x^2 + 120x - 471 \quad \text{dollars} \quad 0 \le x \le 50$$

Use the graph of function P to determine the maximum profit possible.

3. (*FOLD-UP BOX*) Each side of a square piece of cardboard is 65 centimeters. A box of the type in Exercise 21 is made from it. The volume of the resulting box is

$$V(x) = x(65 - 2x)^2$$

Use the graph of function V to determine, to the nearest hundred cubic centimeters, the greatest-volume box that we can create. Keep in mind that the V values are huge and the range must be set accordingly.

4. (*TRIANGLE AREA*) Consider an isosceles triangle with perimeter 24 centimeters. We wish to determine how long the sides should be in order to maximize the area. This means that we need to establish a function that gives the area and then determine a side length that maximizes the function. To proceed, call the length of each of the two equal sides x. This leaves $24 - 2x$ for the third side (see the left portion of the figure on the next page). From

$$A = \frac{1}{2}bh \quad \text{area of a triangle}$$

we have

$$A = \frac{1}{2}(24 - 2x)h$$

$$A = (12 - x)h$$

To eliminate h, consider the left half of the triangle, and apply the Pythagorean theorem to obtain $h = \sqrt{24x - 144}$.

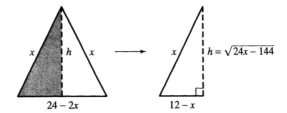

Thus, we have

$$A(x) = (12 - x)\sqrt{24x - 144}$$

Use the graph of A to determine, to the nearest integer, the value of x that maximizes A.

5. **(LAFFER CURVE)** Laffer Curves give the amount of tax revenue, $R(x)$, as a function of the tax rate. The curves vary with economic assumptions. Consider the Laffer-Curve function

$$R(x) = \frac{600x - 6x^2}{12 + x} \quad \text{billion dollars}$$

where x is the tax rate (expressed as a percent). Graph function R, using x in $[0, 100]$ and y in $[0, 400]$.

(a) Find, to the nearest billion dollars, the maximum tax revenue.

(b) Find, to the nearest tenth of a percent, the tax rate that yields the maximum revenue.

4.6 | *ELASTICITY OF DEMAND*

The demand for goods and services is usually affected by changes in the price of those goods and services. For example, when the price of automobiles increases, the demand for them decreases. Manufacturers sometimes offer rebates as a way to decrease auto prices and thus increase demand.

The demand for some goods and services is more sensitive to price increases than the demand for others. A relatively small price increase of 5% on a candy bar (say from 40¢ to 42¢) will have little effect on the demand for candy bars. On the other hand, a 5% increase in the cost of a home loan (which would create correspondingly higher monthly payments) will have a significant, decreasing effect on the demand for new homes. By contrast, the demand for essential surgery is not sensitive to price increases.

It is natural in business to be concerned about the sensitivity of demand changes to price changes. Calculus provides the **elasticity of demand** (E), which gives a numerical measure of the relative sensitivity of percent changes in demand to percent changes in price.

The formula is given next, followed by the derivation of the formula and some examples.

Elasticity of Demand

$$E = -\frac{p}{x} \cdot \frac{dx}{dp}$$

where

E = elasticity of demand
x = demand (quantity)
p = price per unit

Elasticity E is the percent change in demand that will occur for every 1% that the price is changed.

The elasticity formula can be derived by considering a comparison of the percent change in demand, $\Delta x/x$, with the percent change in price, $\Delta p/p$. The ratio is

$$\frac{\dfrac{\Delta x}{x}}{\dfrac{\Delta p}{p}}$$

which simplifies to

$$\frac{p}{x} \cdot \frac{\Delta x}{\Delta p}$$

Assuming that x is a differentiable function of p,

$$\lim_{\Delta p \to 0} \frac{\Delta x}{\Delta p} = \frac{dx}{dp}$$

If we let $\Delta p \to 0$ for the entire ratio, we obtain the instantaneous rate of change of the ratio, which we call elasticity E.

$$E = \lim_{\Delta p \to 0} \frac{p}{x} \cdot \frac{\Delta x}{\Delta p} = \frac{p}{x} \cdot \lim_{\Delta p \to 0} \frac{\Delta x}{\Delta p} = \frac{p}{x} \cdot \frac{dx}{dp}$$

Ordinarily, when the price p increases, the quantity demanded x decreases. When the price decreases, the quantity demanded increases. Graphically, this relationship between x and p would appear as a curve with a negative slope. (See Figure 34.) The derivative dx/dp is the slope of the tangent to the curve and is negative. It follows that the expression derived for the elasticity is always negative. Because economists prefer to use positive values here, *a minus is placed in front of the formula in order that the E values will be positive.* Thus

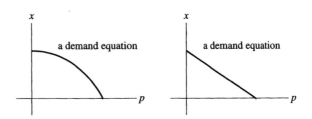

Figure 34 When price *p* increases, the quantity demanded *x* decreases.

$$E = -\frac{p}{x} \cdot \frac{dx}{dp}$$

EXAMPLE 1 **ELASTICITY OF DEMAND**

APPLIED

Suppose the demand equation is $x = 180 - 2p$.

(a) Determine the elasticity of demand.

(b) Calculate the elasticity for $p = 30$.

(c) Calculate the elasticity for $p = 70$.

SOLUTION **(a)** Elasticity E is computed using

$$E = -\frac{p}{x} \cdot \frac{dx}{dp}$$

From the demand equation $x = 180 - 2p$, it follows that

$$\frac{dx}{dp} = -2$$

Two substitutions can now be made into the formula for E. We can use -2 for dx/dp and $180 - 2p$ for x. The result is

$$E = -\frac{p}{180 - 2p}(-2) \qquad \text{or} \qquad E = \frac{2p}{180 - 2p}$$

(b) When $p = 30$ (that is, the price is $30),

$$E = \frac{2(30)}{180 - 2(30)} = \frac{60}{120} = .5$$

An elasticity of 1/2 means that a price increase of 1% will result in a 1/2% decrease in demand. This is an example of **inelastic demand,** in which the magnitude of the change in demand is less than that of the change in price.

(c) When $p = 70$ (that is, the price is $70),

$$E = \frac{2(70)}{180 - 2(70)} = \frac{140}{40} = 3.5$$

An elasticity of 3.5 means that for every 1% the price is increased, there will be a 3.5% decrease in demand. This is an example of **elastic demand,** in which the magnitude of the change in demand is greater than that of the change in price.   ◆

The example leads naturally to the three classifications of elasticity.

If $E < 1$, the demand is called *inelastic*.

If $E > 1$, the demand is called *elastic*.

If $E = 1$, the demand has *unit elasticity*.

The case of **unit elasticity** was not covered in Example 1. If $E = 1$, then a price increase of 1% will cause a 1% change (decrease) in demand.

EXAMPLE 2   *INELASTIC DEMAND*

APPLIED

Suppose the demand equation is $x = 120 - 5p$. Determine for what prices the demand will be inelastic.

SOLUTION   The demand will be inelastic when $E < 1$; that is, when

$$-\frac{p}{x}\frac{dx}{dp} < 1$$

Here $x = 120 - 5p$, from which

$$\frac{dx}{dp} = -5$$

Upon substituting -5 for dx/dp and $120 - 5p$ for x in the inequality, we obtain

$$-\frac{p}{120 - 5p}(-5) < 1 \qquad \text{or} \qquad \frac{5p}{120 - 5p} < 1$$

Multiply both sides of the simplified inequality by $120 - 5p$, which is positive for all p between 0 and 24. (Also, $120 - 5p$ is the *quantity x*, which cannot be negative.) The result:

$$5p < 120 - 5p$$
$$10p < 120$$
$$p < 12$$

Thus, the demand will be inelastic when the price is less than $12.   ◆

Some fascinating results can be obtained now by considering the fact that revenue equals quantity x times price p. That is,

$$R = x \cdot p$$

If demand is inelastic (E < 1), then raising prices will increase revenue. Why? Because demand will decrease by a smaller percentage than prices increase, when demand is inelastic. As a result, the product xp (that is, revenue) will actually increase.

Similarly, *if demand is elastic (E > 1), then lowering prices will increase revenue.* It is left for you to construct the explanation (see Exercise 18).

It follows that *revenue is maximum when demand is of unit elasticity (E = 1).* The graph in Figure 35 may clarify this point.

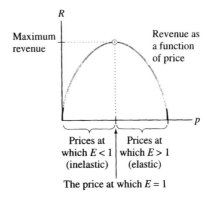

Figure 35 Revenue is maximum when demand is of unit elasticity

In summary,

1. If demand is inelastic, then *raising* prices will increase revenue.
2. If demand is elastic, then *lowering* prices will increase revenue.
3. Total revenue is *maximum* when demand is of unit elasticity.

4.6   Exercises

In Exercises 1–4, determine the elasticity of demand for the given function at the given price.

1. $x = 50 - 3p$, $p = 10$ **2.** $x = 78 - 5p$, $p = 12$

3. $x = \sqrt{200 - p}$, $p = 40$ **4.** $x = \sqrt{300 - 2p}$, $p = 85$

In Exercises 5–8, determine the elasticity of demand for the given function.

5. $x = 321 - p^2$ **6.** $x = 400 - .5p^2$

7. $x = \dfrac{200}{p}$ **8.** $x = \dfrac{100}{\sqrt{p}}$

9. **(LOTTERY TICKET SALES)** A state lottery believes that the number of tickets it can sell weekly is given by $x = 500{,}000 - 40{,}000p^2$ for $1 \leq p \leq 3$, where p is the price in dollars.
   (a) How many tickets can be sold at $1.00 each?
   (b) How many tickets can be sold at $3.00 each?
   (c) Find the elasticity of demand when tickets are priced at $2.00 each.

10. **(DEMAND FOR LUMBER)** Suppose that the demand for a certain lumber is given by $x = 3000 - 250p$, for $0 \leq p \leq 12$, where p is the price in dollars per linear foot and x is the number of linear feet demanded. Determine the elasticity of demand when the price is $2.00 per linear foot.

11. **(UNIT ELASTICITY)** Suppose that the demand equation is $x = 800 - 16p$ for $0 \leq p \leq 50$. Determine the price at which the demand has unit elasticity.

12. **(ELASTICITY)** Determine the elasticity of demand E for the demand equation $x = a - pb$, where a and b are positive constants and p is between 0 and a/b.

13. **(PRICE INCREASE)** Suppose that the demand equation is $x = 112 - 8p$ for $0 \leq p \leq 14$. If the price is $3, what percent decrease in demand will be created by increasing the price 2%?

14. **(PRICE INCREASE)** Suppose that the demand equation is $x = 360 - 12p$ for $0 \leq p \leq 30$. If the price is $5, what percent decrease in demand will be created by increasing the price 3%?

15. **(PRICE INCREASE)** Suppose the demand is given by $x = 280 - 8p$ for $0 \leq p \leq 35$. At what price (p in dollars) will it be true that for every 1% the price is increased, there will be a 4% decrease in demand?

16. **(PRICE DECREASE)** Suppose the demand is given by $x = 300 - 15p$ for $0 \leq p \leq 20$. At what price (p in dollars) will it be true that for every 1% the price is decreased, there will be a .5% increase in demand?

W 17. **(PUBLIC RADIO)** A local public radio station has priced a year's membership at $30. Its demand equation is $x = 10{,}000 - 80p$ for $0 \leq p \leq 125$, where x is the number of members and p is the price (in dollars) per membership. Will raising the price to $35 increase or decrease revenue? Explain.

W 18. **(ELASTIC DEMAND)** Explain why lowering prices will increase revenue when demand is elastic.

W 19. **(WHOLESALER'S PRICE)** If a brick wholesaler is currently selling bricks at 90¢ each and the demand is given by $x = 10{,}000 - 80p$ for $0 \leq p \leq 125$ cents, should the wholesaler increase or decrease his price to increase revenue? Explain.

20. **(MAXIMUM REVENUE)** If the demand is $x = 432 - p^2$ for $0 \leq p \leq 20$ dollars, determine the price p at which revenue is maximum.

21. **(MAXIMUM REVENUE)** Suppose $x = 1200 - 20\sqrt{p}$ for $0 \leq p \leq 3600$ is the demand for a commodity having price p dollars. For what price will the revenue be maximum?

22. **(MINERAL CARTEL)** A mineral cartel is pricing its ore to maximize revenue. If the demand for the ore is $x = 50{,}000 - 40p$ tons when the price is p dollars per ton, what should be the price of a ton of ore?

23. **(CAR WASH)** A car wash company wants to price a wash at just the right price (p dollars) to maximize its revenue. If the weekly demand is known to be $1000 - 2p^3$, what should be its wash price?

 TECHNOLOGY *EXERCISES*

1. **(LOTTERY TICKET SALES)** A county lottery estimates that the number of tickets x it can sell at p dollars each is

$$x = 94{,}000 - 4250p^2 \qquad 1 \leq p \leq 4$$

Use the graph of the demand equation, with p in [1, 4] and x in [0, 100,000].

(a) How many tickets can be sold at $2.75 each?

(b) What price should the lottery charge in order to sell 80,225 tickets?

2. *(ELASTICITY)* Graph the elasticity function

$$E = \frac{2.1p}{1315 - p}$$

to determine the price p (in dollars and cents) at which revenue is maximum. Use p in $[0, 600]$ and E in $[0, 2]$. Zoom and trace as needed.

Key Terms and Ideas

increasing function	concavity	absolute maximum
decreasing function	concave down	absolute minimum
relative maximum point	concave up	applied maximum/minimum problems
relative minimum point	point of inflection	elasticity of demand
critical number	second derivative test	inelastic demand
first derivative test	sketching a graph	elastic demand
relative extrema	absolute extrema	unit elasticity
relative extreme point		

Review Exercises for Chapter 4

Determine where each function given in Exercises 1–4 is increasing and where it is decreasing.

1. $f(x) = -2x^2$
2. $f(x) = x^3 - 5$

3. $g(x) = \dfrac{2x}{x - 1}$
4. $g(x) = \dfrac{100}{x}$

Find the critical numbers of each function in Exercises 5–10.

5. $f(x) = x^3 - 6x^2 - 36x + 5$ **6.** $f(x) = 10 - 2x^3$
7. $f(x) = 8\sqrt{x}$ **8.** $f(x) = 5 - \sqrt[3]{x}$

9. $f(x) = \dfrac{x}{x^2 + 1}$ **10.** $f(x) = 12x - 2x^{3/2}$

Determine all relative extreme points and sketch the graph of each function in Exercises 11–14.

11. $f(x) = x^3 - 3x^2 + 5$ **12.** $f(x) = -x^3 + 3x - 4$

13. $f(x) = 1 - x^{2/3}$ **14.** $f(x) = 1 + 6x^{2/3}$

In Examples 15–18, find all relative extreme points of the function, if any. Do not sketch the graph.

15. $f(x) = x^4 - 8x^3 + 17$ **16.** $f(x) = 75x - x^3$
17. $g(x) = 6x^{1/3} - 20$ **18.** $g(x) = 16x + 6x^{4/3}$

Determine where the graph of each function in Exercises 19–20 is concave up and where it is concave down.

19. $f(x) = 4x^3 - 11x + 1$ **20.** $f(x) = \dfrac{x - 2}{x}$

Find the point of inflection of each function in Exercises 21–22.

21. $f(x) = x^3 - 12x^2 + 17x - 4$

22. $f(x) = -x^3 - 9x^2 - 50x + 3$

23. Use the words *positive*, *negative*, and *zero* to complete the table. Refer to the graph of f shown.

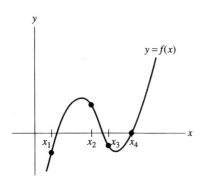

	$f(x)$	$f'(x)$	$f''(x)$
$x = x_1$	(a)	(b)	(c)
$x = x_2$	(d)	(e)	(f)
$x = x_3$	(g)	(h)	(i)
$x = x_4$	(j)	(k)	(l)

24. The questions that follow refer to the functions graphed in the figure below. Match the graph of the function—f or g or h—with the descriptive phrase.
(**a**) Increasing at an increasing rate.
(**b**) Increasing at a decreasing rate.
(**c**) Increasing at a constant rate.
(**d**) The slope of the curve is decreasing.
(**e**) The curve is concave down on (x_1, x_2).
(**f**) The second derivative is 0 on (x_1, x_2).

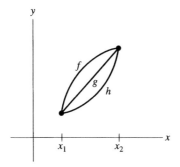

In Exercises 25–26, find the absolute extrema on the given interval.

25. $f(x) = x^3 + 3x^2 - 105x + 20$ on $[-8, 8]$

26. $f(x) = x^3 - 6x^2 + 9x + 2$ on $[1, 3.5]$

27. (**MINIMUM MARGINAL COST**) Suppose that the function $C(x) = x^3 - 42x^2 - 180x + 500$ gives the cost of producing x items. At what production level is the marginal cost minimum?

28. (**MAXIMUM REVENUE**) If the demand equation for your product is $p = 80 - .2x$, how many units should you sell in order to maximize your revenue?

29. (**SWIMMING POOL**) A wealthy family plans to have a rectangular swimming pool built on their estate grounds. If the perimeter of the pool will be 240 feet, what dimensions (length and width) will produce the pool of largest area?

30. (**PLAYGROUND AREA**) The parks department plans to fence in a 2304-square-meter rectangular area for a children's playground. What should be the dimensions in order to use the least amount of fencing?

31. (**ELASTICITY**) Determine the elasticity for $p = 10$ if the demand equation is $x = 200 - 4p$.

32. (**ELASTICITY**) If the demand equation is $x = 150 - 3p$, determine for what price the demand will be inelastic.

W 33. (**UNDULENT FEVER**) The graph shows the decline in the number of cases of undulent fever n in the United States. The disease was a serious concern until the 1960s. The graph is typical for diseases that have been virtually eradicated.

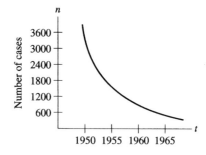

(**a**) Is dn/dt positive, negative, or zero? Explain.
(**b**) Is d^2n/dt^2 positive, negative, or zero? Explain.

34. (**INCREASING PROFIT**) Let $P(x) = 28x - x^2$ dollars be the profit from the manufacture and sale of x toys. When (for what x) is the profit increasing?

W 35. Is it possible for y to be increasing when dy/dt is decreasing? Explain.

W 36. Can the curve shown next be the graph of a function that has *exactly one* critical number? Explain.

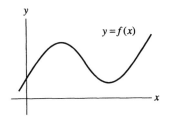

W 37. Consider $f(x) = 2x^4 + 3$. Is $(0, 3)$ a point of inflection? Explain.

W 38. Is the graph of $f(x) = x^3 - 9x^2 + 7x + 81$ concave up or concave down at the point $(5, 16)$? Explain.

39. Suppose $f''(x) = 12(x - 5)^2$. For what values of x is the graph of f concave up?

W 40. Consider $f(x) = 5x^{2/3} - x^{5/3}$. Determine whether the function has a point of inflection. *If it does*, find that point and explain why it is indeed a point of inflection. *If it does not*, explain why not.

41. Consider $f(x) = x^3(x - 7)^4$, which has three critical numbers. Two of the critical numbers are 0 and 7. Find the other critical number.

W 42. Draw simple graphs of four functions—one with a rounded relative maximum at x_1, one with a pointed relative maximum at x_1, one with a rounded relative minimum at x_1, and one with a pointed relative minimum at x_1. Study the concavity of each graph near x_1, considering the curve both to the left and the right of x_1. Compare your findings.

W 43. If $(x_1, f(x_1))$ is a point of inflection, then which dotted portion (a, b, or c) is the correct extension of the graph of f? Explain.

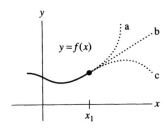

W 44. (***CORPORATE PROFITS***) The Bureau of Economic Analysis provides data on after-tax corporate profits (y) over a period of time (x). Consider the graph of corporate profits over the interval from 1987 to 1993 (see the figure).

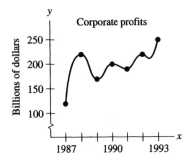

(a) What are the signs of y' and y'' from 1987 to 1988? Explain.

(b) Did absolute maximum corporate profits occur in 1988? Explain.

(c) Did absolute minimum corporate profits occur in 1987? Explain.

W 45. (***CONSUMER PRICE INDEX***) Data from the Bureau of Labor Statistics shows the change in the consumer price index (CPI) from 1983 to 1990. In the graph that follows, x is the year and y is the CPI (expressed as a percentage of the 1983 CPI). Describe the nature of the second derivative of the CPI function on the interval from 1983 to 1990, and explain what it means in this setting.

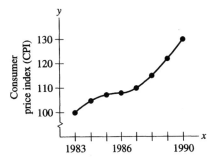

46. (***CERAMICS***) The temperature inside a kiln used to bake clay pottery is given by

$$T(x) = -.4x^2 + 32x + 73 \quad °F$$

Here x is the number of minutes the kiln is on and $0 \le x \le 80$. What is the hottest temperature reached?

47. *(MUSCLE CONTRACTION)* The speed S at which a muscle contracts depends on the weight W placed on it. The relationship is

$$S = \frac{a}{W + b} - c$$

where a, b, and c are positive constants. Obtain dS/dW and use it to show that S is a decreasing function; that is, as the weight on the muscle increases, the speed of contraction decreases.

48. *(FOYER CARPET)* The entrance foyer of a large house has the shape of a large semicircle described by $y = \sqrt{100 - x^2}$, where x and y are in feet. Determine the dimensions of the rectangular carpet of largest area that can be placed in the foyer.

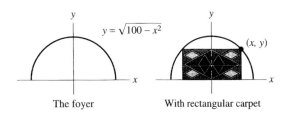

The foyer   With rectangular carpet

49. *(STORAGE FACILITY)* A builder wants to create a storage facility by walling in 486 square feet. She will also use a wall to subdivide the region into two storage compartments. Determine the width x to select in order to use the least amount of material for the walls.

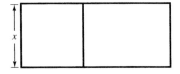

50. *(CABLE TV)* A cable TV company has 12,000 customers and charges $16 per month for basic service. The managers believe they will lose 400 customers for every dollar they raise the monthly charge. Determine the monthly charge that will maximize their revenue, and find that maximum revenue.

51. *(JOGGING TRACK)* A 1-mile jogging track is to be constructed. It will have two straight portions and two (equal) curved semicircular portions. Determine the radius x that should be chosen for the semicircles so that the area enclosed by the track will be the largest possible.

52. Shown next is the graph of $y = f'(x)$ for x in the interval $[-2, 7]$. For what values of x is the original function f decreasing?

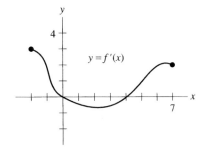

Chapter Projects and Essays

Many of the projects and essays lend themselves to group activity, although most can be completed by individual effort.

1. MATHEMATICAL WORDS

BACKGROUND   Each of the words listed below has been used in our study of calculus. (The sections in which the words were used are given in parentheses.) Clearly, these words are "mathematical," but each word also has a nonmathematical meaning and use.

a. derivative (3.1)   **b.** inflection (4.3)   **c.** implicit (3.8)

d. critical (4.1)   **e.** continuous (2.2)   **f.** infinite (2.4, 2.5)

g. limit (2.1)

THE PROJECT   Use a good English dictionary to look up each of the words listed. In each case, try to determine (and write down) the one nonmathematical meaning that seems to link it to the mathematical word. Proceed to compare the nonmathematical meaning with the mathematical meaning, and explain how they are similar.

2. AIRLINE TICKET SALES

BACKGROUND   Exercises 43 and 44 of Section 4.5 offer one simple example of an airline selling a block of tickets to a wholesaler at deep-discount prices in an attempt to maximize revenue. Perhaps you can get a better look at how the management of an airline thinks and acts as it tries to sell tickets in order to fly with its aircraft as nearly full as possible.

THE PROJECT   Contact a major airline, perhaps by starting with a local or 800 number from your phone book. Obtain the name of a person or office to contact by phone, letter, fax, or e-mail. That person will probably be in the public relations department or the marketing office. Try to obtain general information on how the airline maximizes revenue from ticket sales. When, how, and to what extent does it sell to wholesalers? Airlines regularly run discount sales to the public, with big ads in the newspaper and on radio and TV. How are such sales related to sales to wholesalers? Where does the airline fall between the extremes of carrying few passengers at high prices and carrying many passengers at very low prices?

EXPONENTIAL AND LOGARITHMIC FUNCTIONS

When a geologist found this pygmy mammoth (*Mammuthus exilis*) skeleton on Santa Rosa Island, California, he had stumbled across the remains of a long-extinct mammal. Paleontologists armed with carbon-14 detection instruments discovered that the creature had expired 10,000 years ago.

Carbon-14 occurs naturally in living things and gradually decays after life ceases. After measuring the remaining carbon-14 in an object, scientists can estimate its age by referring to the appropriate exponential function.

You are about to begin the study of some special kinds of functions—exponential functions and logarithmic functions. You will have the opportunity to consider the graphs of these functions and investigate the various limits and derivatives associated with them. An unusual number, called *e*, will be introduced. And, of course, a variety of interesting applications await you.

5.1 | *EXPONENTIAL FUNCTIONS*

There are many applications in which the rate of growth of a quantity is proportional to the amount of the quantity present. In such cases, as the amount increases, so does the rate of growth. The expression *exponential growth* is used to describe these situations. Bacteria in a laboratory culture provide an example of such exponential growth. When the compounding of interest is done in a special manner called "continuous compounding," the balance in the account grows exponentially.

Exponential functions provide the means to study such growth situations. The expressions involved have a form we have not seen yet—the base is constant and the exponent is a variable. Here are two examples.

$$f(x) = 3^x \qquad y = .5^x$$

(Notice how 3^x differs from x^3, which has a variable base and a constant exponent.)

In general,

Exponential Functions

An exponential function f has the form

$$f(x) = b^x$$

where x is any real number, $b > 0$, and $b \neq 1$.

Because the exponent x can be any real number, the domain of f is all the real numbers.

The graph of an exponential function such as $f(x) = 3^x$ provides a picture of these new functions and a chance to visualize exponential growth. In Table 1, we have selected values for x, computed the corresponding y values (3^x), and then passed a smooth curve through the points. See Figure 1.

If desired, points between any two of these points can be obtained by using the $\boxed{y^x}$ key of a calculator or the $\boxed{\wedge}$ key of a graphing calculator. (See Table 2.) The 3^x values are approximate, of course.

x	$y = 3^x$
0	1
1	3
2	9
-1	1/3
-2	1/9

Table 1

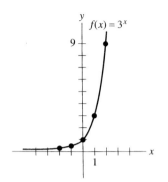

x	3^x
.5	1.73
1.4	4.66
$-.6$	.52
-1.2	.27

Table 2

Figure 1 An exponential function

A graph of $f(x) = .5^x$ can be obtained in a similar manner. Figure 2 shows some points and the graph. This graph illustrates *exponential decay* rather than exponential growth.

x	$y = .5^x$
0	1
1	.5
2	.25
-1	2
-2	4
-3	8

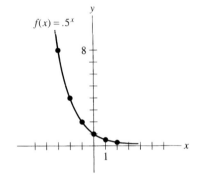

Figure 2

Note

When evaluating an expression such as $4 \cdot 3^x$ for different values of x, keep in mind the usual order of operations—exponents are applied before multiplication is carried out, unless *parentheses* indicate otherwise. Thus, for $x = 2$, we have $4 \cdot 3^x = 4 \cdot 3^2 = 4 \cdot 9 = 36$.

One particular exponential function stands out because of its calculus properties and its widespread natural applications. In fact, it is sometimes called "*the* exponential function." The base of this exponential function is the irrational number "*e*," which is approximately equal to 2.7182818284.

$$e \approx 2.718$$

A study of the expression

$$\left(1 + \frac{1}{n}\right)^n$$

will lead to a formal definition of the number e. Using a calculator to study the value of the expression for various values of n, observe how the value of the expression gets closer and closer to e as n gets larger and larger.

n	$\left(1 + \dfrac{1}{n}\right)^n$
1	2
10	2.59374246
100	2.704813829
1000	2.716923932
10,000	2.718145927
1,000,000	2.718280469
1,000,000,000	2.718281827

A formal definition of e, based on our work, is given next.

Definition of e

$$e = \lim_{n \to \infty} \left(1 + \frac{1}{n}\right)^n$$

The number e was named by Leonhard Euler (1707–1783), the great Swiss mathematician, who used the definition to calculate e to 23 decimal places.

Note

If you find it strange that e has a formal definition of an algebraic nature, recall that the number π (which is approximately 3.14) is defined as the ratio of the circumference of a circle to its diameter—that is, $\pi = C/d$.

The exponential function with base e is written

$$f(x) = e^x$$

Figure 3
Leonhard Euler (1707–1783)

Figure 4 shows the graph of $f(x) = e^x$, where x can be any real number. The e^x values are approximate and can be obtained by hand (using 2.7 for e) or by using the $\boxed{e^x}$ key of a calculator or graphing calculator.

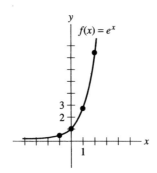

$y = e^x$

x	y
0	1
1	2.7
2	7.4
−1	.4

Figure 4 The exponential function $f(x) = e^x$

From the graph you can see that as x gets larger and larger, e^x also gets larger and larger. In fact,

$$\lim_{x \to \infty} e^x = \infty$$

From this fact it follows that

$$\lim_{x \to \infty} \frac{1}{e^x} = 0 \qquad \text{or, equivalently,} \qquad \lim_{x \to \infty} e^{-x} = 0$$

The graph also shows that

$$\lim_{x \to -\infty} e^x = 0$$

Of course, the usual properties of exponents apply to expressions involving e.

$$e^x \cdot e^y = e^{x+y} \qquad\qquad (e^x)^y = e^{xy}$$

$$\frac{e^x}{e^y} = e^{x-y} \qquad\qquad e^{-x} = \frac{1}{e^x}$$

$$e^1 = e \qquad\qquad e^0 = 1$$

EXAMPLE 1   Simplify the expressions.

(a) $5 - 2e^0$ **(b)** $\dfrac{e^x}{e}$ **(c)** $(e^{3t})^2$

SOLUTION   **(a)** $5 - 2e^0 = 5 - 2 \cdot 1 = 5 - 2 = 3$

(b) $\dfrac{e^x}{e} = \dfrac{e^x}{e^1} = e^{x-1}$ **(c)** $(e^{3t})^2 = e^{3t \cdot 2} = e^{6t}$ ◆

Compound Interest and *e*

We will now see how the number *e* is related to compound interest. Suppose you deposit *P* dollars into an account that pays annual interest rate *r*, with interest compounded *m* times a year. After *t* years the balance *A* in the account will be

$$A = P\left(1 + \frac{r}{m}\right)^{mt}$$

When interest is compounded, the depositor receives interest on the interest as well as on the original investment (principal). The more compoundings per year, the greater the balance will become. The short table below demonstrates this idea for an investment of $1000 at 7% per year.

m compoundings per year	balance after 1 year
1 (annually)	$1070.00
4 (quarterly)	$1071.86
12 (monthly)	$1072.29
365 (daily)	$1072.50

It is natural to wonder what might result if there were thousands or millions of compoundings. The number *e* enters the picture when an infinite number of compoundings per year—that is, "continuous compounding"—is considered. We then have

$$\lim_{m \to \infty} P\left(1 + \frac{r}{m}\right)^{mt}$$

A few manipulations are needed to obtain the desired result.

$$\lim_{m \to \infty} P\left(1 + \frac{r}{m}\right)^{mt} = P \cdot \lim_{m \to \infty}\left(1 + \frac{r}{m}\right)^{mt} = P\left[\lim_{m \to \infty}\left(1 + \frac{r}{m}\right)^{\frac{m}{r}}\right]^{rt}$$

Let *m/r* be equal to *n*. Then *r/m* is $1/n$ and $n \to \infty$ as $m \to \infty$. We obtain

$$\lim_{m \to \infty} P\left(1 + \frac{r}{m}\right)^{mt} = P\left[\lim_{n \to \infty}\left(1 + \frac{1}{n}\right)^{n}\right]^{rt} = Pe^{rt}$$

since the limit inside the brackets is *e*.

In summary, if *P* dollars is invested at annual interest rate *r* **compounded continuously** for *t* years, the total amount accrued will be $A = Pe^{rt}$.

> ## Continuous Compounding
>
> $$A = Pe^{rt}$$
>
> P = amount invested
> r = annual interest rate
> t = number of years
> A = amount accrued

The formula $A = Pe^{rt}$ can be used to show that with continuous compounding, the $1000 at 7% would become $1072.51 in 1 year. The interest is just slightly more than with daily compounding.

Such growth of money is but one example of **exponential growth** applications that involve formulas of this type. When the amount present *decreases* instead, then the application is called **exponential decay.**

Note

In the examples that follow, the value of e^x for specific values of x is determined by a calculator. (Alternatively, there is Table 1 at the back of the book.)

EXAMPLE 2   CONTINUOUS COMPOUNDING

A retiree invests $10,000 at 8% interest per year compounded continuously. How much will she have after 3 years?

SOLUTION   Use the formula for continuous compounding.

$$A = Pe^{rt}$$

with

$$P = \$10,000 \qquad t = 3 \qquad r = .08 \qquad \text{Express the percent as a decimal.}$$

The result is

$$A = \$10,000 \cdot e^{(.08)(3)} = \$10,000 \cdot e^{.24} \approx \$10,000(1.2712) = \$12,712$$

After 3 years she will have $12,712. *Also,* note that calculators and tables provide only *approximate* values of $e^{.24}$ and most other e^x values. This is why the "approximately equal to" symbol was used here.   ♦

EXAMPLE 3   PRESENT VALUE

How much should you invest now at 7% interest per year, compounded continuously, in order to have $6000 in 5 years?

SOLUTION   Use the continuous compounding formula.

$$A = Pe^{rt}$$

with

$$A = \$6000 \qquad r = .07 \qquad t = 5$$

The result is

$$\$6000 = P \cdot e^{(.07)(5)}$$
$$\$6000 = Pe^{.35}$$

Thus, the amount that must be invested, P, is

$$P = \frac{\$6000}{e^{.35}} \approx \frac{\$6000}{1.419} \quad \text{or} \quad \$4228$$

You must invest $4228 now at 7% in order to have $6000 in 5 years.

This amount invested, $4228, is known as the **present value.** In general, the present value is the amount that must be invested now in order to have a specified amount at some time in the future.   ♦

Here is a list of other applications of exponential functions that involve essentially the same formula used for continuous compounding. In each case, the rate of change is proportional to the amount present.

1. Increase or decrease in the population of a city

2. Increase or decrease in the number of bacteria in a culture

3. Decrease in the amount of radioactive material present

4. Effect of insecticides on an insect population

5. Epidemic spread of a disease

Because a knowledge of logarithms is usually needed to solve the problems, these applications will be presented in the next section, after logarithms have been introduced.

Logistic Growth

Logistic growth functions describe situations in which the environment inhibits what would otherwise be unrestricted exponential growth. The population begins to grow exponentially but then levels off because of such problems as overcrowding and lack of food. In many instances it is more realistic to assume logistic growth rather than unlimited growth.

A typical logistic growth curve is shown in Figure 5.

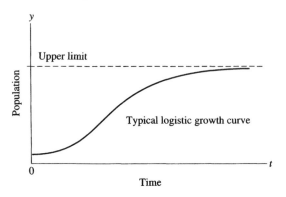

Figure 5 A logistic growth curve

EXAMPLE 4   LOGISTIC GROWTH

The fish population in a breeding lake is growing according to the logistic growth function

$$y = \frac{2000}{1 + 49e^{-.3t}}$$

where y is the number of fish present after t months.

(a) How many fish are present at the beginning?

(b) How many fish are present after 10 months?

(c) What is the maximum number of fish supported by this lake?

SOLUTION   **(a)** At the beginning, $t = 0$, and the logistic growth function has the value

$$y = \frac{2000}{1 + 49 \cdot e^0} = \frac{2000}{50} = 40$$

There are 40 fish at the beginning.

(b) After 10 months, $t = 10$, and the logistic growth function has the value

$$y = \frac{2000}{1 + 49e^{-3}}$$

By calculator, $e^{-3} \approx .05$, and

$$y \approx \frac{2000}{1 + 2.45} \approx 580$$

Approximately 580 fish are present after 10 months.

(c) The maximum number of fish would exist, in theory, when $t \to \infty$. Accordingly, we consider the limit

$$\lim_{t \to \infty} e^{-.3t} = \lim_{t \to \infty} \frac{1}{e^{.3t}}$$

As $t \to \infty$, so does $.3t \to \infty$. This means that $e^{.3t} \to \infty$ also. The expression $1/e^{.3t}$ approaches 0 as $e^{.3t}$ approaches ∞. Now we can determine the limit of y as t approaches ∞.

$$\lim_{t \to \infty} \frac{2000}{1 + 49e^{-.3t}} = \frac{2000}{1 + 49 \cdot 0} = \frac{2000}{1} = 2000$$

We conclude that the maximum number of fish this lake will support is 2000. (See Figure 6.) ◆

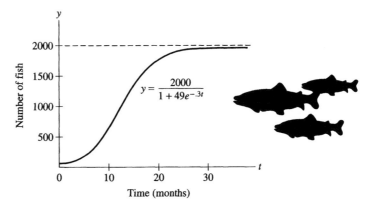

Figure 6 The logistic growth curve for the fish population in a breeding lake

Learning Curve

Psychologists have found that people often learn very quickly at first. Then the rate of learning slows. Eventually, the person reaches a plateau that he or she cannot exceed. For example, someone learning typing will eventually reach a speed (words per minute) that he or she is unlikely to exceed. The general equation of such **learning curves** is

$$y = c(1 - e^{-kt})$$

where t is the time spent learning and y is the amount learned. The plateau, or upper limit, of the amount learned is c. Figure 7 shows a graph of a learning curve.

Exercise 37 provides an opportunity to study a specific learning curve.

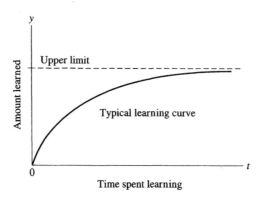

Figure 7

5.1   Exercises

Sketch a graph of each function in Exercises 1–8.

1. $f(x) = 2^x$

2. $f(x) = 4^x$

3. $f(x) = 2^{-x}$

4. $f(x) = 3^{-x}$

5. $y = .4^x$

6. $y = .6^x$

7. $y = 3 \cdot 2^x$

8. $y = 2 \cdot 3^x$

Sketch a graph of each function in Exercises 9–16.

9. $f(x) = e^x$

10. $f(x) = e^{-x}$

11. $f(x) = e^{x+1}$

12. $f(x) = e^{x-1}$

13. $y = 1 + e^x$

14. $y = 2 + e^x$

15. $y = e^x - 2$

16. $y = e^x - 1$

Simplify each expression in Exercises 17–26.

17. $4e^0$

18. $9e^0$

19. $2 - 7e^0$

20. $2e^0 - 10$

21. $\dfrac{e^{2x}}{e}$

22. $\dfrac{e}{e^x}$

23. $e^{3x}e$

24. $e^{7x}e$

25. $(e^{2x})^3$

26. $(e^{3x})^2$

27. (*CONTINUOUS COMPOUNDING*) If $1000 is invested at 8% annual interest compounded continuously, how much will accrue in 5 years?

28. (*CONTINUOUS COMPOUNDING*) If $4000 is invested at 7% annual interest compounded continuously, how much will accrue in 3 years?

29. (*PRESENT VALUE*) A couple wishes to invest now for their young child's college education. How much should they invest at 9% interest per year compounded continuously in order to have $30,000 in 14 years?

30. (*PRESENT VALUE*) Meiko is setting aside money for a future vacation trip. How much should she invest at 7% interest per year compounded continuously so that she will have $2500 in 3 years?

31. (*MUTUAL FUND*) A mutual fund claims that its portfolio value grew at the annual rate of 12% compounded continuously from January 1986 to January 1995. If $10,000 had been invested in the fund in January 1986 what would it have been worth in January 1995?

32. (*REAL ESTATE*) A corporation has purchased its new headquarters for $40,000,000. If the building appreciates at the rate of 6% per year compounded continuously, what will be its value 10 years after purchase?

33. *(FISH POPULATION)* The fish population of a lake is growing according to the logistic growth function

$$y = \frac{1500}{1 + 29e^{-.4t}}$$

where y is the number of fish present after t months.

(a) How many fish are present at the beginning?

(b) How many fish are present after 5 months?

(c) What is the maximum number of fish that can be supported by this lake?

34. *(BACTERIA GROWTH)* A bacteria culture is growing according to the logistic growth function

$$y = \frac{10,000,000}{1 + 5000e^{-.1t}}$$

Here y is the number of bacteria present at t hours.

(a) To the nearest thousand, how many bacteria are present initially?

(b) How large can this culture become?

W (c) Assuming the culture is in a petri dish with a food supply, explain why the growth is logistic rather than exponential.

35. *(FRUIT GROWTH)* The diameter of a fruit grows logistically. For one variety of plums,

$$y = \frac{50}{1 + 24e^{-.36t}}$$

where y is the diameter of the plum in millimeters after t days.

(a) To the nearest millimeter, what is the diameter of a plum after 10 days?

(b) What is the diameter of a full-grown plum?

W (c) Explain why this fruit growth is more accurately described by a logistic function rather than by an exponential function.

36. *(FRUIT FLY BREEDING)* A biology student is breeding fruit flies in a closed container. Suppose the fly population grows according to

$$y = \frac{20}{1 + 9e^{-.2t}}$$

where y is the number of flies present after t days.

(a) How many fruit flies are present after 2 weeks?

(b) How many fruit flies will there be eventually?

(c) Complete the table below. Then use these points, along with the information from parts (a) and (b), to sketch a rough graph of the function.

t	y
0	
6	
10	
20	
25	

37. *(LEARNING TEST)* To test learning, a psychologist asks people to memorize a long sequence of digits, checking with them every few minutes to see how many digits they have memorized. Assume the learning is described by

$$y = 18(1 - e^{-.3t})$$

where y is the number of digits memorized and t is the time in minutes.

(a) Using the equation given, verify that the number of digits memorized at the beginning is zero.

(b) Approximately how many digits will people have memorized in 1, 2, 3, 4, 5, and 10 minutes?

(c) According to the equation, what is the upper limit on the number of digits people can memorize in this manner?

(d) Sketch a rough graph of $y = 18(1 - e^{-.3t})$ based on your answers to parts (a), (b), and (c).

38. *(PROFIT)* If $C(x) = 20xe^{-.03x}$ dollars is the cost of making x units, and $R(x) = 20xe^{.02x}$ dollars is the revenue from the sale of x units, determine the profit from the production and sale of 10 units.

39. *(COST)* Suppose x units of a product can be supplied at a cost of $30e^{-.02x}$ dollars each.

(a) Determine the cost function $C(x)$.

(b) Determine the cost of 5 units.

40. *(PROFIT)* If x lamps can be supplied at $20e^{-.03x}$ dollars each and sold at $25 each, find the profit function.

W 41. (S&P 500) Consider the Standard and Poor's 500 index of stocks, from mid-1983 to mid-1987.

year	points		year	points
1983	140		1985	180
1984	160		1986	220
1985	180		1987	310

Which years, 1983–1985 or 1985–1987, would you consider a time of exponential growth in the S&P 500 index? Explain.

42. The number e can also be defined as

$$e = \lim_{h \to 0} (1 + h)^{1/h}$$

Use h values such as 1, .1, .001, .00001, and .0000001 to create a convincing table, as was done for the original definition of e given in the text.

43. Consider $f(x) = b^x$ for $b = 1$ in order to see why b^x is not considered exponential when $b = 1$. Sketch a graph of $f(x) = b^x$ for $b = 1$.

W 44. Compare exponential growth functions and logistic growth functions.
(a) In what portion of the graph are they similar?
(b) In what portion of the graph are they different? Explain *how* they are different and *why* each type of function should be expected to behave the way it does.

W 45. Review the graph of the exponential function $f(x) = e^x$ (Figure 4).
(a) What is the nature of the tangent lines to the graph of f, and how is this related to the increasing and/or decreasing nature of the function?
(b) Comment on the concavity of the graph of $f(x) = e^x$.

W 46. Explain why many growth situations that might appear to be exponential are, in fact, logistic.

47. Graphs of $f(x) = 3^x$ and $f(x) = .5^x$ were presented early in the section. For each of these functions,
(a) Write the equation of its asymptote.
(b) Write the limit that shows why that line is indeed an asymptote.

In Exercises 48–51, plot the given points and indicate which of the following curves, *if any*, can be passed through them: exponential, logistic, learning.

48. (0,0), (1,1), (3,2), (6,3)

49. (0,1), (2,2), (4,4), (6,6), (8,7)

50. (0,2), (2,3), (4,6), (5,9)

51. (0,3), (3,5), (5,7), (7,8), (9,7)

TECHNOLOGY EXERCISES

1. (FRUIT FLY BREEDING) In Exercise 36, the function

$$y = \frac{20}{1 + 9e^{-.2x}}$$

gave the number of fruit flies y present after x days.

(a) Use the graph of the function to determine the approximate number of fruit flies present after 9 days. Use x in [0, 40] and y in [0, 30].

(b) Use the graph to determine how many days it will take before there will be 18 fruit flies.

(c) Is the x coordinate of the point of inflection closer to 6, 12, 18, 21, or 24?

(d) Write the equation of the horizontal asymptote.

2. Use the graphs of $y = xe^x$ and $y = 12 - x$ to find, to the nearest tenth, all x such that $xe^x = 12 - x$. Use x in $[-2, 10]$ and y in $[-2, 15]$.

3. Use the graphs of $y = .8e^x$ and $y = .3x^2 + 4$ to find, to the nearest tenth, all x such that $.8e^x = .3x^2 + 4$.

4. The ideas of *exponential growth* and *exponential decay* were mentioned briefly in the section. (They are covered more thoroughly in the next section.) Graph each pair of exponential functions, and decide which shows growth and which shows decay.

   (a) $y = 2^x$ and $y = 2^{-x}$ **(b)** $y = e^x$ and $y = e^{-x}$ **(c)** $y = 4^x$ and $y = .25^x$

5. Determine the value of

$$\lim_{x \to -\infty} e^x$$

by graphing $y = e^x$ and tracing the curve out to the left. Use the window $[-1, 5]$ for y.

6. In the section, we used a calculator to generate a table in order to approximate e. Another way to use the definition of e to obtain an approximation is to graph the function

$$y = \left(1 + \frac{1}{x}\right)^x$$

Then the y values can be studied as x gets larger and larger. Select x in the successively larger intervals $[0,100]$, $[0, 1000]$, $[0,10,000]$, $[0,100,000]$, and $[0,1,000,000]$. In each case, trace the curve all the way out to the right to obtain an approximation of e.

W **7.** Graph $y = e^{|x|}$.

   (a) Describe any symmetry that appears in the graph.

   (b) Explain how and why the graph differs from the graph of $y = e^x$.

8. Graph $y = e^{-x}$.

W **(a)** Explain how and why the graph differs from the graph of $y = e^x$.

   (b) At $x = 1.5$, the slope of the tangent line to the graph of $y = e^x$ is 4.48. What is the slope of the tangent line to the graph of $y = e^{-x}$ at $x = -1.5$?

5.2 | LOGARITHMIC FUNCTIONS

The study of **logarithms** is motivated by the need to solve exponential equations such as

$$b^x = a$$

for x. To be able to express x in terms of a and b in this setting requires a manipulation not yet presented. In fact, a new notation must be introduced in order to solve this problem. In view of this, we define $x = \log_b a$ to mean the same as $b^x = a$.

Logarithm Notation

$$x = \log_b a$$

means the same as

$$b^x = a$$

where $b > 0$, $b \neq 1$, and x is any real number.

The equation $x = \log_b a$ is read as "x is the *logarithm* of a to the base b" or as "x is the logarithm to the base b of a." Notice that the logarithm is equal to x, and x is the exponent. Thus, *a logarithm is an exponent*. In this case, x is the exponent to which b must be raised to produce a.

The number a results from raising positive base b to some power x. Consequently, a is always positive in $b^x = a$. In turn, this means that a must be positive in $x = \log_b a$. In other words, $\log_b a$ is defined only for $a > 0$.

The logarithm of a negative number (or zero) is not defined.

Here are some examples of equations written in logarithmic form, along with their equivalent exponential form.

logarithmic equation	exponential equation
$\log_3 9 = 2$	$3^2 = 9$
$\log_2 8 = 3$	$2^3 = 8$
$\log_4 1 = 0$	$4^0 = 1$
$\log_{10} .01 = -2$	$10^{-2} = .01$
$\log_e 20 \approx 3$	$e^3 \approx 20$
$\log_e e = 1$	$e^1 = e$
$\log_e 1 = 0$	$e^0 = 1$

Note

The two most popular bases for logarithms are 10 and e. Logarithms using base 10 are called **common logarithms,** and "$\log_{10}$" is written simply "log." When no base is written, base 10 is assumed. Logarithms using base e are called **natural logarithms,** and "$\log_e$" is written "ln."

$$\log_{10} x \quad \text{is written} \quad \log x$$

$$\log_e x \quad \text{is written} \quad \ln x$$

The equations $\log_e e = 1$ and $\log_e 1 = 0$ (given in the table above) are useful for making simplifications. They are restated next using the "ln" notation.

$$\ln e = 1$$

$$\ln 1 = 0$$

We now show the use of logarithms for manipulation and equation solving.

EXAMPLE 1   Solve for x: $3^x = 11$

SOLUTION   Rewriting the equation in logarithmic form will solve it for x.

$$x = \log_3 11 \qquad\qquad\qquad ◆$$

EXAMPLE 2   Solve for x: $10^{7x} = 9$

SOLUTION   Rewriting the exponential equation in logarithmic form will isolate the exponent $7x$.

$$7x = \log 9$$

$$x = \frac{\log 9}{7} \qquad \text{dividing both sides by 7} \qquad ◆$$

EXAMPLE 3   Solve for x: $4e^{5x} = 12$

SOLUTION   Recent experience makes it seem natural to want to write this equation in logarithmic form in order to solve for the exponent. But in order for us to rewrite an equation in logarithmic form, the base and exponent must be alone on one side. Indeed, that was the case in the definition of logarithm notation as well as in Examples 1 and 2. And, of course, it will also be the case here after both sides of the equation $4e^{5x} = 12$ are divided by 4.

$$\frac{4e^{5x}}{4} = \frac{12}{4}$$

$$e^{5x} = 3$$

$$5x = \ln 3 \qquad \text{logarithmic form}$$

$$x = \frac{\ln 3}{5} \qquad \text{dividing both sides by 5} \qquad ◆$$

EXAMPLE 4   Solve for x: $\ln 7x = 50.$

SOLUTION   Just as exponential equations can be solved by changing to logarithmic form, so can logarithmic equations be solved by changing to exponential form.

$$\log_e 7x = 50$$

$$7x = e^{50} \qquad \text{exponential form}$$

$$x = \frac{e^{50}}{7}$$

$\blacklozenge$

EXAMPLE 5   Solve for x: $3 \ln 2x = 10$.

SOLUTION   The logarithm must be alone before the equation can be changed to exponential form. Divide both sides by 3 to accomplish this.

$$3 \ln 2x = 10$$

$$\ln 2x = \frac{10}{3}$$

$$2x = e^{10/3} \qquad \text{exponential form}$$

$$x = \frac{e^{10/3}}{2}$$

$\blacklozenge$

A sketch of the graph of the **natural logarithm function** $f(x) = \ln x$ (where $x > 0$) can be made by obtaining several points and then passing a curve through them. Values for $\ln x$ can be obtained by using the ⟨**ln**⟩ key of a calculator or graphing calculator. If you do not use a calculator, it is easier to obtain points when the equation $y = \ln x$ is written in exponential form as $x = e^y$. Then you can select y values and obtain corresponding x values.

Figure 8 shows a table of points and a graph of the natural logarithm function.

$y = \ln x$

x	y
1	0
2.7	1
7.4	2
.4	-1

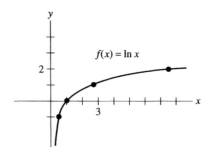

Figure 8 The natural logarithm function

It can be seen by looking at the graph of $y = \ln x$ (or by using a calculator) that as x gets larger and larger, so does $\ln x$ get larger and larger. In fact,

$$\lim_{x \to \infty} \ln x = \infty$$

This result will be needed in Chapter 7. The graph also shows that

$$\lim_{x \to 0^+} \ln x = -\infty$$

Two particularly important results are given next. Each is a restatement of the definition of the natural logarithm: that $y = \ln x$ means the same as $x = e^y$.

1. $e^{\ln x} = x$ for $x > 0$

2. $\ln e^x = x$ for all real x

The first result, $e^{\ln x} = x$, is true because when this exponential equation is written in its equivalent logarithmic form, it becomes $\log_e x = \ln x$, which is clearly a true statement. The second result, $\ln e^x = x$, is true because when it is rewritten in exponential form, it becomes $e^x = e^x$, which is a true statement.

EXAMPLE 6   Simplify each expression.   **(a)** $4 \ln e^7$ **(b)** $1 + e^{\ln 3x}$

SOLUTION   **(a)** $4 \ln e^7 = 4 \cdot \ln e^7$

                     $= 4 \cdot 7$ since $\ln e^x = x$

                     $= 28$

   (b) $1 + e^{\ln 3x} = 1 + 3x$ since $e^{\ln u} = u$ ◆

There are three important properties of logarithms that are useful in manipulations. These properties are stated next for natural logarithms, although they are also true for other bases. The numbers a and b must be positive; otherwise $\ln a$ and $\ln b$ would not be defined.

Properties of Logarithms

1. $\ln (a \cdot b) = \ln a + \ln b$

2. $\ln \dfrac{a}{b} = \ln a - \ln b$

3. $\ln a^p = p \cdot \ln a$

where $a > 0$, $b > 0$, and p is any real number.

The properties are used to expand or condense algebraic expressions. The expanding of algebraic expressions will prove particularly useful with differentiation in Section 5.4. The condensing of algebraic expressions will be useful for simplification.

EXAMPLE 7   Use the properties of logarithms to expand each expression.

(a) $\ln \dfrac{x + 2}{x + 5}$ (b) $\ln 3^{2x}$ (c) $\ln e^3\, x$

SOLUTION   (a) Using logarithm property 2 yields

$$\ln \frac{x + 2}{x + 5} = \ln (x + 2) - \ln (x + 5)$$

(b) Using logarithm property 3 yields

$$\ln 3^{2x} = 2x \ln 3$$

(c) $\ln e^3\, x = \ln e^3 + \ln x$ by logarithm property 1

              $= 3 + \ln x$ because $\ln e^x = x$ for any x ◆

EXAMPLE 8   Use properties of logarithms to condense each expression.

(a) $\ln 3 + \ln x$ (b) $\ln x - \ln 2$ (c) $2 \ln x$

SOLUTION   (a) $\ln 3 + \ln x = \ln 3x$ using property 1

(b) $\ln x - \ln 2 = \ln \dfrac{x}{2}$ using property 2

(c) $2 \ln x = \ln x^2$ using property 3   ◆

Exponential Growth and Decay

In Section 5.1 it was mentioned that a knowledge of logarithms is needed to solve most of the exponential growth problems described there. Now we can consider those applications, each of which uses the following formula.

Exponential Growth and Decay

The amount A (of money, bacteria, etc.) present at any time t is given by

$$A = Ce^{kt}$$

where

C = the amount at the beginning
k = the rate of growth (if positive)
     or decay (if negative)

Exponential growth (or decay) occurs when the rate of increase (or decrease) of A is proportional to the amount present (A).

When we say that the formula $A = Ce^{kt}$ applies to situations in which the rate of growth is proportional to the amount present, we mean that as the amount present increases, so does the rate of growth. Exercise 102 of Section 5.3 offers the opportunity to show that when $A = Ce^{kt}$, the rate of growth is indeed proportional to the amount present. Later on, the formula will be derived from a differential equation based on this "proportional" idea.

> *Note*
>
> In the examples that follow, the value of ln x for specific positive values of x is determined by using a calculator. If a calculator is not available, use Table 2 at the back of the book.

EXAMPLE 9 **CONTINUOUS COMPOUNDING**

At what annual interest rate, compounded continuously, should money be invested in order to double in 8 years?

SOLUTION In $A = Ce^{kt}$, the interest rate we seek is k, the growth rate. The time is $t = 8$ years. To say that money doubles is to say that the amount C at the beginning becomes $2C$ (that is, *double C*) in 8 years. Thus, $A = Ce^{kt}$ becomes

$$2C = Ce^{k(8)}$$

$$2 = e^{8k} \qquad \text{dividing both sides by } C$$

Changing to logarithmic form in order to solve for k yields

$$8k = \ln 2$$

$$k = \frac{\ln 2}{8} \approx \frac{.6931}{8} \approx .087$$

The decimal number .087 is equivalent to 8.7%. Thus, the money should be invested at 8.7% in order to double in 8 years. In this example, 8 years is the **doubling time.** ◆

EXAMPLE 10 **BACTERIA GROWTH**

The number of bacteria in a culture increases from 400 to 1000 in 3 hours. Assuming bacteria growth to be exponential, how many bacteria will be present in the culture after 10 hours?

SOLUTION In order to determine the number of bacteria present after 10 hours, we must have a formula of the form $A = Ce^{kt}$ in which both C and k are known. Then we can substitute 10 for t and obtain the corresponding "amount" A.

To begin, we know that C is 400, because the statement of the problem implies that there are 400 bacteria in the culture at the beginning. Thus we have

$$A = 400e^{kt}$$

We also know that A is 1000 when $t = 3$, since the number of bacteria increases to 1000 in 3 hours.

$$1000 = 400e^{k(3)}$$

This equation can be solved to determine k and thus produce a completed formula of the form $A = Ce^{kt}$. Begin by dividing both sides by 400.

$$2.5 = e^{3k}$$

To solve for k, we obtain the logarithmic form.

$$3k = \ln 2.5$$

$$k = \frac{\ln 2.5}{3} \approx \frac{.9163}{3} \quad \text{or} \quad .305$$

Thus, the formula is

$$A = 400e^{.305t}$$

After 10 hours, when $t = 10$, the number of bacteria A is 8446, as shown next.

$$A = 400e^{.305(10)} = 400e^{3.05} \approx 400(21.115) = 8446$$

A graph showing the bacteria growth is given in Figure 9.

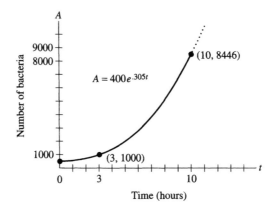

Figure 9 Exponential growth of bacteria   ◆

EXAMPLE 11   ***HALF-LIFE OF A RADIOACTIVE ELEMENT***

Radium is a radioactive element that decays exponentially. The half-life of radium is approximately 1600 years. If we begin with an 80-gram mass of radium, how many grams will remain 200 years from now?

SOLUTION   The **half-life** of a radioactive element is the amount of time it takes for half of the mass of the element to decay (that is, decompose into some other material). A half-life of 1600 years means that the 80 grams of radium will be 40 grams of radium when $t = 1600$, with the decay occurring exponentially over the 1600-year period. In terms of $A = Ce^{kt}$, we have

$$40 = 80e^{k(1600)}$$

or, upon dividing both sides by 80,

$$.5 = e^{1600k}$$

The value of k can be determined by writing this exponential equation in logarithmic form.

$$1600k = \ln .5$$

$$k = \frac{\ln .5}{1600} \approx \frac{-.6931}{1600} \approx -.0004$$

The decay rate is $-.0004$. The *minus* indicates a decay or decrease.

If the k value $-.0004$ is used in $A = Ce^{kt}$ for this situation in which we have 80 grams of radium, then we will have the formula for the amount of radium at any time t, namely

$$A = 80e^{-.0004t}$$

In 200 years, $t = 200$, and the amount of radium remaining is

$$A = 80e^{-.0004(200)} = 80e^{-.08} \approx 80(.9231) \approx 73.85$$

Approximately 73.85 grams of radium will remain 200 years from now.

A graph showing the radioactive decay of radium is given in Figure 10.

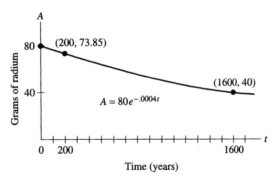

Figure 10 Radioactive decay of radium ◆

APPLIED

EXAMPLE 12 ***RADIOCARBON DATING AND THE FROZEN STONE AGE MAN***

Dr. Willard Libby won a Nobel Prize for developing *radiocarbon dating*, which is used by archaeologists to determine the age of ancient objects they uncover. While alive, all plants and animals acquire a certain amount of carbon-14, depending on their weight. Because carbon-14 decays (half-life approximately 5730 years), plants and animals are continually

acquiring carbon-14 to replace the amount lost by decay. After death, no new carbon-14 is acquired, so the amount present is gradually depleted by decay.

In 1991, hikers discovered the well-preserved body of a man frozen in the Alps. (See Figure 11.) Archaeologists used radiocarbon dating of a piece of his flesh to confirm that he lived in the Stone Age. The flesh contained 53% of the carbon-14 that would be found in a living man. Now, we will proceed to determine the age of the body.

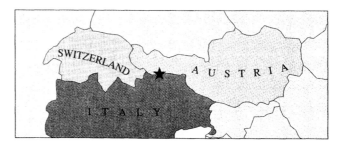

Figure 11 The star shows where the Stone Age man was found.

SOLUTION Using $A = Ce^{kt}$ and the fact that the half-life of carbon-14 is 5730 years, we can determine the decay constant k. Note that whatever the mass C of carbon-14 at the beginning, after 5730 years it will be reduced to half of C, or $.5C$. Thus, we have

$$.5C = Ce^{k(5730)}$$

$$.5 = e^{5730k} \quad \text{dividing both sides by } C$$

$$5730k = \ln .5 \quad \text{logarithmic form}$$

$$k = \frac{\ln .5}{5730} \approx \frac{-.6931}{5730} \approx -.00012$$

The decay constant is $-.00012$, and the decay formula appears as

$$A = Ce^{-.00012t}$$

Since the flesh contained 53% of the carbon-14 that a living body would contain, we can replace A by $.53C$ (53% of C).

$$.53C = Ce^{-.00012t}$$

This equation can be solved for t, the time of death of the man. In steps, divide both sides by C and then change to logarithm form to isolate the t term.

$$.53 = e^{-.00012t}$$

$$-.00012t = \ln .53$$

$$t = \frac{\ln .53}{-.00012} \approx \frac{-.6349}{-.00012} = 5291$$

We conclude that the body was approximately 5300 years old when found in 1991.

Realistically, the method does not pinpoint the age to the nearest year. Rounding to the nearest hundred years is reasonable in such cases. ◆

Note

The carbon-14 dating method can be used to date only objects that are less than 50,000 years old. Older objects contain less than .25% carbon-14 and cannot be dated accurately in this manner. Instead, *potassium-argon dating is* used. All living plants and animals contain potassium-40. Upon death, the potassium-40 decays (to argon-40) with a half-life of 1.3 billion years.

Effective Rate of Interest

When a bank offers you an annual interest rate of 6% compounded continuously, it is really paying you more than 6%. Because of compounding, the 6% is in fact a yield of 6.18% for the year. To see this, consider investing $1 at 6% per year compounded continuously for 1 year. The total return is

$$A = Pe^{rt} = 1 \cdot e^{.06(1)} = e^{.06} = \$1.0618$$

If we subtract from $1.0618 the $1 we invested, the return is $.0618, which is 6.18% of the amount invested. The 6% annual interest rate of this example is called the **nominal rate,** and the 6.18% is called the **effective rate.** In practice, the effective rate is calculated using a formula based on the reasoning we used.

> **Effective Rate**
>
> If r is the annual interest rate (nominal rate) and the interest is compounded continuously, then the **effective rate** is
>
> $$e^r - 1$$

EXAMPLE 13 *EFFECTIVE RATE*

APPLIED

(a) A savings and loan association pays an annual interest rate (nominal rate) of 7.5%. What is the effective rate?

(b) A bank offers an effective rate of 5.41%. What is the nominal rate?

SOLUTION **(a)** The effective rate is $e^r - 1$. Here $r = 7.5\%$, or .075. Thus,

$$e^r - 1 = e^{.075} - 1 \approx 1.0779 - 1 = .0779$$

The effective rate is 7.79%. Because we rounded the value of $e^{.075}$ to four decimal places, the effective rate came out to the nearest hundredth of a percent.

(b) The effective rate is given as 5.41%, which is .0541 in decimal form. The effective rate is also known to be $e^r - 1$, *where r is the nominal rate.* Thus,

$$e^r - 1 = .0541 \qquad \text{or} \qquad e^r = 1.0541$$

Changing to logarithm notation, we have

$$r = \ln 1.0541 \approx .0527$$

This means the nominal rate is 5.27%.   ♦

5.2   Exercises

In Exercises 1–6, write each exponential equation in logarithmic form.

1. $2^5 = 32$ **2.** $3^4 = 81$

3. $10^2 = 100$ **4.** $10^{-2} = .01$

5. $e^0 = 1$ **6.** $e^m = u$

In Exercises 7–14, write each logarithmic equation in exponential form.

7. $\log_3 9 = 2$ **8.** $\log_2 64 = 6$

9. $\log 100 = 2$ **10.** $\log .01 = -2$

11. $\log .1 = -1$ **12.** $\ln 1 = 0$

13. $\ln e = 1$ **14.** $\ln x = t$

In Exercises 15–20, solve each equation for x.

15. $e^x = 3$ **16.** $e^x = 4$

17. $e^{3x} = 2$ **18.** $e^{2x} = 13$

19. $3e^{5x} = 42$ **20.** $2e^{4x} = 20$

In Exercises 21–28, solve each equation for x.

21. $\ln x = -2$ **22.** $\ln x = 6$

23. $\ln 4x = 30$ **24.** $\ln 10x = 50$

25. $\ln 3x = 0$ **26.** $\ln 4x = 1$

27. $5 \ln 3x = 40$ **28.** $7 \ln 5x = 28$

Simplify each expression in Exercises 29–38.

29. $\ln e^4$ **30.** $\ln e^{18}$

31. $5 \ln e^2$ **32.** $4 \ln e$

33. $e \ln 1$ **34.** $-e^{\ln 9}$

35. $1 + 2e^{\ln 3}$ **36.** $2 + 5e^{\ln 3}$

37. $\ln \sqrt{e}$ **38.** $\ln \dfrac{1}{e}$

In Exercises 39–44 use logarithm properties to expand each expression. (Simplify afterward, if possible.)

39. $\ln xy$ **40.** $\ln 4x$

41. $\ln ex$ **42.** $\ln e^2x$

43. $\ln \sqrt{x}$ **44.** $\ln \dfrac{1}{x}$

In Exercises 45–52, apply logarithm properties to condense each expression.

45. $\ln x + \ln 2$ **46.** $\ln 3 + \ln x$

47. $\ln 4 - \ln x$ **48.** $\ln (x + 1) - \ln 2$

49. $3 \ln x$ **50.** $-2 \ln x^{-3}$

51. $\ln 5 + 2 \ln x$ **52.** $2 \ln 3 + 3 \ln x$

🖩 *The use of calculators is recommended for the applied problems that follow. However, the same answers (or nearly the same answers) can be obtained by using the tables at the back of the book.*

53. (*COMPOUND INTEREST*) If $4000 is invested at 7% interest per year compounded continuously, how long will it take to double the original investment?

54. (*COMPOUND INTEREST*) If $5000 is invested at 9% interest per year compounded continuously, how long will it take to double the original amount invested?

55. (*COMPOUND INTEREST*) At what annual interest rate, compounded continuously, will money triple in 12 years?

56. (*COMPOUND INTEREST*) At what annual interest rate, compounded continuously, will money double in 9 years?

57. (*POPULATION GROWTH*) In 1995, the population of the greater Fort Myers, Florida, area was 335,000. It was predicted that the population would increase to 450,000 by the year 2000.
   (a) Determine k for this exponential growth.
W (b) Use a sentence or two to explain what k means in this setting.

58. (*INSECT POPULATION GROWTH*) The insect population in a large field is estimated to be 50,000. An entomologist thinks the population is likely to grow at the rate of 3% a year. How many years will it take for the population to reach 120,000?

59. (*BACTERIA GROWTH*) Assuming the number of bacteria in a culture doubles every hour, how long will it take to have a million bacteria if we begin with 2500 bacteria?

60. (*FRUIT FLY POPULATION GROWTH*) A fruit fly population doubles every 10 days. If there are now 60 fruit flies, how many will there be in two weeks?

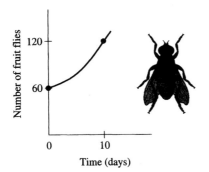

61. (*LAND APPRECIATION*) Suppose that an acre of land purchased in mid 1991 for $20,000 is worth $54,000 in mid 1996.

   (a) What is the annual rate of growth of this investment, assuming continuous compounding?
   (b) If the land continues to appreciate at the same rate, in what year will it be worth $80,000?

62. (*MUTUAL FUND APPRECIATION*) Maureen invested $4000 in a mutual fund in June 1990. In June 1995 her investment was worth $13,500.

   (a) What is the annual rate of growth of this investment, assuming continuous compounding?
   (b) If the mutual fund continues to appreciate at the same rate, how much will her investment be worth in June 1998?

Maureen's investment, from 1990 to 1995

63. (*DISTRESS SALE*) Six months ago, a company was selling 200,000 units per month. Since then, however, sales have fallen and have been given by

$$S(t) = 200,000\, e^{-.12t} \qquad 0 \le t \le 6$$

where $S(t)$ is the number of units sold and t is the time in months. If sales continue to decrease and follow this model, the company will hold a distress sale when the sales per month have fallen to 50,300 units.

   (a) How many units per month is the company selling now (that is, for $t = 6$)?
   (b) If sales decrease according to the model, when will sales be reduced to 50,300 units per month, which will trigger the distress sale?

64. (*HALF-LIFE*) How much of a 300-gram mass of lead 210 will remain after 200 years? The half-life of lead 210 is 22 years.

65. (*HALF-LIFE*) If an element has a half-life of 14 years, how much of a 90-gram mass of the element will still remain after 100 years?

66. (*RADIOCARBON DATING*) The recent discovery of ancient two-wheeled chariots in Kazakhstan indicates that chariots were used at least 1000 years earlier than had previously been thought. A wood wheel from one of these chariots contains 62.5% of the carbon-14 found in a living tree. To the nearest hundred years, how old is this ancient chariot? (Use 5730 years as the half-life of carbon-14. Obtain k to 5 decimal places.)

67. (*RADIOCARBON DATING*) In 1994, archaeologists in Alaska discovered the frozen body of a Thule-culture girl wearing a bird-skin parka. Only 91% of the original carbon-14 remained. To the nearest hundred years, when did the girl die? (Use 5730 years as the half-life of carbon-14. Obtain k to 5 decimal places.)

68. (*RADIATION IN MEDICINE*) Doctors use the radiation from cobalt-60 to arrest the growth of cancer cells. Cobalt-60 has a half-life of 5.27 years.
(a) Find the decay constant k.
(b) How much of a 2-microgram mass of cobalt-60 remains after 20 years?

69. (*NUCLEAR TESTING*) Atmospheric testing of nuclear weapons introduced radioactive strontium-90 into the environment. Because it is now present in food and water and is chemically similar to calcium, strontium-90 does occur in milk and bones, and it can cause bone cancer. The half-life of strontium-90 is 28 years.

(a) Determine the decay constant k.
(b) A treaty banning the atmospheric testing of nuclear weapons was signed in 1963. Assuming that there has been no such testing since 1963 and that there will be no such testing in the future, by what year will the level of strontium-90 be reduced to 10% of the amount present in 1963?

70. (*RADON DECAY*) The following graph shows the decay of the radioactive element polonium-210, the deadly product of radon decay. Examine the graph to determine, to the nearest 10 days, the half-life of polonium-210.

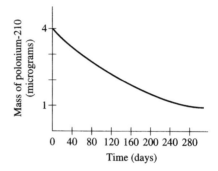

71. (*RADIOACTIVE TRACERS*) Iodine-131 is used in medicine as a radioactive tracer. When the radioactive element is combined with other elements, it can be sent through the body and monitored by a radiation detector. Because iodine-131 concentrates in the thyroid gland and the liver, it is used to study thyroid and liver problems. Iodine-131 has a half-life of 8.6 days.
(a) Determine the decay constant k.
(b) What percent of the iodine-131 remains in the body 5 weeks after its use as a tracer?

72. (*AIDS VIRUS*) Researchers have found that when drugs are used in the late stages of AIDS, the half-life of the virus population present is 2 days. (Unfortunately, although drugs destroy half of the virus population every 2 days, many new virus particles are constantly being made and released.) On the basis of this premise, what percent of the virus population present today will still be living 3 weeks from now? (Use four decimal places for the decay constant k.)

73. (*DRUG CONCENTRATION*) A drug taken intravenously is removed from the blood at a rate that declines exponentially. If the concentration of the drug is 50 units per volume when administered and the decay constant is known to be $-.04$, determine the following, assuming that time is measured in minutes.
(a) The concentration after 30 minutes
(b) The concentration after 2 hours
(c) The time it takes the body to *eliminate* 90% of the drug from the bloodstream

74. **(DRUG CONCENTRATION)** Redo Exercise 73 assuming that the concentration of the drug is 200 units per volume when administered and that the decay rate is $-.05$.

75. **(REVENUE)** A producer can sell x units at the price per unit (dollars) given by the following demand function.

$$D(x) = \frac{50}{\ln (x + 3)}$$

(a) Determine the function that gives the revenue from the sale of x units.

(b) What is the revenue from the sale of 30 units?

76. **(DEMAND)** If the demand function of Exercise 75 were instead

$$D(x) = \frac{50}{\ln x}$$

what restriction would need to be placed on x?

77. **(LARVAE DEVELOPMENT)** A study of mosquito larvae yields the following formula for duration D of development as a function of the environment temperature T.

$$\log D = a - b \log T$$

The numbers a and b are constants, a being the number of day-degrees required for completion of a developmental stage and b being the minimum temperature at which development can proceed.

(a) The given equation is solved for $\log D$, rather than for D. Solve it for D.

(b) Solve the equation for T.

78. **(EARTHQUAKE MEASUREMENT)** The *Richter scale* is used to measure and report the magnitude of earthquakes. Specifically, for Southern California,

$$M = \log \frac{I}{I_0}$$

where M is the magnitude of the earthquake, I_0 is the smallest measurable intensity, and I is the intensity of the earthquake being measured.

(a) What magnitude on the Richter scale would correspond to an earthquake of intensity $1000I_0$ (1000 times the intensity of I_0)?

(b) How much greater is the intensity of an earthquake of magnitude 5 than that of an earthquake of magnitude 3?

79. **(DOUBLING RATE)** The time and interest rate needed for money to double can be studied by considering $A = Pe^{rt}$ with A being equal to $2P$ (double P).

(a) Use $2P$ for A and determine an equation that gives r in terms of t.

(b) Use the result of part (a) to complete the following table of doubling rates and times (in years).

t	5	6	7	8	9	10	11	12	(years to double)
r									(interest rate)

80. **(DOUBLING TIME)** Redo Exercise 79 by obtaining t in terms of r and completing the table that follows.

r	5	6	7	8	9	10	11	12	(interest rate)
t									(years to double)

* *In Exercises 81–86, assume continuous compounding.*

81. **(EFFECTIVE RATE)** A savings and loan association offers an annual interest rate (nominal rate) of 6.3%. What is the effective rate?

82. **(EFFECTIVE RATE)** Your bank offers an annual interest rate (nominal rate) of 5.7%. What is the effective rate?

83. **(NOMINAL RATE)** A credit union offers an effective rate of 6.12%. What is the nominal rate?

84. **(NOMINAL RATE)** A savings bank offers an effective rate of 5.94%. What is the nominal rate?

85. **(EFFECTIVE AND NOMINAL RATES)** The graph on the next page shows the difference D between the effective rate and the nominal rate as a function of the nominal rate n. Answer the following questions on the basis of the graph.

(a) As the nominal rate increases, the difference between the effective rate and the nominal rate _____ .

(b) Is D' positive, negative, or zero?

(c) Is D'' positive, negative, or zero?

(d) Use the words *increasing* and/or *decreasing* to fill in the blanks. "The function D is _____ at a(n) _____ rate."

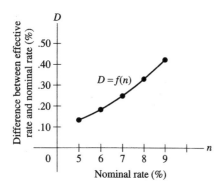

86. (*EFFECTIVE AND NOMINAL RATES*) How much interest (in dollars) will you get in a year if you deposit $2000 into an account that pays as follows?
(a) An effective rate of 5.82%
(b) A nominal rate of 6.31%

87. In Sections 5.1 and 5.2 you were introduced to four exponential-related graphs—exponential growth, exponential decay, logistic growth, and the learning curve.

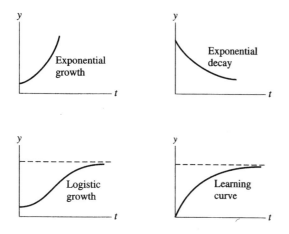

Read each of the situations presented in parts (a) through (i) and decide which of the four types of graphs would best describe it.

(a) (*LUNCH BUSINESS*) A restaurant advertises its lunch specials extensively. As a result, its lunch business begins to increase exponentially. The "lunch hour" is from 11 a.m. to 1:30 p.m. and the restaurant seats 124 people.

(b) (*PIZZA MAKING*) Some inexperienced pizza makers have begun work at a pizzeria. Their productivity will improve with experience.

(c) (*DRUG ELIMINATION*) A nurse gives a patient a drug intravenously. The body acts to remove the drug from the blood at an exponential rate and distributes it to organs that will either use it or eliminate it. Our focus is on the amount of the drug remaining in the blood.

(d) (*POPULATION GROWTH*) Although the human population of the world has been growing at a rate of approximately 2% per year, this kind of growth will be restricted by limited space, shortages of food, lack of medical care, and other problems.

(e) (*INVESTING FOR RETIREMENT*) To accumulate money for retirement needs, Sylvia invests $3000 at 7% annual interest compounded continuously.

(f) (*USE OF ENZYMES*) Increasing the concentration of regular enzymes increases the rate of chemical reaction exponentially. However, the rate of reaction has a bound or limit that cannot be exceeded, regardless of the amount of regular enzyme used.

(g) (*LARVA GROWTH*) After a very short period of slow growth, the housefly larva grows quickly. In fact, its weight doubles every 13 hours. Finally, its growth rate slows considerably.

(h) (*SPREAD OF A RUMOR*) Sociologists studying the spread of a rumor have observed that rumors spread at an exponential rate for a while. However, there is a limited audience (say, at a school), so there is an eventual slowdown in the rate at which the rumor spreads.

(i) (*RAT IN A MAZE*) A psychologist places a rat in a maze and studies its failures and successes as it eventually determines a path that will lead it out of the maze.

88. (PH) In chemistry, the pH of a solution is defined as follows:

$$pH = -\log [H^+]$$

where H^+ is the hydrogen concentration (in moles per liter). A "neutral" solution such as water has a pH of 7. Acid solutions have pH values less than 7, and alkaline solutions have pH values greater than 7.

(a) Use the fact that the hydrogen ion concentration of pure water is .0000001 (or 10^{-7}) mole per liter to verify that the pH of water is 7.

(b) What is the pH of acid rain in which the concentration of hydrogen ions is .000031 mole per liter?

(c) What is the concentration of hydrogen ions in the stomach during digestion if the hydrochloric acid solution has a pH of 3.2?

(d) What is the pH of a shampoo in which the concentration of hydrogen ions is .000000009 mole per liter?

89. (COOKING A ROAST) If a cool object (such as meat to be cooked) is placed in a warm environment (such as an oven), the cooler object will be warmed according to a formula that is similar to one we have been using. Specifically, the temperature y of the object placed in a warm environment is given by $y = S - Ce^{kt}$, where S is the temperature of the warmer environment, t is the time the object is in the environment, k is the rate-of-warming constant, and C is a constant that is readily determined from y and S. Assume that a roast at 60°F (slightly cooler than room temperature) is placed in a 375° oven. After 45 minutes, the roast's temperature is 120°.

(a) What is the value of the constant C?

(b) Determine the rate-of-warming constant k.

(c) How many minutes will it take for the roast to be at a temperature of 160° (cooked)?

90. (MAKING ICE) When a warm body is placed in a cooler environment, the body will cool according to the equation $y = Ce^{kt} + S$, where S is the temperature of the cool environment, y is the temperature of the warm body, t is the time, k is the rate-of-cooling constant, and C is a constant. Suppose that 70° tap water is used to fill an ice cube tray and then the tray is placed in a freezer that is kept at 15°F.

(a) Determine C.

(b) Determine the cooling constant k if the water temperature has been reduced to 45° in 15 minutes.

(c) What will be the temperature of the water after 30 minutes?

91. In the formula $A = Ce^{kt}$, C is the amount at the beginning. Prove this statement by showing that $A = C$ when $t = 0$.

W 92. Throughout this section there are statements such as "ln x for $x > 0$" and "ln a for $a > 0$." Why must there be this restriction that we cannot have logarithms of negative numbers or zero?

W 93. We have claimed that a logarithm is an exponent. In $\log_b a = c$, the logarithm ($\log_b a$) is equal to c. Is c an exponent? Explain.

W 94. (HALF-LIFE) Explain the concept of half-life by using 64 grams of an element with a half-life of 10 years. Include a time period of 30 years in your explanation.

W 95. Review the graph of the natural logarithm function $f(x) = \ln x$ (Figure 8).

(a) What is the nature of the tangent lines to the graph of f and how is this related to the increasing and/or decreasing nature of the function?

(b) Make a comment about the concavity of the graph of $f(x) = \ln x$.

96. Using $k = -.00012$, show that the amount of carbon-14 remaining after 50,000 years is less than .25%. This exercise is a reference to the note after Example 12.

W 97. Explain why the domain of $f(x) = \ln (x - 2)$ is all the real numbers that are greater than 2.

W 98. If the effective rate y is given by $y = e^r - 1$ for nominal rate r, is the nominal rate given by $r = \ln (y + 1)$? Explain.

TECHNOLOGY *EXERCISES*

1. (HALF-LIFE) The graph of $y = 4e^{-.13x}$ shows the decay of a radioactive element, where x is the time in days and y is the mass in micrograms. Study the graph for x in $[0, 20]$ and estimate, to the nearest day, the half-life of the element.

2. Graph: $f(x) = \ln |x|$

   (a) For what value of x is $f'(x)$ undefined?

   W (b) Explain your answer to part (a).

3. (a) Obtain an approximate solution of the equation $3^x = 5.9$ by graphing $y = 3^x$ and $y = 5.9$ and determining, to the *nearest tenth*, the x coordinate of their point of intersection.

   (b) Graph $y = 3^x - 5.9$ and determine where the graph crosses the x axis. Compare this result with that of part (a).

4. Repeat the procedure of Exercise 3(a) to approximate the solution, to the *nearest hundredth*, of the equation $2^x = 7.3$.

5. Use the graphs of $y = \ln 4x$ and $y = 2.3$ to approximate the solution of $\ln 4x = 2.3$ to the nearest tenth.

6. Graph: $f(x) = 3e^{\ln x} - 2 \ln e^x$

   W (a) Describe the graph.

   (b) Return to the function and simplify the expression that defines it.

   W (c) Why is the displayed graph visible only for $x > 0$?

7. **(DEPRECIATION)** A machine depreciates so that its value after x years is

   $$y = 2900e^{-.052x} \quad \text{dollars}$$

   Graph the function using x in $[0, 40]$ and y in $[0, 3000]$.

   (a) To the nearest year, when is the value of the machine $1250?

   (b) To the nearest hundred dollars, what is the value of the machine after $9\frac{1}{2}$ years?

8. The functions $y = e^x$ and $y = \ln x$ are *inverses* of each other, which means that their graphs are reflections of each other (mirror images) in the line $y = x$. To see this, graph the two functions and the line $y = x$ using the windows $[-2, 8]$ for x and y and using Zoom Square.

   (a) Repeat this approach using the functions $y = e^{2x}$ and $y = \frac{1}{2} \ln x$. Do the functions appear to be inverses?

   (b) Graph the functions $y = e^{|x|}$ and $y = \ln |x|$ using the standard windows $[-10, 10]$ for x and y. Also graph $y = x$. Are the functions inverses?

   W (c) Graph the function $y = \frac{1}{x}$ using the window $[.25, 4]$ for x and y. Also graph the line $y = x$. Use Zoom Square. Describe how the graph of the inverse of this function would appear.

9. Graph the effective rate function

   $$y = e^x - 1$$

   where x is the annual interest rate (nominal rate). Use the window $[0, .1]$ for x and y. Answer these questions on the basis of the graph.

(a) To the nearest tenth of a percent, what is the effective rate when the nominal rate is 6.2%?

(b) To the nearest tenth of a percent, what is the nominal rate when the effective rate is 5.7%?

5.3 | *DIFFERENTIATION OF EXPONENTIAL FUNCTIONS*

In some ways, the world can be more complex and less predictable than suggested by traditional mathematical models. In their book *Turbulent Mirror*, John Briggs and F. David Peat explore chaos theory, a field of mathematics that deals with turbulence, irregularity, unpredictability, and discontinuity in biological systems and elsewhere.

Briggs and Peat explore the limitations of both exponential population growth and an alternative that compares with logistic growth.

A thorough analysis of the predator-prey interaction of pike (predator) and trout (prey) is given, along with the effect of permitting fishing. All of this sets the stage for a discussion of the "chaotic" growth behavior of a population of gypsy moths.

It is natural to wonder about differentiating the exponential and logarithmic functions. We can now proceed to obtain a rule for differentiating $f(x) = e^x$. In the next section we will consider the derivative of $f(x) = \ln x$.

As suggested in Chapter 3, the *definition* of the derivative is often used when no rule for differentiation appears to be at hand. Accordingly, to determine $f'(x)$ for $f(x) = e^x$, we proceed by using the definition of the derivative.

$$f'(x) = \lim_{\Delta x \to 0} \frac{f(x + \Delta x) - f(x)}{\Delta x}$$

$$= \lim_{\Delta x \to 0} \frac{e^{x + \Delta x} - e^x}{\Delta x}$$

$$= \lim_{\Delta x \to 0} \frac{e^x \cdot e^{\Delta x} - e^x}{\Delta x} \qquad \text{since } e^{x + \Delta x} = e^x \cdot e^{\Delta x}$$

$$= \lim_{\Delta x \to 0} \frac{e^x (e^{\Delta x} - 1)}{\Delta x} \qquad \text{factorying out } e^x$$

Next, apply the theorem "the limit of a product is the product of the limits."

$$f'(x) = \lim_{\Delta x \to 0} e^x \cdot \lim_{\Delta x \to 0} \frac{e^{\Delta x} - 1}{\Delta x}$$

In the first limit, $\Delta x \to 0$ has no effect on e^x. The limit as $\Delta x \to 0$ of e^x is e^x.

$$f'(x) = e^x \cdot \lim_{\Delta x \to 0} \frac{e^{\Delta x} - 1}{\Delta x} \qquad (*)$$

As we shall see, the limit that remains is equal to 1.

$$\lim_{\Delta x \to 0} \frac{e^{\Delta x} - 1}{\Delta x} = 1$$

The limit can be considered informally by using a calculator to show that as Δx gets closer and closer to zero, the expression gets closer and closer to 1. The calculated entries in the table are correct to nine decimal places. The table presents a plausible case for the limit being 1.

Δx	$\dfrac{e^{\Delta x} - 1}{\Delta x}$
.1	1.051709181
.01	1.005016708
.001	1.000500160
.0001	1.000050000
.00001	1.000000000

Because that limit is 1, we have at last, from equation (∗),

$$f'(x) = e^x \cdot 1 = e^x$$

Thus,

$$\frac{d}{dx}(e^x) = e^x$$

That the derivative of e^x is itself e^x is a most unusual result. This property makes e the natural choice of base when applications involve exponential functions. Also, $y = e^x$ and $y = ce^x$ are the only functions (other than $y = 0$) with the property that the derivative of the function is equal to the function.

EXAMPLE 1 Differentiate $f(x) = x^3 e^x$.

SOLUTION The expression $x^3 e^x$ is a product; $x^3 e^x = x^3 \cdot e^x$. Using the product rule for differentiation, we have the following result.

$$f'(x) = x^3 \cdot \frac{d}{dx}(e^x) + e^x \cdot \frac{d}{dx}(x^3)$$
$$= x^3 \cdot e^x + e^x \cdot 3x^2$$
$$= x^3 e^x + 3x^2 e^x$$

The expression can be simplified algebraically by factoring out $x^2 e^x$ from each term. The result is

$$f'(x) = x^2 e^x (x + 3)$$

This factored form is desirable for determining critical numbers.   ♦

EXAMPLE 2 Determine $\dfrac{dy}{dx}$ if $y = \dfrac{e^x + 7}{x^2}$.

SOLUTION Applying the quotient rule yields

$$\frac{dy}{dx} = \frac{(x^2)(e^x) - (e^x + 7)(2x)}{(x^2)^2} = \frac{x^2 e^x - 2xe^x - 14x}{x^4}$$

This expression can be simplified (that is, the fraction reduced) by factoring x out of the numerator and denominator and then eliminating the x's by division.

$$\frac{dy}{dx} = \frac{xe^x - 2e^x - 14}{x^3}$$ ◆

EXAMPLE 3   If $y = \sqrt{e^x - x}$, determine dy/dx.

SOLUTION   Rewrite the expression with a numerical exponent.

$$y = (e^x - x)^{1/2}$$

Differentiation, using the general power rule, yields

$$\frac{dy}{dx} = \frac{1}{2}(e^x - x)^{-1/2} \cdot \frac{d}{dx}(e^x - x) = \frac{1}{2}(e^x - x)^{-1/2}(e^x - 1)$$

The factor $(e^x - x)^{-1/2}$ can be written in the denominator as $(e^x - x)^{1/2}$ or as $\sqrt{e^x - x}$. The final result is

$$\frac{dy}{dx} = \frac{e^x - 1}{2\sqrt{e^x - x}}$$ ◆

The chain rule can be applied to obtain the derivative of e^u, where u is a function of x. Here

$$\frac{dy}{dx} = \frac{dy}{du} \cdot \frac{du}{dx}$$

becomes

$$\frac{d}{dx}(e^u) = \frac{d}{du}(e^u) \cdot \frac{du}{dx}$$

and then

$$\frac{d}{dx}(e^u) = e^u \cdot \frac{du}{dx}$$

EXAMPLE 4   Obtain the derivative of $y = e^{8x}$.

SOLUTION $$\frac{dy}{dx} = \frac{d}{dx}(e^{8x}) = e^{8x} \cdot \frac{d}{dx}(8x) = e^{8x} \cdot 8 = 8e^{8x}$$ ◆

EXAMPLE 5   If $y = (1 + e^{3x})^{12}$, determine dy/dx.

SOLUTION   The general power rule must be applied here.

$$\frac{dy}{dx} = 12(1 + e^{3x})^{11} \cdot \frac{d}{dx}(1 + e^{3x})$$

$$= 12(1 + e^{3x})^{11}(e^{3x} \cdot 3)$$

$$= 36e^{3x}(1 + e^{3x})^{11} \qquad \text{rearranging and simplifying} \qquad \blacklozenge$$

APPLIED

EXAMPLE 6   *RISING PRICES OF NEW HOMES*

According to the U.S. Bureau of the Census, the average price of new single-family homes rose sharply during the period 1982–1987. The function

$$p(t) = 71 + 2t + e^{.6t}$$

gives the approximate price $p(t)$ in thousands of dollars at any time from mid-1982 ($t = 0$) to mid-1987 ($t = 5$).

(a) Show that new home prices were increasing throughout the interval from 1982 to 1987.

(b) At what rate were the prices changing in mid-1985?

SOLUTION   **(a)** Recall that a function is increasing when its derivative is positive. We have

$$p'(t) = 2 + .6e^{.6t}$$

Note that $e^{.6t} > 0$ for all t, so $.6e^{.6t} > 0$ and $2 + .6e^{.6t} > 0$ for all t. Thus, $p'(t) > 0$ for all t, so $p(t)$ is increasing for all t in the interval. We conclude that new-home prices were increasing throughout the interval from 1982 to 1987.

(b) For the rate of change in mid-1985, we seek $p'(3)$.

$$p'(t) = 2 + .6e^{.6t}$$
$$p'(3) = 2 + .6e^{1.8} \approx 5.6$$

New-home prices were changing at the rate of $5600 per year in mid-1985. $\blacklozenge$

EXAMPLE 7   Determine all critical numbers of $f(x) = 1 + xe^x$.

SOLUTION   Begin by obtaining $f'(x)$.

$$f'(x) = xe^x + e^x = e^x(x + 1)$$

To find the critical numbers of this function, consider the numbers for which the derivative is zero. Since e^x is never zero, $f'(x) = (e^x)(x + 1)$ is zero only when the factor $x + 1$ is zero—that is, when $x = -1$. Thus, -1 is the only critical number. $\blacklozenge$

EXAMPLE 8   Use implicit differentiation to find dy/dx.

$$xe^y + ye^x = x$$

SOLUTION   To begin,

$$\frac{d}{dx}(xe^y) + \frac{d}{dx}(ye^x) = \frac{d}{dx}(x)$$

Observe that since y is (implicitly) a function of x, the term xe^y is a *product* of two functions of x, namely x and e^y. Similarly, ye^x is also a product of two functions of x, namely y and e^x.

This means that the product rule must be used in the differentiation. Continuing,

$$x \cdot e^y \cdot \frac{dy}{dx} + e^y \cdot 1 + y \cdot e^x + e^x \cdot \frac{dy}{dx} = 1$$

Isolating the dy/dx terms produces

$$xe^y \frac{dy}{dx} + e^x \frac{dy}{dx} = 1 - e^y - ye^x$$

To obtain dy/dx, factor out dy/dx and then divide both sides of the equation by the coefficient of dy/dx.

$$(xe^y + e^x)\frac{dy}{dx} = 1 - e^y - ye^x$$

$$\frac{dy}{dx} = \frac{1 - e^y - ye^x}{xe^y + e^x} \qquad \blacklozenge$$

Up to this point, the only exponential functions being differentiated have been those involving base e. A knowledge of logarithms can be used to enable us to determine the derivatives of exponential functions having other bases.

To begin, consider $f(x) = a^x$, where a is a positive number. Next, using properties studied earlier in the chapter, we can rewrite a^x as a power of e. This will enable us to differentiate it.

$$a^x = e^{\ln a^x} \qquad \text{since } e^{\ln u} = u$$
$$= e^{x \ln a} \qquad \text{since } \ln a^p = p \ln a$$

We can now proceed to find the derivative of a^x by differentiating $e^{x \ln a}$.

$$f'(x) = \frac{d}{dx}(a^x) = \frac{d}{dx}(e^{x \ln a}) = e^{x \ln a} \cdot \frac{d}{dx}(x \ln a)$$

Keep in mind that because a is a constant, $\ln a$ is also a constant. This means that the derivative of $x \ln a$ is simply $\ln a$, and

$$f'(x) = e^{x \ln a} \cdot \ln a$$
$$= a^x \ln a \qquad \text{replacing } e^{x \ln a} \text{ by } a^x$$

Thus,

$$\frac{d}{dx}(a^x) = a^x \ln a$$

EXAMPLE 9 Find $f'(x)$. (a) $f(x) = 3^x$ (b) $f(x) = 10^x$

SOLUTION (a) The expression 3^x is of the form a^x.

$$f'(x) = 3^x \ln 3$$

(b) The expression 10^x is of the form a^x.

$$f'(x) = 10^x \ln 10$$ ♦

If the chain rule is applied to obtain the derivative of a^u, where u is a function of x, the result is

$$\frac{d}{dx}(a^u) = a^u \frac{du}{dx} \ln a$$

EXAMPLE 10 Find the derivative of $f(x) = 4^{x^2+1}$.

SOLUTION The expression 4^{x^2+1} is of the form a^u, where $u = x^2 + 1$.

$$f'(x) = \frac{d}{dx}(4^{x^2+1}) = 4^{x^2+1} \cdot 2x \ln 4$$ ♦

5.3   Exercises

Determine the derivative of each function in Exercises 1–12.

1. $y = x^2 e^x$

2. $y = -e^x$

3. $y = 5e^x$

4. $y = \dfrac{e^x}{x}$

5. $f(x) = (e^x + 2)^4$

6. $f(x) = \sqrt{1 - e^x}$

7. $y = \dfrac{e^x + 1}{x}$

8. $y = \dfrac{x}{e^x + 1}$

9. $f(x) = \dfrac{1}{(e^x + x)^3}$

10. $f(x) = \dfrac{1}{(2x + e^x)^2}$

11. $f(x) = \dfrac{e^x}{e^x + 1}$

12. $f(x) = \dfrac{e^x - 1}{e^x + 1}$

Determine the derivative of each function in Exercises 13–30.

13. $f(x) = e^{6x-1}$

14. $f(x) = 2e^{-3x}$

15. $f(x) = e^{-x^2}$

16. $f(x) = e^{1+x^3}$

17. $f(x) = e^{\sqrt{x}}$

18. $f(x) = e^{1/x}$

19. $y = .4e^{-5x^2}$

20. $y = .5e^{2x}$

21. $y = xe^{-x}$

22. $y = x^2 e^{-x}$

23. $f(x) = \dfrac{e^{3x}}{x+1}$

24. $f(x) = \dfrac{1 + 3x}{e^{2x}}$

25. $y = \dfrac{e^x + e^{-x}}{2}$

26. $y = \dfrac{e^x - e^{-x}}{2}$

27. $f(x) = \dfrac{5x}{e^x}$

28. $f(x) = \dfrac{3}{e^x}$

29. $y = (1 + e^{5x})^{10}$

30. $y = (2 + e^{4x})^7$

In Exercises 31–34, determine $f''(x)$.

31. $f(x) = e^{3x}$

32. $f(x) = 2e^{-x}$

33. $f(x) = xe^x$

34. $f(x) = e^{x^2}$

In Exercises 35–42, determine the values of x for which the function is increasing and the values of x for which it is decreasing.

35. $f(x) = 3e^{5x}$

36. $f(x) = -2e^{4x}$

37. $f(x) = 1 + e^{-2x}$

38. $f(x) = 3 - e^{-x}$

39. $f(x) = 1 + xe^{x}$

40. $f(x) = xe^{2x}$

41. $f(x) = e^{x^2}$

42. $f(x) = (1 + x)e^{2x}$

For each function in Exercises 43–50, determine (a) all critical numbers and (b) all relative extrema.

43. $y = x^2 e^x$

44. $y = x^3 e^x$

45. $y = xe^{x/2}$

46. $y = x^2 e^{3x}$

47. $y = x^2 e^{-x}$

48. $y = xe^{-2x}$

49. $y = (1 + x)e^{3x}$

50. $y = (x - 1)e^{2x}$

W 51. For $f(x) = e^x$, focus on $f'(x)$ to explain why the exponential function has no relative extrema. Be complete in explaining your search for critical numbers.

W 52. Repeat Exercise 51 using $f(x) = e^{-x}$.

Sketch the graph of each function in Exercises 53–56. Use calculus methods to assist you.

53. $y = x - e^x$

54. $y = e^{-x^2}$

55. $y = e^x + e^{-x}$

56. $y = e^x - e^{-x}$

57. (*COST/MARGINAL COST*) x units of a commodity can be supplied at a cost of $50e^{-.04x}$ dollars *each*.
  (a) Construct the cost function $C(x)$.
  (b) Determine the marginal cost.
  (c) Determine the cost of 10 units and the marginal cost when $x = 10$ units.
  (d) Determine when marginal cost is zero.

58. (*MARGINAL REVENUE*) If $R(x) = 1000e^{.02x}$ dollars is the revenue from the sale of x units of a product, determine the marginal revenue.

59. (*MARGINAL PROFIT*) If the cost of producing x units is $C(x) = 40xe^{-.02x}$ dollars, and if the revenue from the sale of x units is $R(x) = 40xe^{.03x}$ dollars, find the marginal profit function.

60. (*INCREASING PROFIT*) A manufacturer's profit from the production and sale of x units is given by $P(x) = 25xe^{-.2x}$ dollars. When is the profit increasing?

61. (*MAXIMUM PROFIT*) Let the cost of producing x units be $C(x) = 30xe^{-x/10}$ dollars and the revenue from the sale of

x units be $R(x) = 50xe^{-x/10}$ dollars. What production level will maximize the profit?

62. (*ATMOSPHERIC PRESSURE*) The atmospheric pressure P in pounds per square inch at a height of x miles above sea level is given by

$$P = 14.7e^{-.21x}$$

  (a) Find the pressure 10 miles above sea level.
  (b) What is the rate of change in the atmospheric pressure 10 miles above sea level?

63. (*POLLUTANT CONCENTRATION*) The concentration of pollutants in a river decreases exponentially as the distance downstream from the source of the pollution increases. Suppose that

$$c(x) = .001e^{-2x}$$

gives the concentration of pollutants in grams per cubic centimeter, where x is the number of miles downstream from the source of pollution.
  (a) Determine the concentration of pollutants at the source of pollution and 1 mile downstream.
  (b) Determine the rate of change of the concentration of pollutants with respect to the distance downstream from the source of pollution.

64. Determine the slope of the line tangent to the curve $y = e^x$ at any point (x, y).

65. Determine the slope of the line tangent to the curve $y = 1 + e^{4x}$ at the point $(0, 2)$.

66. Determine the slope of the line tangent to the curve $y = 2xe^{-x}$ at the point $(0, 0)$.

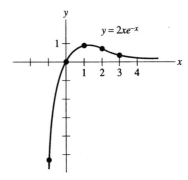

67. Determine the equation of the line tangent to the graph of $y = e^x$ at the point where the slope of the tangent line is e.

68. Determine the equation of the line tangent to the graph of $y = e^x$ at the point where the slope of the tangent line is 1.

Use implicit differentiation to find dy/dx in Exercises 69–78.

69. $x + y + xe^y = 10$ **70.** $x + y + ye^x = 2$

71. $xe^y - ye^x = y$ **72.** $x^2 + y^2 - e^{2y} = 0$

73. $e^{x+y} + x^2 + y^2 = 0$ **74.** $e^{y+1} + e^{2x} + 3y = 2x$

75. $e^{xy} - 2x = y + 3$ **76.** $x^2 + 3e^{xy} - y^2 = 1$

77. $xe^{y^2} + x^2e^y = y$ **78.** $ye^{x^2} - 3xy + x^2 = y$

Determine the derivative of each function in Exercises 79–92.

79. $y = 2^x$ **80.** $y = 1.5^x$

81. $y = 7^{4x}$ **82.** $y = 2^{3x}$

83. $f(x) = 3^{-x^2}$ **84.** $f(x) = 3^{1/x}$

85. $f(x) = 2 \cdot 9^{1+x^2}$ **86.** $f(x) = 4 \cdot 3^{-x^2}$

87. $y = x \cdot 2^{3x}$ **88.** $y = x^2 10^x$

89. $y = \dfrac{3^x}{2x}$ **90.** $y = \dfrac{x + 1}{2^x}$

91. $f(x) = \dfrac{1 - 10^{2x}}{3x}$ **92.** $f(x) = \dfrac{x^2}{1 + 2^x}$

Determine the derivative of each function in Exercises 93–98. Be careful. Think!

93. $y = e^3 + 1$ **94.** $y = \sqrt{e}$

95. $y = e^2 x$ **96.** $y = \dfrac{ex}{7}$

97. $y = \dfrac{x}{1 + e}$ **98.** $y = \dfrac{x}{e}$

99. The graph of $f(x) = 2^{-x^2}$ has one relative maximum point. Find it.

W 100. Given $y = \dfrac{e^{3x}}{4}$, should the *quotient rule* be used to determine dy/dx? Explain.

W 101. Given $y = 5e^{2x}$, should the *product rule* be used to determine dy/dx? Explain.

102. This exercise is intended to show that when $A = Ce^{kt}$, the rate of growth is proportional to the amount present.
(a) Differentiate $A = Ce^{kt}$ to obtain dA/dt.
(b) In $dA/dt = k \cdot Ce^{kt}$, replace Ce^{kt} by A since we are given that $A = Ce^{kt}$. The result is

$$\frac{dA}{dt} = k \cdot A$$

which says that the rate of change of A is a constant times A—that is, it is proportional to the amount present A.

W 103. (*ALGAE GROWTH*) The growth of an algae population is given by the logistic growth curve shown next. Explain how you can tell from the graph that the growth rate is greatest at the point of inflection.

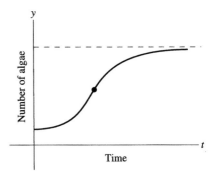

TECHNOLOGY EXERCISES

1. Graph: $f(x) = x - e^{x-4}$

(a) Find, to the nearest tenth, the coordinates of the relative maximum point.

(b) Where is the graph concave up?

2. Graph $f(x) = 7 - .6e^x - .6e^{-x}$ and determine the interval on which the function is increasing.

3. Graph $f(x) = e^{-x}/x^2$. Use x in $[-6, 4]$ and y in $[-1, 8]$.

   (a) Is $f'(1)$ positive, negative, zero, or undefined?

   (b) Is $f''(-4)$ positive or negative?

   (c) Determine any horizontal asymptote(s).

4. Graph: $f(x) = (e^x + e^{-x})/2$

   (a) Determine the coordinates of the relative minimum point.

   (b) Is $f''(2)$ positive, negative, or zero?

5. Approximate the critical number of $f(x) = 2xe^{3x} - x$, to the *nearest thousandth*, by using the following steps. Obtain $f'(x)$ and then graph it. Study the graph to see where $f'(x) = 0$.

6. Redo Exercise 5 using $f(x) = \dfrac{4x}{e^x} - 1.1x$.

5.4 DIFFERENTIATION OF LOGARITHMIC FUNCTIONS

To obtain a formula for the derivative of the logarithmic function $f(x) = \ln x$, we begin with a result from Section 5.2.

$$e^{\ln x} = x$$

Differentiating both sides of this equation yields

$$\frac{d}{dx}(e^{\ln x}) = \frac{d}{dx}(x)$$

$$e^{\ln x} \cdot \frac{d}{dx}(\ln x) = 1$$

Since $e^{\ln x} = x$, we can substitute x for $e^{\ln x}$ on the left side of the equation above.

$$x \cdot \frac{d}{dx}(\ln x) = 1 \qquad \text{after substituting}$$

$$\frac{d}{dx}(\ln x) = \frac{1}{x}$$

This is a most important result. We insist that $x > 0$, so that $\ln x$ is defined.

$$\frac{d}{dx}(\ln x) = \frac{1}{x} \qquad x > 0$$

EXAMPLE 1 Find $f'(x)$ when $f(x) = x^2 \ln x$.

SOLUTION The expression $x^2 \ln x$ is the product of x^2 and $\ln x$. Consequently, the product rule will be used for the differentiation.

$$f'(x) = x^2 \cdot \frac{d}{dx}(\ln x) + (\ln x) \cdot \frac{d}{dx}(x^2)$$

$$= x^2 \cdot \frac{1}{x} + (\ln x) \cdot 2x$$

$$= x + 2x \ln x$$

If desired (say, for determining critical numbers), the expression $x + 2x \ln x$ can be factored and written as $x(1 + 2 \ln x)$.   ◆

EXAMPLE 2 Differentiate $y = 6(\ln x)^3$.

SOLUTION $\dfrac{dy}{dx} = \dfrac{d}{dx}[6(\ln x)^3] = 6 \cdot \dfrac{d}{dx}(\ln x)^3 = 6 \cdot 3(\ln x)^2 \cdot \dfrac{1}{x} = \dfrac{18(\ln x)^2}{x}$ ◆

EXAMPLE 3 Find dy/dx for $y = \dfrac{\ln x}{x^2}$.

SOLUTION The quotient rule applies here.

$$\frac{dy}{dx} = \frac{d}{dx}\left(\frac{\ln x}{x^2}\right) = \frac{x^2 \cdot \dfrac{1}{x} - (\ln x)(2x)}{(x^2)^2} = \frac{x - 2x \ln x}{x^4}$$

At this point, x can be factored out of the numerator and denominator in order to simplify (reduce) this fraction.

$$\frac{dy}{dx} = \frac{x(1 - 2 \ln x)}{x(x^3)} = \frac{1 - 2 \ln x}{x^3}$$ ◆

If the chain rule is applied to obtain the derivative of $y = \ln u$, where u is a function of x, then

$$\frac{dy}{dx} = \frac{dy}{du} \cdot \frac{du}{dx} = \frac{d}{du}(\ln u) \cdot \frac{du}{dx} = \frac{1}{u} \cdot \frac{du}{dx}$$

$$\frac{d}{dx}(\ln u) = \frac{1}{u} \cdot \frac{du}{dx}$$

EXAMPLE 4 Differentiate $y = \ln (x^2 + 1)$.

SOLUTION   In this example, $u = x^2 + 1$.

$$\frac{dy}{dx} = \frac{d}{dx} \ln (x^2 + 1) = \frac{1}{x^2 + 1} \cdot \frac{d}{dx}(x^2 + 1) = \frac{1}{x^2 + 1} \cdot 2x = \frac{2x}{x^2 + 1} \qquad \blacklozenge$$

A look at the final form of the derivative obtained in Example 4 suggests that for some situations, a different form of the derivative would simplify the differentiation process. Instead of

$$\frac{1}{u} \cdot \frac{du}{dx}$$

we can use

$$\frac{du/dx}{u}$$

$$\frac{d}{dx}(\ln u) = \frac{du/dx}{u}$$

The differentiation of Example 4 can now be done in one step, as

$$\frac{d}{dx} \ln (x^2 + 1) = \frac{2x}{x^2 + 1}$$

This alternative form of the derivative of $\ln u$ is often a better choice, but not always. The alternative form will be of great value when techniques of integration are studied in Chapter 7.

EXAMPLE 5   Given $y = \ln (x^3 + 9)^5$, find dy/dx.

SOLUTION   Using the formula for the derivative of $\ln u$, we have

$$\frac{dy}{dx} = \frac{\dfrac{d}{dx}(x^3 + 9)^5}{(x^3 + 9)^5}$$

Now, applying the general power rule yields

$$\frac{dy}{dx} = \frac{5(x^3 + 9)^4 \cdot 3x^2}{(x^3 + 9)^5}$$

The factor $(x^3 + 9)^4$ appears in both the numerator and the denominator. When it is eliminated by division, the result is

$$\frac{dy}{dx} = \frac{15x^2}{x^3 + 9}$$

This is the final result, but *observe now how property 3 of logarithms could have been used to simplify the procedure*. Using this property,

$$y = \ln (x^3 + 9)^5$$

can be written as

$$y = 5 \ln (x^3 + 9)$$

Now the calculus is much easier.

$$\frac{dy}{dx} = 5 \cdot \frac{d}{dx} \ln (x^3 + 9) = 5 \cdot \frac{3x^2}{x^3 + 9} = \frac{15x^2}{x^3 + 9}$$ ◆

EXAMPLE 6   Determine the derivative of $f(x) = \ln \sqrt{1 + x^2}$.

SOLUTION   Begin by changing the radical to an exponent.

$$f(x) = \ln (1 + x^2)^{1/2}$$

The calculus will be simpler if property 3 of logarithms is used to rewrite $\ln (1 + x^2)^{1/2}$ as $\frac{1}{2} \ln (1 + x^2)$.

$$f(x) = \frac{1}{2} \ln (1 + x^2)$$

$$f'(x) = \frac{1}{2} \cdot \frac{2x}{1 + x^2} = \frac{x}{1 + x^2}$$

If you are not convinced of the value of this shortcut approach, try determining the derivative of $f(x) = \ln (1 + x^2)^{1/2}$ without using property 3.   ◆

EXAMPLE 7   Find all relative extrema of $f(x) = 2x - \ln 2x$.

SOLUTION   Begin the search for critical numbers by finding $f'(x)$.

$$f'(x) = 2 - \frac{1}{x}$$

Now determine where $f'(x)$ is zero or undefined.

It is clear that $f'(x)$ is undefined when $x = 0$. Unfortunately, the original function $f(x) = 2x - \ln 2x$ is also undefined for $x = 0$, because $\ln 0$ is not defined. This means that 0 is *not* a critical number.

$f'(x)$ is zero when

$$2 - \frac{1}{x} = 0$$

$$\frac{1}{x} = 2$$

$$2x = 1$$

$$x = \frac{1}{2}$$

And because $f(\frac{1}{2})$ is defined, $\frac{1}{2}$ is a critical number.

The second derivative is easy to obtain, so use the second derivative test to see whether $f\left(\frac{1}{2}\right)$ is a relative extremum.

$$f''(x) = \frac{1}{x^2}$$

and

$$f''\left(\frac{1}{2}\right) = 4 > 0$$

Because $f''\left(\frac{1}{2}\right) > 0$, function f has a relative minimum at $\frac{1}{2}$, and $f\left(\frac{1}{2}\right)$ is that relative minimum value.

$$f\left(\frac{1}{2}\right) = 2 \cdot \frac{1}{2} - \ln\left(2 \cdot \frac{1}{2}\right) = 1 - 0 = 1$$

Thus, 1 is a relative minimum function value, the only relative extremum of the function $f(x) = 2x - \ln 2x$. See Figure 12. ◆

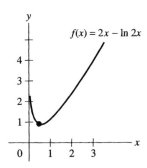

$f(x) = 2x - \ln 2x$

Figure 12

EXAMPLE 8 Is the graph of the function $f(x) = 2x^2 - 5 \ln x$ increasing or decreasing at the point $(1, 2)$?

SOLUTION Determine $f'(1)$. If $f'(1) > 0$, then the graph is increasing at $(1, 2)$. If $f'(1) < 0$, then the graph is decreasing at $(1, 2)$.

$$f'(x) = 4x - \frac{5}{x}$$

$$f'(1) = 4 - 5 = -1 < 0$$

Because $f'(1) < 0$, the graph of f is decreasing at $(1, 2)$. ◆

EXAMPLE 9 RURAL-URBAN MIGRATION

In the developing world, worsening rural poverty has led to increased migration to the cities. The World Resources Institute predicts specific increases in the percentage of the population that will be living in such cities between 1995 and 2025. The function

$$f(t) = .75 + .002t + .01 \ln(t + 1)$$

estimates the percentage of the Latin American population that will live in cities from 1995 ($t = 0$) to 2025 ($t = 30$).

(a) What percentage of the Latin American population will live in cities in 2005?

(b) At what rate will the percentage of the population in the cities be changing in 2005?

SOLUTION **(a)** Since $t = 10$ for the year 2005, we seek $f(10)$.

$$f(10) = .75 + .002(10) + .01 \ln 11 = .794$$

Thus, 79.4% of the population will live in cities in 2005.

(b) For the rate of change, we seek $f'(10)$.

$$f'(t) = .002 + \frac{.01}{t+1}$$

$$f'(10) = .002 + \frac{.01}{11} \approx .0029$$

The percentage of the population in the cities will be changing (increasing) at the rate of .29% per year in 2005. ♦

EXAMPLE 10   Use implicit differentiation to find dy/dx.

$$3x + y + \ln(xy) = 0$$

SOLUTION   First note that it will be easier to differentiate $\ln(xy)$ if we write it instead as $\ln x + \ln y$, making use of property 1 of logarithms. Thus far we have

$$3x + y + \ln x + \ln y = 0$$

Differentiating term by term yields

$$3 + \frac{dy}{dx} + \frac{1}{x} + \frac{1}{y} \cdot \frac{dy}{dx} = 0$$

Fractions can be eliminated by multiplying each term (both sides of the equation) by the common denominator xy. The result:

$$3xy + xy\frac{dy}{dx} + y + x\frac{dy}{dx} = 0$$

Next, isolate the dy/dx terms.

$$xy\frac{dy}{dx} + x\frac{dy}{dx} = -3xy - y$$

Then

$$(xy + x)\frac{dy}{dx} = -(3xy + y)$$

Finally,

$$\frac{dy}{dx} = -\frac{3xy + y}{xy + x}$$ ♦

EXAMPLE 11   Derive a formula for $\dfrac{d}{dx}\ln|x|$. (You will need this formula in Chapter 6.)

SOLUTION   Consider that x can be positive or negative.

(i)   *When $x > 0$*

This means that $|x| = x$ and so $\ln|x| = \ln x$. Thus,

$$\frac{d}{dx}\ln|x| = \frac{d}{dx}\ln x = \frac{1}{x}$$

(ii) *When* $x < 0$

This means that $|x| = -x$ and so $\ln |x| = \ln (-x)$. Thus,

$$\frac{d}{dx} \ln |x| = \frac{d}{dx} \ln (-x)$$

The differentiation can be continued using the formula for the derivative of $\ln u$, with $u = -x$.

$$\frac{d}{dx} \ln (-x) = \frac{1}{-x} \cdot \frac{d}{dx} (-x) = \frac{1}{-x} \cdot (-1) = \frac{1}{x}$$

Parts (i) and (ii) suggest that whether x is positive or negative, the derivative of $\ln |x|$ is the same, namely $1/x$. ◆

$$\frac{d}{dx} \ln |x| = \frac{1}{x}$$

There are formulas for differentiating logarithms that have bases other than e, but such logarithms usually do not occur in settings requiring differentiation. In view of this, our coverage will be brief and a formula for such differentiation is presented next without proof. An example follows.

$$\frac{d}{dx} \log_a u = \frac{1}{u} \cdot \frac{du}{dx} \cdot \frac{1}{\ln a}$$

EXAMPLE 12 If $y = \log_{10}(x^2 + 1)$, find dy/dx.

SOLUTION $$\frac{dy}{dx} = \frac{d}{dx} \log_{10}(x^2 + 1) = \frac{1}{x^2 + 1} \cdot 2x \cdot \frac{1}{\ln 10} = \frac{2x}{(x^2 + 1) \ln 10}$$ ◆

Logarithmic Differentiation

In Section 5.3 we differentiated functions of the form e^x and a^x, where the base is a constant and the exponent is a variable. In Chapter 3 we differentiated functions of the form x^n—such as x^2, x^3, x^4, x^{-1}—where the base is a variable and the exponent is a constant. Next we consider differentiation of functions in which *both* the base and the exponent are variables. A procedure known as **logarithmic differentiation** will be demonstrated in Example 13.

EXAMPLE 13 Let $y = x^x$ (and $x > 0$). Determine dy/dx.

SOLUTION The preceding paragraph outlined the nature of this problem. We have no formula for differentiating x^x, in which both the base and the exponent are variables. Logarithms will be introduced in order to "eliminate" the exponent. From

$$y = x^x$$

It follows that

$$\ln y = \ln x^x$$

By logarithm property 3,

$$\ln y = x \ln x$$

Note that we no longer have a variable base raised to a variable power. The exponent has been "eliminated" by the use of logarithms. We can now proceed with the calculus by differentiating both sides. Keep in mind that in differentiating $\ln y$, the y is itself a function of x. Also note that $x \ln x$ is a product.

$$\frac{d}{dx}(\ln y) = \frac{d}{dx}(x \cdot \ln x)$$

$$\frac{1}{y} \cdot \frac{d}{dx}(y) = x \cdot \frac{d}{dx}(\ln x) + \ln x \cdot \frac{d}{dx}(x)$$

$$\frac{1}{y} \frac{dy}{dx} = x \cdot \frac{1}{x} + (\ln x) \cdot 1$$

$$\frac{1}{y} \frac{dy}{dx} = 1 + \ln x$$

Now multiply both sides of the equation by y in order to solve for dy/dx.

$$\frac{dy}{dx} = y(1 + \ln x)$$

Since $y = x^x$, make the substitution of x^x for y. In this way, the derivative will be a function of x explicitly, just as the original function was given explicitly in terms of x. The result:

$$\frac{dy}{dx} = x^x(1 + \ln x)$$

The graph of $y = x^x$ is shown in Figure 13.   ◆

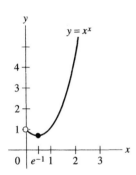

Figure 13
The graph of $y = x^x$. The relative minimum occurs at $x = e^{-1}$. Can you verify that e^{-1} is a critical number?

> *Note*
> An alternative to logarithmic differentiation is presented in Exercise 92.

Logarithmic differentiation can also be used to *prove* that the derivative of x^r is rx^{r-1} for any real number r. To begin,

$$y = x^r$$

It follows that

$$\ln y = \ln x^r$$
$$\ln y = r \ln x$$
$$\frac{1}{y}\frac{dy}{dx} = r \cdot \frac{1}{x} \qquad \text{by differentiation}$$
$$\frac{dy}{dx} = y \cdot r \cdot \frac{1}{x}$$

Upon substituting x^r for y,

$$\frac{dy}{dx} = x^r \cdot r \cdot \frac{1}{x} = r \cdot x^r \cdot x^{-1} = rx^{r-1}$$

5.4 Exercises

Find the derivative of each function in Exercises 1–12.

1. $y = \ln x$

2. $y = 3 \ln x$

3. $y = x \ln x$

4. $y = (\ln x)^3$

5. $y = \dfrac{\ln x}{x}$

6. $y = \dfrac{2x}{\ln x}$

7. $y = \dfrac{x+1}{\ln x}$

8. $y = \dfrac{1}{(\ln x)^2}$

9. $f(x) = \sqrt{\ln x}$

10. $f(x) = e^x \ln x$

11. $f(x) = \dfrac{x}{1 + \ln x}$

12. $f(x) = x(\ln x)^2$

Find the derivative of each function in Exercises 13–24.

13. $y = \ln (x^2 + 7)$

14. $y = \ln (1 + 2x)$

15. $y = \ln (2x + 1)^3$

16. $y = \ln (x^2 - 3)^4$

17. $f(x) = \ln \dfrac{1}{x}$

18. $f(x) = \dfrac{\ln x}{e^x}$

19. $f(x) = \ln \sqrt{x}$

20. $f(x) = \ln (x^2 - e^x)$

21. $f(x) = \ln \dfrac{x}{x+1}$

22. $f(x) = \ln \dfrac{x+1}{x}$

23. $y = \ln (xe^x)$

24. $y = x^2 \ln \sqrt{x}$

25. Determine the equation of the line tangent to the graph of $f(x) = 3 \ln x$ at the point $(1, 0)$.

26. Determine the equation of the line tangent to the graph of $f(x) = 6x - \ln x^2$ at the point $(1, 6)$.

Find the second derivative of each function in Exercises 27–32.

27. $f(x) = x \ln x$

28. $f(x) = x^2 \ln x$

29. $f(x) = (\ln x)^2$

30. $f(x) = (\ln x)^3$

31. $f(x) = \dfrac{\ln x}{x}$

32. $f(x) = \dfrac{\ln x^2}{x}$

33. **(MARGINAL REVENUE)** Suppose $R(x) = 70x + 100 \ln x$ is the revenue in dollars when x units are sold.
(a) Determine the marginal revenue function.
(b) What is the marginal revenue when the production level is 20 units?

34. **(REVENUE/MARGINAL REVENUE)** Suppose that the price p at which x units $(x > 1)$ can be sold is given by the demand equation

$$p = 60 + \frac{10}{\ln x}$$

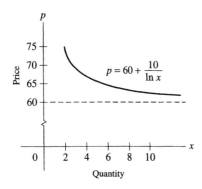

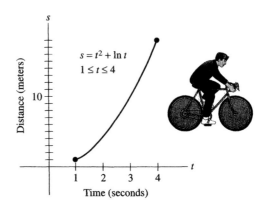

(a) Determine the revenue function.

(b) Determine the marginal revenue function.

35. (*COST/MARGINAL COST*) Suppose that the price p at which x units can be produced is given by the supply equation

$$p = 3 \ln (x + 1)$$

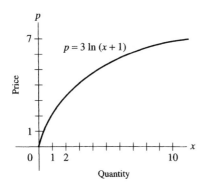

(a) Determine the cost function.

(b) Determine the marginal cost function.

36. (*BICYCLE VELOCITY*) Suppose that a bicyclist is traveling according to $s = t^2 + \ln t$ for $1 \le t \le 4$. Distance s is measured in meters, and time t is in seconds.

(a) Determine the function that gives the velocity of the bicycle at any time t, where $1 \le t \le 4$.

(b) What is the bicycle's velocity after 1 second, after 2 seconds, and after 4 seconds?

37. (*INCREASING CRIME*) According to F.B.I. data, the number of crimes $c(t)$ reported to police between 1984 ($t = 0$) and 1991 ($t = 7$) is given by

$$c(t) = 11.9 + .1t + \ln(t + 1)$$

Show that c is an increasing function for $0 \le t \le 7$, which means that crime was increasing during the years 1984–1991.

38. Determine the rate of change of y with respect to x for the function $y = \ln x$, when $x = 1/2$.

For each function in Exercises 39–44, determine whether its graph is increasing or decreasing at the given point.

39. $f(x) = \ln x^2$ at $(1, 0)$

40. $f(x) = x \ln x$ at $(1, 0)$

41. $f(x) = \dfrac{\ln x}{x}$ at $(1, 0)$

42. $f(x) = \ln \dfrac{1}{x}$ at $\left(\dfrac{1}{e}, 1 \right)$

43. $f(x) = \dfrac{x + 1}{\ln x}$ at $(e, e + 1)$

44. $f(x) = \dfrac{x + 2}{1 + \ln x}$ at $(1, 3)$

Find all critical numbers and all relative extrema, if any, for each function in Exercises 45–52.

45. $f(x) = 2x - 6 \ln x$ **46.** $f(x) = x^2 - 18 \ln x$

47. $f(x) = \dfrac{\ln x^2}{x}$ **48.** $f(x) = \dfrac{\ln x}{x^2}$

49. $f(x) = x^2 \ln x$ **50.** $f(x) = x \ln x$

51. $f(x) = \ln (2x - x^2)$ **52.** $f(x) = \ln (3x - x^3)$

Sketch the graph of each function in Exercises 53–56.

53. $y = x - \ln x$ **54.** $y = x \ln x$

55. $y = \ln (x^2 + 1)$ **56.** $y = x^2 \ln x$

Use implicit differentiation to find dy/dx in Exercises 57–64.

57. $3 \ln x + xy + y = 1$ **58.** $y^2 - \ln y + 2x = 6$

59. $x^2 + 2y + \ln (xy) = 0$ **60.** $xy^3 + \ln (xy) = 5x$

61. $x \ln y - y \ln x = 8$ **62.** $x^2 \ln x + y^2 \ln y = 2$

63. $e^x \ln y - 3xy + x = 10$ **64.** $e^y \ln x + xy^2 = y$

Find the derivative of each function in Exercises 65–72.

65. $y = \log_{10} x$ **66.** $y = \log_3 x$

67. $y = \log_2 9x$ **68.** $y = \log_2 3x^2$

69. $y = x \log_{10}(1 - 3x)$ **70.** $y = x^2 \log_2 5x$

71. $y = \dfrac{\log_{10} x}{x}$ **72.** $y = \dfrac{\log_2 x}{x + 1}$

Use logarithmic differentiation (see Example 13) to obtain dy/dx for each function in Exercises 75–80.

73. $y = x^{2x}$ **74.** $y = (2x)^x$

75. $y = (x + 1)^x$ **76.** $y = (x + 1)^{2x}$

77. $y = x^{1/x}$ **78.** $y = x^{x + 1}$

79. $y = (3x)^{x + 1}$ **80.** $y = (x - 1)^{x + 1}$

81. As an alternative to the formulas in Section 5.3, use logarithmic differentiation to obtain dy/dx for each of the given functions.
(a) $y = 3^x$ **(b)** $y = 2^x$
(c) $y = 5^{3x}$ **(d)** $y = 4^{x^2}$

82. Use a calculator to investigate the limit

$$\lim_{x \to 0^+} x \ln x$$

83. Use a calculator to investigate the limit

$$\lim_{x \to \infty} \frac{\ln x}{x}$$

84. Given $y = 7 \ln x$, should the *product rule* be used to determine dy/dx? Explain.

85. Given $y = \dfrac{\ln x}{2}$, should the *quotient rule* be used to determine dy/dx? Explain.

86. Explain why -1 is not a critical number of the function $y = \ln (3x - x^3)$.

87. Is the graph of $y - x + y \ln x = 1 - e$ increasing or decreasing at the point $\left(e, \tfrac{1}{2}\right)$?

88. For $f(x) = \ln x$, we have $f'(x) = 1/x$. It would appear that $f'(x) > 0$ for $x > 0$ and $f'(x) < 0$ for $x < 0$. Can we conclude that f is increasing for $x > 0$ and decreasing for $x < 0$? Explain.

89. For $f(x) = \ln x$, use $f'(x)$ to explain why the natural logarithm function has no relative extrema. Be complete in the explanation of your search for critical numbers.

90. Let $y = u^v$, where u and v are functions of x. Use logarithmic differentiation to obtain the result

$$\frac{dy}{dx} = u^v \left[\frac{v}{u} \cdot \frac{du}{dx} + (\ln u) \frac{dv}{dx} \right]$$

91. Consider the slope of the tangent line to the graph of $y = \ln x$, where $x = 1, 10, 100,$ and 1000. Where will the slope of the tangent line be zero, or is that not possible? Explain.

92. *Alternative to logarithmic differentiation* (which was demonstrated in Example 13).
The expression x^x can be written as follows:

$$x^x = e^{\ln x^x} \quad \text{or} \quad x^x = e^{x \ln x}$$

Now x^x can be differentiated by differentiating $e^{x \ln x}$.

$$\frac{d}{dx} x^x = \frac{d}{dx} e^{x \ln x} = e^{x \ln x} \cdot \frac{d}{dx} (x \ln x)$$

$$= e^{x \ln x} \left[x \cdot \frac{1}{x} + (\ln x) \cdot 1 \right]$$

$$= e^{x \ln x}(1 + \ln x)$$

$$= x^x(1 + \ln x)$$

Redo Exercises 73 and 75 by using this alternative method.

93. If $f(x) = \ln x$, determine $f^{(40)}(x)$, the 40th derivative. (*Hint*: Obtain a few derivatives and then determine a pattern.)

TECHNOLOGY *E X E R C I S E S*

1. Graph $f(x) = 3.2 + 1.8x - 2 \ln x$.

   (a) Find, to the nearest tenth, the coordinates of the relative minimum point.

   (b) Where is the graph concave up?

2. Graph $f(x) = x + e^x - 20 \ln x$. Determine whether the graph is increasing or decreasing at the given points.

   (a) $(3, f(3))$ **(b)** $(1, f(1))$ **(c)** $(2, f(2))$

3. Graph the function

$$f(x) = \frac{x^2 - 10 \ln x}{2x}$$

   (a) Is $f'(2)$ positive, negative, zero, or undefined?

   (b) Is $f''(1)$ positive or negative?

4. Graph the appropriate function and study it in order to evaluate the limit.

$$\lim_{x \to \infty} \frac{14 \ln x}{5x}$$

5. Approximate the larger critical number of $f(x) = x^2 - 2x - x \ln x$, to the *nearest hundredth*, by using the following steps. Obtain $f'(x)$ and then graph it. Study the graph to see where $f'(x) = 0$.

Key Terms and Ideas

exponential functions	learning curve	half-life
e	logarithm	radiocarbon dating
continuous compounding	common logarithms	nominal rate
exponential growth	natural logarithms	effective rate
exponential decay	natural logarithm function	derivative of e^u
present value	properties of logarithms	derivative of $\ln u$
logistic growth	doubling time	logarithmic differentiation

Review Exercises for Chapter 5

In Exercises 1–8, solve each equation for x.

1. $5e^{7x} = 30$ **2.** $10^{3x} = 4$

3. $3 \ln 4x = 18$ **4.** $\log 4x = 2$

5. $4e^{.03x} = 2$ **6.** $e^{-.004x} = 7$

7. $5 - \ln x = 0$ **8.** $1 - 2 \ln x = 0$

Simplify each expression in Exercises 9–12.

9. $-e^{\ln 7}$ **10.** $xe^{\ln x}$

11. $\ln \dfrac{1}{e^2}$ **12.** $-e \ln e$

Determine the derivative of each function in Exercises 13–26.

13. $y = x^4 e^4$ **14.** $y = \dfrac{e^x}{x^2}$

15. $f(x) = (3 - e^x)^7$ **16.** $f(x) = \sqrt{1 + e^x}$

17. $f(x) = x^3 e^{-3x}$ **18.** $f(x) = \sqrt{x + e^{4x}}$

19. $f(x) = e^{3x} \ln x$ **20.** $f(x) = \sqrt{1 + \ln x}$

21. $y = x^2 (\ln x)^2$ **22.** $y = x^2 \ln x^2$

23. $f(x) = \ln \dfrac{1}{x^2}$ **24.** $f(x) = \dfrac{\ln x}{x^2}$

25. $y = x \ln x - x$ **26.** $y = x^2 \ln \sqrt{x}$

In Exercises 27–30, find all critical numbers of the given function.

27. $f(x) = 4x - 3e^x$ **28.** $f(x) = .5e^x - x$

29. $y = \ln (x - 3) - \dfrac{x}{7}$ **30.** $y = x - \ln 2x$

In Exercises 31–32, use implicit differentiation to find dy/dx.

31. $5 \ln y + e^{3y} = 2x$ **32.** $4 \ln x + e^{2y} = 3y$

33. (*PRESENT VALUE*) How much should be invested now at 7.5% interest per year, compounded continuously, in order to have $10,000 in 4 years?

34. (*DECLINING REAL ESTATE VALUE*) If the value of an old industrial property declines at the rate of 3% per year, what percent of its current value will it have 10 years from now?

35. (*FUNGUS GROWTH*) If a fungus doubles in size every 7 hours, how many times its present size will it be in 32 hours?

36. (*POPULATION GROWTH*) The population of Cary, North Carolina, increased from 21,800 in 1980 to 65,000 in 1995. Assuming exponential growth, determine the growth constant k and express it as a percent.

37. (*POPULATION GROWTH*) The population of a small sunbelt town has grown from 5000 to 8400 in 4 years. If the exponential growth continues at the same rate, what will the population be in another 4 years?

38. (*HOUSE APPRECIATION*) In 1994, houses in the Raleigh, North Carolina, area appreciated 7.8%. If appreciation continues at this rate for 10 years, what will be the value of a house that was worth $120,000 before the 10-year appreciation began?

39. (*MEDICARE*) In 1994, the annual cost of the Medicare program was $160 billion, and the cost was increasing at the rate of 10% per year.
   (a) If the growth rate were to remain at 10%, what would be the annual cost of Medicare in 2002?
   (b) The Republicans offered a plan to reduce the growth rate to 6.4% per year. Under their plan, what would be the annual cost of Medicare in 2002?

40. (*NUMBER OF ZEBRAS*) As a result of 6 months of severe drought, the number of zebras in a region has been reduced from 400 to 320. Assuming an exponential decline and assuming the drought continues, what will be the zebra population in another 4 months?

41. (*RADIOCARBON DATING*) Discovery of an 8000-year-old skeleton in a mountain cave in Colorado was announced in 1994. What percent of the original carbon-14 was contained in the skeleton? (Use 5730 years as the half-life of carbon-14. Obtain k to five decimal places.)

42. (*MOSQUITO GROWTH*) The mosquito population in a swampy region is growing according to

$$A = 9000e^{.02t}$$

where A is the number of mosquitos present after t days.

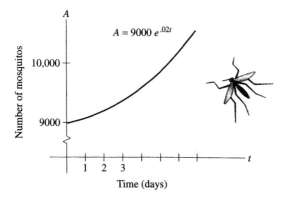

(a) When will the mosquito population be at 30,000?
(b) What is the rate of change of the mosquito population (expressed as mosquitos per day) when the population is 30,000?

43. (*SPREAD OF AN EPIDEMIC*) A logistic growth function can often be used to describe the spread of an epidemic through a city. For example, if y is the number of cases of the flu after t weeks, then we may have

$$y = \frac{200,000}{1 + 1999e^{-.8t}}$$

(a) How many cases of flu were there at the beginning, when the epidemic was first declared?
(b) How many cases of flu were there after 5 weeks?
(c) What is the maximum number of people in this city who can get the flu?

44. (*RADIOACTIVE DECAY*) If a 3-microgram mass of a radioactive element decays according to

$$A(t) = 3e^{-.001t}$$

determine the limit

$$\lim_{t \to \infty} A(t)$$

45. (*PHOTOSYNTHESIS*) Studies of leaves and photosynthesis led to the formula

$$\log P = a - b \log A$$

in which P is the rate at which photosynthesis occurs and A is the age of the leaf.

(a) Solve the equation for P.
(b) Solve the equation for A.

46. (*PROFIT*) Profit on the production and sale of x items is given by

$$P(x) = 50e^{.01x} - 80$$

Use calculus to determine whether profit is increasing or decreasing when $x = 10$ units.

W 47. (*FOOD STAMP PROGRAM*) Which one of the functions of time t given below could be used to describe a decrease in the demand y for food stamps in a region? Give an explanation.

(i) $y = 2500e^{.01t}$ **(ii)** $y = 4000e^{-.02t}$

(iii) $y = 1.4t - 2300$ **(iv)** $y = \dfrac{3500}{1 + 24e^{-.1t}}$

W 48. Read each of the descriptions presented below and decide which of the three situations best fits the graph shown here. Also, explain why the other two situations do not fit the graph.

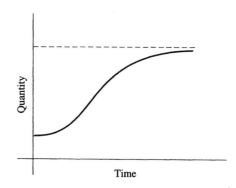

(i) Publicity about a beautiful valley community surrounded by steep, uninhabitable mountains leads to rapid population growth in the valley.
(ii) As people and local governments become more familiar with recycling, the amount of material being recycled will increase.
(iii) With the widespread use of personal computers, the number of typewriters being made has been declining in recent years.

W 49. What happens when you use a calculator to determine $\ln 0$ or $\ln(-1)$? Explain why it happens.

50. Determine whether the graph of the function given by $f(x) = e^x - 2\ln(x + 1)$ is increasing or decreasing at the point $(0, 1)$.

51. Use a calculator to investigate the limit

$$\lim_{x \to \infty} \frac{\ln x}{\sqrt{x}}$$

52. Use calculus to determine the smallest value that $(1 - \ln x)^2$ can have.

W 53. In Example 7 of Section 5.4, the graph of f is concave up for all x in the domain. Explain why.

54. (*LEARNING CURVE*) Consider the general learning curve equation

$$y = c(1 - e^{-kt})$$

(a) Show in steps how the equation can be manipulated into the form

$$y = c - c(e^{-t})^k$$

(b) With the help of a limit from Section 5.1, show that the plateau, or upper limit, for y is c.

55. (*CATENARY*) Electric lines and telephone lines are often hung suspended between poles that support them. The shape of the hanging cable is a curve called a *catenary* (see the figure).

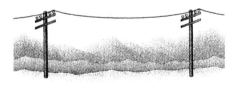

Algebraically, a catenary involves a sum of exponential expressions. Consider a telephone line that hangs between two poles placed 50 feet apart.

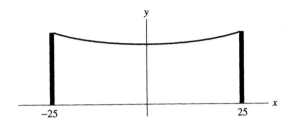

The curve is described by

$$y = 25e^{x/50} + 25e^{-x/50}$$

(a) Intuitively, we sense that the lowest point of the telephone line should be halfway between the two poles. Determine the height of the telephone line at its lowest point.

(b) Determine the height of the telephone line at its highest point.

(c) Determine the *sag* in the telephone line—that is, the difference between the maximum and minimum heights.

(d) Verify the intuitive suggestion of part (a) by showing that 0 is the critical number of the function and that the critical number 0 is indeed associated with a minimum.

56. (*FINDING HALF-LIFE*) Use the data given for the radioactive element polonium-210 to determine its half-life.

Number of days	10	35
Grams remaining	1.142	1.009

CHAPTER PROJECTS AND ESSAYS

Many of the projects and essays lend themselves to group activity, although most can be completed by individual effort.

1. EXPONENTIAL AND RELATED FUNCTIONS

BACKGROUND   Throughout the chapter there have been examples of exponential growth, exponential decay, logistic growth, and the learning curve. Exercise 87 of Section 5.2 lists nine examples.

THE PROJECT   Using the sources suggested below, obtain a collection of examples of these four types of functions. Note the type in each case, and give a brief explanation or justification. Use examples not given in this textbook. Here is a sample:

Example	Type	Explanation/Justification
Fish population of a breeding lake	Logistic growth	The population will grow exponentially for a while, but limited space and food will cause the growth to level off.

Sources to Consult: (1) Talk to instructors in other fields—especially the natural sciences, the social sciences, and business. (2) Brainstorm with other students. (3) Look through magazines such as *Business Week* and *Scientific American*.

2. LEONHARD EULER

BACKGROUND   Swiss mathematician Leonhard Euler is mentioned, and his photograph is reproduced, in Section 5.1. He was an amazingly productive mathematician and the most prolific writer in the history of mathematics. Although Euler was not a teacher by profession, his work had a great impact on the teaching and learning of mathematics.

THE PROJECT   Locate books on the history of mathematics or other books or articles that contain information on the accomplishments of Leonhard Euler. Select information about him and prepare an essay. Include, *among other things*,

(a) Mathematical symbols and notations that Leonhard Euler introduced.

(b) A brief description of any books he wrote that seem related to this calculus course.

(c) An explanation of the handicap Euler overcame in later life and how he overcame it.

(d) A measure of the volume of his work.

(e) A description of the capacity of his mind for calculations.

6

INTEGRATION

The amount of water passing through a dam varies throughout a day. An engineer, knowing the formula relating time to the amount of water leaving the site, can use the antiderivative, or integral, to calculate the total number of gallons of water entering a reservoir each day. Adjustments to the flow can then be made in order to prevent flooding during heavy rains.

*T*he previous three chapters presented a thorough study of the calculus operation called differentiation. The definition of *derivative* was motivated by our desire to define the slope of the tangent line. Many other applications followed.

In this chapter, we begin the study of another calculus operation. Once again, there will be a geometric interpretation and many nongeometric applications. But this time you have a head start, because this operation is related to differentiation. One name for this operation is *integration*. However, its other name, *antidifferentiation,* provides a hint of what is about to unfold.

6.1   ANTIDIFFERENTIATION

The preceding chapters focused on the calculus operation called differentiation, in which we begin with a function f and obtain the derivative f'. Interpreting f' as a rate of change of f led to a variety of applications. By contrast, there are situations in which we know the rate of change and seek the function. We need to be able to reverse the differentiation process in such cases.

One view of the calculus operation called **antidifferentiation** is that of reversing differentiation—that is, beginning with the derivative f' and obtaining from it an **antiderivative** f.

$$f \xrightarrow{\quad \text{differentiation} \quad} f'$$
$$f' \xrightarrow{\quad \text{antidifferentiation} \quad} f$$

Another view of antidifferentiation suggests that we may seek an antiderivative even though no differentiation has taken place; we begin with a function f and obtain an antiderivative denoted by F.

Rules for antidifferentiation are easy to obtain from known differentiation rules, since the process essentially reverses the effect of differentiation. Before obtaining rules for antidifferentiation, let us consider an example and some notation.

EXAMPLE 1   Antidifferentiate $f(x) = 3x^2$.

SOLUTION   We need to determine the function F that yields $f(x) = 3x^2$ when differentiated. It does not take long to realize that the derivative of x^3 is $3x^2$.

We might conclude that the antiderivative of $f(x) = 3x^2$ is $F(x) = x^3$, since

$$\frac{d}{dx}(x^3) = 3x^2$$

But it is also true that

$$\frac{d}{dx}(x^3 + 1) = 3x^2 \qquad \frac{d}{dx}(x^3 + 4) = 3x^2 \qquad \frac{d}{dx}(x^3 - 3) = 3x^2$$

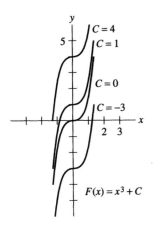

In fact,

$$\frac{d}{dx}(x^3 + C) = 3x^2 \qquad \text{for any constant } C$$

In view of this, we say that the antiderivative of $f(x) = 3x^2$ is

$$F(x) = x^3 + C \qquad \qquad \blacklozenge$$

The example has demonstrated why antiderivatives are written in this most general "plus C" form. Here are a few more examples of functions and their antiderivatives. Also, notice that *differentiation can be used to check antiderivatives*. The derivative of the antiderivative is equal to the function.

function	antiderivative	check
$f(x) = 2x$	$F(x) = x^2 + C$	$\dfrac{d}{dx}(x^2 + C) = 2x$
$f(x) = 6$	$F(x) = 6x + C$	$\dfrac{d}{dx}(6x + C) = 6$
$f(x) = e^x$	$F(x) = e^x + C$	$\dfrac{d}{dx}(e^x + C) = e^x$

Note

We now state without proof a result that is consistent with the result of Example 1.
If functions F and G are both antiderivatives of the same function f, then F(x) and G(x) can differ only by an added constant.

Just as there are special notations for the derivative, there is also a special notation for antiderivatives. The antiderivative of f is denoted by

$$\int f(x)\, dx$$

The symbol $\int$ is called an **integral sign** and was introduced by Leibniz. $f(x)$ is the **integrand.** The dx specifies that this is the integral of $f(x)$ with respect to x. (Later, we will say more about dx and how it is related to Δx and to differentials.) $\int f(x)\, dx$ is called an **indefinite integral**. The indefinite integral is the same as the most general antiderivative. The process of antidifferentiation can also be called **integration.** To integrate is to antidifferentiate.

Notation such as $\int f(x)\, dx$ clearly indicates integration. Nevertheless, the directions accompanying examples and exercises may say such things as "perform the antidifferentiation" or "evaluate" or "calculate" or "perform the integration."

EXAMPLE 2 Perform the integration: $\int 3x^2\, dx$

SOLUTION Here we are asked to antidifferentiate (integrate) $3x^2$. In fact, this is the problem of Example 1: only the notation is different. Thus, from previous experience we know that

$$\int 3x^2\, dx = x^3 + C$$

The number C is called the **constant of integration.** ◆

Recall the differentiation formula

$$\frac{d}{dx}(x^n) = nx^{n-1}$$

The corresponding antidifferentiation formula is given next.

Power Rule

$$\int x^n\, dx = \frac{x^{n+1}}{n+1} + C \qquad n \neq -1$$

To antidifferentiate (integrate) a power of x, increase the exponent by 1 and then divide by the new exponent.

The formula is true because the derivative of $\dfrac{x^{n+1}}{n+1} + C$ is in fact x^n, as we now show. (Note that when $n = -1$ the expression is not defined.)

$$\frac{d}{dx}\left(\frac{x^{n+1}}{n+1} + C\right) = \frac{d}{dx}\left(\frac{x^{n+1}}{n+1}\right) + \frac{d}{dx}(C) = \frac{(n+1)x^n}{(n+1)} + 0 = x^n$$

EXAMPLE 3 Perform the indicated antidifferentiation: $\int x^4\, dx$

SOLUTION

$$\int x^4\, dx = \frac{x^{4+1}}{4+1} + C = \frac{x^5}{5} + C$$

Note that in using the formula for $\int x^n\, dx$, we added 1 to the exponent and then divided by the new exponent. As a check, the derivative of $x^5/5 + C$ is x^4.

The check:

$$\frac{d}{dx}\left(\frac{x^5}{5} + C\right) = \frac{5x^4}{5} + 0 = x^4$$

◆

EXAMPLE 4 Determine $\int t^{-3}\, dt.$

SOLUTION

$$\int t^{-3}\, dt = \frac{t^{-3+1}}{-3+1} = \frac{t^{-2}}{-2} + C = -\frac{1}{2t^2} + C$$

◆

EXAMPLE 5 Perform the integration: $\int \frac{1}{\sqrt{x}}\, dx$

SOLUTION To begin, write $\sqrt{x}$ as $x^{1/2}$.

$$\int \frac{1}{\sqrt{x}}\, dx = \int \frac{1}{x^{1/2}}\, dx$$

Rewriting the integrand as a power of x, we obtain

$$\int x^{-1/2}\, dx$$

We can now apply the antidifferentiation formula. Add 1 to the exponent and divide by the new exponent. The result is

$$\frac{x^{1/2}}{1/2} + C$$

which simplifies to

$$2x^{1/2} + C \quad or \quad 2\sqrt{x} + C$$

◆

The three rules given next are based on differentiation rules. Each one can be proved by differentiating the right-hand side to obtain the integrand given on the left-hand side. (Keep in mind that the derivative of the antiderivative of a function is the function.)

Properties of Indefinite Integrals

$$\int [f(x) + g(x)]\, dx = \int f(x)\, dx + \int g(x)\, dx$$

$$\int [f(x) - g(x)]\, dx = \int f(x)\, dx - \int g(x)\, dx$$

$$\int k f(x)\, dx = k \int f(x)\, dx \qquad k = \text{constant}$$

In words, *the integral of a sum is the sum of the integrals*, *the integral of a difference is the difference of the integrals*, and *the integral of a constant times a function is that constant times the integral of the function.*

EXAMPLE 6 Evaluate $\int (x^2 + x^{3/2})\, dx$.

SOLUTION

$$\int(x^2 + x^{3/2})\, dx = \int x^2\, dx + \int x^{3/2}\, dx$$

$$= \frac{x^3}{3} + \frac{x^{5/2}}{5/2} + C$$

$$= \frac{x^3}{3} + \frac{2}{5}x^{5/2} + C$$

Notice that although there were two separate integrals along the way, there is only one constant of integration (C) shown in the final result. There is no need to list two constants, because the sum of two constants is simply one constant. Using the one constant C is sufficient. ◆

EXAMPLE 7   Perform the antidifferentiation: $\int(4x^2 - 3x)\, dx$

SOLUTION

$$\int(4x^2 - 3x)\, dx = \int 4x^2\, dx - \int 3x\, dx$$

$$= 4\int x^2\, dx - 3\int x\, dx$$

$$= 4 \cdot \frac{x^3}{3} - 3 \cdot \frac{x^2}{2} + C$$

$$= \frac{4x^3}{3} - \frac{3x^2}{2} + C$$ ◆

As you know, if k is a constant, then the derivative of kx is k. Reversing the direction of this process yields the following antidifferentiation rule.

Integral of a Constant

$$\int k\, dx = kx + C$$

where k is a constant.

EXAMPLE 8   Perform the integration: $\int 7\, dx$

SOLUTION

$$\int 7\, dx = 7x + C$$ ◆

EXAMPLE 9   Perform the integration: $\int dx$

SOLUTION

$$\int dx = \int 1\, dx = x + C$$ ◆

EXAMPLE 10   Perform the integration: $\displaystyle\int \left(5x^4 - \frac{3}{x^2} + 6\right) dx$

SOLUTION

$$\int \left(5x^4 - \frac{3}{x^2} + 6\right) dx = \int 5x^4\, dx - \int \frac{3}{x^2}\, dx + \int 6\, dx$$

$$= 5\int x^4\, dx - 3\int x^{-2}\, dx + \int 6\, dx$$

$$= \frac{5x^5}{5} - \frac{3x^{-1}}{-1} + 6x + C$$

$$= x^5 + \frac{3}{x} + 6x + C \qquad \blacklozenge$$

Two other integration formulas follow from differentiation formulas. The first is from Section 5.3, the second from Section 5.4.

$$\int e^x\, dx = e^x + C \qquad\qquad \int \frac{1}{x}\, dx = \ln |x| + C$$

If $x > 0$, then $\ln |x|$ can be written $\ln x$. Also, since $1/x$ is the same as x^{-1}, we now have a formula for $\int x^{-1}\, dx$, the case of $\int x^n\, dx$ when $n = -1$.

EXAMPLE 11   Determine $\displaystyle\int (e^x + 3x)\, dx.$

SOLUTION

$$\int (e^x + 3x)\, dx = \int e^x\, dx + \int 3x\, dx$$

$$= e^x + 3\int x\, dx$$

$$= e^x + \frac{3x^2}{2} + C \qquad \blacklozenge$$

EXAMPLE 12   Determine $\displaystyle\int \left(t - \frac{1}{t}\right) dt.$

SOLUTION

$$\int \left(t - \frac{1}{t}\right) dt = \int t\, dt - \int \frac{1}{t}\, dt$$

$$= \frac{t^2}{2} - \ln |t| + C \qquad \blacklozenge$$

EXAMPLE 13   Calculate $\displaystyle\int \frac{1 + 3x^3}{x}\, dx.$

SOLUTION   The integrand can be separated into two fractions. Then we can integrate.

$$\int \frac{1 + 3x^3}{x}\, dx = \int \left(\frac{1}{x} + \frac{3x^3}{x} \right) dx$$

$$= \int \frac{1}{x}\, dx + \int 3x^2\, dx$$

$$= \ln |x| + x^3 + C \qquad \blacklozenge$$

The formula shown next is needed for some of the applications presented later in the chapter. Verification of the formula follows.

$$\int e^{kx}\, dx = \frac{1}{k}e^{kx} + C \qquad k \neq 0$$

The formula can be verified by showing that the derivative of $\frac{1}{k}e^{kx} + C$ is e^{kx}.

$$\frac{d}{dx}\left(\frac{1}{k}e^{kx} + C \right) = \frac{d}{dx}\left(\frac{1}{k}e^{kx} \right) + \frac{d}{dx}(C) = \frac{1}{k}\cdot \frac{d}{dx}(e^{kx}) + 0 = \frac{1}{k}\cdot e^{kx}\cdot k = e^{kx}$$

EXAMPLE 14   Evaluate the integrals.

(a) $\int e^{3x}\, dx$ **(b)** $\int e^{-2x}\, dx$ **(c)** $\int e^{.02x}\, dx$ **(d)** $\int 4e^{.1x}\, dx$

SOLUTION   **(a)** $\int e^{3x}\, dx = \frac{1}{3}e^{3x} + C$

(b) $\int e^{-2x}\, dx = \frac{1}{-2}e^{-2x} + C = -\frac{1}{2}e^{-2x} + C$

(c) $\int e^{.02x}\, dx = \frac{1}{.02}e^{.02x} + C = 50e^{.02x} + C$

(d) $\int 4e^{.1x}\, dx = 4\int e^{.1x}\, dx = 4\cdot \frac{1}{.1}e^{.1x} + C = 4(10)e^{.1x} + C = 40e^{.1x} + C \qquad \blacklozenge$

6.1   Exercises

Perform each antidifferentiation in Exercises 1–8.

1. $\int 8x\, dx$

2. $\int 4x\, dx$

3. $\int 6x^2\, dx$

4. $\int 5x^2\, dx$

5. $\int t^3\, dt$

6. $\int 4x^3\, dx$

7. $\int 10x^5\, dx$

8. $\int 5x^5\, dx$

Evaluate each indefinite integral in Exercises 9–22.

9. $\int x^{-2}\, dx$

10. $\int t^{-5}\, dt$

11. $\int 3x^{-4}\, dx$

12. $\int 10x^{-6}\, dx$

13. $\int \dfrac{1}{x^5}\, dx$

14. $\int \dfrac{1}{x^3}\, dx$

15. $\int \dfrac{20}{z^6}\, dz$

16. $\int \dfrac{6}{t^4}\, dt$

17. $\int \sqrt{x}\, dx$

18. $\int \sqrt[3]{x}\, dx$

19. $\int x^{3/4}\, dx$

20. $\int t^{3/2}\, dt$

21. $\int x^{-2/3}\, dx$

22. $\int x^{-3/4}\, dx$

Perform each integration in Exercises 23–32.

23. $\int 3\, dx$

24. $\int 10\, dx$

25. $\int (x^2 + 6x)\, dx$

26. $\int (4x^3 - 7)\, dx$

27. $\int (\sqrt{x} - 3x^2)\, dx$

28. $\int (1 - \sqrt{t})\, dt$

29. $\int (x^{-1/2} + 9)\, dx$

30. $\int (1 - x^{-1/2})\, dx$

31. $\int (t^2 - 8t + 1)\, dt$

32. $\int (x^2 + 7x - 2)\, dx$

Determine the value of each integral in Exercises 33–56.

33. $\int e^x\, dx$

34. $\int e^t\, dt$

35. $\int (2x - e^x)\, dx$

36. $\int (e^x - x^4)\, dx$

37. $\int (e^x + 1)\, dx$

38. $\int (x^2 - e^x)\, dx$

39. $\int \dfrac{1}{z}\, dz$

40. $\int \dfrac{7}{t}\, dt$

41. $\int \left(\dfrac{4}{x} + 6x\right) dx$

42. $\int \left(\dfrac{2}{x} - 4x\right) dx$

43. $\int \dfrac{1}{5x}\, dx$

44. $\int \dfrac{1}{7x}\, dx$

45. $\int (3 + x^{-1})\, dx$

46. $\int (x^{-1} + 3x^2)\, dx$

47. $\int e^{7x}\, dx$

48. $\int e^{4x}\, dx$

49. $\int 5e^x\, dx$

50. $\int 3e^x\, dx$

51. $\int (e^{.05t} + 1)\, dt$

52. $\int (e^{.01t} + 2)\, dt$

53. $\int e^{-6x}\, dx$

54. $\int e^{-2x}\, dx$

55. $\int e^{-.01x}\, dx$

56. $\int e^{-.02x}\, dx$

Evaluate each indefinite integral in Exercises 57–62.

57. $\int \dfrac{1 + 2x^2}{x}\, dx$

58. $\int \dfrac{x^3 - 4}{x}\, dx$

59. $\int \dfrac{t + 1}{t^{1/2}}\, dt$

60. $\int \dfrac{1 - t^2}{t^{1/2}}\, dt$

61. $\int \dfrac{x^2 + x}{\sqrt{x}}\, dx$

62. $\int \dfrac{1 + \sqrt{x}}{x}\, dx$

Evaluate each indefinite integral in Exercises 63–66.

63. $\int \dfrac{e^x + 1}{e^x}\, dx$

64. $\int \dfrac{1 - e^{2x}}{e^x}\, dx$

65. $\int x^2(1 + x)\, dx$

66. $\int \dfrac{1}{x}\left[x + \dfrac{1}{x}\right] dx$

In Exercises 67–70, consider each integral and determine which of the four expressions given is equal to the integral.

67. $\int xe^x\, dx$

    (i) $xe^x + e^x + x + C$ **(ii)** $xe^x - e^x + C$

    (iii) $e^x - xe^x - x + C$ **(iv)** $xe^x - x + C$

68. $\int x^2 e^x\, dx$

    (i) $x^3 e^x + 2xe^x + C$

    (ii) $x^2 e^x - xe^x + C$

    (iii) $x^2 e^x - 2xe^x + 2e^x + C$

    (iv) $2x^2 e^x + xe^x - e^x + C$

69. $\int \ln x \, dx$

    (i) $\dfrac{1}{x} + C$ **(ii)** $x + \ln x + C$

    (iii) $x + x \ln x + C$ **(iv)** $x \ln x - x + C$

70. $\int 4x \ln x \, dx$

    (i) $4x \ln x - x + C$ **(ii)** $2x^2 \ln x - x^2 + C$

    (iii) $x^2 \ln x - 2x^2 + C$ **(iv)** $2x \ln x + x^2 + C$

W 71. Consider a function such as $f(x) = x^2 + 5$ or $f(x) = \sqrt{x}$ or some other function f.

    (a) If you integrate the function f and then differentiate the result, will the final result be function f?

    (b) If you differentiate function f and then integrate the result, will you then have function f? Explain.

W 72. In the formula for the integral of e^{kx}, it is stated that k cannot be 0. What problem arises when $k = 0$?

W 73. Can we integrate x^n for all real values of n? If not, explain why not. If so, explain the different cases.

W 74. Consider the two functions graphed at the top of the next column. Which graph is the function f, and which is the antiderivative F? Explain.

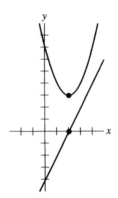

W 75. The next figure shows the graph of F, an antiderivative of f. Describe the appearance of the graph of G, another antiderivative of f, given that $G(3) = 2$.

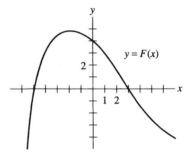

TECHNOLOGY *EXERCISES*

W 1. Consider $f(x) = 2x + 3$. Obtain $F(x)$ for which $C = 1$. Graph both f and F using x in $[-6, 6]$ and y in $[-4, 10]$.

    (a) What can be said of the graph of f at the x value for which F has a relative minimum?

    (b) Compare the graph of f to the left and right of the relative minimum point of F. (Focus on the x axis.)

W 2. Consider $f(x) = 3x^2 - 10x + 2.5$. Obtain $F(x)$ for which $C = 7.3$. Graph both f and F.

    (a) What can be said of the graph of F at the x values for which $f(x) = 0$?

    (b) Consider the number x_1 for which $f'(x_1) = 0$. What is happening to the graph of F at the point $(x_1, F(x_1))$?

W 3. Consider $f(x) = .3x^2$. Graph three antiderivatives—those for $C = 0$, $C = 3$, and $C = -4$.

    (a) What is true of the slope of the tangent line to each of the three curves at the same x value (say $x = -2$)?

(b) How do you explain the result in part (a)?

Note Using a computer algebra system, you can graph several antiderivatives of a function along with tangent lines to each curve. Consider redoing the last exercise with the aid of such software, perhaps even using x values other than -2.

Note *Mathematica* and *Maple* can perform integration of functions. The integral

$$\int (x^2 + 6)\, dx$$

can be evaluated as follows.

Mathematica: `Integrate [x ^ 2 + 6, x]`

Maple: `int(x ^ 2 + 6, x);`

Consider trying such software on Exercises 35, 43, and 57.

6.2 | *SOME APPLICATIONS OF ANTIDIFFERENTIATION*

This section includes a variety of applications of antidifferentiation. In each instance, the value of the constant C will need to be determined for the specific situation. When this is done, the resulting antiderivative is called a **particular antiderivative** or may be thought of as a *particular solution*. To begin, here is an example that demonstrates how the value of C can be determined when specific information is given.

EXAMPLE 1 Find $f(x)$ if $f'(x) = 3x^2 + 2x - 1$ and $f(2) = 14$.

SOLUTION $f(x)$ is determined from its derivative $f'(x)$ by antidifferentiation.
Because $f'(x) = 3x^2 + 2x - 1$, we have

$$f(x) = \int (3x^2 + 2x - 1)\, dx$$

$$f(x) = x^3 + x^2 - x + C$$

The value of C can be determined by using the fact that $f(2) = 14$. Recall that $f(2) = 14$ means that when $x = 2$, $f(x) = 14$. Upon substituting 2 for x and 14 for $f(x)$ in $f(x) = x^3 + x^2 - x + C$, we have

$$14 = 2^3 + 2^2 - 2 + C$$
$$14 = 10 + C$$
$$C = 4$$

Thus C is 4 and the function is

$$f(x) = x^3 + x^2 - x + 4$$

Note that because we have determined the value of C, this function can be called a "particular" antiderivative of $f'(x)$.   ◆

EXAMPLE 2   Determine the equation of the curve that has slope $2x$ and passes through the point $(3, 11)$.

SOLUTION   Because the slope is $2x$, we can write

$$\frac{dy}{dx} = 2x$$

It follows that

$$y = \int 2x\, dx \qquad \text{or} \qquad y = x^2 + C$$

The curve passes through $(3, 11)$, which means that $y = 11$ when $x = 3$. So let $x = 3$ and $y = 11$ in the equation $y = x^2 + C$.

$$11 = 3^2 + C \qquad \text{or} \qquad C = 2$$

We can now replace C by 2 in the equation $y = x^2 + C$. The result is

$$y = x^2 + 2$$ ◆

EXAMPLE 3   **OBTAINING COST FROM MARGINAL COST**

A company finds that the marginal cost when x units of merchandise are produced is $50 - .08x$ dollars. If the fixed cost (overhead) is \$700, determine

(a) the cost of producing x units   **(b)** the cost of producing 10 units

SOLUTION   Recall that marginal cost is the derivative of cost (see Section 3.4). Using $C(x)$ for the cost function, we have

$$C'(x) = 50 - .08x$$
$$C(x) = \int (50 - .08x)\, dx$$
$$C(x) = 50x - .04x^2 + C$$

Because the fixed cost (overhead) is \$700, we know that the cost of producing zero units is \$700. In other words, $C(0) = 700$. This information can be used to determine the constant C.

$$C(0) = 50(0) - .04(0)^2 + C$$
$$700 = 0 - 0 + C$$
$$C = 700$$

Thus,

(a) $C(x) = 50x - .04x^2 + 700$

(b) $C(10) = 50(10) - .04(10)^2 + 700 = 1196$

The cost of producing 10 units is $1196. Figure 1 shows the cost function.

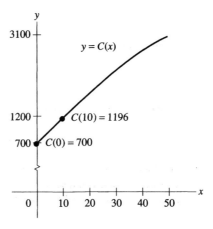

Figure 1 The cost function determined in Example 3 ◆

EXAMPLE 4 *ROCKET FLIGHT*

A toy rocket is shot vertically upward from the ground with an initial velocity of 300 feet per second. The acceleration due to gravity is −32 feet per second per second—negative because it is downward. (No other acceleration is applied to the rocket.)

(a) Find a formula for the rocket's velocity *t* seconds after the launch.

(b) Find a formula for the rocket's distance above the ground at any time *t*.

SOLUTION **(a)** Recall from Chapter 3 that acceleration is the derivative of velocity.

$$a = \frac{dv}{dt}$$

The acceleration is given as −32, so we have

$$\frac{dv}{dt} = -32$$

Antidifferentiation yields

$$v = \int (-32)\, dt \qquad \text{or} \qquad v = -32t + C$$

To determine C, use the fact that the initial velocity is 300 feet per second. This means $v = 300$ when $t = 0$. Substituting these two numbers into the equation $v = -32t + C$ yields

$$300 = -32(0) + C \qquad \text{or} \qquad 300 = C$$

Thus we have

$$v = -32t + 300$$

(b) Recall from Chapter 3 that velocity is the derivative of distance.

$$v = \frac{ds}{dt}$$

And since $v = -32t + 300$, we have

$$\frac{ds}{dt} = -32t + 300$$

Antidifferentiation yields

$$s = \int (-32t + 300)\, dt \qquad \text{or} \qquad s = -16t^2 + 300t + C$$

To determine C, note that at the beginning (when $t = 0$), the rocket's distance s above the ground is zero, because it is shot upward from the ground. Substituting 0 for t and 0 for s into $s = -16t^2 + 300t + C$ yields

$$0 = -16(0)^2 + 300(0) + C \qquad \text{or} \qquad C = 0$$

Thus,

$$s = -16t^2 + 300t \qquad\qquad\qquad \blacklozenge$$

APPLIED

EXAMPLE 5 *A LEARNING EXPERIMENT*

To test learning, a psychologist asks people to memorize a long sequence of digits. Assume that the rate at which digits are being memorized is

$$\frac{dy}{dt} = 5.4e^{-.3t} \qquad \text{words per minute}$$

where y is the number of digits memorized and t is the time in minutes.

(a) Find y as a function of t, which gives the number of digits memorized after t minutes.

(b) How many digits will be memorized after 5 minutes?

SOLUTION **(a)** From the given equation

$$\frac{dy}{dt} = 5.4e^{-.3t}$$

we can obtain y by antidifferentiation.

$$y = \int 5.4e^{-.3t}\, dt = 5.4 \int e^{-.3t}\, dt = \frac{5.4}{-.3}e^{-.3t} + C = -18e^{-.3t} + C$$

To determine C, we use the fact that in the beginning (when $t = 0$), the number of digits memorized is zero (that is, $y = 0$). Thus, $y = 0$ when $t = 0$ and

$$0 = -18e^{-.3(0)} + C$$
$$0 = -18(1) + C$$
$$C = 18$$

Thus, the number of digits memorized (y) as a function of time (t) is

$$y = 18 - 18e^{-.3t}$$

A graph of the function is given in Figure 2.

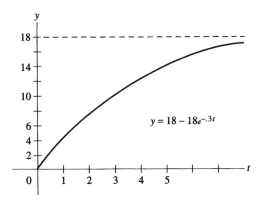

Figure 2 The learning function of Example 5: The number of digits memorized as a function of time

(b) After 5 minutes ($t = 5$), the number of digits memorized is

$$y = 18 - 18e^{-.3(5)}$$
$$= 18 - 18e^{-1.5}$$
$$\approx 18 - 18(.2231)$$
$$= 18 - 4.0158$$
$$\approx 14$$

Approximately 14 digits will be memorized after 5 minutes. ◆

6.2 Exercises

In Exercises 1–10, determine the particular antiderivative $f(x)$. See Example 1.

1. $f'(x) = 3x^2 - 2x + 5$, $f(1) = 8$

2. $f'(x) = 12x^2 + 6x$, $f(2) = 27$

3. $f'(x) = -3x^{-4}$, $f(1) = 3$

4. $f'(x) = 1 - \dfrac{20}{x^3}$, $f(1) = 20$

5. $f'(x) = 1 + 3\sqrt{x}$, $f(4) = 16$

6. $f'(x) = 8x^{1/3} + 3x^{1/2}$, $f(1) = 7$

7. $f'(x) = \dfrac{1}{x}$, $f(1) = 5$

8. $f'(x) = 3 - \dfrac{1}{x}$, $f(1) = 8$

9. $f'(x) = e^{2x} + 8x$, $f(0) = 2$

10. $f'(x) = 1 + 10e^{5x}$, $f(0) = 2$

In Exercises 11–16, find the equation of the curve that has the given slope and passes through the given point.

11. Slope $2x$ and through $(3, 14)$

12. Slope $4x - 2$ and through $(0, 3)$

13. Slope $\sqrt{x}$ and through $(9, 19)$

14. Slope $3/x$ and through $(1, 3)$

15. Slope e^x and through $(0, 1)$

16. Slope $2e^x$ and through $(0, 3)$

(COST) In Exercises 17–20, determine the cost function $C(x)$ that corresponds to the marginal cost given.

17. Marginal cost $= 40 - .06x$,   fixed cost $= \$200$

18. Marginal cost $= 10 - .02x$,   fixed cost $= \$150$

19. Marginal cost $= \dfrac{10}{\sqrt{x}}$,   fixed cost $= \$50$

20. Marginal cost $= \dfrac{2}{\sqrt{x}}$,   fixed cost $= \$10$

21. (COST) If the marginal cost when x units are produced is $100 - .50x$ dollars and the overhead is $\$40$, what is the cost of producing 10 units?

22. (REVENUE) Let $R(x)$ be the revenue a company receives from the sale of x units of its product. If its marginal revenue $R'(x)$ is $100 - .2x$ dollars, determine
(a) $R(x)$
(b) The revenue from the sale of 20 units
Assume there is no revenue when zero units are sold.

(REVENUE) In Exercises 23–25, determine the revenue function $R(x)$ that corresponds to the marginal revenue given. Assume there is no revenue when zero units are sold.

23. Marginal revenue $= 50 - .4x$

24. Marginal revenue $= 100 - .03x^2$

25. Marginal revenue $= 10 - e^{.05x}$

(PROFIT) In Exercises 26–29, determine the profit function $P(x)$ that corresponds to the given marginal profit.

26. Marginal profit $= 35 - .6x^2$, $P(0) = -\$50$

27. Marginal profit $= 100 + .4x - .06x^2$, $P(0) = 0$

28. Marginal profit $= 50 - .3\sqrt{x}$, $P(0) = -\$130$

29. Marginal profit $= 70 - e^{.01x}$, $P(0) = -\$30$

30. (VELOCITY/DISTANCE) A ball is shot vertically upward from the edge of a building with initial velocity 352 feet per second. The building is 768 feet tall. Acceleration due to gravity is -32 feet per second per second.
(a) Determine the equations that describe the velocity of the ball and its distance from the ground.
(b) How far above the ground is the ball after 6 seconds, and how fast is it going then?

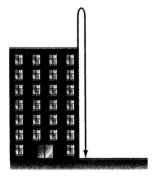

31. (VELOCITY/DISTANCE) A tourist accidentally drops his camera from the top of a cliff that is 576 feet above the water below. Assume the acceleration due to gravity to be -32 feet per second per second.
(a) Determine the velocity $v(t)$ of the camera at any time t during its fall.
(b) Determine $s(t)$, the height of the camera above the water at any time t during its fall.
(c) How fast is the camera falling 4 seconds after it is dropped?
(d) How long will it take the camera to hit the water? (*Hint*: What is the value of s when the camera hits the water?)

32. (VELOCITY/DISTANCE) A woman gets into her car and then drives it with a constant acceleration of 22 feet per second per second.
(a) Determine the velocity function.
(b) Determine the distance function.
(c) How far does the car go in 6 seconds?

33. (VELOCITY/DISTANCE) On the *moon* the magnitude of the acceleration due to gravity is less than that on the earth; it is approximately -5.3 feet per second per second. Consider a ball thrown upward from the surface of the moon with an initial velocity of 120 feet per second.
(a) Obtain a function that gives the velocity of the ball at any time t.

(b) Determine a function that shows the distance of the ball from the moon's surface at any time t.

34. (TREE HEIGHT) The height h (in feet) of a tree is a function of time t (in years). Suppose you begin ($t = 0$) by planting a 5-foot tree in your yard and the tree grows to maturity according to the formula

$$\frac{dh}{dt} = .3 + \frac{1}{\sqrt{t}} \qquad t > 0$$

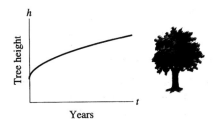

(a) Determine a formula for the height of the tree at any time t.

(b) Find the height of the tree after 1 year, 4 years, 9 years, and 16 years.

35. (FLU OUTBREAK) From data collected, the health office estimates that a flu virus is spreading through the county at the rate of $5t^{2/3} + 22$ people per day.

(a) If n is the number of people who have the flu at any time t, where t is the time in days, complete the equation. $dn/dt =$ _____

(b) If 50 people had the flu at the beginning of the outbreak, determine an equation that expresses n as a function of t.

(c) How many people have the flu after 8 days?

36. (FLU EPIDEMIC) A flu epidemic is spreading at the rate

$$\frac{dn}{dt} = 180t - 6t^2$$

where n is the number of people who are sick with flu on any particular day t after the outbreak started.

(a) Determine an equation for n as a function of t. Assume no one has the flu at the beginning (when $t = 0$).

(b) How many people have the flu the tenth day after the outbreak begins?

37. (INHIBITING GROWTH) A colony of 2000 bacteria is introduced to a growth-inhibiting environment and grows at the rate

$$\frac{dn}{dt} = 30 + 2t$$

where n is the number of bacteria present at any time t (t is measured in hours).

(a) Determine a function that gives the number of bacteria present at any time t.

(b) How many bacteria are present after 3 hours?

38. (INHIBITING GROWTH) Redo Exercise 37 assuming that the colony has 1000 bacteria and that

$$\frac{dn}{dt} = 50 + 2t$$

39. (MOLD GROWTH) The weight of a mold is growing exponentially at the rate of

$$\frac{dw}{dt} = e^{.2t} \qquad \text{milligrams per hour}$$

How much will the mold weigh in 10 hours if it weighs 70 milligrams now?

40. (TEMPERATURE) The rate of change of the temperature T inside a furnace after x minutes ($0 \le x \le 20$) is

$$\frac{dT}{dx} = 2x + 15 \qquad \text{degrees per minute}$$

Assume the temperature inside the furnace is 200°F initially.

(a) Find the formula for the temperature at any time x.

(b) What is the temperature inside the furnace after 14 minutes?

41. (ARTERY PLAQUE) Plaque buildup on the inside walls of an artery reduces the diameter of the artery (and thus reduces the blood flow). Suppose that an artery has a diameter of .4 centimeter and the diameter (d) is decreasing at the rate

$$\frac{dd}{dt} = -.03e^{-.001t} \qquad \text{centimeters per year.}$$

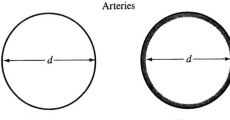

Arteries

No plaque
(full diameter)

Plaque
(reduced diameter)

(a) Determine d as a function of t.

(b) What will the diameter of the artery be after 10 years?

42. **(COAL PRODUCTION)** After t hours of operation, a coal mine is producing coal at the rate of $30 + 2t - .03t^2$ tons of coal per hour. Find a formula for the total output of the coal mine after t hours of operation.

43. **(ATMOSPHERIC PRESSURE)** The rate at which atmospheric pressure P changes as the height x above sea level changes is

$$\frac{dP}{dx} = -3.087e^{-.21x}$$

(P is measured in pounds per square inch and x is in miles, which means that dP/dx is in pounds per square inch per mile.)

   Determine P as a function of x. At sea level, P is 14.7 pounds per square inch.

44. **(GEOMETRY)** The rate of change of the area of a circular region with respect to its radius is

$$\frac{dA}{dr} = 2\pi r$$

Use this fact, and the fact that $A = 0$ when $r = 0$, to determine the area of a circular region when the radius is 4 centimeters.

45. **(GEOMETRY)** The rate of change of the volume of a spherical balloon with respect to its radius is

$$\frac{dV}{dr} = 4\pi r^2$$

Use this fact, and the fact that $V = 0$ when $r = 0$, to determine the volume of the balloon when its radius is 6 centimeters.

W 46. **(COST)** Explain in words how you can determine the cost function when you are given the marginal cost function and the fixed cost (or overhead).

W 47. **(PROFIT)** Exercises 26–29 give the value of $P(0)$.
   (a) What is the meaning of $P(0)$?
   (b) What does it mean when $P(0)$ is negative?

48. Use antidifferentiation to determine a function that has a rounded relative minimum at (2, 1).

W 49. Given $f'(x)$, what specific information is needed in order to determine a particular antiderivative $f(x)$?

 TECHNOLOGY EXERCISES

1. (a) Determine the equation of the curve that has slope $1.5x$ and passes through the point (0, 2).

   W (b) Graph the curve and the lines $y = -3x - 1$ and $y = 1.5x + 1.25$. Use the window $[-5, 5]$ for x and the window $[0, 10]$ for y. Comment on the relationship of the lines to the curve.

   W (c) What is the slope of the curve at $x = -2$? How does this tie in with the line $y = -3x - 1$?

   W (d) Redo part (c) using $x = 1$ and the line $y = 1.5x + 1.25$.

2. **(VELOCITY/DISTANCE)** At time x seconds, the velocity of a ball shot upward from the surface of the moon is given by

$$y = -5.3x + 87 \quad \text{feet per second}$$

   From a graph of the appropriate function, answer the following questions. Use x in $[0, 40]$ and y in $[0, 800]$.

   (a) How high is the ball at $x = 8.84$ seconds?

   (b) When is the ball 667 feet above the surface of the moon?

W **(c)** What is the position of the ball at $x = 35$ seconds?

3. *(Cost)* A company finds that the marginal cost when x units of merchandise are produced is $110 - .04x$ dollars. The fixed cost is $850. Obtain the cost function and use its graph to determine the number of units that can be produced for $7190. Use x in $[0, 100]$ and $C(x)$ in $[0, 12,000]$.

4. *(Artery Plaque)* From Exercise 41, graph the diameter function d using t in $[0, 30]$ and d in $[0, 1]$ and use it to answer the following questions.

  (a) How many years will it take before the diameter of the artery is reduced to .2 centimeter?

  (b) How many years will it take before plaque fills the entire artery?

6.3 | *THE DEFINITE INTEGRAL AS THE AREA UNDER A CURVE*

Srinivasa Ramanujan was a mathematical genius who grew up in poverty near Madras, India. He taught himself mathematics, including calculus, from the few books he was able to borrow. A number of Ramanujan's theorems deal with evaluating definite integrals and approximating the value of definite integrals. He is also famous for his formulas for infinite series and his results in number theory.
   Ramanujan studied forms and patterns for their own sake, with no thought or concern for how his pure mathematics might be applied. Now, years after his death in 1920, some of his results are being used in real-world applications in physics, mathematics, and computer science. Ramanujan's "Notebooks" are still being studied today by mathematicians.

As we prepare to introduce the definite integral, the need will arise for a compact way of writing sums. Consider the sum of the integers from 1 through 50.

$$1 + 2 + 3 + \cdots + 50$$

We shall use the capital Greek letter sigma (Σ) to specify a sum. Along with sigma, a letter such as i, j, or k is used as the *index*, or counter. The first and last values of the index are written on the sigma as shown next.

$$1 + 2 + 3 + \cdots + 50 = \sum_{i=1}^{50} i$$

This particular example of **sigma notation,** or **summation notation,** specifies a sum of numbers of the form "i," where i begins at 1 and counts up to 50. Thus, it specifies the sum of the integers from 1 through 50.
   Here is another sum written in sigma notation.

$$\sum_{j=2}^{5} j(j - 2)$$

This one represents the sum of terms of the form $j(j - 2)$. The j values begin at 2 and count up to 5; that is, j is 2, 3, 4, 5.

$$\sum_{j=2}^{5} j(j - 2) = 2(2 - 2) + 3(3 - 2) + 4(4 - 2) + 5(5 - 2)$$
$$= 2(0) + 3(1) + 4(2) + 5(3)$$
$$= 0 + 3 + 8 + 15$$
$$= 26$$

The index can also be used for subscripts. Consider the sum

$$x_1 + x_2 + x_3 + x_4 + \cdots + x_n$$

Using summation notation, this sum can be written as

$$\sum_{i=1}^{n} x_i$$

EXAMPLE 1 Evaluate the sum

$$\sum_{i=1}^{3} f(x_i)$$

assuming

$$f(x) = x^2 \qquad x_1 = 2 \qquad x_2 = 3 \qquad x_3 = 7$$

SOLUTION

$$
\begin{aligned}
\sum_{i=1}^{3} f(x_i) &= f(x_1) + f(x_2) + f(x_3) \\
&= f(2) + f(3) + f(7) \\
&= 2^2 + 3^2 + 7^2 \\
&= 4 + 9 + 49 \\
&= 62
\end{aligned}
$$

♦

Area and the Definite Integral

The study of geometry includes formulas for determining the area bounded by such geometric figures as circles, triangles, and rectangles (see Figure 3). In this section we will develop the calculus necessary to determine the area of other types of regions—regions bounded by various curves (see Figure 4). We will also pursue a variety of applications and the role of antidifferentiation in this setting.

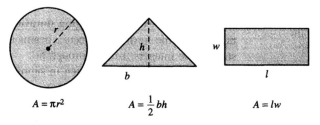

$A = \pi r^2$ $\qquad A = \frac{1}{2} bh$ $\qquad A = lw$

Figure 3 Areas enclosed by geometric figures

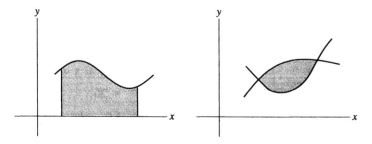

Figure 4 Regions bounded by curves

To begin, let us consider the area bounded by the graph of $y = f(x)$, the x axis, and the vertical lines $x = a$ and $x = b$. This is usually called simply **the area under the curve.** We will be considering the interval from $x = a$ to $x = b$, and we will assume that the graph of $y = f(x)$ is continuous—that is, it has no breaks or gaps. We will also assume that $f(x) \geq 0$ for all x between a and b. The area we are considering is shown shaded in Figure 5 below.

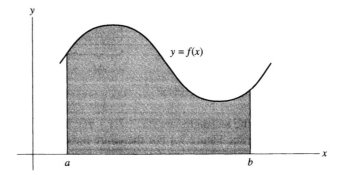

Figure 5 The area under a curve

At this time we have no means of determining the *exact* value of the shaded area. However, we can approximate the area by using rectangles, because it is an easy matter to determine the area of any rectangle. In view of this, let us create a rectangular approximation of the area under the curve.

We begin by dividing the interval from a to b into n equal subintervals. Because the whole interval has width $b - a$, it follows immediately that the width of each of the n subintervals is

$$\frac{b - a}{n}$$

We shall call this width Δx. That is

$$\Delta x = \frac{b - a}{n}$$

One rectangle will be constructed for each subinterval, and the width of each rectangle will be Δx. The length of each rectangle will be the distance between the x axis and the graph, measured vertically at the right end of each subinterval. This is illustrated in Figure 6. Here $n = 4$, so there are 4 subintervals, each of width Δx. If the area of each rectangle is computed, and then all four areas are added, the result will be an approximation to the area under the curve.

The area of a rectangle is computed as length times width. Here the width is Δx in each instance. The length is the distance from the x axis to the graph. That distance is the value of $f(x)$ for the particular x. If we call the x values x_1, x_2, x_3, and x_4, then the lengths of

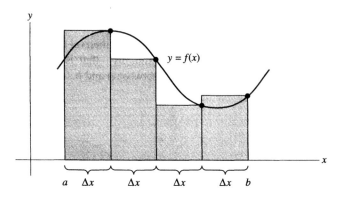

Figure 6 Rectangles constructed to approximate the area under the curve.

the rectangles are $f(x_1), f(x_2), f(x_3),$ and $f(x_4)$. The area of the first rectangle is $f(x_1) \cdot \Delta x$. (See Figure 7.) For the entire region,

$$\text{Area} = f(x_1)\Delta x + f(x_2)\Delta x + f(x_3)\Delta x + f(x_4)\Delta x$$

See Figure 8.

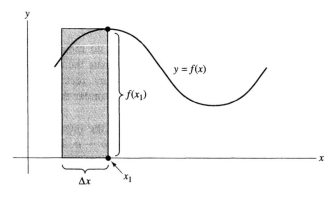

Figure 7 The area of this (shaded) rectangle is $f(x_1) \cdot \Delta x$.

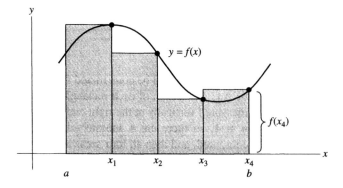

Figure 8 The entire region

Using summation notation, we express the total area of the rectangles as

$$\text{Area} = \sum_{i=1}^{4} f(x_i)\,\Delta x$$

This is a rough approximation to the area under the curve. The approximation can be improved by using more rectangles. Compare the approximation shown by using four rectangles (Figure 9) and the better approximation obtained by using eight rectangles (Figure 10).

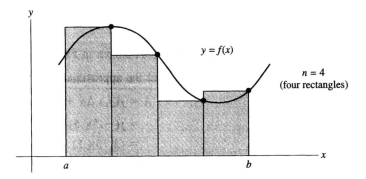

Figure 9 A rough approximation

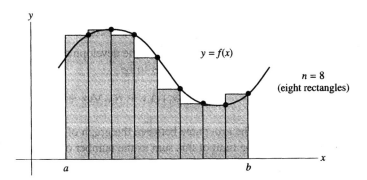

Figure 10 A better approximation

EXAMPLE 2   Approximate the area bounded by the graph of $f(x) = 4 - x^2$, the x axis, and the lines $x = -1$ and $x = 1$.

(a) Use $n = 2$ subintervals.   (b) Use $n = 4$ subintervals.

SOLUTION   (a) If $n = 2$ subintervals are used, then

$$\Delta x = \frac{b - a}{n} = \frac{1 - (-1)}{2} = 1$$

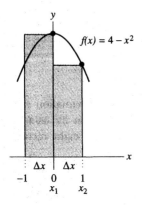

Figure 11
The rectangles of
Example 2(a)

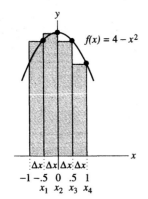

Figure 12
The rectangles of
Example 2(b)

The rectangles are shown in Figure 11.

The area of the approximating rectangles is

$$A = f(x_1)\,\Delta x + f(x_2)\,\Delta x$$
$$= f(0)\cdot 1 + f(1)\cdot 1$$
$$= (4 - 0^2)\cdot 1 + (4 - 1^2)\cdot 1$$
$$= 7$$

(b) If $n = 4$ subintervals are used, then

$$\Delta x = \frac{b - a}{n} = \frac{1 - (-1)}{4} = .5$$

The rectangles are shown in Figure 12.

The area of the approximating rectangles is

$$A = f(x_1)\,\Delta x + f(x_2)\,\Delta x + f(x_3)\,\Delta x + f(x_4)\,\Delta x$$
$$= f(-.5)(.5) + f(0)(.5) + f(.5)(.5) + f(1)(.5)$$
$$= (3.75)(.5) + (4)(.5) + (3.75)(.5) + (3)(.5)$$
$$= 7.25$$

The approximation to the area under the curve improves as the number of rectangles n increases. In the next section, you will be able to determine that the exact area is $7\frac{1}{3}$ square units. ◆

Returning now to the development of the area under the graph of $y = f(x)$, we find the area of n rectangles to be

$$A = f(x_1)\,\Delta x + f(x_2)\Delta x + f(x_3)\,\Delta x + \cdots + f(x_n)\,\Delta x = \sum_{i=1}^{n} f(x_i)\,\Delta x$$

The *exact* area between the graph of $y = f(x)$ and the x axis (on the interval from a to b) is the limit of this sum as the number of rectangles n approaches infinity. Thus, assuming the limit exists,

$$A = \lim_{n \to \infty} \sum_{i=1}^{n} f(x_i)\,\Delta x$$

Saying that $n \to \infty$ is the same as saying that $\Delta x \to 0$, since the width of each rectangle gets smaller and smaller as the number of rectangles increases. Thus, we can also write

$$A = \lim_{\Delta x \to 0} \sum_{i=1}^{n} f(x_i)\,\Delta x$$

This limit is given a special name and notation. It is known as the **definite integral** of f from a to b.

The Definite Integral of f from a to b

If f is continuous on $[a,b]$, then the **definite integral** of f from a to b is given by

$$\int_a^b f(x)\, dx = \lim_{\Delta x \to 0} \sum_{i=1}^n f(x_i)\, \Delta x$$

assuming the limit exists. The interval $[a,b]$ is divided into n equal subintervals of width Δx, where Δx is $(b - a)/n$, and x_i is the rightmost point in the ith interval.

Recall that we began with the area under a curve and insisted that $f(x) \geq 0$ on the interval from $x = a$ to $x = b$. This means that the definite integral represents the area under the curve only when $f(x) \geq 0$. Nevertheless, we shall see other applications that do not require that $f(x) \geq 0$.

We have defined the definite integral as the limit of a sum. That sum is an example of a more general type called a *Riemann sum*, named for the German mathematician Bernhard Riemann (1826–1866).

6.3   Exercises

In Exercises 1–8, compute the value of each expression and simplify it completely.

1. $\displaystyle\sum_{i=1}^5 i^2$

2. $\displaystyle\sum_{i=0}^{10} (i + 2)$

3. $\displaystyle\sum_{k=1}^6 (2k + 1)$

4. $\displaystyle\sum_{j=-1}^5 2j$

5. $\displaystyle\sum_{j=0}^5 j(j + 3)$

6. $\displaystyle\sum_{k=1}^4 3k$

7. $\displaystyle\sum_{n=1}^3 \frac{n + 1}{2n}$

8. $\displaystyle\sum_{n=0}^3 \frac{n}{n + 1}$

In Exercises 9–13, use summation notation to write each expression in condensed form.

9. $1 + 2 + 3 + 4 + 5 + 6 + 7 + 8 + 9$

10. $1 + \dfrac{1}{2} + \dfrac{1}{3} + \dfrac{1}{4} + \cdots + \dfrac{1}{100}$

11. $4 + 5 + 6 + \cdots + n$

12. $\dfrac{3}{7} + \dfrac{4}{7} + \dfrac{5}{7} + \cdots + \dfrac{20}{7}$

13. $\dfrac{1}{2} + \dfrac{2}{3} + \dfrac{3}{4} + \dfrac{4}{5} + \cdots + \dfrac{49}{50}$

Use summation notation to write each expression in Exercises 14–18 in a condensed form.

14. $x_1 + x_2 + x_3 + x_4 + x_5 + x_6$

15. $a_1 x_1 + a_2 x_2 + a_3 x_3 + \cdots + a_{10} x_{10}$

16. $x_1^2 + x_2^2 + x_3^2 + \cdots + x_n^2$

17. $f(x_0) + f(x_1) + f(x_2) + f(x_3) + \cdots + f(x_n)$

18. $a_0 x^0 + a_1 x^1 + a_2 x^2 + \cdots + a_{n-1} x^{n-1}$

Evaluate each sum in Exercises 19–22.

19. $\sum\limits_{i=1}^{4} f(x_i)$ assuming that $f(x) = x^3$, $x_1 = 0$, $x_2 = 1$, $x_3 = 2$, and $x_4 = 3$

20. $\sum\limits_{i=1}^{3} x_i f(x_i)$ assuming $f(x) = 3x$, $x_1 = 1$, $x_2 = 2$, and $x_3 = 3$

21. $\sum\limits_{i=1}^{3} f(x_i)\,\Delta x$ assuming $f(x) = x^2$, $x_1 = 1$, $x_2 = 3$, $x_3 = 5$, and $\Delta x = 2$

22. $\sum\limits_{i=1}^{5} f(x_i)\,\Delta x$ assuming $f(x) = 4x$, $x_1 = 0$, $x_2 = .5$, $x_3 = 1$, $x_4 = 1.5$, $x_5 = 2$, and $\Delta x = .5$

In Exercises 23–30, use rectangles to approximate the area bounded by the graph of function f, the x axis, and the two vertical lines given. Use n subintervals. Refer to Example 2.

23. $f(x) = x^2 + 2$, $x = 0$, $x = 2$, $n = 2$

24. $f(x) = x^2 + 2$, $x = 0$, $x = 2$, $n = 4$

25. $f(x) = 6 - x^2$, $x = -1$, $x = 1$, $n = 4$

26. $f(x) = 10 - x^3$, $x = 0$, $x = 2$, $n = 4$

27. $f(x) = 1 + x^3$, $x = 0$, $x = 2$, $n = 4$

28. $f(x) = 5 + \sqrt{x}$, $x = 0$, $x = 4$, $n = 4$

29. $f(x) = e^x$, $x = 0$, $x = 2$, $n = 4$

30. $f(x) = \dfrac{1}{x}$, $x = 1$, $x = 4$, $n = 4$

W 31. We have used n rectangles of width Δx in order to approximate the area under a curve. What is the relationship between n and Δx?

W 32. When we approximate the area under a curve, why is the approximation better when more rectangles are used?

W 33. When we introduced the area between the graph of $y = f(x)$ and the x axis, we insisted that $f(x) \geq 0$. Why does this matter? Consider the illustration below, in which $f(x) < 0$.

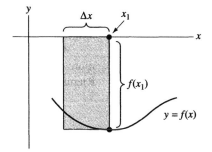

TECHNOLOGY *EXERCISES*

```
Prgm1:RECTANGL
:Disp "A"
:Input A
:Disp "B"
:Input B
:Disp "N"
:Input N
:0→S
:1→I
:(B-A)/N→D
:Lbl 1
:A+I*D→X
:Y₁→R
:R*D+S→S
:I+1→I
:If I≤N
:Goto 1
:Disp "AREA ="
:Disp S
```

All of the exercises in this set require the use of a program that uses rectangles to approximate the area under a curve. The program given here (for the TI-81 and TI-82) follows the approach of Example 2 and Exercises 23–30. Be sure to enter the function (integrand) as Y1 before requesting the program.

1. Consider the function of Exercise 23, $f(x) = x^2 + 2$. Find the approximate area between the curve and the x axis from $x = 0$ to $x = 2$ as follows.

    (a) Use $n = 2$ and compare with Exercise 23.

    (b) Use $n = 4$, 10, 50, 100, and 500 and notice that improvement in the approximation. (The exact area is $6\frac{2}{3}$.)

2. Consider the function of Exercise 27, $f(x) = 1 + x^3$. Find the approximate area between the curve and the x axis from $x = 0$ to $x = 2$ as follows.

    (a) Use $n = 4$ and compare with Exercise 27.

    (b) Obtain better approximations by using $n = 10$, 50, 100, and 500.

3. Find the approximate area between the graph of $f(x) = x + e^{.09x}$ and the x axis from $x = 1$ to $x = 5$. Use $n = 10, 25,$ and 50 and note the improvement in the approximation.

4. **(a)** Use $n = 10, 50,$ and 100 in the approximation of the area between the graph of the function $f(x) = x - x^3$ and the x axis from $x = 0$ to $x = 1$.

   (b) Use still larger n to see whether you can guess the exact area.

6.4 | *THE FUNDAMENTAL THEOREM OF CALCULUS*

Perhaps you were surprised to see that the notation used for the definite integral looks so much like the notation used for antidifferentiation. As it happens, determining the area under a curve is indeed related to antidifferentiation. Consider the two applications that follow.

1. **(a)** Distance can be determined from velocity by antidifferentiation. From $v = ds/dt$, it follows that

$$s = \int v\, dt$$

   (b) Distance can also be determined as the area under the graph of a velocity function. Consider a train traveling at $v = 60$ miles per hour for 3 hours. As shown in Figure 13, the area is 180, which is in fact the distance traveled in 3 hours at 60 miles per hour. If the velocity were to vary, then we would have the situation illustrated in Figure 14.

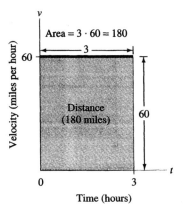

Figure 13 Distance as the area under the graph of a velocity function

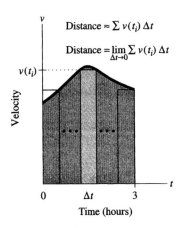

Figure 14 Distance as the area under the graph of a (variable) velocity function

2. (a) Total cost can be determined from marginal cost by antidifferentiation.

$$C(x) = \int C'(x)\, dx$$

(b) In a manner similar to the distance example with variable velocity, total cost $C(x)$ can be determined as the area under the graph of the marginal cost function $y = C'(x)$. See Figure 15.

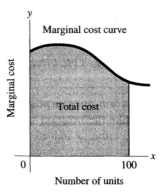

Figure 15 The shaded area represents the total cost of producing 100 units

Assuming that f is nonnegative and continuous at all x in the interval from a to b, the area $A(x)$ under the graph of f from a to x (as shown in Figure 16) is given by

$$A(x) = \int_a^x f(x)\, dx$$

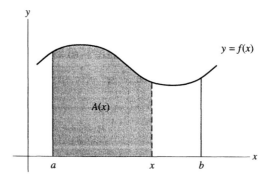

Figure 16 The area under the graph of f from a to x

Next we will show that A is an antiderivative of f. The shaded area in Figure 17 is $A(x + \Delta x) - A(x)$. This shaded area can be approximated by the rectangle having width Δx and length $f(x)$. The area of this approximating rectangle is $f(x) \cdot \Delta x$. Thus,

$$A(x + \Delta x) - A(x) \approx f(x)\, \Delta x$$

or

$$\frac{A(x + \Delta x) - A(x)}{\Delta x} \approx f(x) \qquad \text{dividing by } \Delta x$$

The smaller Δx becomes, the better this approximation. In the limit, we have

$$\lim_{\Delta x \to 0} \frac{A(x + \Delta x) - A(x)}{\Delta x} = f(x)$$

or

$$A'(x) = f(x)$$

Thus, A is an antiderivative of f.

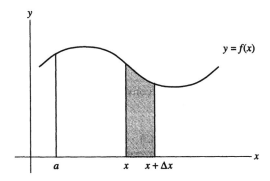

Figure 17 The shaded area is $A(x + \Delta x) - A(x)$.

Knowing that A is an antiderivative of f, and letting F represent any antiderivative of f, we have the following result (which can be proved formally):

$$A(x) = F(x) + C \qquad (C = \text{some constant})$$

Considering that

$$A(b) = \int_a^b f(x)\, dx \qquad \text{and} \qquad A(a) = \int_a^a f(x)\, dx = 0$$

it follows that

$$\int_a^b f(x)\, dx = A(b)$$

$$= A(b) - A(a)$$
$$= (F(b) + C) - (F(a) + C)$$
$$= F(b) - F(a)$$

This result,

$$\int_a^b f(x)\ dx = F(b) - F(a)$$

is so important to the study of calculus that it is known as the **Fundamental Theorem of Calculus.** It provides a key link between differential calculus and integral calculus.

The Fundamental Theorem of Calculus

If f is continuous on the closed interval $[a, b]$, then

$$\int_a^b f(x)\ dx = F(b) - F(a)$$

where F is any antiderivative of f.

Note

1. As a convenience, we will use the notation

$$[F(x)]_a^b$$

for $F(b) - F(a)$ when evaluating definite integrals, beginning in Example 1.

2. The numbers a and b are called **limits of integration.** Specifically, b is the **upper limit** and a is the **lower limit.**

Using the Fundamental Theorem

To evaluate the definite integral of f from a to b by using the Fundamental Theorem of Calculus, follow these steps.

1. Determine an antiderivative of f.

2. Evaluate the antiderivative F at the upper limit; that is, obtain $F(b)$.

3. Evaluate the antiderivative F at the lower limit; that is, obtain $F(a)$.

4. Subtract as follows: $F(b) - F(a)$.

EXAMPLE 1 Evaluate $\displaystyle\int_1^2 x^2\, dx$ using the Fundamental Theorem of Calculus.

SOLUTION For this integral, $f(x) = x^2$. Thus, $F(x) = x^3/3$, and so

$$\int_1^2 x^2\, dx = \left[\frac{x^3}{3}\right]_1^2 \qquad \text{This is } \left[F(x)\right]_a^b$$

$$= \frac{(2)^3}{3} - \frac{(1)^3}{3} \qquad \text{This is } F(b) - F(a).$$

$$= \frac{8}{3} - \frac{1}{3} = \frac{7}{3} \qquad\qquad\qquad\qquad \blacklozenge$$

Note

Because the Fundamental Theorem of Calculus says we can use *any* antiderivative, *we will always use the antiderivative with $C = 0$.* However, if you did use some other value of C, it would be eliminated in the process anyway. If $x^3/3 + C$ (rather than just $x^3/3$) had been used in Example 1, we would have had

$$\left[\frac{x^3}{3} + C\right]_1^2 = \left(\frac{8}{3} + C\right) - \left(\frac{1}{3} + C\right) = \frac{7}{3} + C - C = \frac{7}{3}$$

EXAMPLE 2 Evaluate the definite integral: $\displaystyle\int_0^4 (5x + 3)\, dx$

SOLUTION

$$\int_0^4 (5x + 3)\, dx = \left[\frac{5x^2}{2} + 3x\right]_0^4$$

$$= \left(\frac{5(4)^2}{2} + 3(4)\right) - \left(\frac{5(0)^2}{2} + 3(0)\right)$$

$$= (40 + 12) - (0 + 0)$$

$$= 52 \qquad\qquad\qquad\qquad \blacklozenge$$

EXAMPLE 3 Integrate: $\displaystyle\int_0^1 (1 - e^t)\, dt$

SOLUTION

$$\int_0^1 (1 - e^t)\, dt = \left[t - e^t\right]_0^1$$

$$= (1 - e^1) - (0 - e^0)$$

$$= 1 - e - 0 + 1$$

$$= 2 - e \qquad\qquad\qquad\qquad \blacklozenge$$

EXAMPLE 4   Determine the (exact) area under the curve $y = \sqrt{x}$ from $x = 1$ to $x = 4$.

SOLUTION   The area is shown shaded in Figure 18.

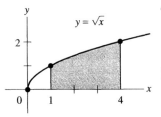

Figure 18
The area under $y = \sqrt{x}$
from $x = 1$ to $x = 4$

The area under the curve $y = f(x)$ from $x = a$ to $x = b$ is given by the definite integral

$$\int_a^b f(x) \, dx$$

In this instance, $f(x) = \sqrt{x}$, $a = 1$, and $b = 4$. Thus,

$$\text{Area} = \int_1^4 \sqrt{x} \, dx = \int_1^4 x^{1/2} \, dx = \left[\frac{x^{3/2}}{3/2}\right]_1^4 = \left[\frac{2}{3}x^{3/2}\right]_1^4$$

$$= \frac{2}{3} \cdot 4^{3/2} - \frac{2}{3} \cdot 1^{3/2} = \frac{2}{3} \cdot 8 - \frac{2}{3} \cdot 1 = \frac{16}{3} - \frac{2}{3} = \frac{14}{3}$$

The area between the graph of $y = \sqrt{x}$ and the x axis on the interval $[1, 4]$ has been shown to be 14/3, or 4 2/3 square units.   ◆

EXAMPLE 5   Determine the area under the curve $y = 1/x$ from $x = 1$ to $x = 7$.

SOLUTION   The area is

$$\int_1^7 \frac{1}{x} \, dx = \left[\ln |x|\right]_1^7 = \ln 7 - \ln 1 = \ln 7 - 0 = \ln 7 \qquad ◆$$

Note

Example 5 showed that $\ln 7$ is the area under the graph of $y = 1/x$ from $x = 1$ to $x = 7$. Can you see that for any $t > 0$,

$$\ln t = \int_1^t \frac{1}{x} \, dx$$

This is a calculus interpretation of the natural logarithm. See Figure 19.

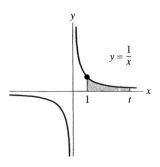

Figure 19 The shaded area is $\ln t$

The three properties given next resemble familiar properties of indefinite integrals (from Section 6.1). We will use them when they are needed.

Properties of Definite Integrals

$$\int_a^b [f(x) + g(x)]\, dx = \int_a^b f(x)\, dx + \int_a^b g(x)\, dx$$

$$\int_a^b [f(x) - g(x)]\, dx = \int_a^b f(x)\, dx - \int_a^b g(x)\, dx$$

$$\int_a^b k f(x)\, dx = k \int_a^b f(x)\, dx \qquad k = \text{constant}$$

6.4   Exercises

It has been shown that the area under the graph of a velocity function is the (total) distance traveled and that the area under the marginal cost curve is the total cost. In Exercises 1–8, interpret the area under the graph of each function.

1. (*MARGINAL REVENUE*) The function gives the marginal revenue when x units have been sold.

2. (*MARGINAL PROFIT*) The function gives the marginal profit when x units have been produced and sold.

3. (*GASOLINE CONSUMPTION*) The function gives the rate at which gasoline was consumed in the United States from 1964 to 1976.

4. (*SALES INCREASE*) The function gives the rate at which a corporation's sales have grown from 1988 to 1993.

5. (*INTEREST RATES*) The function gives the interest rates paid by a bank on its money market account from 1984 to 1992.

6. (*FLU EPIDEMIC*) The function gives the rate (in people per day) at which a flu virus is spreading from the fourth day through the tenth day of the epidemic.

7. (*YEAST CULTURE*) The function gives the rate (in milligrams per hour) at which a yeast culture has been growing this week.

8. (*POPULATION GROWTH*) The function gives the rate at which a city's population has grown from 1990 to 1996.

Evaluate each definite integral in Exercises 9–28.

9. $\int_0^3 8x\, dx$

10. $\int_1^2 3x^2\, dx$

11. $\int_1^4 x^2\, dx$

12. $\int_2^6 (3t - 8)\, dt$

13. $\int_0^2 (1 + x^3)\, dx$

14. $\int_0^2 (y^3 - y)\, dy$

15. $\int_1^6 (5t - t^2)\, dt$

16. $\int_3^4 (1 - 2x + 3x^2)\, dx$

17. $\int_0^3 (x^2 + 2x - 5)\, dx$

18. $\int_0^6 (x^2 - 8x + 17)\, dx$

19. $\int_0^1 (e^x - 2x)\, dx$

20. $\int_0^1 (x^2 + e^x)\, dx$

21. $\int_2^5 \frac{1}{t^2}\, dt$

22. $\int_3^4 \frac{2}{x^2}\, dx$

23. $\int_4^9 6\sqrt{x}\, dx$

24. $\int_0^8 \sqrt[3]{x}\, dx$

25. $\int_1^3 \frac{1}{x}\, dx$

26. $\int_2^e \frac{1}{x}\, dx$

27. $\int_0^{100} e^{.05x}\, dx$

28. $\int_0^{50} e^{.04x}\, dx$

Evaluate each definite integral in Exercises 29–34.

29. $\int_1^2 \frac{3x^2 + 4}{x}\, dx$

30. $\int_1^e \frac{1 + x^3}{x}\, dx$

31. $\int_e^4 \frac{t + 1}{t^2}\, dt$

32. $\int_2^e \frac{1 - t^2}{t}\, dt$

33. $\int_1^9 \frac{1 + x}{\sqrt{x}}\, dx$

34. $\int_4^9 \frac{x + \sqrt{x}}{x}\, dx$

Determine each area in Exercises 35–46.

35. The area under $y = x^2$ from $x = 0$ to $x = 3$.

36. The area under $y = x^2 + 3$ from $x = 1$ to $x = 4$.

37. The area under $y = 9 - x^2$ from $x = 1$ to $x = 2$.

38. The area under $y = -5x - x^2$ from $x = -3$ to $x = 0$.

39. The area under $y = 3x - x^2$ from $x = 0$ to $x = 2$.

40. The area under $y = \sqrt{x}$ from $x = 9$ to $x = 16$.

41. The area under $y = \sqrt[3]{x}$ from $x = 1$ to $x = 8$.

42. The area under $y = e^x$ from $x = 0$ to $x = 2$.

43. The area under $y = 1/x$ from $x = 1$ to $x = 6$.

44. The area under $y = 1/x$ from $x = 1$ to $x = e$.

45. The area under $y = e^{.5x}$ from $x = 0$ to $x = 2$.

46. The area under $y = e^{.2x}$ from $x = 0$ to $x = 10$.

Determine each area shaded in Exercises 47–50.

47.

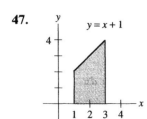

$y = x + 1$

48.

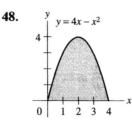

$y = 4x - x^2$

49.

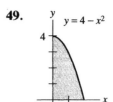

$y = 4 - x^2$

50.

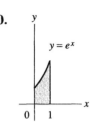

$y = e^x$

51. A property of definite integrals is

$$\int_a^a f(x)\, dx = 0$$

Verify this property for the three integrals given below by evaluating the integrals and showing that in each instance the integral is zero.

$$\int_2^2 6x\, dx \qquad \int_1^1 x^2\, dx \qquad \int_{-2}^{-2} (x^3 + 1)\, dx$$

52. Another property of definite integrals enables us to split an integral into two integrals by changing the limits of integration. Specifically, for any number c in the interval from a to b.

$$\int_a^b f(x)\, dx = \int_a^c f(x)\, dx + \int_c^b f(x)\, dx$$

Verify this property for the two examples given below by evaluating all integrals and showing that in each case, the integral on the left is indeed equal to the sum of the two integrals on the right.

(a) $\int_0^5 (4x + 3)\, dx = \int_0^2 (4x + 3)\, dx + \int_2^5 (4x + 3)\, dx$

(b) $\int_1^8 3x^2\, dx = \int_1^4 3x^2\, dx + \int_4^8 3x^2\, dx$

W 53. Give an intuitive geometric interpretation of why you would expect the integral property of Exercise 51 to be true.

W 54. Give an intuitive geometric interpretation of why you would expect the integral property of Exercise 52 to be true. It may help to draw the graph of $y = f(x)$ defined on an interval $[a, b]$ with c in the interval.

Evaluate each definite integral in Exercises 55–60.

55. $\displaystyle\int_{-1}^{0} \frac{e^x - 1}{e^x}\, dx$ **56.** $\displaystyle\int_{1}^{2} \frac{2x + e^x}{xe^x}\, dx$

57. $\displaystyle\int_{0}^{3} |x|\, dx$ **58.** $\displaystyle\int_{-2}^{0} |x|\, dx$

59. $\displaystyle\int_{0}^{2} \frac{x^2 - 9}{x - 3}\, dx$ **60.** $\displaystyle\int_{0}^{2} \frac{x^3 + 8}{x + 2}\, dx$

W 61. Reread the statement of the Fundamental Theorem of

Calculus, and then explain why it cannot be used to evaluate

$$\int_{1}^{5} f(x)\, dx$$

for the function graphed here.

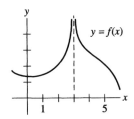

TECHNOLOGY *EXERCISES*

In Exercises 1–2, find the area enclosed by the given curve and the x axis. Begin by graphing the function to see at what integers it crosses the x axis. Then set up and carry out the integration.

1. $y = 3\sqrt{x} - x$ **2.** $y = 3x + 2x^2 + 2x^3 - x^4$

In Exercises 3–4, find the area enclosed by the given curve and the x axis. Begin by graphing the function to find, to the nearest tenth, where it crosses the x axis. Then set up and carry out the integration.

3. $y = 1 - 3x - x^2$ **4.** $y = 2.2\sqrt{x} - 1.2x$

Note You can shade the area enclosed by a curve and the x axis below it. On TI calculators, the **DRAW** instruction with **Shade** option will accomplish this. Specifically,

$$\text{Shade } (0, 6-x^2)$$

will draw the graph of the function $y = 6 - x^2$ and shade the area below the graph of $y = 6 - x^2$ and above the x axis ($y = 0$). Try it.

You may also want to try shading under the curves in Exercises 1–4 above.

5. Consider the region under the graph of $y = 50 - 3x^2$ from $x = 1$ to $x = 4$.

   (a) Use the RECTANGL program from Section 6.3 to approximate the area in the region, using $n = 10$, 50, and 100. Be sure to enter the function (integrand) as Y1 before requesting the program.

   (b) Use integration to determine the exact area.

Note   *Mathematica* and *Maple* can also evaluate *definite integrals*. The integral

$$\int_1^4 (x^2 + 7)\, dx$$

can be evaluated as follows.

Mathematica: `Integrate [x^2 + 7, {x, 1, 4}]`

Maple: `int(x^2 + 7, x = 1..4);`

If you have access to such software, use it to evaluate the integrals of Exercises 15, 19, and 33.

6.5 | *SOME APPLICATIONS OF THE DEFINITE INTEGRAL*

This section presents an introduction to applications of the definite integral. The first three examples here can be compared with those of Section 6.2 to see the similarities and differences between applications of the antiderivative (indefinite integral) and the definite integral.

APPLIED

EXAMPLE 1   *OBTAINING COST FROM MARGINAL COST*

A company's marginal cost when x units of merchandise have been produced is $50 - .08x$ dollars. The fixed cost is $700.

(a) Determine the cost of producing x units.

(b) Find the cost of producing 10 units.

(c) Find the cost of producing 15 units.

(d) What is the total cost of raising production from 10 units to 15 units?

SOLUTION   Parts (a) and (b) are the same as Example 3 from Section 6.2, where we found by antidifferentiating $C'(x) = 50 - .08x$ that $C(x) = 50x - .04x^2 + 700$ dollars and $C(10) = \$1196$.

(c) Let $x = 15$ in $C(x) = 50x - .04x^2 + 700$ to obtain $C(15) = \$1441$.

(d) Using parts (b) and (c), we find that the total cost of raising production from 10 units to 15 units is

$$C(15) - C(10) = \$1441 - \$1196 = \$245. \qquad \blacklozenge$$

Note

The answer to part (d) of Example 1 is the value of $C(15) - C(10)$. We began with $C'(x)$. That should look like a familiar form. It is an example of the Fundamental Theorem of Calculus and could have been obtained *directly* from a definite integral. Specifically,

$$\int_{10}^{15} C'(x)\ dx = C(15) - C(10)$$

This means that the cost of raising production from 10 units to 15 units could have been determined simply as

$$\int_{10}^{15} (50 - .08x)\ dx = \left[50x - .04x^2\right]_{10}^{15}$$
$$= (750 - 9) - (500 - 4)$$
$$= 245 \quad \text{dollars}$$

Note that there was no need to determine the constant 700. In fact, part (d) could have been done without first doing parts (a), (b), and (c).

In the next two examples you will see how the concept explained in the note above can be applied to completely different settings.

EXAMPLE 2 *FALLING OBJECT*

A ball is dropped from a high-altitude balloon. If the ball falls with velocity $v = 32t$ feet per second, how far does the ball travel during the first 4 seconds?

SOLUTION   We are given $v = 32t$. Since v is the same as ds/dt or $s'(t)$, we can write

$$s'(t) = 32t$$

The total distance traveled from $t = 0$ to $t = 4$ is $s(4) - s(0)$, or

$$\int_0^4 s'(t)\, dt = \int_0^4 32t\, dt = \left[16t^2\right]_0^4 = 256 \quad \text{feet}$$

The ball falls 256 feet in the first 4 seconds. (Notice that the height of the balloon does not matter, unless it is lower than 256 feet, in which case the ball hits the ground within the first 4 seconds.)

EXAMPLE 3   **PETROLEUM CONSUMPTION IN JAPAN**

APPLIED

The rate at which petroleum was consumed in Japan is given approximately by $c'(t) = .08t + 1.64$ billion barrels per year from 1987 ($t = 0$) to 1992 ($t = 5$). Determine the total amount of petroleum consumed from 1987 to 1992. (See Figure 20.)

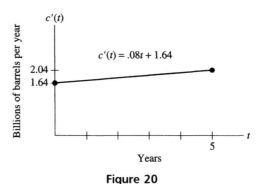

Figure 20

SOLUTION   The function $c'(t) = .08t + 1.64$ gives the *rate* of consumption, dc/dt, so the consumption itself $c(t)$ is an antiderivative of the given function $c'(t)$. Specifically, the total amount of petroleum consumed from 1987 ($t = 0$) to 1992 ($t = 5$) is given by the following definite integral:

$$\int_0^5 c'(t)\, dt = \int_0^5 (.08t + 1.64)\, dt = \left[.04t^2 + 1.64t\right]_0^5 = 1.0 + 8.2 = 9.2$$

The total consumption of petroleum was 9.2 billion barrels.

Average Value of a Function

You probably know that the average value of n numbers $x_1, x_2, x_3, \ldots, x_n$ is

$$\frac{x_1 + x_2 + x_3 + \cdots + x_n}{n}$$

To obtain the average value of a *function* over an interval, consider n functional values spread out evenly over the interval. The average of the n functional values $f(x_1)$, $f(x_2)$, $f(x_3)$, . . . , $f(x_n)$ is

$$\frac{f(x_1) + f(x_2) + f(x_3) + \cdots + f(x_n)}{n}$$

or

$$f(x_1) \cdot \frac{1}{n} + f(x_2) \cdot \frac{1}{n} + f(x_3) \cdot \frac{1}{n} + \cdots + f(x_n) \cdot \frac{1}{n}$$

If each term is multiplied by 1 in the form

$$\frac{b - a}{b - a}$$

the average will appear as

$$\frac{1}{b - a} \cdot f(x_1) \frac{b - a}{n} + \frac{1}{b - a} \cdot f(x_2) \frac{b - a}{n} + \cdots + \frac{1}{b - a} \cdot f(x_n) \cdot \frac{b - a}{n}$$

The fraction $(b - a)/n$ should look familiar; it's the Δx from Section 6.3, where the interval $[a, b]$ was divided into n equal subintervals. If we substitute Δx for each $(b - a)/n$, the result is

$$\frac{1}{b - a} f(x_1) \, \Delta x + \frac{1}{b - a} f(x_2) \, \Delta x + \cdots + \frac{1}{b - a} f(x_n) \, \Delta x$$

Factoring out $1/(b - a)$ from each term yields

$$\frac{1}{b - a} [f(x_1) \, \Delta x + f(x_2) \, \Delta x + \cdots + f(x_n) \, \Delta x] \qquad \text{or} \qquad \frac{1}{b - a} \sum_{i=1}^{n} f(x_i) \, \Delta x$$

Letting the number of functional values approach infinity will give the average value of the function.

$$\lim_{n \to \infty} \frac{1}{b - a} \sum_{i=1}^{n} f(x_i) \, \Delta x = \frac{1}{b - a} \int_{a}^{b} f(x) \, dx$$

Thus,

Average Value of a Function

The **average value of $f(x)$** over the interval $[a, b]$ is

$$\frac{1}{b - a} \int_{a}^{b} f(x) \, dx$$

EXAMPLE 4   Find the average value of $f(x) = 3x^2 + 4x - 5$ over the interval $[1, 3]$.

SOLUTION   The average value is

$$\frac{1}{3-1}\int_1^3 (3x^2 + 4x - 5)\,dx = \frac{1}{2}\int_1^3 (3x^2 + 4x - 5)\,dx$$

$$= \frac{1}{2}[x^3 + 2x^2 - 5x]_1^3$$

$$= \frac{1}{2}[(27 + 18 - 15) - (1 + 2 - 5)]$$

$$= 16 \qquad \qquad \blacklozenge$$

APPLIED

EXAMPLE 5   **BLOOD FLOW THROUGH AN ARTERY**

Blood does not flow with a constant velocity. It flows fastest in the center of an artery and slowest next to the wall of the artery. In fact, the velocity v at any distance x from the center can be expressed as a function of x. For example, for an artery of radius .2 centimeter, the velocity is

$$v = 40 - 990x^2$$

The distance x is measured in centimeters, and the velocity is in centimeters per second. See Figure 21.

fastest

.2 cm

slowest

Figure 21 Blood flow through an artery

It is natural to wonder what is the *average* velocity of the blood flowing through the artery. Using

$$\text{Average value of } f(x) = \frac{1}{b-a}\int_a^b f(x)\,dx$$

the average velocity $\bar{v}$ is

$$\bar{v} = \frac{1}{.2 - 0}\int_0^{.2} (40 - 990x^2)\,dx$$

Keep in mind that x is in the interval [0, .2] because x is the distance from the center. That distance could be as small as zero (at the center) or as large as .2 (at the artery wall). Continuing,

$$\bar{v} = \frac{1}{.2} \int_0^{.2} (40 - 990x^2)\, dx = 5[40x - 330x^3]_0^{.2}$$

$$= 5\{[(40)(.2) - (330)(.2)^3] - [(40)(0) - (330)(0)^3]\}$$

$$= 26.8 \text{ centimeters per second}$$

We have used an equation developed by French physician J. L. M. Poiseuille in 1842. The equation will be different if an artery of different radius is used. The length of the artery and the person's blood pressure also affect the equation. Some assumptions were made in order to simplify the example.   ♦

Volume

In this presentation you will see how a definite integral can be used to find the **volume of a solid of revolution.** Such a solid is produced by revolving a plane region (an area) about a line (such as the x axis). Consider the plane region shown shaded in Figure 22.

Now, imagine revolving this region about the x axis. As it spins around the axis, it sweeps out a three-dimensional figure—a solid of revolution. See Figure 23.

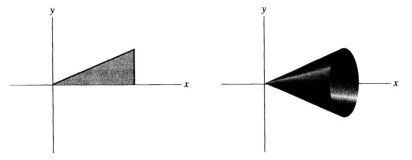

Figure 22 A plane region— to be revolved about the x axis

Figure 23 A solid of revolution

This particular solid is cone-shaped. A formula for finding the volume of such solids of revolution can be obtained in a manner similar to the way the basic area formula was obtained. Consider a function $y = f(x)$ that is nonnegative and continuous on an interval $[a, b]$. Divide this interval of width $b - a$ into n equal subintervals of width Δx. We then have

$$\Delta x = \frac{b - a}{n}$$

Let us draw the rectangles as we did in Section 6.3. The heights of the rectangles are $f(x_1)$, $f(x_2)$, and so on. See Figure 24 on the next page.

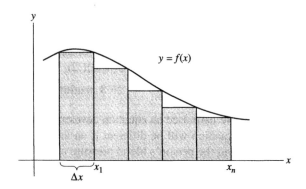

Figure 24 Rectangles in the region under the curve

As the region is spun around the x axis, each rectangle generates a cylinder. For example, the first rectangle with width Δx and height $f(x_1)$ generates a cylinder having radius $f(x_1)$ and height Δx. See Figures 25 and 26.

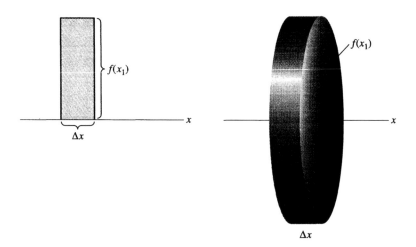

Figure 25 A rectangle generates a cylinder

The volume of a cylinder is $\pi r^2 h$, where r is the radius and h is the height. Here $r = f(x_1)$ and $h = \Delta x$. Thus, the volume of the first cylinder generated is $\pi[f(x_1)]^2 \Delta x$. The volume of the second cylinder is $\pi[f(x_2)]^2 \Delta x$. The total volume generated by revolving all n rectangles is

$$\pi[f(x_1)]^2 \Delta x + \pi[f(x_2)]^2 \Delta x + \cdots + \pi[f(x_n)]^2 \Delta x$$

In summation notation, we have

$$V = \sum_{i=1}^{n} \pi[f(x_i)]^2 \Delta x \qquad n \text{ cylinders}$$

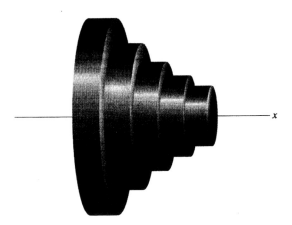

Figure 26 The rectangles generate cylinders

This volume is approximately the volume of the solid of revolution. The larger n becomes, the smaller Δx becomes, and the better is the approximation. The exact volume of the solid is the limit of this sum as $n \rightarrow \infty$ or as $\Delta x \rightarrow 0$.

$$V = \lim_{\Delta x \to 0} \sum_{i=1}^{n} \pi[f(x_i)]^2 \, \Delta x \qquad \text{the entire solid}$$

The limit on the right is the definite integral shown next.

Volume

The **volume** V of the solid produced by revolving the region bounded by $y = f(x)$ and the x axis (between $x = a$ and $x = b$) about the x axis is

$$V = \int_a^b \pi[f(x)]^2 \, dx$$

provided that f is continuous on $[a, b]$.

APPLIED

EXAMPLE 6   *VOLUME*

Find the volume of the solid produced by revolving about the x axis the region bounded by $y = \sqrt{x}$, the x axis, $x = 1$, and $x = 3$.

SOLUTION   A graph of the region being revolved is shown in Figure 27 on the next page.

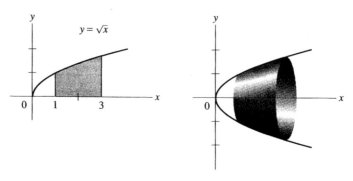

Figure 27 The region and the volume of revolution

$$V = \int_1^3 \pi \left[\sqrt{x}\right]^2 dx = \pi \int_1^3 x\, dx = \pi \left[\frac{x^2}{2}\right]_1^3 = \pi \left[\frac{9}{2} - \frac{1}{2}\right] = 4\pi$$

The volume is 4π cubic units. ◆

6.5   Exercises

1. **(COST)** Suppose the marginal cost when x units of merchandise have been produced is $40 - .06x$ dollars. What is the cost of increasing the number of units produced from 5 to 10?

2. **(OIL CONSUMPTION)** Assume the rate of oil consumption over a 4-year period was $c'(t) = 10e^{.05t}$ billions of barrels per year. Determine the total amount of oil consumed during the period.

3. **(SALES)** A corporation's sales have grown at the rate $ds/dt = 1800 - 200e^{.01t}$, where s is the amount of sales in dollars and t is the time in days. Determine the total amount of sales for the first 100 days.

4. **(SALES)** A corporation's sales are declining at the rate $s' = 2000e^{-.01t}$, where s is the amount of sales in dollars, t is time in days, and $t = 0$ today.
  (a) Determine the total amount of sales, to the nearest hundred dollars, for the next 100 days.
  (b) Determine the total amount of sales for the hundred days after that (that is, for the second hundred days).

W 5. **(PROFIT)** A computer manufacturer has a marginal profit function $P'(x) = 300 - .2x$ dollars, where x is the number of personal computers produced. The company is currently producing 1400 computers. Would it be wise for it to raise the production level to 1700 computers? Explain.

6. **(FALLING STONE)** A stone is dropped from a high cliff and falls with velocity $v = 32t$ feet per second. How far does the stone travel during the first 3 seconds?

7. **(FALLING STONE)** On the moon a stone is dropped from a high cliff and falls with velocity $v = 5.3t$ feet per second. How far does the stone travel during the first 3 seconds?

8. **(CAR TRAVEL)** A car is traveling at the rate of $v = 12t$ feet per second.
  (a) How far does it travel in the first 5 seconds?
  (b) How far does it travel during the 10th second?

9. **(SPREAD OF FLU VIRUS)** A flu virus is spreading at the rate of $dn/dt = 5 + 3\sqrt{t}$ people per day. Here n is the number of people and t is the time in days. How many people will get the flu between the ninth and sixteenth days?

10. **(TREE GROWTH)** Assume that a small tree will grow to maturity according to

$$\frac{dh}{dt} = 2 + \frac{1}{2\sqrt{t}} \qquad t > 0$$

where h is the height of the tree in feet and t is the time in years.

(a) How much does the tree grow between the first and fourth years?

(b) How much does it grow between the fourth and ninth years?

11. **(AIR POLLUTION)** In response to pressure from the mayor and the city council, the owners of a local factory have agreed to reduce the volume of polluted gas spewed into the air at their plant. Accordingly, over the next 6 months ($0 \le t \le 180$ days), the rate of pollution dp/dt will be given by

$$\frac{dp}{dt} = 3000 - 10t \qquad \text{cubic meters per day}$$

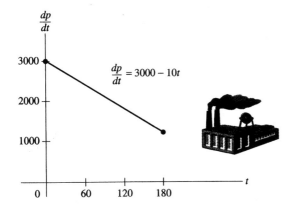

Find the total volume of polluted gas that will be vented into the atmosphere over the next 6 months.

12. **(POPULATION INCREASE)** It is anticipated that the county's population will be increasing at the rate of $10{,}000e^{.04t}$ people per year for the next t years. What will be the county's total increase in population in the next 5 years, on the basis of this rate?

13. **(PETROLEUM CONSUMPTION)** The rate at which petroleum was consumed in India was approximately $c'(t) = 21t + 281$ million barrels per year from 1983 ($t = 0$) to 1987 ($t = 4$). Determine the total amount of petroleum consumed from 1983 to 1987.

14. **(NATURAL GAS USE)** The rate at which natural gas was used as a fuel in U.S. industry from 1988 ($t = 0$) to 1991

($t = 3$) was approximately $c'(t) = .3t + 7.6$ trillion cubic feet per year. Find the total industrial consumption of natural gas from 1988 to 1991.

15. **(WATER USAGE)** The rate at which water is used in a small Maryland town depends on the time of day. From 2 p.m. ($t = 2$) to 10 p.m. ($t = 10$), water is used at the rate of $36t - 3t^2$ gallons per hour. Find the total number of gallons of water used over this 8-hour period.

In Exercises 16–24, determine the average value of each function over the given interval.

16. $f(x) = x^2$ over $[0, 1]$

17. $f(x) = x^2 + 4$ over $[0, 1]$

18. $f(x) = 3x^2 - 2x + 10$ over $[1, 4]$

19. $f(x) = x^2 + 6x - 2$ over $[0, 3]$

20. $f(x) = \sqrt{x}$ over $[4, 9]$

21. $f(x) = \dfrac{1}{\sqrt{x}}$ over $[9, 16]$

22. $f(x) = e^{2x}$ over $[0, 1]$

23. $f(x) = e^{.01x}$ over $[0, 100]$

24. $f(x) = \dfrac{1}{x}$ over $[1, e]$

25. **(BLOOD FLOW)** Find the average velocity of the blood flowing through an artery having radius .25 centimeter. Assume $v = 63 - 960x^2$. (See Example 5.)

26. **(BLOOD FLOW)** Find the average velocity of blood flowing through an artery having radius .18 centimeter. Assume $v = 32 - 1020x^2$. (See Example 5.)

27. **(FALLING STONE)** A stone dropped from a high cliff falls with velocity $v = 32t$ feet per second. What is the stone's average velocity during the first 5 seconds?

28. **(HEATED METAL)** As heat is applied to a metal bar, its temperature T increases. After t seconds the temperature of the bar is

$$T(t) = 70e^{.02t}$$

(a) What is the temperature of the bar initially?

(b) What is its temperature after 20 seconds?

(c) What is the average temperature of the bar during the first 20 seconds?

29. (TREE GROWTH) Suppose a small tree grows so that its height h after t years is

$$h = 1.4t + .6\sqrt{t} + 7 \quad \text{feet}$$

What is the average height of the tree from the fourth year to the ninth year?

30. (BACTERIA COUNT) The number of bacteria present in a particular culture is

$$A = 200e^{.3t}$$

Where A is the number of bacteria present after t hours. Determine the average number of bacteria present during the first 10 hours.

31. (COMPOUND INTEREST) If you deposit $3000 into a savings account that pays 8% interest per year compounded continuously for 10 years, what will be the average amount of money in your account during the 10-year period?

32. (BUYER POWER) If an economist estimates that the buying power b of the dollar will be

$$b = .98^t$$

in t years, what will be the average buying power of the dollar during the next 2 years?

W 33. Use the calculus formula for average value to determine the average value of $f(x) = 5$ over the interval $[1, 8]$. Comment on the answer and suggest an easy, noncalculus method of determining the same result.

W 34. Use calculus to determine the average value of $f(x) = x^3$ over the interval $[-2, 2]$. Then sketch a graph of the function and use the graph to explain the result of the integration.

(VOLUME) In Exercises 35–50, find the volume of the solid produced by revolving about the x axis the region whose boundary is given. (*Note:* $y = 0$ is the equation of the x axis.)

35. $y = \sqrt{x}$, the x axis, $x = 2$, $x = 4$

36. $y = 2x$, $y = 0$, $x = 1$, $x = 3$

37. $y = x + 1$, the x axis, $x = 0$, $x = 4$

38. $y = 2x + 3$, the x axis, $x = 0$, $x = 5$

39. $y = x^2 + 1$, $y = 0$, $x = 0$, $x = 1$

40. $y = x^3$, the x axis, $x = 1$, $x = 2$

41. $y = \sqrt{x + 2}$, $y = 0$, $x = 0$, $x = 8$

42. $y = e^x$, the x axis, $x = 0$, $x = 1$

43. $y = e^{2x}$, the x axis, $x = 0$, $x = 3$

44. $y = \dfrac{1}{x}$, the x axis, $x = 1/4$, $x = 1$

45. $y = \dfrac{1}{\sqrt{x}}$, the x axis, $x = e$, $x = 10$

46. $y = \sqrt[3]{x}$, $y = 0$, $x = 1$, $x = 8$

47. $y = 1 + \dfrac{1}{x}$, $y = 0$, $x = 1$, $x = 2$

48. $y = 1 + \sqrt{x}$, $y = 0$, $x = 1$, $x = 4$

49. $y = x^2 - 5x$, $y = 0$, $x = 5.1$, $x = 5.5$

50. $y = 1.4e^x$, $y = 0$, $x = 1.3$, $x = 2.4$

51. (VOLUME) If the region bounded by the line $y = \frac{r}{h}x$, the x axis, and $x = h$ is revolved about the x axis, the result will be a cone. Use calculus to determine the volume of the cone. (From geometry, a cone with radius r and height h has volume $V = \frac{1}{3}\pi r^2 h$, which is the answer.)

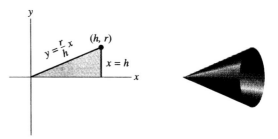

W 52. When seeking the *area* under the graph of $y = f(x)$, we insisted that $f(x) \geq 0$. However, we imposed no such restriction when seeking the corresponding *volume* produced by revolving the area. Explain.

53. (PETROLEUM CONSUMPTION) Consider the graph of c' given in Example 3. Because c' is a linear function, there is a geometric (noncalculus) way to obtain the result—the total amount of petroleum consumed over the 5-year period.

W (a) Explain the geometric method.

    (b) What answer do you obtain by using the geometric method?

54. Use the geometric approach referred to in Exercise 53 to solve the following problems given earlier in the exercises of this section.

    (a) Exercise 8(a)

    (b) Exercise 11

    (c) Exercise 14

TECHNOLOGY *EXERCISES*

1. In Example 4, the average value of $f(x) = 3x^2 + 4x - 5$ over the interval $[1, 3]$ was determined to be 16. Graph the function f using x in $[1, 3]$ and y in $[0, 40]$. Trace to approximately $y = 16$. Does this seem reasonable as an average value for the function?

2. Graph $f(x) = 8 - x - x^2$.

   (a) Determine the interval (endpoints to the nearest tenth) on which the function values are positive.

   (b) Use calculus to find the average value of the function on that interval.

3. Redo Exercise 2 using $f(x) = 1.5 + x - .5x^2$ and endpoints to the nearest integer.

4. Graph $f(x) = .5x^2 - 3x + 2.5$.

   (a) Determine the interval (endpoints to the nearest integer) on which the function values are negative.

   (b) Use calculus to find the volume obtained when the region enclosed by the curve and the x axis is revolved about the x axis.

6.6 | SURPLUS

Now we will combine our knowledge of supply and demand with what we know about the area under a curve to study the idea of surplus. To begin, consider a graph (Figure 28) showing a typical demand curve $p = D(x)$ and supply curve $p = S(x)$. Recall that x is the number of units and p is the price per unit.

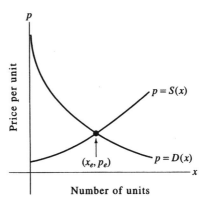

Figure 28 Supply and demand curves

Recall from Section 1.5 that the point (x_e, p_e) where the two curves meet is called the **equilibrium point;** it is the point where supply equals demand. To buy x_e units at price p_e dollars each, a consumer would spend $x_e \cdot p_e$ dollars. The amount $x_e p_e$ happens to be the area of a rectangle—the rectangle shown shaded in Figure 29. The length of the rectangle is x_e and the width is p_e.

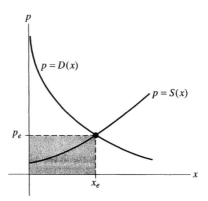

Figure 29 The area of the rectangle is $x_e p_e$

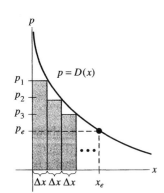

Figure 30
Some consumers are willing to pay more than p_e dollars

However, if we examine the demand curve alone (see Figure 30), we see that there are consumers willing to pay more than p_e dollars. For example, they will pay approximately p_1 dollars for each of the first Δx units, p_2 dollars for each of the next Δx units, and so on. The sum $p_1 \, \Delta x + p_2 \, \Delta x + \cdots + p_e \, \Delta x$ is the approximate cost of buying x_e units at the higher prices.

The exact cost of buying x_e units this more expensive way is the area under the graph of $p = D(x)$ between $x = 0$ and $x = x_e$, namely

$$\int_0^{x_e} D(x) \, dx$$

Thus, the consumer who can buy x_e units at the equilibrium price p_e will save an amount equal to

$$\int_0^{x_e} D(x) \, dx - x_e p_e$$

This amount of savings is called the **consumer's surplus.**

Consumer's Surplus

$$\int_0^{x_e} D(x) \, dx - x_e p_e$$

EXAMPLE 1   CONSUMER'S SURPLUS

APPLIED

Let $p = D(x) = 15 - \frac{1}{2}x$ dollars and $p = S(x) = \frac{3}{2}x + 1$ dollars. Find the equilibrium point and the consumer's surplus.

SOLUTION   The equilibrium point is the point where the graphs of $p = D(x)$ and $p = S(x)$ meet. The point is found in this example by setting $15 - \frac{1}{2}x$ equal to $\frac{3}{2}x + 1$.

$$15 - \frac{1}{2}x = \frac{3}{2}x + 1$$

$$2x = 14$$

$$x = 7$$

And when $x = 7$, $p = 23/2$ or 11.5. Thus, the equilibrium point (x_e, p_e) is $(7, 11.5)$.

The consumer's surplus is given by

$$\int_0^{x_e} D(x)\, dx - x_e p_e = \int_0^7 \left(15 - \frac{1}{2}x\right) dx - (7)(11.5)$$

$$= \left[15x - \frac{1}{4}x^2\right]_0^7 - 80.5$$

$$= 105 - 12.25 - 80.5 = 12.25$$

The consumer's surplus is $12.25.   ◆

From the producer's point of view, there is also a saving to be realized by selling at the equilibrium price. The supply curve shows that some suppliers are willing to sell units at a lower price, in which case the amount they receive is the area under the supply curve from $x = 0$ to $x = x_e$. See Figure 31.

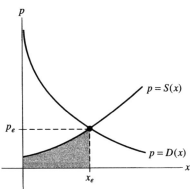

Figure 31 The amount received (area under the curve) is $\int_0^{x_e} S(x)\, dx$.

By selling at the equilibrium price, the producer receives $x_e p_e$. Thus, the producer's gain by selling at the equilibrium price is

$$x_e p_e - \int_0^{x_e} S(x)\, dx$$

This amount is called the **producer's surplus.**

Producer's Surplus

$$x_e p_e - \int_0^{x_e} S(x)\, dx$$

EXAMPLE 2 PRODUCER'S SURPLUS

Find the producer's surplus for the conditions of Example 1.

SOLUTION   In Example 1 we determined the equilibrium point:

$$(x_e,\, p_e) = (7,\, 11.5)$$

Using this information and the given supply function $S(x) = \frac{3}{2}x + 1$, the producer's surplus is

$$x_e p_e - \int_0^{x_e} S(x)\, dx = (7)(11.5) - \int_0^7 \left(\frac{3}{2}x + 1\right) dx$$

$$= 80.5 - \left[\frac{3x^2}{4} + x\right]_0^7$$

$$= 80.5 - (36.75 + 7) = 36.75$$

The producer's surplus is $36.75.   ◆

6.6   Exercises

(SURPLUS) In Exercises 1–12, both a supply function and a demand function are given. Determine (a) the equilibrium point, (b) the consumer's surplus, and (c) the producer's surplus. Assume the monetary unit is dollars.

1. $S(x) = 2x + 7$, $D(x) = 40 - x$

2. $S(x) = 3x + 16$, $D(x) = 100 - x$

3. $S(x) = \frac{3}{2}x + 4$, $D(x) = 30 - \frac{1}{2}x$

4. $S(x) = \frac{4}{3}x + 2$, $D(x) = 20 - \frac{2}{3}x$

5. $S(x) = .25x + 1$, $D(x) = 15 - .25x$

6. $S(x) = .3x + 2$, $D(x) = 10 - .2x$

7. $S(x) = \frac{1}{10}x^2 + 1$, $D(x) = 11 - \frac{3}{10}x^2$

8. $S(x) = .2x^2 + 5$, $D(x) = 77 - .3x^2$

9. $S(x) = 2\sqrt{x} + 1$, $D(x) = 13 - \sqrt{x}$

10. $S(x) = \dfrac{3}{2}\sqrt{x} + 3$, $\quad D(x) = 15 - \dfrac{1}{2}\sqrt{x}$

11. $S(x) = x^2 + 1$, $\quad D(x) = 13 - x$

12. $S(x) = x^2 + 5$, $\quad D(x) = 29 - 2x$

W 13. Refer to the graph in Figure 29. Describe (clearly and

completely) the region that represents the consumer's surplus.

W 14. Refer to the graph in Figure 31. Describe (clearly and completely) the region that represents the producer's surplus.

TECHNOLOGY *EXERCISES*

1. Given the supply function $S(x) = 1 + .3x^{1.5}$ and the demand function $D(x) = 10e^{-.1x}$, determine the equilibrium point (coordinates to the nearest tenth).

2. Given the supply function $S(x) = 1.7 + \sqrt{.2x}$ and the demand function $D(x) = 9.5e^{-.2x}$, determine the equilibrium point (coordinates to the nearest tenth).

3. Graph the supply and demand functions

$$S(x) = 3.76 + .2x^{1.5} \qquad D(x) = 3.06 + 8e^{-.2x}$$

(a) Determine the equilibrium point (x_e, p_e), coordinates to the nearest integer.

(b) Graph $y = p_e$ on the interval $[0, x_e]$ and shade under the graph of S from 0 to x_e. The unshaded area above the graph of S is now split into two regions—consumer's surplus and producer's surplus. Which is greater? *Shading note*: On TI calculators, the shading is accomplished by using

$$\text{Shade } (0, 3.76 + .2x^{1.5}, 1, 0, x_e)$$

Additional shading information is given in the note that accompanies the Technology Exercises of Section 6.7.

4. Redo Exercise 3 using $S(x) = 2.2 + .6x^{1.5}$ and $D(x) = 2.9 + .6e^{-.1x}$.

6.7 | ***AREA IN THE PLANE***

The development of the definite integral produced a natural application—area under a curve. By area under a curve we mean the area of the region between the graph of $y = f(x)$ and the x axis over some interval (from $x = a$ to $x = b$) for which $f(x) \geq 0$. See Figure 32.

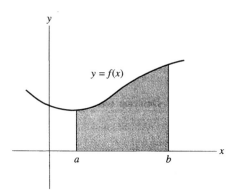

Figure 32 The area under a curve

We can easily extend the area concept to include the area *between* two curves. Let the curves be graphs of the functions $y = f(x)$ and $y = g(x)$ and consider the region between them from $x = a$ to $x = b$. (See Figure 33.)

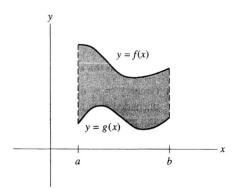

Figure 33 The region between two curves

The area of this region can be computed as the area under the curve $y = f(x)$ *minus* the area under the curve $y = g(x)$, as can be seen from the drawings in Figure 34. The *unshaded* region in the drawing in Figure 34(b) is the area between the two curves, and it is, in fact, the area under $y = f(x)$ minus the area under $y = g(x)$. Thus, assuming that both functions are continuous and that the graph of $y = f(x)$ is above the graph of $y = g(x)$ everywhere on the interval from a to b, the **area between the curves** from $x = a$ to $x = b$ is

$$\int_a^b f(x)\ dx - \int_a^b g(x)\ dx \qquad \text{"top curve } \textit{minus} \text{ bottom curve"}$$

The two integrals can be combined as

$$\int_a^b [f(x) - g(x)]\ dx$$

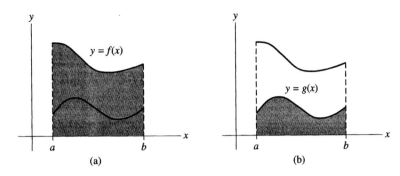

Figure 34 (a) Shaded is the area under $y = f(x)$.
(b) Shaded is the area under $y = g(x)$.

Area Between Two Curves

The area between the graphs of $y = f(x)$ and $y = g(x)$, from $x = a$ to $x = b$, is

$$\int_a^b [f(x) - g(x)] \, dx$$

provided that f and g are continuous on $[a, b]$ and $f(x) \geq g(x)$.

For area, we have insisted that the integrand be nonnegative. As long as $f(x) \geq g(x)$, the integrand $f(x) - g(x)$ will indeed be nonnegative. (Add $-g(x)$ to both sides of the inequality $f(x) \geq g(x)$ and the result is $f(x) - g(x) \geq 0$.) Note that this is true even if $g(x)$ is negative or if both $f(x)$ and $g(x)$ are negative.

EXAMPLE 1 Find the area between the curves $y = x^2 + 1$ and $y = x - 2$ from $x = -1$ to $x = 2$.

SOLUTION Begin with a graph of the two functions and shade in the desired region, as shown in Figure 35.

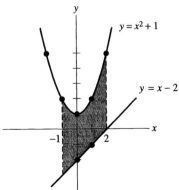

Figure 35 The area between the curves

Clearly $y = x^2 + 1$ is the greater (top) function, so call it f. Thus $f(x) = x^2 + 1$ and $g(x) = x - 2$, and

$$\text{Area} = \int_a^b [f(x) - g(x)]dx = \int_{-1}^2 [(x^2 + 1) - (x - 2)]dx$$

$$= \int_{-1}^2 (x^2 - x + 3) \, dx = \left[\frac{x^3}{3} - \frac{x^2}{2} + 3x \right]_{-1}^2$$

$$= \left(\frac{8}{3} - 2 + 6 \right) - \left(-\frac{1}{3} - \frac{1}{2} - 3 \right) = 10\frac{1}{2}$$ ◆

EXAMPLE 2   Find the area of the region enclosed by the curves $y = x^2$ and $y = 2x$.

SOLUTION   The statement of the example gives no values for a and b. However, the curves intersect and create an enclosed region. Thus, the x coordinates of the points of intersection will be the a and b values. A graph makes this more apparent. The desired region is shown shaded in Figure 36.

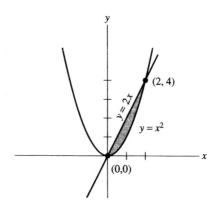

Figure 36 The area between the curves

Several observations need to be made.

1. From Figure 36, we see that $y = 2x$ is the greater ("top") function, so let $f(x) = 2x$ and $g(x) = x^2$.

2. The graphs intersect at the points $(0, 0)$ and $(2, 4)$—that is, where $x = 0$ and where $x = 2$. Thus, $a = 0$ and $b = 2$ for the limits of integration. The area will be determined from $x = 0$ to $x = 2$.

3. The area is

$$\int_0^2 [(2x) - (x^2)] \, dx = \int_0^2 (2x - x^2) \, dx = \left[x^2 - \frac{x^3}{3} \right]_0^2 = \frac{4}{3}$$

4. In *this* example, the points of intersection (0, 0) and (2, 4) might have been chosen as points to plot, so by luck you might have just happened upon the points of intersection. But often the points of intersection must be found algebraically by solving a system of two equations in the unknowns x and y. In this example, we would solve the system

$$\begin{cases} y = x^2 \\ y = 2x \end{cases}$$

The method of substitution can be used. Because $y = x^2$ and $y = 2x$, it follows that $x^2 = 2x$. Solving yields

$$x^2 = 2x$$
$$x^2 - 2x = 0$$
$$(x)(x - 2) = 0$$
$$x = 0, \quad x = 2 \qquad \text{as we expected!}$$

The corresponding y values can be found by substituting these x values into either $y = x^2$ or $y = 2x$. *However*, we have no need for the y values in this application. ◆

EXAMPLE 3   Find the area enclosed by $y = x^2 - 4x + 3$ and the x axis.

SOLUTION   This example is different because the selected portion of the graph of the function $y = x^2 - 4x + 3$ is *below* the x axis. The region is shown shaded in Figure 37.

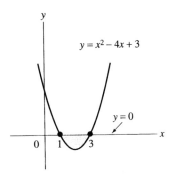

Figure 37 The region is below the *x* axis

From the graph you can see that the area we seek is from $x = 1$ to $x = 3$. Notice how the x axis (the line $y = 0$) serves as the greater (top) function by helping to form the enclosed region. Thus, $f(x) = 0$ and $g(x) = x^2 - 4x + 3$.

$$\text{Area} = \int_1^3 [(0) - (x^2 - 4x + 3)]\, dx = \int_1^3 (-x^2 + 4x - 3)\, dx$$

$$= \left[-\frac{x^3}{3} + 2x^2 - 3x \right]_1^3 = \frac{4}{3}$$

The limits of integration ($x = 1$ and $x = 3$) *can* be determined algebraically. They are the numbers for which $g(x) = x^2 - 4x + 3$ equals zero. Solving the equation $x^2 - 4x + 3 = 0$ yields $x = 1$ and $x = 3$. ◆

Note

To find the area of the region between a curve $y = f(x)$ and the x axis, *when the region is entirely below the x axis*, use either one of these equivalent methods.

$$\int_a^b [0 - f(x)]\, dx \qquad \text{as done in Example 3}$$

$$\int_a^b [-f(x)]\, dx \qquad \text{simplified form of the above}$$

If you are careless and compute this type of area as simply

$$\int_a^b f(x)\, dx$$

your result will be negative.

EXAMPLE 4 Determine the area between $y = x^2 - 4$ and the x axis from $x = 1$ to $x = 4$.

SOLUTION You will get the *wrong* result if you do not graph the function and instead simply write down the integral

$$\int_1^4 (x^2 - 4)\, dx = 9 \qquad \text{wrong!}$$

A graph shows why this approach is wrong. The desired area is shaded in Figure 38.

The area is in fact the sum of two areas, one to the left of $x = 2$ and one to the right of it. Thus,

$$\text{Area} = \int_1^2 [0 - (x^2 - 4)]\, dx + \int_2^4 (x^2 - 4)\, dx$$

$$= \int_1^2 (4 - x^2)\, dx + \int_2^4 (x^2 - 4)\, dx = \left[4x - \frac{x^3}{3}\right]_1^2 + \left[\frac{x^3}{3} - 4x\right]_2^4$$

$$= \left[\left(8 - \frac{8}{3}\right) - \left(4 - \frac{1}{3}\right)\right] + \left[\left(\frac{64}{3} - 16\right) - \left(\frac{8}{3} - 8\right)\right]$$

$$= \frac{5}{3} + \frac{32}{3} = \frac{37}{3} \qquad ◆$$

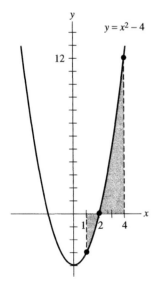

Figure 38
A region that consists of two areas—one above the x axis and one below it

EXAMPLE 5   Determine the area of the region enclosed by $y = x^3$ and $y = x$.

SOLUTION   The graph is shown in Figure 39, where the desired region is shaded.

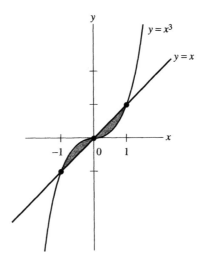

Figure 39 The area enclosed by the curves

The region is in fact two separate regions. Notice that for the region on the left, x goes from -1 to 0, and $y = x^3$ is the greater function. However, for the region on the right, x goes from 0 to 1, and $y = x$ is the greater function. Thus,

$$
\begin{aligned}
\text{Area} &= \int_{-1}^{0} [(x^3) - (x)] \, dx + \int_{0}^{1} [(x) - (x^3)] \, dx \\
&= \int_{-1}^{0} (x^3 - x) \, dx + \int_{0}^{1} (x - x^3) \, dx \\
&= \left[\frac{x^4}{4} - \frac{x^2}{2} \right]_{-1}^{0} + \left[\frac{x^2}{2} - \frac{x^4}{4} \right]_{0}^{1} \\
&= (0 - 0) - \left(\frac{1}{4} - \frac{1}{2} \right) + \left(\frac{1}{2} - \frac{1}{4} \right) - (0 - 0) = \frac{1}{2}
\end{aligned}
$$

Incidentally, the points of intersection of $y = x^3$ and $y = x$ can be found algebraically by solving the system

$$
\begin{cases} y = x^3 \\ y = x \end{cases}
$$

By substitution, $x^3 = x$. Then $x^3 - x = 0$, or $(x)(x^2 - 1) = 0$. Considering the factors equal to zero separately leads to $x = 0$, $x = 1$, and $x = -1$.   ◆

6.7 Exercises

In Exercises 1–8, determine the area between the two curves. Graphing is recommended.

1. $y = x^2 + 2$ and $y = x$ from $x = 0$ to $x = 6$

2. $y = x^2 + 4$ and $y = x - 1$ from $x = 0$ to $x = 3$

3. $y = x + 5$ and $y = \sqrt{x}$ from $x = 0$ to $x = 4$

4. $y = 2x + 4$ and $y = \sqrt{x}$ from $x = 1$ to $x = 9$

5. $y = \sqrt{x}$ and $y = 9 - x$ from $x = 0$ to $x = 1$

6. $y = \sqrt{x}$ and $y = 7 - x$ from $x = 1$ to $x = 4$

7. $y = 1 - x^2$ and $y = x + 4$ from $x = -3$ to $x = 1$

8. $y = 2 - x^2$ and $y = 5 - x$ from $x = -1$ to $x = 1$

Determine each area shaded in Exercises 9–12.

9.

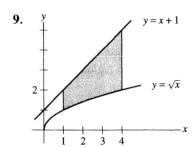

10.

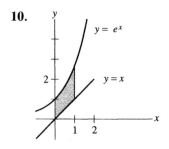

11.

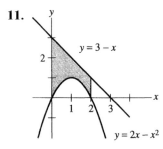

12.

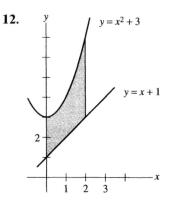

In Exercises 13–23, determine the area enclosed by the curves. Graphing is recommended.

13. $y = x^2$ and $y = 3x$

14. $y = x^2$ and $y = 4x$

15. $y = x^2 + 1$ and $y = 2x + 1$

16. $y = x^2 - 2$ and $y = 3x - 2$

17. $y = x^3$ and $y = x^2$ (Graph very carefully.)

18. $y = 4 - x^2$ and $y = x^2 - 4$

19. $y = \sqrt{x}$ and $y = x^2$

20. $y = x^2 + 3x + 2$ and $y = 3x + 6$

21. $y = x^2 - 2x + 1$ and $y = -2x + 2$

22. $y = e^x$, $y = e$, and $x = 0$

23. $y = e^x$, $y = 1$, and $x = 1$

In Exercises 24–30, determine the area between the curve and the x axis. For some curves, the desired area is entirely below the x axis. For other curves, part of the desired area is below the x axis and part is above the x axis. See Examples 3 and 4. Graphing is recommended.

24. $y = x^2 - 5x + 4$ from $x = 1$ to $x = 4$

25. $y = x^2 - 2x - 3$ from $x = -2$ to $x = 2$

26. $y = x^2 - 1$ from $x = 0$ to $x = 4$

27. $y = x^2 - 4$ from $x = -1$ to $x = 4$

28. $y = x^2 - 3x$ from $x = 0$ to $x = 3$

29. $y = x^2 - 2x$ from $x = 1$ to $x = 3$

30. $y = -e^{-x}$ from $x = 0$ to $x = 1$

In Exercises 31–39, determine the area enclosed by the curves. In each case the region enclosed consists of two regions. A careful study of the graphs is essential.

31. $y = x^3$ and $y = 4x$ **32.** $y = x^3$ and $y = 9x$

33. $y = -x^3$ and $y = -x$ **34.** $y = x^3 + 1$ and $y = x + 1$

35. $y = x^3 - 4$ and $y = x - 4$

36. $y = x^3 - 12x$ and $y = 0$

37. $y = x^3 - 3x$ and $y = 0$

38. $y = x^4$ and $y = 4x^2$

39. $y = x^4$ and $y = x^2$

W 40. Explain how to select the *greater* function when finding the area between the graphs of two functions.

41. *(CONSUMER'S SURPLUS)* Consider the consumer's surplus as the area between the curves $y = D(x)$ and $y = p_e$ and obtain a definite integral that represents the consumer's surplus.

42. *(PRODUCER'S SURPLUS)* Use an approach similar to that suggested in Exercise 41 to obtain a definite integral that represents producer's surplus.

In Exercises 43–48 determine the area enclosed by the curves.

43. $y = x^3 - 3x + 3$ and $y = 2x^2 + 3$

44. $y = x^3 - 2x + 1$ and $y = x^2 + 1$

45. $y = \dfrac{1}{x}$, $y = \dfrac{1}{e}$, and $x = 2$

46. $y = \sqrt{x}$, $y = \dfrac{1}{x}$, and $x = 4$

47. $y = |x|$ and $y = -x^2 + 2$

48. $y = |2x|$ and $y = -x^2 + 3$

49. Determine the area of the shaded region.

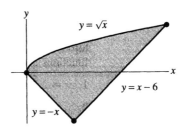

50. Determine the area of the shaded region.

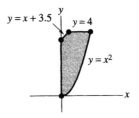

W 51. Consider the graph of function f shown here. Is

$$\int_1^{10} f(x)\, dx$$

positive or negative? Explain.

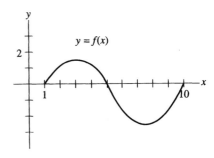

W 52. Does the integral in Exercise 51 give the area between the graph of $y = f(x)$ and the x axis? Explain.

TECHNOLOGY *E X E R C I S E S*

To determine the area between two curves, you must determine which function is the greater (or top) function f and which is the smaller (or bottom) function g. In Exercises 1–4, graph the two functions to determine which is f and which is g on the given interval.

1. $y = 2\sqrt{x + 6}$, $y = .3x^4 + 2$ on $[-1, 1]$

2. $y = 5 + \ln x$, $y = 3 + e^{-2x}$ on $[2, 7]$

3. $y = x^3 + x - 5$, $y = 10 - .5x^2$ on $[-1, 2]$

4. $y = 8 - .1x^3$, $y = x + \ln x$ on $[0, 2]$

To determine the area enclosed by two curves, you must determine where the curves intersect. In Exercises 5–6, determine (to the nearest tenth) the x coordinates of the two points of intersection of the given curves.

5. $y = 1 + \ln x$ and $y = x^2 - 8x + 15$

6. $y = x^2 + x - 6$ and $y = \sqrt{x^2 + 10}$

In Exercises 7–8, use graphs to determine (to the nearest tenth) the x coordinates of the points of intersection of the given curves. Then use calculus to determine the area between the curves.

7. $y = x^2 - 5.8x + 1$ and $y = 1.2x - 4$

8. $y = 1 + 4x - x^2$ and $y = x^2 - 6x + 10$

Note   You can shade the area between two curves by means of an instruction similar to the one used in Section 6.4. The instruction

$$\text{Shade } (x^2 - 4, 2x + 1)$$

will draw and shade the area that is above $y = x^2 - 4$ and below $y = 2x + 1$. Try it. The instruction

$$\text{Shade } (\sqrt{x}, x + 3, 1, 2, 6)$$

will draw and shade the area that is above $y = \sqrt{x}$ and below $y = x + 3$, between $x = 2$ and $x = 6$. The "1" specifies full shading. Try it.

Key Terms and Ideas

antidifferentiation	power rule	limits of integration
antiderivative	particular antiderivative	average value of $f(x)$
integral sign	sigma notation	volume of a solid of revolution
integrand	summation notation	equilibrium point
indefinite integral	area under a curve	consumer's surplus
integration	definite integral	producer's surplus
constant of integration	Fundamental Theorem of Calculus	area between two curves

Review Exercises for Chapter 6

Evaluate each indefinite integral in Exercises 1–12.

1. $\int (8x + 2)\, dx$

2. $\int \frac{x}{2}\, dx$

3. $\int (10x^4 - x^2)\, dx$

4. $\int (3 - x^7)\, dx$

5. $\int (1 + \sqrt{x})\, dx$

6. $\int x^{-2/3}\, dx$

7. $\int \frac{3}{t^2}\, dt$

8. $\int 4t^{-3}\, dt$

9. $\int \frac{2}{x}\, dx$

10. $\int \frac{5}{\sqrt{x}}\, dx$

11. $\int e^{-.02x}\, dx$

12. $\int 4e^{4x}\, dx$

Evaluate each definite integral in Exercises 13–20.

13. $\int_0^5 (2x - 3)\, dx$

14. $\int_0^2 (x^3 + x)\, dx$

15. $\int_1^2 (3 - t^{-2})\, dt$

16. $\int_0^1 e^{-5x}\, dx$

17. $\int_1^6 \frac{1}{t}\, dt$

18. $\int_2^3 \frac{1}{t^2}\, dt$

19. $\int_1^{10} e^{.04x}\, dx$

20. $\int_0^1 (5 - e^x)\, dx$

Determine each area in Exercises 21–26.

21. The area under $y = x^2 + 2$ from $x = 0$ to $x = 3$

22. The area under $y = 2 + \sqrt{x}$ from $x = 4$ to $x = 9$

23. The area between the curves $y = 4 - x$ and $y = e^x$ from $x = 0$ to $x = 1$

24. The area between the curve $y = x^2 + 1$ and the line $y = x$ from $x = 2$ to $x = 5$

25. The area enclosed by the curve $y = x^2$ and the curve $y = 8 - x^2$

26. The area enclosed by the line $y = x + 2$ and the curve $y = -x^2 + 4x + 2$

27. *(REVENUE)* If the marginal revenue function is $R'(x) = .65 + .002x$ dollars, where x is the number of liter bottles of cola sold, determine the total revenue from the sale of 50 liter bottles of cola.

28. *(PROFIT)* Determine the profit function $P(x)$ if the marginal profit is $80 + .4x$ and $P(0) = -\$40$.

29. *(VELOCITY/DISTANCE)* A man starts his car and then drives it with a constant acceleration of 18 feet per second per second. How far does the car go in 5 seconds?

30. *(PETROLEUM CONSUMPTION)* The rate at which petroleum was consumed in China was approximately

$$c'(t) = 47t + 635$$

million barrels per year from 1984 to 1989. Determine the total amount of petroleum consumed from 1984 to 1989.

31. *(PETROLEUM CONSUMPTION)* The rate at which petroleum was consumed in the United States was approximately

$$c'(t) = .2t + 5.7$$

billion barrels per year from 1985 to 1988. Determine the total amount of petroleum consumed from 1985 to 1988.

32. *(DEPRECIATION)* A business anticipates that $15,000 worth of newly purchased equipment will depreciate at the rate of $3000 - 400t$ dollars per year for 7 years. Use a definite integral to determine the total amount of depreciation that will occur during the first 4 years.

33. *(WATER FLOW)* Water will be added to the city's reservoir tonight for a 4-hour period. The rate at which water is added depends on the time and is given by

$$\frac{dw}{dt} = 1000 + 100t \qquad 0 \le t \le 4$$

where w is the volume in gallons and t is the time in hours. Determine the total amount of water added.

34. *(PERSONAL CONSUMPTION)* The rate of personal consumption expenditures in the U.S. from 1987 to 1992 was approximately

$$c'(t) = .2t + 3.1$$

trillion dollars per year. Determine the total of personal consumption expenditures from 1987 to 1992.

35. (FLU OUTBREAK) There is an outbreak of flu, and the number of people n who will have the flu after t days is

$$n = 8t + 3\sqrt{t}$$

What is the average number of people who will have the flu between the ninth and sixteenth days?

36. (COMPOUND INTEREST) A person deposits $5000 into a savings account that pays 7% interest per year compounded continuously for 6 years. What is the average amount of money in the account during the 6-year period?

37. Find the average value of $f(x) = x^{2/3}$ over the interval [8, 27].

38. Find the average value of the function $f(x) = 1/x^2$ over the interval [1, 5].

39. (VOLUME) Find the volume of the solid produced by revolving about the x axis the region bounded by $y = 2e^x$, $y = 0$, $x = -1$, and $x = 0$.

40. (VOLUME) Find the volume of the solid produced by revolving about the x axis the region bounded by $y = 1 + \sqrt[3]{x}$, $y = 0$, $x = 8$, and $x = 27$.

41. (SURPLUS) Suppose $S(x) = .4x + 3$ dollars and $D(x) = 15 - .2x$ dollars. Determine the equilibrium point, the consumer's surplus, and the producer's surplus.

42. (SURPLUS) Suppose $S(x) = .1x^2 + 2$ dollars and $D(x) = 11 - .2x^2$ dollars. Determine the equilibrium point, the consumer's surplus, and the producer's surplus.

43. Use summation notation to write the expression $x_1 f(x_1) + x_2 f(x_2) + \cdots + x_n f(x_n)$.

44. Use rectangles to approximate the area bounded by the graph of $f(x) = 12 - x^2$, the x axis, and the lines $x = -1$ and $x = 3$. Use $n = 4$ subintervals.

45. Consider the three-color region shown next.

    (a) Determine the *red* shaded area.
    (b) Determine the *yellow* shaded area.
    (c) Determine the *green* shaded area.
    (d) Compare your results from parts (a), (b), and (c).

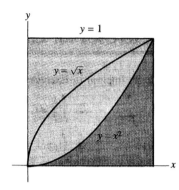

46. Consider the region shown below.

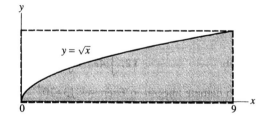

    (a) Determine the volume of the paraboloid obtained by revolving about the x axis the (shaded) region bounded by $y = \sqrt{x}$, the x axis, and $x = 9$.
    (b) Determine the volume of the cylinder obtained when the rectangle shown (dashed lines) is revolved about the x axis.
    (c) Do your results agree with the statement that the paraboloid carves out a volume equal to half of the cylinder it sits in?

47. Consider a curve such that
    (i) The slope of the curve at any point is always twice the x coordinate there.
    (ii) The curve passes through the point (4, 10).
Determine the equation of the curve.

W 48. Consider

$$\int_2^7 (e^x + 2x)\, dx = \left[e^x + x^2\right]_2^7$$

$$\int_{2}^{7} (e^{x} + 2x)\, dx = \left[e^{x} + x^{2} + 1 \right]_{2}^{7}$$

(a) Are both approaches correct? Explain.

(b) Will both approaches produce the same answer? Explain.

49. Use the definition of absolute value (from Section 1.4) to rewrite $|x|$ and then evaluate each integral.

(a) $\displaystyle\int_{3}^{4} |x|\, dx$ (b) $\displaystyle\int_{-2}^{-1} |x|\, dx$ (c) $\displaystyle\int_{-5}^{2} |x|\, dx$

50. The next figure shows the graphs of several antiderivatives of f. Determine the function f.

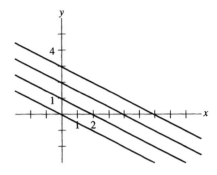

Chapter Projects and Essays

Many of the projects and essays lend themselves to group activity, although most can be completed by individual effort.

1. HISTORY OF INTEGRATION

BACKGROUND The definite integral was presented in Section 6.3 as the area under a curve, where the definition includes the limit of a sum of rectangular areas. Then, in Section 6.4, the Fundamental Theorem of Calculus shows how to evaluate a definite integral by using any antiderivative of the integrand function.

Historically, many individual approaches were used to solve a variety of problems that were, in fact, integration problems.

THE PROJECT Locate books on the history of mathematics or other books or articles that contain information on the history of integration. Investigate several of the mathematicians listed here, and report on the integration-related problems they solved and the methods they used.

Archimedes   Pierre de Fermat
al-Haytham (Alhazen) Evangelista Torricelli
Johann Kepler   John Wallis
Bonaventura Cavalieri

2. VOLUME APPROXIMATION

BACKGROUND In Section 6.3, rectangles were used to obtain approximations to the *area* under a curve. Specific numerical examples were given in Example 2 and Exercises 23–30 of that section.

A similar approach for *volume* was introduced in Section 6.5.

THE PROJECT Use rectangles (which become cylinders when revolved) to approximate the volume produced when the region bounded by $f(x) = .25x^2$ and the x axis (between $x = 0$ and $x = 4$) is revolved about the x axis.

(continued)

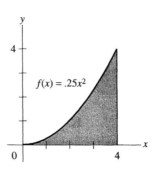

(a) Divide the interval $[0, 4]$ into four equal subintervals so that $\Delta x = 1$. Use $x_1 = 1$, from which it follows that $x_2 = 2$, $x_3 = 3$, and $x_4 = 4$.

(b) Obtain the volumes of the four cylinders by using $V = \pi \, [f(x_i)]^2 \, \Delta x$ for $i = 1, 2, 3, 4$. Then add the results to get the total volume.

(c) Redo parts (a) and (b) by dividing the interval $[0, 4]$ into eight equal subintervals.

(d) Obtain the *exact* volume by integration.

(e) Compare the three results and comment.

TECHNIQUES OF INTEGRATION

7

Of the 21 remaining species of this nectar-sipping Hawaiian bird, 14 are endangered on the islands. Because the pictured species—the i'iwi—has a curved beak for sipping nectar from lobelia blossoms, the trampling of lobelia by wild pigs has threatened the i'iwi's survival. The population of pigs, an introduced species, is now being controlled by park rangers. By tracking the birds' growth after the protective measures, ornithologists can predict the future population of i'iwis using calculus.

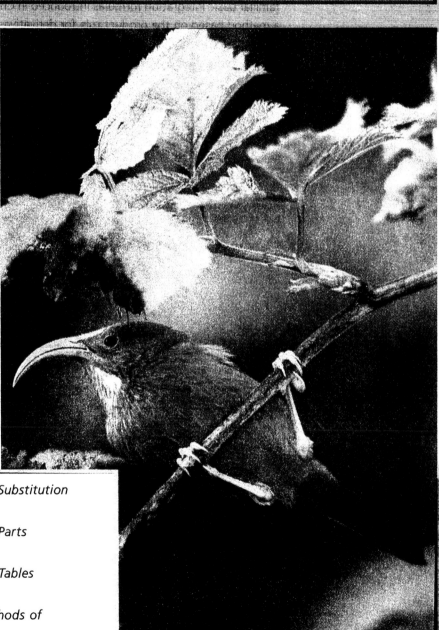

*T*his chapter concentrates on what are known as *techniques of integration.* In Section 7.1, *integration by substitution* will enable you to extend the use of the familiar basic integration formulas introduced in Chapter 6. Then, *integration by parts,* a method based on the product rule for derivatives, offers an opportunity to perform integrations that are completely different from any you have seen before. Next, the use of integration tables opens up a whole new world of possibilities. Finally, numerical methods offer ways of approximating the value of definite integrals. Such methods are needed when the integral cannot be evaluated by any other means.

7.1 | INTEGRATION BY SUBSTITUTION

When the concept of integration was introduced in Chapter 6, several basic properties and formulas were presented. The list is summarized here.

Basic Integral Formulas

1. $\int x^n \, dx = \dfrac{x^{n+1}}{n+1} + C \qquad n \neq -1$

2. $\int k \, dx = kx + C \qquad k = \text{constant}$

3. $\int e^x \, dx = e^x + C$

4. $\int e^{kx} \, dx = \dfrac{1}{k} e^{kx} + C$

5. $\int \dfrac{1}{x} \, dx = \ln |x| + C$

These basic integration formulas were obtained by reversing known differentiation formulas. When this approach is applied to the chain rule, the process is called **integration by substitution,** which is the topic of this section.

To begin, consider $f(x) = (x^3 + 1)^5$. The derivative $f'(x)$ can be obtained by using the chain rule.

$$f'(x) = 5(x^3 + 1)^4 \cdot 3x^2$$

In this differentiation, we let $u = x^3 + 1$, and then du/dx is $3x^2$. The *integration* of $f'(x) = 5(x^3 + 1)^4 \cdot 3x^2$ can be accomplished by making the *same* substitution—let $u = x^3 + 1$. Specifically, in

$$\int 5(x^3 + 1)^4 \cdot 3x^2 \, dx$$

let

$$u = x^3 + 1$$

Then

$$\frac{du}{dx} = 3x^2 \qquad \text{and} \qquad du = 3x^2 \, dx$$

We can now substitute within the integral. Replace $x^3 + 1$ by u and replace $3x^2 \, dx$ by du. The result is

$$\int 5\underbrace{(x^3 + 1)^4}_{u} \cdot \underbrace{3x^2 \, dx}_{du} = \int 5u^4 \, du$$

The integration is now a familiar one, although the variable is u rather than x.

$$\int 5u^4 \, du = \frac{5u^5}{5} + C = u^5 + C$$

To reintroduce x, use $u = x^3 + 1$ to replace u by $x^3 + 1$. The result is

$$(x^3 + 1)^5 + C$$

Thus,

$$\int 5(x^3 + 1)^4 \cdot 3x^2 \, dx = (x^3 + 1)^5 + C$$

Let's consider another example of integration by substitution.

EXAMPLE 1 Evaluate $\int 2x\sqrt{x^2 - 5} \, dx$.

SOLUTION Let $u = x^2 - 5$. Then $du/dx = 2x$ and $du = 2x \, dx$. Also, rearrange the integrand so that the substitution of u for $x^2 - 5$ and du for $2x \, dx$ can be made. The integration will then be an easy matter. Here is the entire procedure.

$$\int 2x\sqrt{x^2 - 5} \, dx = \int \sqrt{x^2 - 5} \; 2x \, dx \qquad \text{rearranging}$$

$$= \int \sqrt{u} \, du \qquad \text{substituting}$$

$$= \int u^{1/2} \, du$$

$$= \frac{2}{3} u^{3/2} + C$$

$$= \frac{2}{3} (x^2 - 5)^{3/2} + C \qquad \text{substituting back}$$

♦

The next example demonstrates how constants can be introduced when needed in order to modify an integral.

EXAMPLE 2   Evaluate $\displaystyle\int (x^2 + 1)^6 \, x \, dx$.

SOLUTION   Let $u = x^2 + 1$. Then $du/dx = 2x$ and $du = 2x \, dx$. Unfortunately, the $2x \, dx$ obtained as du is not the same as the $x \, dx$ in the integral. However, a *constant* factor can be inserted in an integral in the manner demonstrated next. Here we wish to insert a factor of 2 in order to change the $x \, dx$ to $2x \, dx$.

$$\int (x^2 + 1)^6 \, x \, dx = \int (x^2 + 1)^6 \cdot \frac{1}{2} \cdot 2 \cdot x \, dx$$

Since $\frac{1}{2} \cdot 2 = 1$, this is legitimate. In other words, we have merely multiplied the integrand by 1. Clearly, we do not want the 1/2 that now appears in the integrand. Because 1/2 is a *constant* factor, it can be placed outside the integral, just as was done in Section 6.1.

$$\int (x^2 + 1)^6 \, x \, dx = \frac{1}{2} \int (x^2 + 1)^6 \cdot 2x \, dx$$

Now the substitution can be made—u for $x^2 + 1$ and du for $2x \, dx$.

$$\int (x^2 + 1)^6 \, x \, dx = \frac{1}{2} \int u^6 \, du$$

$$= \frac{1}{2} \cdot \frac{u^7}{7} + C$$

$$= \frac{u^7}{14} + C$$

$$= \frac{(x^2 + 1)^7}{14} + C \qquad \blacklozenge$$

EXAMPLE 3   A shortcut based on **Example 2**.

SOLUTION   After evaluating several integrals by substitution, your experience enables you to visualize more. Consider the integral of Example 2.

$$\int (x^2 + 1)^6 \, x \, dx$$

Since $u = x^2 + 1$ and $du = 2x \, dx$, we need a 2 inside the integral (to create $2x$ from x) and a 1/2 in front of the integral (to balance the 2).

$$\frac{1}{2} \int (x^2 + 1)^6 \, 2x \, dx$$

Now, without actually writing another integral, *visualize* that this is in fact

$$\frac{1}{2} \int u^6 \, du$$

which will yield

$$\frac{1}{2} \cdot \frac{u^7}{7} + C$$

With all of this *in mind*, the actual steps that are written are as follows:

$$\int (x^2 + 1)^6 \, x \, dx = \frac{1}{2} \int (x^2 + 1)^6 \, 2x \, dx$$

$$= \frac{1}{2} \cdot \frac{(x^2 + 1)^7}{7} + C = \frac{(x^2 + 1)^7}{14} + C \qquad \blacklozenge$$

Our work suggests an easier way to evaluate such integrals. It also leads to extending the rule

$$\int x^n \, dx = \frac{x^{n+1}}{n + 1} + C \qquad n \neq -1$$

to include integrands of the form u^n, where u is a function of x.

$$\int u^n \, du = \frac{u^{n+1}}{n + 1} + C \qquad n \neq -1$$

where u is a function of x.

EXAMPLE 4   Evaluate $\int (1 - x^3)^4 \, x^2 \, dx$.

SOLUTION   Here $u = 1 - x^3$, and then $du = -3x^2 \, dx$. Thus, we need a factor of -3 inside the integral in order to complete the du. To balance the -3 inserted inside, we must place $-1/3$ outside the integral. The integration:

$$\int (1 - x^3)^4 \, x^2 \, dx = -\frac{1}{3} \int (1 - x^3)^4 (-3x^2) \, dx$$

$$= -\frac{1}{3} \cdot \frac{(1 - x^3)^5}{5} + C = -\frac{(1 - x^3)^5}{15} + C \qquad \blacklozenge$$

EXAMPLE 5   Evaluate $\int (x^2 + 1)^4 \, 3x \, dx$.

SOLUTION   Here $u = x^2 + 1$, and then $du = 2x \, dx$. The given integral contains $3x \, dx$, but we want $2x \, dx$. One simple way to handle this type of situation is to remove the 3. Place the constant factor 3 in front of the integral, leaving $x \, dx$ inside the integral. Then place a 2 inside the integral (to obtain the desired $2x \, dx$) and a $1/2$ in front of the integral. Here is the entire procedure.

$$\int (x^2 + 1)^4 \, 3x \, dx = 3 \int (x^2 + 1)^4 \, x \, dx$$

$$= \frac{1}{2} \cdot 3 \int (x^2 + 1)^4 \, 2x \, dx$$

$$= \frac{3}{2} \int (x^2 + 1)^4 \, 2x \, dx$$

$$= \frac{3}{2} \cdot \frac{(x^2 + 1)^5}{5} + C = \frac{3(x^2 + 1)^5}{10} + C \qquad \blacklozenge$$

EXAMPLE 6   Evaluate the definite integral.

$$\int_0^2 \frac{x}{\sqrt{1 + 2x^2}} \, dx$$

SOLUTION $$\int_0^2 \frac{x}{\sqrt{1 + 2x^2}} \, dx = \int_0^2 \frac{x}{(1 + 2x^2)^{1/2}} \, dx = \int_0^2 (1 + 2x^2)^{-1/2} \, x \, dx$$

Because $u = 1 + 2x^2$, it follows that $du = 4x \, dx$. We need a 4 inside the integral and a 1/4 in front to compensate for it.

$$\int_0^2 \frac{x}{\sqrt{1 + 2x^2}} \, dx = \frac{1}{4} \int_0^2 (1 + 2x^2)^{-1/2} \, 4x \, dx = \frac{1}{4} \left[\frac{(1 + 2x^2)^{1/2}}{1/2} \right]_0^2$$

$$= \frac{1}{4} \cdot \frac{2}{1} \left[\sqrt{1 + 2x^2} \right]_0^2 = \frac{1}{2} \left[(\sqrt{9}) - (\sqrt{1}) \right] = 1 \qquad \blacklozenge$$

Note

We could have evaluated the definite integral of Example 6 by using u in the integration and changing the limits of integration to agree with it. Because $u = 1 + 2x^2$, when (lower limit) x is 0, $u = 1 + 2(0)^2 = 1$. Similarly, when (upper limit) x is 2, $u = 1 + 2(2)^2 = 9$. Thus, we would have

$$\frac{1}{4} \int_1^9 u^{-1/2} \, du = \frac{1}{4} \cdot \frac{2}{1} \left[u^{1/2} \right]_1^9 = \frac{1}{2} (3 - 1) = 1$$

EXAMPLE 7   Evaluate $\int (x^2 + 8x + 1)^5 (x + 4) \, dx$.

SOLUTION   Here $u = x^2 + 8x + 1$ and $du = (2x + 8) \, dx$. If we multiply $(x + 4) \, dx$ by 2, it will become $(2x + 8) \, dx$, which is du. In view of this, we place a 2 inside the integral and 1/2 in front. The integration:

$$\int (x^2 + 8x + 1)^5 (x + 4)\, dx = \frac{1}{2}\int (x^2 + 8x + 1)^5\, 2(x + 4)\, dx$$

$$= \frac{1}{2} \cdot \frac{(x^2 + 8x + 1)^6}{6} + C$$

$$= \frac{(x^2 + 8x + 1)^6}{12} + C \qquad \blacklozenge$$

Other integration formulas can be extended to include integration by substitution. For example, the formula

$$\int e^x\, dx = e^x + C$$

can be extended to

$$\int e^u\, du = e^u + C$$

EXAMPLE 8   Evaluate $\displaystyle\int xe^{x^2}\, dx$.

SOLUTION   First, rearrange the integrand to put the x with the dx.

$$\int xe^{x^2}\, dx = \int e^{x^2}\, x\, dx$$

For this integral, $u = x^2$, which means that $du = 2x\, dx$. Consequently, a 2 must be placed inside the integral to complete the du, and a 1/2 must be placed in front of the integral to compensate for it.

$$\int xe^{x^2}\, dx = \frac{1}{2}\int e^{x^2}\, 2x\, dx$$

The integrand is now of the form $e^u\, du$, so the integration can be completed.

$$\int xe^{x^2}\, dx = \frac{1}{2}e^{x^2} + C \qquad \blacklozenge$$

Another formula that can be extended is

$$\int \frac{1}{x}\, dx = \ln |x| + C$$

The more general formula is

$$\int \frac{1}{u}\, du = \ln |u| + C$$

In view of the usual concern with obtaining du before completing any integration, this integration formula is usually considered in the form shown below. Example 9 will demonstrate why this is done.

$$\int \frac{du}{u} = \ln |u| + C$$

EXAMPLE 9 Evaluate $\int \frac{2x}{x^2 - 1}\, dx.$

SOLUTION *When the integrand is a fraction, the dx can be written in the numerator or at the end of the integrand.* Specifically,

$$\int \frac{2x}{x^2 - 1}\, dx = \int \frac{2x\, dx}{x^2 - 1}$$

Having dx in the numerator means that the entire du will be together in the numerator. In this example, $u = x^2 - 1$, and thus $du = 2x\, dx$. This integral is clearly in the form

$$\int \frac{du}{u}$$

Thus,

$$\int \frac{2x\, dx}{x^2 - 1} = \ln |x^2 - 1| + C \qquad \qquad \blacklozenge$$

EXAMPLE 10 Evaluate $\int \frac{e^x}{e^x - 1}\, dx.$

SOLUTION To begin,

$$\int \frac{e^x}{e^x - 1}\, dx = \int \frac{e^x\, dx}{e^x - 1}$$

Now you can see that the numerator is in fact the differential of the denominator, since $u = e^x - 1$ and $du = e^x\, dx$. Thus, the integral is of the form

$$\int \frac{du}{u}$$

Finally,

$$\int \frac{e^x}{e^x - 1}\, dx = \int \frac{e^x\, dx}{e^x - 1} = \ln |e^x - 1| + C \qquad \qquad \blacklozenge$$

7.1   Exercises

Evaluate each indefinite integral in Exercises 1–20.

1. $\int (x^2 + 3)^5 \, 2x \, dx$

2. $\int (5x + 1)^3 \, 5 \, dx$

3. $\int 2x\sqrt{x^2 - 6} \, dx$

4. $\int 6x\sqrt{1 + 3x^2} \, dx$

5. $\int (3x - 2)^6 \, dx$

6. $\int (x^2 - 10)^3 \, x \, dx$

7. $\int x\sqrt{x^2 - 3} \, dx$

8. $\int x^2\sqrt{1 + x^3} \, dx$

9. $\int (5x^3 + 1)^4 \, x^2 \, dx$

10. $\int (1 - 2x^3)^7 \, x^2 \, dx$

11. $\int \frac{1}{(7x + 2)^3} \, dx$

12. $\int \frac{x}{(1 - x^2)^4} \, dx$

13. $\int \frac{dx}{\sqrt{3x + 2}}$

14. $\int \frac{2 \, dx}{\sqrt{1 - 6x}}$

15. $\int 3(x + 2)^7 \, dx$

16. $\int 2(3x - 1)^6 \, dx$

17. $\int (x^2 - 4x + 1)^5 (x - 2) \, dx$

18. $\int (4x^2 + 4x - 6)^4 (2x + 1) \, dx$

19. $\int (x^{1/2} + 1)^4 \, \frac{1}{x^{1/2}} \, dx$

20. $\int \frac{(1 + \sqrt{x})^3}{\sqrt{x}} \, dx$

Evaluate each definite integral in Exercises 21–32.

21. $\int_0^1 (x + 1)^5 \, dx$

22. $\int_2^3 (x - 2)^4 \, dx$

23. $\int_1^2 (4x - 3)^3 \, dx$

24. $\int_0^1 (5x + 1)^2 \, dx$

25. $\int_2^3 \frac{dx}{(2x - 3)^2}$

26. $\int_1^3 \frac{dx}{(3x + 1)^3}$

27. $\int_0^4 x\sqrt{2x^2 + 4} \, dx$

28. $\int_1^3 x\sqrt{5x^2 + 4} \, dx$

29. $\int_0^4 \frac{x}{\sqrt{1 + 3x^2}} \, dx$

30. $\int_0^4 \frac{x}{\sqrt{x^2 + 9}} \, dx$

31. $\int_1^4 \frac{(1 + \sqrt{x})^2}{\sqrt{x}} \, dx$

32. $\int_1^9 \frac{(\sqrt{x} - 1)^3}{\sqrt{x}} \, dx$

Evaluate each indefinite integral in Exercises 33–42.

33. $\int 3x^2 e^{x^3} \, dx$

34. $\int x^2 e^{x^3} \, dx$

35. $\int e^{x+1} \, dx$

36. $\int e^{2t+1} \, dt$

37. $\int e^{-x} \, dx$

38. $\int e^{7t} \, dt$

39. $\int t e^{3t^2} \, dt$

40. $\int \frac{1}{x^2} e^{1/x} \, dx$

41. $\int (e^x + e^{-x}) \, dx$

42. $\int 2x e^{1 - x^2} \, dx$

Evaluate each indefinite integral in Exercises 43–52.

43. $\int \frac{1}{x + 1} \, dx$

44. $\int \frac{2}{2x + 3} \, dx$

45. $\int \frac{dx}{5x + 2}$

46. $\int \frac{dx}{3x + 4}$

47. $\int \frac{3x^2}{1 + x^3} \, dx$

48. $\int \frac{2x + 5}{x^2 + 5x - 9} \, dx$

49. $\int \frac{x^{1/2}}{1 + x^{3/2}} \, dx$

50. $\int \frac{x^2}{1 - 5x^3} \, dx$

51. $\int \frac{x^2 + 4x}{x^3 + 6x^2 - 15} \, dx$

52. $\int \frac{x^2 - 1}{x^3 - 3x + 1} \, dx$

Evaluate each indefinite integral in Exercises 53–70.

53. $\int \frac{x}{1 + x^2} \, dx$

54. $\int (e^x + 1)^3 \, e^x \, dx$

55. $\int (1 + e^{3t}) \, dt$

56. $\int \frac{1}{(6x - 2)^4} \, dx$

57. $\int \left(\frac{1}{x} + 1 \right) dx$

58. $\int x e^{1 - x^2} \, dx$

59. $\int \frac{e^{2x}}{1 - e^{2x}} \, dx$

60. $\int \frac{e^x}{1 - e^x} \, dx$

61. $\displaystyle\int (\ln x)^4 \cdot \frac{1}{x}\, dx$

62. $\displaystyle\int \frac{\ln x}{x}\, dx$

63. $\displaystyle\int \frac{1}{x(\ln x)^2}\, dx$

64. $\displaystyle\int \frac{1}{x \ln x}\, dx$

65. $\displaystyle\int \left(1 - \frac{1}{e^x}\right) dx$

66. $\displaystyle\int \frac{x^2}{e^{x^3}}\, dx$

67. $\displaystyle\int \frac{\ln x^2}{x}\, dx$

68. $\displaystyle\int \frac{\sqrt{\ln x}}{x}\, dx$

69. $\displaystyle\int \frac{(\ln x)^2}{x}\, dx$

70. $\displaystyle\int \frac{e^x - e^{-x}}{e^x + e^{-x}}\, dx$

Evaluate each definite integral in Exercises 71–82.

71. $\displaystyle\int_0^1 \frac{2x\, dx}{1 + x^2}$

72. $\displaystyle\int_0^2 \frac{x\, dx}{x^2 + 1}$

73. $\displaystyle\int_0^1 \frac{e^x}{1 + e^x}\, dx$

74. $\displaystyle\int_0^1 e^{1-x}\, dx$

75. $\displaystyle\int_0^1 x e^{-x^2}\, dx$

76. $\displaystyle\int_0^1 x^2 e^{x^3}\, dx$

77. $\displaystyle\int_0^{e-1} \frac{1}{x + 1}\, dx$

78. $\displaystyle\int_2^{e+1} \frac{1}{x - 1}\, dx$

79. $\displaystyle\int_1^e \frac{\ln x}{x}\, dx$

80. $\displaystyle\int_1^e \frac{\ln ex}{x}\, dx$

81. $\displaystyle\int_0^{\sqrt{2}} \frac{x\, dx}{3 - x^2}$

82. $\displaystyle\int_0^{\sqrt{5}} \frac{x\, dx}{6 - x^2}$

Evaluate each indefinite integral in Exercises 83–90.

83. $\displaystyle\int e^2\, dx$

84. $\displaystyle\int 3e\, dx$

85. $\displaystyle\int \frac{\ln \sqrt{x}}{x}\, dx$

86. $\displaystyle\int \frac{1}{x} \ln \frac{1}{\sqrt{x}}\, dx$

87. $\displaystyle\int \frac{x^2 + 2x + 4}{x + 1}\, dx$ *Hint:* Try long division.

88. $\displaystyle\int \frac{x}{x + 1}\, dx$ *Hint:* Try long division.

89. $\displaystyle\int \frac{3x}{x - 1}\, dx$

90. $\displaystyle\int \frac{1 + \ln x}{x \ln x}\, dx$

91. Determine the equation of the curve that has slope $4x e^{x^2}$ and passes through the point $(0, 5)$.

92. Determine the equation of the curve that has slope $x/(x^2 + 1)$, and passes through the point $(0, 0)$.

93. Find the average value of $f(x) = \sqrt{2x + 1}$ over the interval $[4, 12]$.

94. Find the average value of $f(x) = x e^{x^2}$ over the interval $[0, 1]$.

95. Determine the area under the curve $y = (7x + 1)^{1/3}$ from $x = 0$ to $x = 1$.

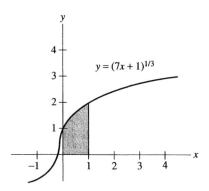

96. Determine the area under the curve $y = \sqrt{4x + 1}$ from $x = 2$ to $x = 6$.

97. *(VOLUME)* Find the volume of the solid produced by revolving about the x axis the region bounded by $y = 1/(2x + 3)$, the x axis, $x = 2$, and $x = 4$.

98. *(VOLUME)* Find the volume of the solid produced by revolving about the x axis the region bounded by $y = (2x - 1)^{1/3}$, the x axis, $x = 1$, and $x = 14$.

99. *(TREE GROWTH)* Suppose a transplanted small tree will grow to maturity according to

$$\frac{dh}{dt} = 3 + \frac{1}{2\sqrt{t + 1}}$$

where h is the height of the tree in feet and t is the time in years since it was transplanted. How much does the tree grow in the first 3 years?

100. *(FLU OUTBREAK)* Suppose the number of people n who will have the flu t days after an outbreak is

$$n = 8t + 3\sqrt{t + 2}$$

What is the average number of people who will have the flu during days 7 through 14 of the outbreak?

101. *(FILLING A TANK)* Oil is being piped into a huge storage tank at the rate of $15\sqrt{10t + 9}$ gallons per minute.

How many gallons of oil are piped into the tank in the first 4 minutes?

102. *(MARGINAL COST)* Determine the cost function $C(x)$ if the marginal cost is $1/\sqrt{2x + 1}$ and the fixed cost is $150.

W 103. Compare the two integrals given next.

$$\int (x^2 + 1)^{18}\, 2\, dx \qquad \int (2x + 1)^{18}\, dx$$

(a) Which integral can be evaluated by methods studied thus far? Explain why and how.

(b) Which integral cannot be evaluated by methods studied thus far? Explain.

W 104. As you know,

$$\int \frac{du}{u} = \ln |u| + C$$

(a) Do we need to keep the absolute value symbols around u in such cases as $\ln |x^2 + 3|$ and $\ln |e^x + 1|$? Explain.

(b) Do we need to keep the absolute value symbols around u in such cases as $\ln |x + 5|$ and $\ln |x^3|$? Explain.

TECHNOLOGY *EXERCISES*

In Exercises 1–2, use graphs to determine, to the nearest integer, the x coordinates of the points of intersection of the given curves. Then use calculus to determine the (approximate) area enclosed by the curves.

1. $y = x\sqrt{.5x^2 + 1}$ and $y = 5x - x^2$

2. $y = \dfrac{1}{\sqrt{2x + 1}}$ and $y = -x^2 + 6x - 8$

3. Consider the region under the curve $y = 6\sqrt{5x + 1}$ from $x = 0$ to $x = 3$.

(a) Use the RECTANGL program (from Section 6.3) to approximate the area of the region, using $n = 10$, 50, and 100. Be sure to enter the function (integrand) as Y1 before requesting the program.

(b) Use integration to determine the exact area.

Note If you used a computer algebra system for some integration in Chapter 6, you may want to use it again here, perhaps on Exercises 9, 27, 33, and 69.

7.2 | *INTEGRATION BY PARTS*

Considering the product rule from an integration point of view leads to another method of integration called **integration by parts.** The derivative formula for a product of two functions of x, called u and v, was stated in Section 3.5 as

$$\frac{d}{dx}(u \cdot v) = u \cdot \frac{dv}{dx} + v \cdot \frac{du}{dx}$$

To prepare for integration, consider differential form, obtained by multiplying both sides of this equation by dx.

$$d(u \cdot v) = u \cdot dv + v \cdot du$$

Next, subtract $v \, du$ from both sides and then integrate.

$$u \, dv = d(uv) - v \, du$$

$$\int u \, dv = \int d(uv) - \int v \, du$$

or

Integration by Parts

$$\int u \, dv = uv - \int v \, du$$

Integration performed by using this formula is called *integration by parts* and is set up by fitting your integral to the integral on the left side,

$$\int u \, dv$$

Your integral contains two parts—a function u and the differential of some other function v. An example should provide some feeling for the process.

EXAMPLE 1   Evaluate $\int xe^x \, dx$.

SOLUTION   This integral cannot be evaluated by any of the formulas we have studied so far. *If* the factor x were not present, we could readily integrate the e^x that remained. You will see that the process of integration by parts produces a new integral—one without the factor x. To begin, using the integration by parts formula,

$$\int u \, dv = uv - \int v \, du$$

The integral we are asked to evaluate is always called $\int u \, dv$. Thus,

$$\int xe^x \, dx \quad \text{is} \quad \int u \, dv$$

One part of the integrand must be chosen as u, and what remains must then be dv. A guideline for making these choices is given after this introductory example. In this instance, we will select

$$u = x \quad \text{and} \quad dv = e^x \, dx$$

If $u = x$, then by differentiation, $du = dx$. Also, if $dv = e^x \, dx$, then by antidifferentiation, $v = e^x$. In summary,

$$u = x \quad \rightarrow du = dx$$
$$dv = e^x \, dx \rightarrow \quad v = e^x$$

These four pieces—values for u, du, dv, and v—can now be used in the formula for integration by parts.

$$\int xe^x \, dx = uv - \int v \, du = x \cdot e^x - \int e^x \, dx$$
$$= xe^x - e^x + C \qquad \text{answer}$$

The choices of $u = x$ and $dv = e^x \, dx$ were correct. Had we chosen instead $u = e^x$ and $dv = x \, dx$, then we would have obtained $du = e^x \, dx$ and $v = x^2/2$. If those four pieces had been used in the integration by parts formula, the result would have been

$$\int xe^x \, dx = x \cdot \frac{x^2}{2} - \int \frac{x^2}{2} e^x \, dx$$

Clearly, this result is worse than the integral we began with. Our experience suggests a guideline (given next) that is often useful.   ◆

Guideline

When using integration by parts, it is often wise to let u equal the part of the integrand that you would like to eliminate—unless what remains for dv cannot be integrated.

With this guideline in mind, you may want to reread the beginning of Example 1.

EXAMPLE 2   Examine each integral for integration by parts and select u.

(a) $\int x(x + 3)^4 \, dx$ **(b)** $\int x^2 e^x \, dx$ **(c)** $\int x^2 \ln x \, dx$

SOLUTION   **(a)** $\int x(x + 3)^4 \, dx \ldots$ Let $u = x$ and $dv = (x + 3)^4 \, dx$.

(b) $\int x^2 e^x \, dx \ldots$ Let $u = x^2$ and $dv = e^x \, dx$.

(c) $\int x^2 \ln x \, dx \ldots$ Let $u = \ln x$ and $dv = x^2 \, dx$.

Note that you cannot let $u = x^2$ here, because doing so would leave $\ln x \, dx$ as dv, and you would not be able to integrate $\ln x$ to get v.   ◆

EXAMPLE 3   Determine $x^2 e^x \, dx$.

SOLUTION   From Example 2, part (b), we know that we should let $u = x^2$. Then

$$u = x^2 \quad \rightarrow du = 2x \, dx$$
$$dv = e^x \, dx \rightarrow \quad v = e^x$$

Thus,

$$\int u \, dv = uv - \int v \, du$$

is

$$\int x^2 e^x \, dx = x^2 e^x - \int 2x e^x \, dx$$

$$= x^2 e^x - 2 \int x e^x \, dx$$

The integral obtained here by parts cannot be integrated *directly*, although it is an improvement. The integrand of the original was $x^2 e^x$, and this one is $x e^x$. Also, in Example 1 we saw how this integral,

$$\int x e^x \, dx$$

can itself be evaluated by parts. Thus, to proceed from

$$\int x^2 e^x \, dx = x^2 e^x - 2 \int x e^x \, dx$$

we will use a second application of integration by parts, this time to evaluate $\int x e^x \, dx$. As was done in Example 1, let $u = x$ and $dv = e^x \, dx$. Then $du = dx$ and $v = e^x$. As a result, we have

$$\int x^2 e^x \, dx = x^2 e^x - 2\left(x e^x - \int e^x \, dx \right)$$

$$= x^2 e^x - 2x e^x + 2 \int e^x \, dx$$

$$= x^2 e^x - 2x e^x + 2 e^x + C$$

Thus, after two applications of integration by parts,

$$\int x^2 e^x \, dx = x^2 e^x - 2xe^x + 2e^x + C \qquad \text{answer} \qquad \blacklozenge$$

EXAMPLE 4 Evaluate the definite integral.

$$\int_0^1 xe^x \, dx$$

SOLUTION The purpose of this example is to show evaluation of a *definite* integral using integration by parts. In Example 1, we obtained along the way

$$\int xe^x \, dx = xe^x - \int e^x \, dx$$

Evaluating the definite integral, we have

$$\int_0^1 xe^x \, dx = \left[xe^x \right]_0^1 - \int_0^1 e^x \, dx$$

$$= (1 \cdot e^1 - 0 \cdot e^0) - \left[e^x \right]_0^1$$

$$= e^1 - 0 - (e^1 - e^0)$$

$$= e - 0 - e + 1$$

$$= 1 \qquad \blacklozenge$$

The following two important results from Section 5.2 will be needed for evaluating definite integrals.

$$\ln e = 1 \qquad\qquad \ln 1 = 0$$

Present Value of an Income Stream

A business may generate a continuous stream of income over a period of t years. The rate of income will probably vary and thus be a function of t, say $f(t)$. The **present value of an income stream** is the amount P that must be invested now at the current interest rate r in order to produce in t years the same amount that would be produced by the income stream.

In Section 5.1, present value P was computed from $A = Pe^{rt}$, which can also be written as $P = Ae^{-rt}$, where A is the value t years from now. In other words, e^{-rt} is multiplied by the amount we expect to have in t years.

In considering a variable income stream, we would replace the constant A by $f(t)$, and the present value would be the sum of (a theoretically infinite number of) terms of the form $f(t)e^{-rt}$. The present value of an income stream over T years is then given by the following definite integral.

> ## Present Value of an Income Stream
> ## (over T years)
>
> $$P = \int_0^T f(t)e^{-rt}\, dt$$
>
> P = the present value
>
> $f(t)$ = the rate at which income
>   is generated
>
> t = the time in years
>
> r = the prevailing annual
>   interest rate

APPLIED

EXAMPLE 5 *PRESENT VALUE OF AN INCOME STREAM*

A small corporation's 5-year projection shows its income t years from now as

$$f(t) = 40{,}000 + 10{,}000t \qquad \text{dollars per year}$$

Assuming an annual interest rate of 8%, find the present value of the income stream over the 5-year period.

SOLUTION The present value of the income stream is given by

$$P = \int_0^T f(t)e^{-rt}\, dt$$

where

$$f(t) = 40{,}000 + 10{,}000t \qquad r = .08 \qquad T = 5$$

Thus, we have

$$P = \int_0^5 (40{,}000 + 10{,}000t)e^{-.08t}\, dt$$

$$= \int_0^5 40{,}000e^{-.08t}\, dt + \int_0^5 10{,}000te^{-.08t}\, dt$$

The second integral requires integration by parts, with $u = 10{,}000t$ and $dv = e^{-.08t}\, dt$ (and then $du = 10{,}000\, dt$ and $v = -12.5e^{-.08t}$).

$$P = \left[40{,}000 \cdot \frac{1}{-.08}e^{-.08t}\right]_0^5 + \left[-125{,}000te^{-.08t}\right]_0^5 - \int_0^5 (-125{,}000e^{-.08t})\, dt$$

$$= \left[-500{,}000e^{-.08t}\right]_0^5 - \left[125{,}000te^{-.08t}\right]_0^5 + \int_0^5 125{,}000e^{-.08t}\, dt$$

$$= (164{,}840) - (418{,}938) + \left[-1{,}562{,}500e^{-.08t}\right]_0^5$$

$$= 164{,}840 - 418{,}938 + 515{,}156 \qquad \text{using } e^{-.4} \text{ to 4 decimal places}$$

$$= 261{,}058$$

The present value of the income stream over the 5-year period is $261,058. ◆

7.2   Exercises

In Exercises 1–20, evaluate each indefinite integral by using integration by parts.

1. $\displaystyle\int xe^{2x}\, dx$

2. $\displaystyle\int xe^{-x}\, dx$

3. $\displaystyle\int x \ln x\, dx$

4. $\displaystyle\int x \ln (x + 1)\, dx$

5. $\displaystyle\int x^2 \ln x\, dx$

6. $\displaystyle\int x^2 \ln 3x\, dx$

7. $\displaystyle\int (x + 1)e^x\, dx$

8. $\displaystyle\int x(e^x + 1)\, dx$

9. $\displaystyle\int \frac{\ln x}{x^2}\, dx$

10. $\displaystyle\int \ln x\, dx$

11. $\displaystyle\int x(x + 3)^4\, dx$

12. $\displaystyle\int x(x - 4)^5\, dx$

13. $\displaystyle\int \frac{x}{(x + 7)^3}\, dx$

14. $\displaystyle\int \frac{x}{(x + 2)^5}\, dx$

15. $\displaystyle\int \frac{\ln x}{\sqrt{x}}\, dx$

16. $\displaystyle\int x^3 \ln x\, dx$

17. $\displaystyle\int x^3 e^x\, dx$

18. $\displaystyle\int \sqrt{x} \ln x\, dx$

19. $\displaystyle\int x(x + 2)^{-3}\, dx$

20. $\displaystyle\int x\sqrt{1 + x}\, dx$

In Exercises 21–30, evaluate each definite integral by parts.

21. $\displaystyle\int_1^2 xe^x\, dx$

22. $\displaystyle\int_0^1 x^2 e^x\, dx$

23. $\displaystyle\int_1^e \ln x\, dx$

24. $\displaystyle\int_0^1 (x + 1)e^x\, dx$

25. $\displaystyle\int_0^1 x(1 + e^x)\, dx$

26. $\displaystyle\int_0^4 \ln (x + 1)\, dx$

27. $\displaystyle\int_{-1}^0 \frac{x}{e^x}\, dx$

28. $\displaystyle\int_1^e x \ln x\, dx$

29. $\displaystyle\int_2^3 30x(x + 1)^4\, dx$

30. $\displaystyle\int_3^5 90x(x - 3)^8\, dx$

Evaluate each indefinite integral in Exercises 31–40. Note that *only some* of the integrals require the use of integration by parts.

31. $\displaystyle\int xe^{x^2}\, dx$

32. $\displaystyle\int x(e^{2x} + 3)\, dx$

33. $\displaystyle\int \frac{\ln x}{x}\, dx$

34. $\displaystyle\int x \ln x\, dx$

35. $\displaystyle\int \ln 2x\, dx$

36. $\displaystyle\int \frac{1}{x \ln x}\, dx$

37. $\displaystyle\int x\sqrt{1 + x}\, dx$

38. $\displaystyle\int \frac{x}{x^2 + 3}\, dx$

39. $\displaystyle\int x\sqrt{1 + x^2}\, dx$

40. $\displaystyle\int x^{-2} \ln x\, dx$

In Exercises 41–46, evaluate each integral by parts. These integrals provide practice for work with problems involving the present value of an income stream.

41. $\displaystyle\int xe^{-.04x}\, dx$

42. $\displaystyle\int xe^{-.02x}\, dx$

43. $\displaystyle\int 12xe^{-.08x}\, dx$

44. $\displaystyle\int 4xe^{-.1x}\, dx$

45. $\displaystyle\int xe^{-.05x}\, dx$

46. $\displaystyle\int xe^{-.08x}\, dx$

47. (*INCOME STREAM*) A small corporation's 4-year projection shows its income t years from now as

$$f(t) = 20,000 + 3000t \quad \text{dollars per year}$$

Assuming an annual interest rate of 5%, find the present value of the income stream over the 4-year period.

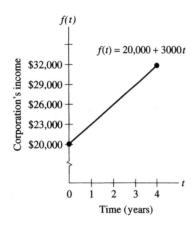

48. (*INCOME STREAM*) Suppose your business will produce income at the rate of $f(t) = 20t$ thousand dollars per year for the next 5 years. Using an annual interest rate of 8%, find the present value of the income stream. Note that t is time in years.

49. (*INCOME STREAM*) Assume that the natural gas from a well will produce a continuous stream of income of

$$f(t) = 7000 - 300t$$

dollars per year for t years. If the prevailing annual interest rate is 8%, find the present value of the income stream over the first 6 years of operation.

50. (*INCOME STREAM*) The owners of a factory estimate that new machinery they have installed will contribute to their revenue at the rate of

$$f(t) = 8000 - 400t$$

dollars per year for t years. Determine the present value of the income stream over the first 4 years, assuming an annual interest rate of 10%.

51. (*WILDLIFE PRESERVATION*) The population of a rare bird species had been reduced to fewer than 60 birds. Since then, conservationists have managed to protect the birds' environment. The bird population is now growing at the rate

$$\frac{dP}{dt} = 1 + \ln t \qquad t \geq 1$$

where P is the number of birds and t is the time in years.

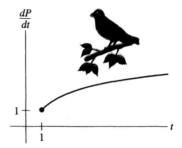

Assuming that the bird population was 60 birds after 1 year, determine P, the population at any time t.

52. (*MARGINAL REVENUE*) Determine the revenue function $R(x)$ for $x \geq 1$ if the marginal revenue is $x \ln x$ and the revenue from the sale of one unit is $1.75.

53. (*MEDICATION*) A medicine is absorbed into the bloodstream for t minutes at the rate of

$$M(t) = te^{-.1t}$$

milligrams per minute. How much medicine is absorbed into the bloodstream during the first 20 minutes?

54. (*MUSHROOM GROWTH*) A mushroom sprouts, and its volume grows for t hours at the rate of

$$M(t) = 3te^{-.4t}$$

cubic centimeters per hour. What is the volume of the mushroom after 8 hours?

55. Find the average value of $f(x) = xe^x$ over the interval $[0, 1]$.

56. Find the average value of $f(x) = \ln 2x$ over the interval $[e, 10]$.

57. Determine the equation of the curve that has slope $\ln x$ and passes through the point $(1, -1)$.

58. Determine the equation of the curve that has slope $4x \ln x$ and passes through the point $(1, -1)$.

59. Determine the area under the curve $y = xe^{-x}$ from $x = 1$ to $x = 3$.

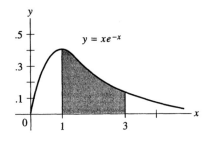

60. Determine the area under the curve $y = (x - 1)e^x$ from $x = 1$ to $x = 2$.

61. *(VOLUME)* Find the volume of the solid produced by revolving about the x axis the region bounded by $y = xe^x$, the x axis, $x = 0$, and $x = 1$.

62. *(VOLUME)* Find the volume of the solid produced by revolving about the x axis the region bounded by $y = \sqrt{x} \ln x$, the x axis, $x = e$, and $x = 5$.

W 63. Suppose we plan to use integration by parts to evaluate

$$\int \ln x \, dx$$

Is $u = 1$ and $dv = \ln x \, dx$ a good choice? Explain.

 TECHNOLOGY *EXERCISES*

W 1. Graph $f(x) = x^3 e^{x^2}$. Determine the average value of this function over the interval $[-2, 2]$. Is there an easy way to obtain the result? Explain.

2. Use a computer algebra system to perform the integration of Exercises 5, 9, and 37.

7.3 *INTEGRATION BY TABLES*

Although you have learned ways to evaluate a variety of integrals, there are still many integrals you would be unable to evaluate. Consider the following:

$$\int \sqrt{x^2 + 7} \, dx \qquad \int \frac{1}{4x^2 - 9} \, dx \qquad \int \frac{1}{1 + e^{-3x}} \, dx$$

Each of these three integrals can be evaluated by using methods that are beyond the scope of this text. But even with advanced techniques, some integration problems can be very difficult and time-consuming. Consequently, lists (or tables) of integration formulas have been devised to simplify matters.

To begin the study of **integration by tables,** glance at the integrals given in Table 5 in the Appendix. This is a short list of integral formulas, intended only to help demonstrate the use of integral tables. Ordinarily, tables of integrals are much longer, as in the references given next.

1. *CRC's Standard Mathematical Tables.* The Chemical Rubber Company (CRC). 59 pages of integration formulas.

2. *Mathematical Handbook,* by Murray R. Spiegel. Schaum's Outline Series, McGraw-Hill Book Co. 44 pages of integration formulas.

3. *Table of Indefinite Integrals*, by G. Petit Bois. Dover Publications. 150 pages of integration formulas.

The three examples that follow illustrate the process of evaluating an integral by means of a table.

EXAMPLE 1   Evaluate $\displaystyle\int \sqrt{x^2 + 7}\, dx.$

SOLUTION   This integral fits the form of formula 8 in Table 5, namely

$$\int \sqrt{u^2 + a^2}\, du$$

Here $u = x$ and $a = \sqrt{7}$ (from $a^2 = 7$). Since $u = x$, we have $du = dx$. The formula

$$\int \sqrt{u^2 + a^2}\, du = \frac{u}{2}\sqrt{u^2 + a^2} + \frac{a^2}{2} \ln \left| u + \sqrt{u^2 + a^2} \right| + C$$

becomes

$$\int \sqrt{x^2 + 7}\, dx = \frac{x}{2}\sqrt{x^2 + 7} + \frac{7}{2} \ln \left| x + \sqrt{x^2 + 7} \right| + C \qquad \blacklozenge$$

EXAMPLE 2   Evaluate $\displaystyle\int \frac{dx}{4x^2 - 9}.$

SOLUTION   This integral fits the form of formula 16 in Table 5, namely

$$\int \frac{du}{u^2 - a^2}$$

Here $u = 2x$ (from $u^2 = 4x^2$) and $a = 3$ (from $a^2 = 9$). Note, however, that if $u = 2x$, then $du = 2\, dx$. Hence we must modify the original integral by inserting a factor of 2 in the integrand and 1/2 outside the integral.

$$\int \frac{dx}{4x^2 - 9} = \frac{1}{2}\int \frac{2\, dx}{4x^2 - 9} = \frac{1}{2}\int \frac{2\, dx}{(2x)^2 - (3)^2}$$

The formula

$$\int \frac{du}{u^2 - a^2} = \frac{1}{2a} \ln \left| \frac{u - a}{u + a} \right| + C$$

becomes

$$\int \frac{dx}{4x^2 - 9} = \frac{1}{2}\int \frac{2\, dx}{4x^2 - 9} = \frac{1}{2}\left(\frac{1}{2(3)} \ln \left| \frac{2x - 3}{2x + 3} \right| \right) + C$$

$$= \frac{1}{12} \ln \left| \frac{2x - 3}{2x + 3} \right| + C \qquad \blacklozenge$$

EXAMPLE 3   Evaluate $\displaystyle\int \frac{dx}{1 + e^{-3x}}.$

SOLUTION   This integral fits the form of formula 18 in Table 5, namely

$$\int \frac{du}{1 + e^u}$$

Here $u = -3x$. This means that $du = -3\, dx$ and our original integral must be modified as follows:

$$\int \frac{dx}{1 + e^{-3x}} = -\frac{1}{3}\int \frac{-3\, dx}{1 + e^{-3x}}$$

Thus, the formula

$$\int \frac{du}{1 + e^u} = u - \ln(1 + e^u) + C$$

can be applied as

$$\int \frac{dx}{1 + e^{-3x}} = -\frac{1}{3}\int \frac{-3\, dx}{1 + e^{-3x}}$$

$$= -\frac{1}{3}[(-3x) - \ln\,(1 + e^{-3x})] + C$$

$$= x + \frac{1}{3}\ln\,(1 + e^{-3x}) + C \qquad\qquad\qquad ◆$$

A special type of integration formula, called a **reduction formula**, is used to simplify an integral containing a power of some expression. The simplified integral that results will contain a *reduced* (lower) power of some expression. Such reduction formulas are used to produce integrals that are easier to integrate. Two reduction formulas appear in our integral table. The next example shows how such formulas can be used.

EXAMPLE 4   Evaluate $\int (\ln x)^2\, dx$.

SOLUTION   Using the first reduction formula (formula 19 in Table 5) with $u = x$ and $n = 2$ will yield the following:

$$\int (\ln x)^2\, dx = x(\ln x)^2 - 2\int \ln x\, dx$$

The new integral

$$\int \ln x\, dx$$

can be evaluated either by parts (as suggested in Section 7.2, Exercise 10) or by an additional application of formula 19, this time with $n = 1$. Either way,

$$\int \ln x\, dx = x \ln x - x$$

After replacing $\int \ln x \, dx$ by $x \ln x - x + C$ in

$$\int (\ln x)^2 \, dx = x(\ln x)^2 - 2 \int \ln x \, dx$$

we obtain

$$\int (\ln x)^2 \, dx = x(\ln x)^2 - 2(x \ln x - x) + C$$

This simplifies to

$$\int (\ln x)^2 \, dx = x(\ln x)^2 - 2x \ln x + 2x + C \qquad \blacklozenge$$

7.3 Exercises

Use the table of integrals (Table 5 in the Appendix) to evaluate each indefinite integral in Exercises 1–12.

1. $\int \sqrt{x^2 + 16} \, dx$

2. $\int \sqrt{x^2 + 9} \, dx$

3. $\int \sqrt{9x^2 + 5} \, dx$

4. $\int \sqrt{16x^2 + 3} \, dx$

5. $\int \dfrac{dx}{x^2 - 49}$

6. $\int \dfrac{dx}{x^2 - 4}$

7. $\int \dfrac{dx}{25x^2 - 81}$

8. $\int \dfrac{dx}{9x^2 - 64}$

9. $\int \dfrac{dx}{1 + e^{7x}}$

10. $\int \dfrac{dx}{1 + e^{4x}}$

11. $\int \dfrac{dx}{1 + e^{-4x}}$

12. $\int \dfrac{dx}{1 + e^{-2x}}$

Use Table 5 to evaluate each indefinite integral in Exercises 13–36.

13. $\int \dfrac{dx}{\sqrt{x^2 + 25}}$

14. $\int \dfrac{dx}{\sqrt{x^2 + 81}}$

15. $\int \dfrac{dx}{\sqrt{9x^2 + 16}}$

16. $\int \dfrac{dx}{\sqrt{25x^2 + 1}}$

17. $\int \dfrac{dx}{x^2\sqrt{x^2 + 1}}$

18. $\int \dfrac{dx}{25x^2\sqrt{25x^2 + 9}}$

19. $\int \dfrac{dx}{4x^2\sqrt{4x^2 + 3}}$

20. $\int \dfrac{dx}{9x^2\sqrt{5 - 9x^2}}$

21. $\int \dfrac{dx}{x^2\sqrt{4x^2 + 3}}$

22. $\int \dfrac{dx}{x^2\sqrt{5 - 9x^2}}$

23. $\int \dfrac{dx}{x^2 - 9}$

24. $\int \dfrac{dx}{x^2 - 16}$

25. $\int \dfrac{dx}{9x^2 - 1}$

26. $\int \dfrac{dx}{16x^2 - 25}$

27. $\int x^2 \ln x \, dx$

28. $\int x^3 \ln x \, dx$

29. $\int x^5 \ln x \, dx$

30. $\int x^4 \ln x \, dx$

31. $\int \dfrac{dx}{x\sqrt{x^2 + 1}}$

32. $\int \dfrac{dx}{x\sqrt{x^2 + 9}}$

33. $\int \dfrac{dx}{2x\sqrt{4x^2 + 25}}$

34. $\int \dfrac{dx}{4x\sqrt{16x^2 + 1}}$

35. $\int \dfrac{dx}{x\sqrt{9x^2 + 4}}$

36. $\int \dfrac{dx}{x\sqrt{4x^2 + 9}}$

Use a reduction formula from the table of integrals (Table 5) to evaluate each indefinite integral in Exercises 37–44.

37. $\int (\ln x)^3 \, dx$

38. $\int (\ln x)^4 \, dx$

39. $\int \ln x \, dx$

40. $\int (\ln x)^5 \, dx$

41. $\int xe^x \, dx$

42. $\int x^3 e^x \, dx$

43. $\int x^2 e^x \, dx$ **44.** $\int x^4 e^x \, dx$

45. Use properties of logarithms to show that the righthand side of formula 18 (Table 5) can be written as

$$\ln \frac{e^u}{1 + e^u} + C$$

That is, show that

$$\ln \frac{e^u}{1 + e^u} = u - \ln (1 + e^u)$$

46. Find the average value of $f(x) = \sqrt{25x^2 + 9}$ over the interval $[2, 6]$.

47. Find the average value of $f(x) = x^3 \ln x$ over the interval $[1, 3]$.

48. Determine the area under the curve

$$y = \frac{1}{\sqrt{x^2 + 9}}$$

from $x = 0$ to $x = 4$.

49. Determine the area under the curve

$$y = \frac{3}{\sqrt{x^2 - 9}}$$

from $x = 5$ to $x = 7$.

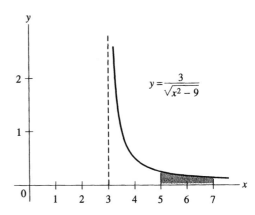

$$y = \frac{3}{\sqrt{x^2 - 9}}$$

W **50.** In Example 4, a reduction formula is used to evaluate

$$\int (\ln x)^2 \, dx$$

This integral can also be evaluated by using two applications of parts. If you were to begin by parts, what would be your choice for u and dv? Explain why your choice is good by indicating what it accomplishes.

TECHNOLOGY *EXERCISES*

Note   Computer algebra systems offer a modern alternative to integration by tables. If a system is available, use it to perform the integration of Examples 1, 3, and 4.

7.4 | *NUMERICAL METHODS OF APPROXIMATION*

Sometimes we encounter definite integrals that cannot be evaluated by any of the methods of integration. In fact, even a larger table of integrals may not include them. In such instances, approximations to the value of

$$\int_a^b f(x) \, dx$$

can be obtained by using **numerical methods** that approximate the area under the curve. You may recall the development of the definite integral in Section 6.3, where *rectangles* were used to approximate the area under the curve. In this section we will seek close approximations by using *trapezoids* (by means of the "trapezoidal rule") and *parabolas* ("Simpson's rule").

We begin our presentation of the **trapezoidal rule** with a graphical example that demonstrates why trapezoids are preferable to rectangles. First, consider a rectangular approximation to the area under a curve. We will use four rectangles. See Figure 1.

Next, let us consider an approximation obtained by using four trapezoids rather than four rectangles. Figure 2 shows that for this function, the trapezoidal approximation is much closer to the actual area under the curve than is the rectangular approximation.

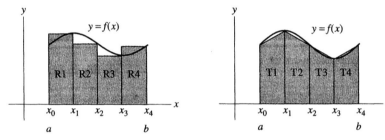

Figure 1 Rectangular approximation to area   **Figure 2** Trapezoidal approximation to area

The sum of the areas of all four trapezoids shown can be determined by using the formula for the area of a trapezoid:

$$A = \frac{1}{2}(b_1 + b_2)h \qquad \begin{cases} b_1 = \text{one base} \\ b_2 = \text{the other base} \\ h = \text{height} \end{cases}$$

Figure 3 shows, for example, that in the first trapezoid (T1) above,

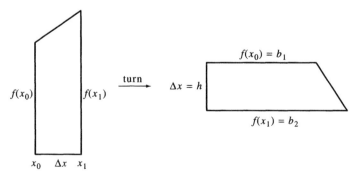

Figure 3

b_1 is $f(x_0)$, b_2 is $f(x_1)$, and h is Δx. (Note that Δx will be used, as in Section 6.3, to represent $x_1 - x_0$, $x_2 - x_1$, etc.) Thus, the areas of the four trapezoids are

$$T_1: \quad A = \frac{1}{2}[f(x_0) + f(x_1)]\Delta x \qquad T_2: \quad A = \frac{1}{2}[f(x_1) + f(x_2)]\,\Delta x$$

$$T_3: \quad A = \frac{1}{2}[f(x_2) + f(x_3)]\,\Delta x \qquad T_4: \quad A = \frac{1}{2}[f(x_3) + f(x_4)]\,\Delta x$$

The total area of all four trapezoids is the sum of these four areas.

$$A = \frac{\Delta x}{2}[f(x_0) + 2f(x_1) + 2f(x_2) + 2f(x_3) + f(x_4)]$$

In general, if n trapezoids are used, then the approximate value of the integral is given by the trapezoidal rule, stated next.

Trapezoidal Rule

If f is continuous on the interval [a, b], then

$$\int_a^b f(x)\, dx \approx \frac{\Delta x}{2}[f(x_0) + 2f(x_1) + 2f(x_2) + \cdots + 2f(x_{n-1}) + f(x_n)]$$

where $\Delta x = (b - a)/n$, $a = x_0$, $b = x_n$, n = number of trapezoids, and $x_1 = x_0 + \Delta x$, $x_2 = x_1 + \Delta x$, $x_3 = x_2 + \Delta x$, ...

The larger the value of n, the more trapezoids will be used and the smaller will be Δx. Using larger n yields a better approximation to the definite integral.

EXAMPLE 1 Use the trapezoidal rule with $n = 4$ to approximate the definite integral.

$$\int_0^2 \frac{1}{16 + x^2}\, dx$$

SOLUTION For this integral,

$$f(x) = \frac{1}{16 + x^2} \qquad a = 0 \qquad b = 2$$

Thus,

$$\Delta x = \frac{b - a}{n} = \frac{2 - 0}{4} = \frac{1}{2} \quad \text{or} \quad .5$$

Because $\Delta x = .5$, each successive x_i is .5 larger than the preceding one. To begin, since $a = 0$, then $x_0 = 0$, and then $x_1 = .5$, $x_2 = 1$, $x_3 = 1.5$, and $x_4 = 2$. Substituting into the formula for the trapezoidal rule yields

$$\int_0^2 \frac{1}{16 + x^2}\, dx \approx \frac{.5}{2}\left[\frac{1}{16 + 0^2} + \frac{2 \cdot 1}{16 + .5^2} + \frac{2 \cdot 1}{16 + 1^2} + \frac{2 \cdot 1}{16 + 1.5^2} + \frac{1}{16 + 2^2}\right]$$

$$\approx .25[.0625 + .1230 + .1176 + .1096 + .0500]$$

$$= .25[.4627]$$

$$\approx .1157$$

This approximation is quite good. The actual value of the integral correct to four decimal places is .1159, as determined by using a larger value of n. This form of integral is also available in tables of integrals.   ◆

Simpson's rule approximates the area under a curve by means of parabolas and provides (in most cases) a better fit and closer approximation than are obtained by using the trapezoidal rule. The formula for Simpson's rule is given next. Some justification of the rule will follow.

Simpson's Rule

If f is continuous on the interval [a, b], then

$$\int_a^b f(x)\, dx \approx \frac{\Delta x}{3}[f(x_0) + 4f(x_1) + 2f(x_2) + 4f(x_3) + \cdots +$$
$$2f(x_{n-2}) + 4f(x_{n-1}) + f(x_n)]$$

where $\Delta x = (b - a)/n$, $a = x_0$, $b = x_n$, *and n must be an* even *integer.* Also, $x_1 = x_0 + \Delta x$, $x_2 = x_1 + \Delta x$, $x_3 = x_2 + \Delta x$, ...

Consider x_0, $x_1 = x_0 + \Delta x$, and $x_2 = x_1 + \Delta x$. The three corresponding points on the graph of $y = f(x)$ are $(x_0, f(x_0))$, $(x_1, f(x_1))$, and $(x_2, f(x_2))$. The area under the parabola through those points can be shown to be

$$A = \frac{\Delta x}{3}[f(x_0) + 4f(x_1) + f(x_2)]$$

A second (nonoverlapping) parabola can be passed through the three points $(x_2, f(x_2))$, $(x_3, f(x_3))$, and $(x_4, f(x_4))$. Its area is

$$A = \frac{\Delta x}{3}[f(x_2) + 4f(x_3) + f(x_4)]$$

The total area of all the approximating parabolas created between $x = a$ and $x = b$ (that is, between x_0 and x_n) is the sum of several expressions of the form shown above. The grand total is shown above in the box as the formula for Simpson's rule. Note that n must be an even number, since if *one* parabola is used, the last x used is x_2; for *two* parabolas the last x is x_4; for *three* parabolas it is x_6; and so on. Figure 4 shows the exact area under a curve between x_0 and x_2 and the approximation using a parabola.

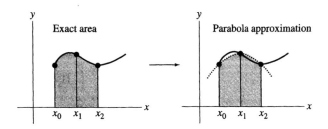

Figure 4 Exact area and approximation using a parabola

EXAMPLE 2 Use Simpson's rule with $n = 4$ to approximate the definite integral. Round all calculations to four decimal places.

$$\int_1^5 \sqrt{x^2 - 1} \, dx$$

SOLUTION For this integral, $f(x) = \sqrt{x^2 - 1}$, $a = 1 = x_0$, and $b = 5 = x_4$. Also,

$$\Delta x = \frac{b - a}{n} = \frac{5 - 1}{4} = 1$$

and so $x_0 = 1$, $x_1 = 2$, $x_2 = 3$, $x_3 = 4$, and $x_4 = 5$. By Simpson's rule,

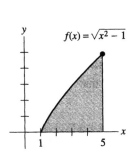

$$\int_1^5 \sqrt{x^2 - 1} \, dx \approx \frac{1}{3}\left[\sqrt{1^2 - 1} + 4 \cdot \sqrt{2^2 - 1} + \right.$$

$$\left. 2 \cdot \sqrt{3^2 - 1} + 4 \cdot \sqrt{4^2 - 1} + \sqrt{5^2 - 1}\right]$$

$$= \frac{1}{3}\left[\sqrt{0} + 4\sqrt{3} + 2\sqrt{8} + 4\sqrt{15} + \sqrt{24}\right]$$

$$\approx \frac{1}{3}[0 + 4(1.7321) + 2(2.8284) + 4(3.8730) + 4.8990]$$

$$= \frac{1}{3}(0 + 6.9284 + 5.6568 + 15.4920 + 4.8990)$$

$$= \frac{1}{3}(32.9762) \approx 10.9921 \qquad \blacklozenge$$

Error Estimates

When using an approximation method such as the trapezoidal rule or Simpson's rule, it is important to know how accurate an approximation the method will produce. The formulas shown next can be used to estimate the **error** E, which is the difference between the actual value and the approximate value. Notice that the formulas give the largest possible error, because they state that E is less than or equal to some number.

Error Estimates

$$\int_a^b f(x)\ dx, \quad n \text{ subintervals}$$

1. *Trapezoidal rule*

$$E \leq \frac{(b-a)^3}{12n^2} \cdot M$$

where M is the maximum value of $|f''(x)|$ on the interval $[a, b]$

2. *Simpson's rule*

$$E \leq \frac{(b-a)^5}{180n^4} \cdot M$$

where M is the maximum value of $|f^{(4)}(x)|$ on the interval $[a, b]$.

EXAMPLE 3 Determine the maximum error in approximating the definite integral

$$\int_1^5 \ln x\ dx$$

(a) Use the trapezoidal rule with $n = 8$.

(b) Use Simpson's rule with $n = 8$.

SOLUTION (a) We will begin by determining M. Since $f(x) = \ln x$, it follows that $f'(x) = 1/x$ and $f''(x) = -1/x^2$. The function f'' has no critical numbers, and the maximum value of $|f''(x)|$ on $[1, 5]$ occurs at the interval endpoint $x = 1$. It follows that $M = |f''(1)| = 1$ and that

$$E \leq \frac{(5-1)^3}{12(8)^2}\,(1) \qquad \text{or} \qquad E \leq .0833$$

The maximum error is .0833.

(b) To obtain M, we determine $f^{(4)}(x) = -6/x^4$. The maximum value of $|f^{(4)}(x)|$ on $[1, 5]$ occurs at $x = 1$. It follows that $M = |f^{(4)}(1)| = 6$. We have then

$$E \leq \frac{(5-1)^5}{180(8)^4} \cdot 6 \qquad \text{or} \qquad E \leq .0083$$

The maximum error is .0083.   ◆

EXAMPLE 4 When the trapezoidal rule is used to approximate

$$\int_1^5 \ln x$$

how large must n be so that $E \le .01$?

SOLUTION To guarantee that $E \le .01$, we must choose n so that

$$\frac{(b - a)^3}{12n^2} \cdot M \le .01$$

From Example 3, we know that M is 1. Also, $b - a = 4$. In steps,

$$\frac{4^3}{12n^2} \cdot 1 \le .01$$

$$16 \le .03n^2$$

$$n^2 \ge 533.33$$

$$n \ge 23.09$$

We must use $n = 24$, because n must be an integer and 23 does not satisfy the inequality $n \ge 23.09$. ◆

In most cases, for the same n value, Simpson's rule provides a better approximation than does the trapezoidal rule. However, the error estimate for Simpson's rule requires the fourth derivative, and for some functions it can be difficult and time-consuming to determine the fourth derivative. In such cases, the trapezoidal rule is the better choice. Simply use a larger n to get the accuracy you seek.

7.4 Exercises

In Exercises 1–10, consider each interval $[a, b]$ to be associated with the definite integral

$$\int_a^b f(x)\, dx$$

and determine the value of Δx to be used with a numerical approximation method such as the trapezoidal rule. Also determine $x_0, x_1, x_2, x_3, \ldots, x_n$.

1. $[0, 4]$, $n = 4$ **2.** $[0, 8]$, $n = 8$

3. $[1, 7]$, $n = 6$ **4.** $[2, 8]$, $n = 6$

5. $[2, 5]$, $n = 6$ **6.** $[2, 3]$, $n = 4$

7. $[2, 6]$, $n = 8$ **8.** $[0, 4]$, $n = 8$

9. $[3, 5]$, $n = 8$ **10.** $[1, 3]$, $n = 8$

In Exercises 11–20, use the trapezoidal rule to approximate each definite integral. Round calculations to four decimal places. *Use a calculator.*

11. $\displaystyle\int_0^2 x^2\, dx, \quad n = 4$ **12.** $\displaystyle\int_0^3 x^3\, dx, \quad n = 6$

13. $\displaystyle\int_0^3 \sqrt{x^2 + 1}\, dx, \quad n = 6$

14. $\displaystyle\int_1^4 \sqrt{x^2 - 1}\, dx, \quad n = 6$

15. $\int_{-1}^{5} \frac{1}{x+2} \, dx$, $\quad n = 6$

16. $\int_{0}^{2} \frac{1}{1+x^2} \, dx$, $\quad n = 4$

17. $\int_{0}^{8} x\sqrt{x+1} \, dx$, $\quad n = 4$

18. $\int_{0}^{4} x^2\sqrt{x+4} \, dx$, $\quad n = 4$

19. $\int_{1}^{5} \ln x \, dx$, $\quad n = 4$

20. $\int_{2}^{5} x \ln x \, dx$, $\quad n = 6$

In Exercises 21–30, use Simpson's rule to approximate each definite integral. Round calculations to four decimal places. *Use a calculator.*

21. $\int_{1}^{5} (x^2 + 3) \, dx$, $\quad n = 4$

22. $\int_{0}^{2} (x^3 + 2) \, dx$, $\quad n = 4$

23. $\int_{0}^{4} \sqrt{x^2 + 1} \, dx$, $\quad n = 4$

24. $\int_{1}^{4} \sqrt{x^2 - 1} \, dx$, $\quad n = 6$

25. $\int_{-1}^{2} \sqrt{x^3 + 1} \, dx$, $\quad n = 6$

26. $\int_{0}^{2} \sqrt{x^4 + 1} \, dx$, $\quad n = 4$

27. $\int_{0}^{2} \frac{1}{x+1} \, dx$, $\quad n = 8$ **28.** $\int_{0}^{4} \frac{1}{x^2 + 9} \, dx$, $\quad n = 8$

29. $\int_{0}^{3} \frac{1}{1+e^x} \, dx$, $\quad n = 6$ **30.** $\int_{0}^{2} e^{x^2} \, dx$, $\quad n = 4$

In Exercises 31–40, use both (a) the trapezoidal rule and (b) Simpson's rule to approximate each definite integral. Round calculations to four decimal places. *Use a calculator.* Then (c) obtain the *exact* value of the integral by ordinary integration. Compare the results.

31. $\int_{0}^{4} x^2 \, dx$, $\quad n = 4$ **32.** $\int_{0}^{3} x^2 \, dx$, $\quad n = 6$

33. $\int_{1}^{4} x^3 \, dx$, $\quad n = 6$ **34.** $\int_{0}^{2} x^3 \, dx$, $\quad n = 4$

35. $\int_{1}^{4} \sqrt{x} \, dx$, $\quad n = 6$ **36.** $\int_{1}^{4} \frac{1}{x^2} \, dx$, $\quad n = 6$

37. $\int_{0}^{1} xe^{x^2} \, dx$, $\quad n = 4$ **38.** $\int_{0}^{1} xe^{x^2} \, dx$, $\quad n = 8$

39. $\int_{0}^{2} x\sqrt{4 - x^2} \, dx$, $\quad n = 8$

40. $\int_{0}^{4} x\sqrt{x^2 + 9} \, dx$, $\quad n = 8$

41. Determine the shaded area in the figure by using each of the following methods:
   (a) The trapezoidal rule with $n = 4$
   (b) Simpson's rule with $n = 4$
   (c) The area of a circular region having radius r is πr^2. The drawing shows a quarter circle. Use $\pi \approx 3.1416$.

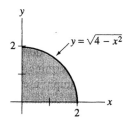

42. Determine the shaded semielliptical area in the figure by using each of the following methods:

   (a) The trapezoidal rule with $n = 6$. Use the interval $[0, 3]$ and double the result.
   (b) Simpson's rule with $n = 6$. Again, use $[0, 3]$ and double the result.

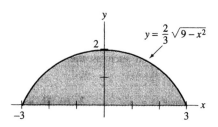

43. Use the trapezoidal rule to approximate the area of the property shown on the next page. The measurements along the street are made every 50 feet.

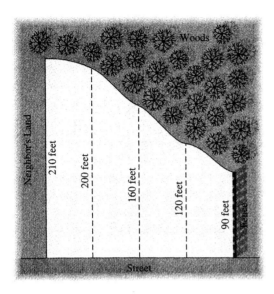

In Exercises 44–49, determine the maximum error in approximating the definite integral using (a) the trapezoidal rule and (b) Simpson's rule.

44. $\int_0^2 x^3 \, dx, \quad n = 4$

45. $\int_0^2 x^4 \, dx, \quad n = 4$

46. $\int_1^3 \ln x \, dx, \quad n = 8$

47. $\int_1^2 \frac{1}{x} \, dx, \quad n = 8$

48. $\int_1^3 \sqrt{x} \, dx, \quad n = 4$

49. $\int_0^1 e^{-x} \, dx, \quad n = 4$

In Exercises 50–53, determine how large n must be so that a trapezoidal rule approximation of the integral will have an error that does not exceed the value given as E.

50. $\int_1^2 \frac{1}{x} \, dx, \quad E = .001$

51. $\int_1^3 \frac{1}{x^2} \, dx, \quad E = .001$

52. $\int_0^2 x^3 \, dx, \quad E = .0001$

53. $\int_0^2 x^4 \, dx, \quad E = .0001$

W 54. What is the reason for using numerical integration methods such as the trapezoidal rule and Simpson's rule?

W 55. Explain why in Exercise 31 Simpson's rule yielded the *exact* value of the integral. *Hint*: Think about the *graph* of the function.

TECHNOLOGY *EXERCISES*

```
Prgm2:TRAPZOID
:Disp "A"
:Input A
:Disp "B"
:Input B
:Disp "N"
:Input N
:0→S
:1→I
:(B-A)/N→D
:Lbl 1
:A+(I-1)D→X
:S+Y₁→S
:A+I*D→X
:S+Y₁→S
:I+1→I
:If I≤N
:Goto 1
:(D/2)*S→S
:Disp "AREA ="
:Disp S
```

In Exercises 1–2, use the TRAPZOID program (program 2) to approximate each definite integral by the trapezoidal rule. Be sure to enter the integrand as function Y1 before requesting the program. (This program was written for the TI-81 and TI-82.)

1. $\int_1^5 \ln x \, dx$

   (a) Use $n = 4$ and compare with the answer to Exercise 19.

   (b) Use $n = 12, 20, 50,$ and 100 and notice the improvement in the approximation. (Compare with 4.047189562, which is correct to nine decimal places.)

2. $\int_1^4 (x + 1) \, dx$

   (a) Use $n = 3, 10,$ and 20 and observe the results.

W (b) In order to understand the results of part (a), graph the function $y = x + 1$. Focus on the region bounded by the graph of the function, the x axis, $x = 1$, and $x = 4$. Explain why the trapezoidal rule will produce the exact area for any n in this instance.

```
Prgm3:SIMPSON
:Disp "A"
:Input A
:Disp "B"
:Input B
:Disp "N EVEN"
:Input N
:0→S
:1→I
:(B-A)/N→D
:Lbl 1
:A+(I-1)D→X
:S+Y₁→S
:A+I*D→X
:S+4Y₁→S
:A+(I+1)D→X
:S+Y₁→S
:I+2→I
:If I<N
:Goto 1
:(D/3)*S→S
:Disp "AREA ="
:Disp S
```

In Exercises 3–4, use the SIMPSON program (program 3) to approximate each definite integral by Simpson's rule. Be sure to enter the integrand as function Y1 before requesting the program.

3. $\int_0^2 \dfrac{1}{x+1}\, dx$

   (a) Use $n = 8$ and compare the result with the answer to Exercise 27.

   (b) Use $n = 12$, 20, and 50 and notice the improvement in the approximation. (Compare with 1.098612289, which is correct to nine decimal places.)

4. $\int_1^5 (x^2 + 3)\, dx$

   (a) Use $n = 4$ and compare the result with the answer to Exercise 21.

W **(b)** Use $n = 10$, 20, and 50. Do you see an improvement in the approximation? Comment.

   (c) Perform the integration in, order to obtain the exact value of the integral.

W **(d)** Consider the nature of the curve $y = x^2 + 3$ and the nature of the curves used as a basis for Simpson's rule. Then explain the ''unusual'' results in this exercise.

Exercises 5–10 can be done using the TRAPZOID and SIMPSON programs (for the TI-81 and TI-82) or computer software.

5. Use the trapezoidal rule to approximate the definite integral of Example 1, namely

$$\int_0^2 \frac{1}{16 + x^2}\, dx$$

Begin with $n = 4$ and continue by using larger and larger n, until your approximation is correct to seven decimal places.

6. Redo Exercise 5 using Simpson's rule instead.

7. Use the approach of Exercise 5 to approximate the definite integral correct to seven decimal places.

$$\int_3^7 \frac{1}{x^2 - 1}\, dx$$

8. Redo Exercise 7 using Simpson's rule instead.

9. Use the approach of Exercise 5 to approximate the definite integral correct to seven decimal places.

$$\int_5^7 \frac{1}{\sqrt{x^2 - 9}}\, dx$$

10. Redo Exercise 9 using Simpson's rule instead.

7.5 | *IMPROPER INTEGRALS*

Recall that the area under the graph of $y = f(x)$ between $x = a$ and $x = b$ is given by

$$\int_a^b f(x)\, dx$$

provided f is continuous and nonnegative between a and b. In probability and statistics (and in some other application areas), the interval between a and b can extend infinitely far in either direction. The three possible types of intervals are shown next. The corresponding integrals are called **improper integrals.**

interval	integral
$[a, \infty)$	$\int_a^\infty f(x)\, dx$
$(-\infty, b]$	$\int_{-\infty}^b f(x)\, dx$
$(-\infty, \infty)$	$\int_{-\infty}^\infty f(x)\, dx$

In order to motivate a definition for the improper integral

$$\int_a^\infty f(x)\, dx$$

let us consider the following definite integral:

$$\int_a^b f(x)\, dx$$

Figure 5 shows the area under the curve for larger and larger values of b.

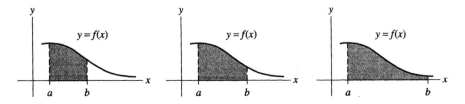

Figure 5 The area under the curve for larger and larger values of b

It seems reasonable to consider the improper integral in question (with upper limit ∞) to be the limit of the integral from a to b as b approaches infinity.

Improper Integral from a to ∞

$$\int_a^\infty f(x)\ dx = \lim_{b \to \infty} \int_a^b f(x)\ dx$$

provided that f is continuous on the interval $[a, \infty)$.

As you can see, evaluating improper integrals will involve determining limits at infinity. Because of this, some special limits at infinity are listed here. Most of these limits also appeared in Chapter 2 or in Chapter 5. You may want to review Section 2.4 on limits at infinity, since variations of these limits may appear. Exercises 1–22 at the end of this section offer a chance to practice determining limits before you need to use them in the improper integrals presented later in the exercises.

Some Limits at Infinity

$$\lim_{x \to \infty} \frac{1}{x^n} = 0 \qquad n > 0$$

$$\lim_{x \to -\infty} \frac{1}{x^n} = 0 \qquad n > 0$$

$$\lim_{x \to \infty} x^n = \infty \qquad n > 0$$

$$\lim_{x \to -\infty} x^n = \begin{cases} \infty & n = 2, 4, 6, \ldots \\ -\infty & n = 1, 3, 5, \ldots \end{cases}$$

$$\lim_{x \to \infty} \sqrt{x} = \infty \qquad \lim_{x \to \infty} \frac{1}{\sqrt{x}} = 0$$

$$\lim_{x \to \infty} e^x = \infty \qquad \lim_{x \to -\infty} e^x = 0$$

$$\lim_{x \to \infty} \frac{1}{e^x} = 0 \qquad \lim_{x \to \infty} e^{-x} = 0$$

$$\lim_{x \to \infty} \ln x = \infty$$

EXAMPLE 1 Evaluate the improper integral.

$$\int_1^\infty \frac{1}{x^2}\ dx$$

SOLUTION To begin, use the definition of the improper integral. Then perform the integration. Finally, evaluate the limit. The steps:

$$\int_1^\infty \frac{1}{x^2}\,dx = \lim_{b\to\infty}\int_1^b \frac{1}{x^2}\,dx = \lim_{b\to\infty}\int_1^b x^{-2}\,dx = \lim_{b\to\infty}\left[\frac{x^{-1}}{-1}\right]_1^b = \lim_{b\to\infty}\left[-\frac{1}{x}\right]_1^b$$

$$= \lim_{b\to\infty}\left[\left(-\frac{1}{b}\right) - \left(-\frac{1}{1}\right)\right] = \lim_{b\to\infty}\left(-\frac{1}{b} + 1\right)$$

Now that the integration has been completed, the limit can be determined. And because $\lim_{b\to\infty}(1/b) = 0$, the final result is simply 1.

$$\int_1^\infty \frac{1}{x^2}\,dx = 1$$

Note that this integral represents the area under the curve $y = 1/x^2$ for $x \ge 1$. Figure 6 shows this area.

♦

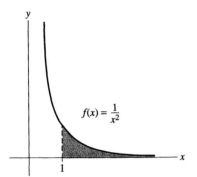

$f(x) = \dfrac{1}{x^2}$

Figure 6

EXAMPLE 2 Evaluate the improper integral.

$$\int_1^\infty \frac{1}{x}\,dx$$

SOLUTION This integral *appears* to be very similar to the integral of the previous example. Even the graph of the function is nearly the same. See Figure 7. However, evaluating the integral will show that the two integrals are quite different indeed.

$$\int_1^\infty \frac{1}{x}\,dx = \lim_{b\to\infty}\int_1^b \frac{1}{x}\,dx = \lim_{b\to\infty}\left[\ln|x|\right]_1^b = \lim_{b\to\infty}(\ln b - \ln 1) = \lim_{b\to\infty}(\ln b) = \infty \quad ♦$$

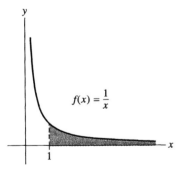

$f(x) = \dfrac{1}{x}$

Figure 7

> **Note**
> The integral just evaluated is said to be **divergent,** since it has no finite numerical value. By contrast, the integral of Example 1,
>
> $$\int_1^\infty \frac{1}{x^2}\,dx$$
>
> is said to be **convergent,** since it has a finite value. There is indeed a finite area under the curve.

APPLIED

EXAMPLE 3 ***POLLUTION OF A RIVER***

A factory has been dumping large quantities of waste into a nearby river. But now, to meet the new government environmental standard, the polluting has been decreased to $e^{-.4t}$ tons per year, where t is the number of years from now. What is the total amount of waste dumped into the river if the polluting continues indefinitely according to the formula?

SOLUTION   The total amount of waste dumped into the river will be

$$\int_0^\infty e^{-.4t}\, dt \quad \text{tons}$$

This integral is evaluated next.

$$\int_0^\infty e^{-.4t}\, dt = \lim_{b \to \infty} \int_0^b e^{-.4t}\, dt = \frac{1}{-.4} \lim_{b \to \infty} \int_0^b e^{-.4t}(-.4)\, dt$$

$$= -2.5 \lim_{b \to \infty} \int_0^b e^{-.4t}(-.4)\, dt = -2.5 \lim_{b \to \infty} \left[e^{-.4t}\right]_0^b$$

$$= -2.5 \lim_{b \to \infty} (e^{-.4b} - e^0) = -2.5 \lim_{b \to \infty} \left(\frac{1}{e^{.4b}} - 1\right)$$

$$= -2.5(0 - 1) = 2.5$$

The total amount of waste dumped into the river will be 2.5 tons, assuming the polluting continues indefinitely into the future. See Figure 8.

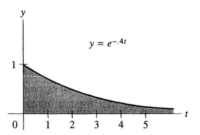

Figure 8 The graph of the function shows the (decreasing) rate of pollution. The area under the graph gives the total pollution that will occur.   ◆

APPLIED

EXAMPLE 4   **CAPITAL VALUE OF A RENTAL PROPERTY**

The **capital value** of a rental property, assuming that it will last indefinitely, is

$$\int_0^\infty Re^{-kt}\, dt$$

where R is the annual rent and k is the current annual rate of interest. (The amount received in rent will then earn interest at this rate.) Determine the capital value of a rental property if the annual rent is \$10,000 and the annual rate of interest is 8%.

SOLUTION   The capital value is

$$\int_0^\infty 10{,}000e^{-.08t}\, dt = \lim_{b \to \infty} \int_0^b 10{,}000e^{-.08t}\, dt = \frac{10{,}000}{-.08} \lim_{b \to \infty} \int_0^b e^{-.08t}(-.08)\, dt$$

$$= -125{,}000 \lim_{b \to \infty} (e^{-.08b} - e^0)$$

$$= -125,000(0 - 1) = 125,000$$

The capital value is $125,000. ◆

Improper integrals of the type

$$\int_{-\infty}^{b} f(x)\ dx$$

are defined and evaluated in a manner comparable to that for the improper integrals you have seen already.

$$\int_{-\infty}^{b} f(x)\ dx = \lim_{a \to -\infty} \int_{a}^{b} f(x)\ dx$$

provided that f is continuous on the interval $(-\infty, b]$.

EXAMPLE 5 Evaluate the improper integral.

$$\int_{-\infty}^{0} e^x\ dx$$

SOLUTION
$$\int_{-\infty}^{0} e^x\ dx = \lim_{a \to -\infty} \int_{a}^{0} e^x\ dx = \lim_{a \to -\infty} \left[e^x \right]_{a}^{0} = \lim_{a \to -\infty} (e^0 - e^a)$$

$$= \lim_{a \to -\infty} (1 - e^a) = 1 - 0 = 1$$

Keep in mind that $e^a \to 0$ as $a \to -\infty$. ◆

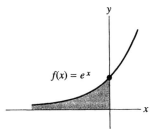

$f(x) = e^x$

Improper integrals of the type

$$\int_{-\infty}^{\infty} f(x)\ dx$$

are defined and evaluated in a way that involves both types of improper integrals you have seen already.

$$\int_{-\infty}^{\infty} f(x)\ dx = \int_{-\infty}^{c} f(x)\ dx + \int_{c}^{\infty} f(x)\ dx$$

provided that f is continuous on the interval $(-\infty, \infty)$.

The number c used in the two integrals can be any real number, although 0 or 1 is often a good choice. If either (or both) of the two integrals diverges, then the original integral also diverges. Otherwise, the original integral converges.

EXAMPLE 6 Evaluate the improper integral.

$$\int_{-\infty}^{\infty} xe^{-x^2}\, dx$$

SOLUTION We will use 0 for c.

$$\int_{-\infty}^{\infty} xe^{-x^2}\, dx = \int_{-\infty}^{0} xe^{-x^2}\, dx + \int_{0}^{\infty} xe^{-x^2}\, dx$$

$$= \lim_{a\to -\infty} \int_{a}^{0} xe^{-x^2}\, dx + \lim_{b\to \infty} \int_{0}^{b} xe^{-x^2}\, dx$$

$$= -\frac{1}{2}\lim_{a\to -\infty} \int_{a}^{0} e^{-x^2}(-2x)\, dx - \frac{1}{2}\lim_{b\to \infty} \int_{0}^{b} e^{-x^2}(-2x)\, dx$$

$$= -\frac{1}{2}\lim_{a\to -\infty} \left[e^{-x^2}\right]_{a}^{0} - \frac{1}{2}\lim_{b\to \infty} \left[e^{-x^2}\right]_{0}^{b}$$

$$= -\frac{1}{2}\lim_{a\to -\infty} (1 - e^{-a^2}) - \frac{1}{2}\lim_{b\to \infty} (e^{-b^2} - 1)$$

$$= -\frac{1}{2}(1 - 0) - \frac{1}{2}(0 - 1) = 0 \qquad \blacklozenge$$

7.5 Exercises

Evaluate each limit in Exercises 1–22.

1. $\lim_{b\to \infty} \dfrac{1}{b^2}$ **2.** $\lim_{b\to \infty} \dfrac{1}{b}$

3. $\lim_{a\to -\infty} \dfrac{2}{a}$ **4.** $\lim_{a\to -\infty} \dfrac{1}{a^2}$

5. $\lim_{b\to \infty} \sqrt{b+1}$ **6.** $\lim_{b\to \infty} \sqrt{b}$

7. $\lim_{b\to \infty} \dfrac{1}{\sqrt{2b}}$ **8.** $\lim_{b\to \infty} \dfrac{1}{\sqrt{b+1}}$

9. $\lim_{b\to \infty} (b^{1/2}+1)$ **10.** $\lim_{b\to \infty} \dfrac{4}{b^3}$

11. $\lim_{b\to \infty} \ln b$ **12.** $\lim_{b\to \infty} 3\ln b$

13. $\lim_{b\to \infty} e^b$ **14.** $\lim_{b\to \infty} e^{-b}$

15. $\lim_{a\to -\infty} (e^a+3)$ **16.** $\lim_{a\to -\infty} e^{-a}$

17. $\lim_{b\to \infty} b^3$ **18.** $\lim_{b\to \infty} b^2$

19. $\lim_{a\to -\infty} \dfrac{1}{e^a}$ **20.** $\lim_{b\to \infty} \dfrac{1}{e^b}$

21. $\lim_{b\to \infty} \left(2 - \dfrac{1}{\sqrt{b}}\right)$ **22.** $\lim_{a\to -\infty} \left(3 + \dfrac{1}{a}\right)$

In Exercises 23–44, evaluate each improper integral if it is convergent. If the integral is divergent, so indicate.

23. $\int_{1}^{\infty} \dfrac{1}{x^3}\, dx$ **24.** $\int_{2}^{\infty} \dfrac{1}{x^3}\, dx$

25. $\int_{1}^{\infty} x^{-4}\, dx$ **26.** $\int_{1}^{\infty} x^{-2}\, dx$

27. $\int_{1}^{\infty} \dfrac{1}{2x}\, dx$ **28.** $\int_{1}^{\infty} \sqrt{x}\, dx$

29. $\displaystyle\int_1^\infty \frac{1}{\sqrt{x}}\,dx$

30. $\displaystyle\int_1^\infty \frac{1}{x^{3/2}}\,dx$

31. $\displaystyle\int_0^\infty e^x\,dx$

32. $\displaystyle\int_1^\infty e^{2x}\,dx$

33. $\displaystyle\int_1^\infty e^{-x}\,dx$

34. $\displaystyle\int_0^\infty e^{-2x}\,dx$

35. $\displaystyle\int_0^\infty \frac{dx}{x+1}$

36. $\displaystyle\int_{-2}^\infty \frac{dx}{x+3}$

37. $\displaystyle\int_0^\infty \sqrt{2x+9}\,dx$

38. $\displaystyle\int_0^\infty \sqrt[3]{x}\,dx$

39. $\displaystyle\int_0^\infty \frac{x}{1+x^2}\,dx$

40. $\displaystyle\int_0^\infty \frac{x^2}{x^3+4}\,dx$

41. $\displaystyle\int_1^\infty \frac{\ln x}{x}\,dx$

42. $\displaystyle\int_e^\infty \frac{dx}{x\ln x}$

43. $\displaystyle\int_0^\infty e^{-x/2}\,dx$

44. $\displaystyle\int_0^\infty e^{-.01x}\,dx$

In Exercises 45–50, determine the requested area.

45. The area under the curve $y = e^{-x}$ for $x \geq 0$

46. The area under the curve $y = e^{-.1x}$ for $x \geq 0$

47. The area under the curve $y = x^{-3}$ for $x \geq 2$

48. The area under the curve $y = \dfrac{1}{x^2}$ for $x \geq 10$

49. The area under the curve $y = \dfrac{1}{(x-1)^2}$ for $x \geq 2$

50. The area under the curve $y = \dfrac{x}{(1+x^2)^2}$ for $x \geq 0$

51. *(WATER POLLUTION)* Let t be the number of years from now. What is the total amount of waste dumped into a lake by a factory that dumps waste at the rate of $5e^{-.1t}$ pounds per year indefinitely?

52. *(AIR POLLUTION)* If radioactive material enters the earth's atmosphere at the rate of $100e^{-.02t}$ pounds per year and this continues indefinitely, what will be the total amount of radioactive material released to the atmosphere?

53. *(REAL ESTATE)* A real estate investment pays the investor indefinitely at the rate of $4000e^{-.08t}$ per year t years from now. Find the total amount received by the investor. The curve in the figure shows the rate at which the real estate investment pays the investor. The area under the curve is the total amount received by the investor.

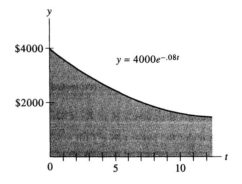

54. *(CAPITAL VALUE)* Determine the capital value of a rental property if the annual rent is \$10,920 and the annual interest rate is 7%.

55. *(CAPITAL VALUE)* Determine the capital value of a rental property if the annual rent is \$6390 and the annual interest rate is 9%.

56. In reference to capital value (Example 4), show that

$$\int_0^\infty Re^{-kt}\,dt = \frac{R}{k}$$

by evaluating the improper integral. Then use the R and k values of Example 4 to obtain the result of that example from R/k rather than from the actual integration shown in that example.

In Exercises 57–68, evaluate each improper integral if it is convergent. If the integral is divergent, so indicate.

57. $\displaystyle\int_{-\infty}^{-1} \frac{1}{x^3}\,dx$

58. $\displaystyle\int_{-\infty}^{-2} 2x^{-3}\,dx$

59. $\displaystyle\int_{-\infty}^{0} e^{3x}\,dx$

60. $\displaystyle\int_{-\infty}^{0} e^{4x}\,dx$

61. $\displaystyle\int_{-\infty}^{0} e^{-2x}\,dx$

62. $\displaystyle\int_{-\infty}^{0} e^{-x}\,dx$

63. $\int_{-\infty}^{0} \dfrac{x}{1 + x^2}\, dx$

64. $\int_{-\infty}^{0} \dfrac{2x}{x^2 + 10}\, dx$

65. $\int_{-\infty}^{0} \dfrac{dx}{(x - 2)^3}$

66. $\int_{-\infty}^{0} \dfrac{dx}{(x - 1)^3}$

67. $\int_{-\infty}^{-2} \dfrac{dx}{(4 - x)^2}$

68. $\int_{-\infty}^{-1} \dfrac{dx}{(1 - x)^2}$

In Exercises 69–74, determine the requested area.

69. The area under the curve $y = e^x$ for $x \le -1$

70. The area under the curve $y = e^{2x}$ for $x \le 0$

71. The area under the curve $y = \dfrac{1}{(x - 1)^2}$ for $x \le -2$

72. The area under the curve $y = \dfrac{1}{(x + 1)^2}$ for $x \le -2$

73. The area under the curve $y = \dfrac{1}{x^3}$ for $x \le -4$

74. The area under the curve $y = \dfrac{1}{(x + 2)^3}$ for $x \le -3$

Evaluate each improper integral in Exercises 75–86. If the integral is divergent, so indicate.

75. $\int_{-\infty}^{\infty} x\, dx$

76. $\int_{-\infty}^{\infty} x^3\, dx$

77. $\int_{-\infty}^{\infty} e^{-x}\, dx$

78. $\int_{-\infty}^{\infty} e^x\, dx$

79. $\int_{-\infty}^{\infty} x^2 e^{-x^3}\, dx$

80. $\int_{-\infty}^{\infty} x^3 e^{-x^4}\, dx$

81. $\int_{-\infty}^{\infty} \dfrac{x}{(1 + x^2)^2}\, dx$

82. $\int_{-\infty}^{\infty} \dfrac{x}{(x^2 + 4)^2}\, dx$

83. $\int_{-\infty}^{\infty} x e^{-2x^2}\, dx$

84. $\int_{-\infty}^{\infty} e^{-3x}\, dx$

85. $\int_{-\infty}^{\infty} \dfrac{x}{\sqrt{x^2 + 1}}\, dx$

86. $\int_{-\infty}^{\infty} \dfrac{x}{\sqrt[3]{x^2 + 1}}\, dx$

87. In Example 1, the improper integral converges, thus giving the area under the curve $y = 1/x^2$, beginning at $x = 1$ and continuing infinitely far to the right. How many square units is that area?

W 88. In Example 2, the improper integral diverges. Give an area interpretation for this situation.

89. (*GABRIEL'S HORN*) When the region under the graph of $y = 1/x$ for $x \ge 1$ is revolved about the x axis, the solid created is called *Gabriel's horn*. Determine the volume of Gabriel's horn.

Gabriel's horn

 TECHNOLOGY *EXERCISES*

W 1. Recall the integral from Example 6.

$$\int_{-\infty}^{\infty} x e^{-x^2}\, dx$$

Graph the function $y = x e^{-x^2}$ and study it to suggest an intuitive explanation of why the integral of Example 6 is equal to 0. Use x in $[-3, 3]$ and y in $[-.5, .5]$.

Note   *Mathematica* and *Maple* can evaluate improper integrals. The integral

$$\int_2^\infty \frac{1}{x^5}\, dx$$

can be evaluated as follows.

         Mathematica: `Integrate [1/x^5, {x, 2, Infinity}]`

         Maple: `int (1/x^5, x = 2..infinity);`

If you have access to such a system, use it to evaluate the integrals of Exercises 23 and 27.

Key Terms and Ideas

integration by substitution	reduction formula	improper integrals
integration by parts	numerical integration methods	divergent integral
income stream (money flow)	trapezoidal rule	convergent integral
present value of an income stream	Simpson's rule	capital value
integration by tables	error estimates	

Review Exercises for Chapter 7

Evaluate each indefinite integral in Exercises 1–24. Use substitution if possible. Otherwise, use parts or the tables.

1. $\displaystyle\int x\sqrt{1 + x^2}\, dx$

2. $\displaystyle\int 2x\sqrt{1 - x^2}\, dx$

3. $\displaystyle\int \frac{x\, dx}{\sqrt{1 + 2x}}$

4. $\displaystyle\int \frac{x}{(x + 1)^2}\, dx$

5. $\displaystyle\int (x - 2)^3\, dx$

6. $\displaystyle\int (x - 5)^4\, dx$

7. $\displaystyle\int x(x - 2)^3\, dx$

8. $\displaystyle\int x(x + 1)^4\, dx$

9. $\displaystyle\int xe^{x^2}\, dx$

10. $\displaystyle\int \frac{x}{e^{x^2}}\, dx$

11. $\displaystyle\int xe^{3x}\, dx$

12. $\displaystyle\int \frac{x}{e^{3x}}\, dx$

13. $\displaystyle\int \frac{x}{\sqrt{x^2 + 1}}\, dx$

14. $\displaystyle\int \frac{1}{\sqrt{x^2 - 1}}\, dx$

15. $\displaystyle\int \frac{1}{\sqrt{x^2 + 1}}\, dx$

16. $\displaystyle\int \frac{1}{x\sqrt{x^2 + 1}}\, dx$

17. $\displaystyle\int \ln 2x\, dx$

18. $\displaystyle\int x \ln 3x\, dx$

19. $\displaystyle\int \frac{\ln 2x}{x}\, dx$

20. $\displaystyle\int \frac{x + 1}{x}\, dx$

21. $\displaystyle\int \frac{e^{2x}}{1 + e^{2x}}\, dx$

22. $\displaystyle\int \frac{e^{3x}}{1 - e^{3x}}\, dx$

23. $\displaystyle\int \frac{1}{1 + e^{2x}}\, dx$

24. $\displaystyle\int \frac{e^{2x} + 1}{e^x}\, dx$

In Exercises 25–28, use (a) the trapezoidal rule and (b)

Simpson's rule to approximate each definite integral. Round calculations to four decimal places. *Use a calculator.*

25. $\int_0^2 \sqrt{9 - x^2}\, dx,\ n = 4$ **26.** $\int_0^2 e^{2x}\, dx,\ n = 4$

27. $\int_1^4 \frac{1}{x^2 + 4}\, dx,\ n = 6$ **28.** $\int_2^5 x \ln x\, dx,\ n = 6$

In Exercises 29–36, evaluate each improper integral if it is convergent. If the integral is divergent, so indicate.

29. $\int_1^\infty \frac{1}{x^4}\, dx$ **30.** $\int_1^\infty \frac{1}{\sqrt[3]{x}}\, dx$

31. $\int_{-\infty}^0 e^{-.5x}\, dx$ **32.** $\int_{-\infty}^0 e^{.5x}\, dx$

33. $\int_2^\infty x^{-2/3}\, dx$ **34.** $\int_0^\infty \frac{dx}{x + 2}$

35. $\int_{-\infty}^\infty \frac{x}{x^2 + 2}\, dx$ **36.** $\int_{-\infty}^\infty x^2\, dx$

37. (**MARGINAL PROFIT**) Determine the profit function $P(x)$ if the marginal profit is $\ln (x + 1)$ and $P(0) = -120$. *Note:* when needed, by division,

$$\frac{x}{x + 1} = 1 - \frac{1}{x + 1}$$

38. Use Simpson's rule to approximate the area under the arch of the monument shown here.

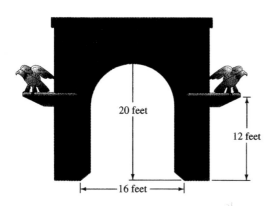

20 feet

12 feet

16 feet

39. (**INCOME STREAM**) A small corporation's 4-year projection shows its income t years from now as

$$f(t) = 30{,}000 + 6000t$$

dollars per year. Assuming an annual interest rate of 5%, find the present value of the income stream over the 4-year period.

40. (**CAPITAL VALUE**) Determine the capital value of a rental property if the annual rent is $9600 and the annual interest is 8%.

41. Determine the area under the curve $y = \ln x$ from $x = 1$ to $x = 4$. (See the figure.)

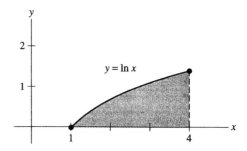

$y = \ln x$

42. Find the area under the curve $y = x \ln x$ from $x = 1$ to $x = 5$.

43. Determine the area between the curves $y = \sqrt{2x + 1}$ and $y = 25 - x^2$ from $x = 0$ to $x = 4$.

44. Find the average value of $f(x) = e^{2x+1}$ over the interval $[-1, 1]$.

45. Find the average value of $f(x) = x\sqrt{x^2 + 9}$ over the interval $[0, 4]$.

46. (**VOLUME**) Find the volume of the solid produced by revolving about the x axis the region bounded by $y = \sqrt{\ln x}$, the x axis, $x = 1$, and $x = e$.

47. Determine the equation of the curve that has slope xe^x and passes through the point $(1, 7)$.

48. (**RED TIDE**) Red-tide algae bloom quickly in the Gulf of Mexico, and the toxin they release kills fish that swim through it. If the algae population grows for t hours at the rate of

$$A(t) = .5te^{-.1t}$$

million algae per hour, how many algae are present after 24 hours?

Chapter Projects and Essays

Many of the projects and essays lend themselves to group activity, although most can be completed by individual effort.

1. INTEGRATION BY TABLES

BACKGROUND Integration by tables was introduced in Section 7.3. The presentation included examples, exercises, and a short table of integrals (Table 5 in the Appendix). Larger tables of integrals are available elsewhere.

THE PROJECT Locate a book (see the beginning of Section 7.3) that contains a large table of integrals. Use the table to evaluate each of the following integrals.

1. $\int \sqrt{x^2 - 1} \, dx$ 　　　 **2.** $\int x^3 \sqrt{x^2 - 9} \, dx$

3. $\int \frac{\sqrt{x^2 - 16}}{x^2} \, dx$ 　　 **4.** $\int \frac{x^3 \, dx}{(x^2 - 25)^{3/2}}$

5. $\int \frac{dx}{x(x^4 - 1)}$ 　　　 **6.** $\int \frac{x \, dx}{x^4 - 16}$

7. $\int (\ln x)^2 \, dx$ 　　　 **8.** $\int \ln (x^2 - 4) \, dx$

9. $\int \frac{dx}{x(x^2 - 4)}$ 　　 **10.** $\int \frac{x^3 \, dx}{\sqrt{x^2 + 9}}$

2. NUMERICAL INTEGRATION

BACKGROUND The trapezoidal rule and Simpson's rule can be considered to be two examples of a more general rule known as the *Newton-Cotes integration formulas*.

The trapezoidal rule gives the area as a sum of areas under line segments (polynomials of degree 1), where each line segment uses two points of the function and approximates the function on the interval between (the x coordinates of) those two points.

Simpson's rule gives the area as a sum of areas under parabolas (polynomials of degree 2), where each parabola uses three points of the function and approximates the function on the interval that includes (the x coordinates of) those three points.

The Newton-Cotes interpolation formulas give the area as a sum of areas under polynomials, where each approximating polynomial uses n points of the function.

THE PROJECT Locate a book on *numerical analysis* or *numerical methods* and read about the "closed" *Newton-Cotes integration formulas*. Then, compute three numerical approximations for a definite integral of your choice. Use

1. The trapezoidal rule (Newton-Cotes using two points for each area)

2. Simpson's rule (Newton-Cotes using three points for each area)

3. Newton-Cotes using four points for each area.

Compare the results.

PROBABILITY AND CALCULUS

8

Should you play the odds? Placing bets on a thoroughbred is tempting when one horse has been picked as a favorite. But even a sure thing can disappoint. A horse named "Editor's Note" was a dubious choice going into the 1996 Belmont Park races, but it broke a nine-race losing streak to win. Such situations are accounted for in the study of probability by "variance" from the expected outcome.

Perhaps it is human nature to wonder about the chances that a particular event will occur. How likely is it to rain today? Your first child was a boy, so how likely is it that your second child will be a girl? What are my chances of winning the lottery this week?

The formal study of probability is considered to have begun about 1654, when Blaise Pascal and Pierre de Fermat studied games of chance and the gambling associated with them.

An English merchant named John Graunt pioneered in a different direction. He studied data available from over 50 years of burial records and then drew conclusions about life expectancy, publishing his results in 1662. His work provided a foundation for the development of life insurance companies, which followed soon afterward.

8.1 PROBABILITY AND CALCULUS

Our everyday life provides casual experiences with probability. The chances of rain may be 70% or 60% or 100% or 0%. When such percents are converted to fractions or decimal numbers, we have

percent	other form
70%	$\frac{7}{10}$ or .7
50%	$\frac{1}{2}$ or .5
100%	1
0%	0

To say that it will rain (that is, rain is a sure thing) is to say that the chance of rain is 100%. By contrast, if an event cannot occur, then its chance of occurring is 0%.

This example suggests that the largest value for a probability is 100%, or 1, and the smallest value is 0%, or 0.

Probability Values

The probability that an event occurs is a number between 0 and 1, inclusive.

The probability of an impossible event is 0.

The probability of a certain event is 1.

Sometimes probabilities can be represented by areas under a curve. In such instances, calculus (integration, in particular) can be used to find the desired probabilities.

Before we introduce formal definitions and the associated calculus, let us consider a simple example that will provide some useful orientation.

Consider an overnight delivery company that guarantees delivery between 9 a.m. and 4 p.m. the next day. In theory, the chance of delivery between 9 a.m. and 4 p.m. is 100%. Furthermore, the company claims that the chance of a morning delivery is 60% (or .6). This means the chance of an afternoon delivery is 40% (or .4). We will assume that a morning delivery (9 a.m.–12 noon) can come at any time in that interval with equal likelihood. Similarly, an afternoon delivery (12 noon–4 p.m.) can come at any time in that interval with equal likelihood. A graph, using a 24-hour clock, that describes this situation is shown in Figure 1.

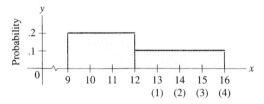

Figure 1 Delivery times and their probabilities

Notice that the area under the graph from $x = 9$ to $x = 12$ is indeed .6—calculated as the area of the rectangle having length 3 (from $12 - 9$) and width .2. Also, the area under the graph from $x = 12$ to $x = 16$ is the .4 we expect. It is calculated as $(4)(.1) = .4$. (The y values .2 and .1 were selected to make this work out.)

We shall use a special notation for probability. $P(9 \leq x \leq 12)$ will mean "the probability that x is between 9 and 12." We then have

$$P(9 \leq x \leq 12) = .6 \qquad\qquad P(12 \leq x \leq 16) = .4$$

You can also see from the graph such probabilities as

$$P(9 \leq x \leq 10) = .2 \qquad\qquad P(9 \leq x \leq 16) = 1$$
$$P(13 \leq x \leq 16) = .3 \qquad\qquad P(10 \leq x \leq 13) = .5$$

Calculus provides the means to determine probabilities when the function is neither constant nor composed of parts that are constants. (The function we considered consisted of two parts, each of which was constant over an interval.) If the graph of f were such that $P(c \leq x \leq d)$ was the area under f from $x = c$ to $x = d$, then, using calculus, we would want to have

$$P(c \leq x \leq d) = \int_{c}^{d} f(x)\, dx$$

A function that can be used in this manner to determine probabilities is called a **probability density function.** The definition of a probability density function is given next. A graph of such a function is shown in Figure 2.

Probability Density Function

Let f be defined over the interval $[a, b]$. Then f is a *probability density function* if

1. $f(x) \geq 0$ for $a \leq x \leq b$

2. $P(a \leq x \leq b) = 1$

The probability that x is between c and d, for c and d in the interval $[a, b]$, is given by

$$P(c \leq x \leq d) = \int_c^d f(x)\, dx$$

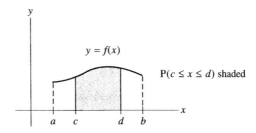

Figure 2 A probability density function

> *Note*
>
> Condition 2 of the definition can be stated as
>
> $$\int_a^b f(x)\, dx = 1$$

EXAMPLE 1   Consider $f(x) = \dfrac{1}{21}x^2$ for x in the interval $[1, 4]$.

   (a) Show that f is a probability density function.

   (b) Determine $P(2 \leq x \leq 3)$, the probability that x is between 2 and 3.

SOLUTION   **(a)** We must show that

     1. $f(x) \geq 0$ for all x in the interval $[1, 4]$

     2. $\displaystyle\int_1^4 f(x)\, dx = 1$

First, $x^2 \geq 0$ for all x in $[1, 4]$, and thus $\frac{1}{21}x^2 \geq 0$ for all x in $[1, 4]$. Second,

$$\int_1^4 \frac{1}{21}x^2 \, dx = \left[\frac{1}{21} \cdot \frac{x^3}{3}\right]_1^4 = \left[\frac{1}{63}x^3\right]_1^4 = \frac{1}{63}(64 - 1) = 1$$

Thus, f is a probability density function.

(b) The probability that x is between 2 and 3 is

$$P(2 \leq x \leq 3) = \int_2^3 \frac{1}{21}x^2 \, dx = \left[\frac{1}{63}x^3\right]_2^3 = \frac{1}{63}(27 - 8) = \frac{19}{63}$$

Thus, $P(2 \leq x \leq 3) = 19/63 \approx .3016.$ ◆

EXAMPLE 2 **LIGHT BULB LIFE**

APPLIED

Suppose the total hours x that a light bulb will burn is given by the probability density function

$$f(x) = .002e^{-.002x} \qquad x \geq 0$$

(a) Verify that f is indeed a probability density function.

(b) Find the probability that a light bulb will burn 300 hours or less.

(c) Find the probability that a light bulb will burn between 100 and 400 hours.

SOLUTION **(a)** Because $e^u > 0$ for any real number u, it follows that

$$.002e^{-.002x} \geq 0 \qquad \text{for } x \geq 0$$

which satisfies condition 1 for a probability density function. Second, since the inequality $x \geq 0$ describes the interval $[0, \infty)$, we must show that

$$\int_0^\infty .002e^{-.002x} \, dx = 1$$

Here is the step-by-step process of evaluation of this improper integral.

$$\int_0^\infty .002e^{-.002x} \, dx = .002 \int_0^\infty e^{-.002x} \, dx = .002 \lim_{b \to \infty} \int_0^b e^{-.002x} \, dx$$

$$= (.002) \cdot \frac{1}{-.002} \lim_{b \to \infty} \left[e^{-.002x}\right]_0^b$$

$$= -\lim_{b \to \infty} \left[e^{-.002b} - e^{-.002(0)}\right] = -\lim_{b \to \infty} \left[e^{-.002b} - 1\right]$$

$$= -\lim_{b \to \infty} e^{-.002b} + 1 = 0 + 1 = 1$$

(b) The probability that a light bulb will burn 300 hours or less is

$$\int_0^{300} .002e^{-.002x}\,dx = .002\int_0^{300} e^{-.002x}\,dx = -\left[e^{-.002x}\right]_0^{300}$$

$$= -\left[e^{-.6} - e^0\right] = -e^{-.6} + 1$$

$$\approx -.5488 + 1 = .4512$$

(c) The probability that a light bulb will burn between 100 and 400 hours is

$$\int_{100}^{400} .002e^{-.002x}\,dx = .002\int_{100}^{400} e^{-.002x}\,dx = -\left[e^{-.002x}\right]_{100}^{400}$$

$$= -\left[e^{-.8} - e^{-.2}\right] \approx -.4493 + .8187$$

$$= .3694$$

See Figure 3.

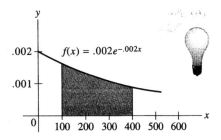

Figure 3 The area of the shaded region is the probability that a light bulb will burn between 100 and 400 hours. ◆

EXAMPLE 3   The function defined by $f(x) = 4x^2$ on $[2, 5]$ is not a probability density function. Multiply f by a constant to create a probability density function.

SOLUTION   Although $f(x) = 4x^2 \geq 0$ for all x in the interval $[2, 5]$, f is not a probability density function because

$$\int_2^5 4x^2\,dx = \left[\frac{4x^3}{3}\right]_2^5 = 156 \neq 1$$

For f to be a probability density function, the integral must be equal to 1. To accomplish this, divide the original function by 156. Thus,

$$g(x) = \frac{4x^2}{156} = \frac{x^2}{39}$$

is a probability density function. (Note that $g(x) \geq 0$ for all x in the interval.)   ◆

8.1 Exercises

In Exercises 1–4, obtain the requested probabilities from the given graph. You may want to refer to the overnight delivery example.

1. (a) $P(5 \le x \le 6)$ (b) $P(6 \le x \le 8)$
  (c) $P(6 \le x \le 9)$ (d) $P(5 \le x \le 9)$

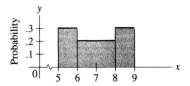

2. (a) $P(2 \le x \le 4)$ (b) $P(4 \le x \le 7)$
  (c) $P(5 \le x \le 7)$ (d) $P(2 \le x \le 7)$

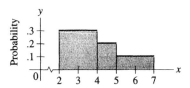

3. (a) $P(7 \le x \le 8)$ (b) $P(5 \le x \le 7)$
  (c) $P(4 \le x \le 8)$ (d) $P(4 \le x \le 7)$

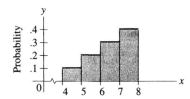

4. (a) $P(6 \le x \le 7)$ (b) $P(7 \le x \le 9)$
  (c) $P(6 \le x \le 8)$ (d) $P(6 \le x \le 9)$

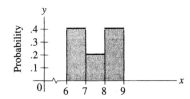

In Exercises 5–12, show that each function f is a probability density function on the given interval.

5. $f(x) = \dfrac{1}{30}x$ on [2, 8] **6.** $f(x) = \dfrac{2x}{15}$ on [1, 4]

7. $f(x) = \dfrac{1}{12}(3x^2 + 2x)$ on [0, 2]

8. $f(x) = \dfrac{1}{42}(2x + 1)$ on [0, 6]

9. $f(x) = \dfrac{3}{38}\sqrt{x}$ on [4, 9] **10.** $f(x) = \dfrac{x^3}{4}$ on [0, 2]

11. $f(x) = \dfrac{10}{9x^2}$ on [1, 10] **12.** $f(x) = \dfrac{1}{6}$ on [4, 10]

In Exercises 13–18, find the requested probabilities associated with the given probability density function.

13. $f(x) = \dfrac{3}{64}x^2$ on [0, 4]

  (a) $P(1 \le x \le 4)$ (b) $P(0 \le x \le 2)$

14. $f(x) = \dfrac{1}{16}x$ on [2, 6]

  (a) $P(2 \le x \le 5)$ (b) $P(3 \le x \le 6)$

15. $f(x) = \dfrac{1}{10}$ on [0, 10]

  (a) $P(1 \le x \le 6)$ (b) $P(7 \le x \le 10)$

16. $f(x) = \dfrac{1}{8}(4 - x)$ on [0, 4]

  (a) $P(0 \le x \le 2)$ (b) $P(1 \le x \le 4)$

17. $f(x) = \dfrac{1}{x}$ on [1, e]

  (a) $P(1 \le x \le 2)$ (b) $P(2 \le x \le e)$

18. $f(x) = \dfrac{3}{76}(1 + \sqrt{x})$ on [1, 9]

  (a) $P(1 \le x \le 4)$ (b) $P(4 \le x \le 9)$

In Exercises 19–24, modify the given function f to create a function g that will be a probability density function on the given interval (see Example 3, if needed).

19. $f(x) = 2x$ on $[1, 8]$ **20.** $f(x) = \sqrt{x}$ on $[1, 4]$

21. $f(x) = x^3$ on $[0, 1]$ **22.** $f(x) = \dfrac{1}{x^2}$ on $[1, 2]$

23. $f(x) = x - 5$ on $[6, 10]$ **24.** $f(x) = x^2$ on $[3, 7]$

25. (*NEWSPAPER SALES*) The probability density function for the number of newspapers x a convenience store will sell in a day is

$$f(x) = .0008x \qquad 0 \le x \le 50$$

What is the probability that the store will sell at least 40 newspapers tomorrow?

26. (*WAITING IN LINE*) The wait in line (x minutes) on the first day of registration is described by the probability density function

$$f(x) = .0002x \qquad 0 \le x \le 100$$

(a) Find the probability that the wait will be 10 minutes or less.
(b) Find the probability that the wait will be between 30 minutes and an hour.
(c) Find the probability that the wait will be at least an hour.

27. (*SMOKE DETECTOR*) A smoke detector flashes every 30 seconds to show that it is operational. The probability density function is

$$f(x) = \frac{1}{30} \qquad 0 \le x \le 30$$

where x is the number of seconds before the next flash. Find the probability that you will see a flash within 6 seconds of looking at the smoke detector.

28. (*WAITING FOR A BUS*) The wait (x minutes) for a bus is described by the probability density function

$$f(x) = \frac{1}{25} \qquad 0 \le x \le 25$$

(a) Find the probability that the wait will be at most 10 minutes.
(b) Find the probability that the wait will be at least 15 minutes.
(c) Verify that f is a probability density function.

29. (*PHONE CALL LENGTH*) A local phone company finds that the probability density function for the length of time (x minutes) of a phone call is

$$f(x) = .25e^{-.25x} \qquad x \ge 0$$

(a) Find the probability that a phone call will last no more than 4 minutes.
(b) Find the probability that a phone call will last between 4 and 10 minutes.

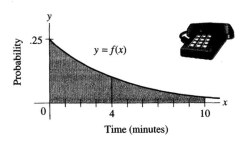

30. (*LIGHT BULB LIFE*) The probability density function for the total time (x hours) that a light bulb will burn is

$$f(x) = .001e^{-.001x} \qquad x \ge 0$$

(a) Verify that f is a probability density function.
(b) Find the probability that a light bulb will burn between 200 and 500 hours.

31. (*LEARNING EXPERIMENT*) A psychologist asks the subjects of her experiment to learn a task that she has devised. The probability density function is determined to be

$$f(x) = \frac{30}{13x^2} \qquad 2 \le x \le 15$$

where x is the number of minutes needed to learn the task. (The task cannot be learned in less than 2 minutes.)

(a) Find the probability that a subject chosen at random will learn the task in 5 minutes or less.
(b) Find the probability that a subject chosen at random will take at least 10 minutes to learn it.

32. (*LEARNING EXPERIMENT*) A psychologist devises a task similar to the one used in Exercise 31. He finds that the probability density function has the form

$$f(x) = \frac{k}{x^2} \qquad 4 \le x \le 20$$

where x is the number of minutes needed to learn the task. The fastest time to learn the task is 4 minutes, and the slowest is 20 minutes.

(a) Determine k.

(b) What is the probability that a participant will learn the task in 10 minutes or less?

W 33. Let f be defined on the interval [0, 10] and let $f(x) \geq 0$ for all x in the interval. Also, suppose that

$$\int_1^4 f(x)\, dx = 2.5$$

Can function f be a probability density function? Explain.

W 34. Suppose you are given a function defined on a closed interval. Explain using words (no mathematical symbols)

how you would determine whether the function is a probability density function.

W 35. Consider the probability density function graphed next, which gives the total hours x that a candle will burn.

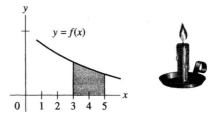

Complete the following sentence: The shaded area is the probability that _____.

TECHNOLOGY EXERCISES

W 1. Graph the probability density function of Example 1. Use x in [1, 4] and y in [0, 1]. From the graph, determine which is greater, $P(1 \leq x \leq 2.5)$ or $P(2.5 \leq x \leq 4)$. Explain.

W 2. Graph the probability density function of Exercise 10. Use x in [0, 2] and y in [−1, 3]. From the graph, determine which is greater, $P(0 \leq x \leq 1.5)$ or $P(1.5 \leq x \leq 2)$. Explain.

Note You may benefit from using the Shade instruction in the two exercises above. The basics of shading were explained in three technology notes (Sections 6.4, 6.6, and 6.7). To shade under the graph of $y = x^2$ from $x = 3$ to $x = 5$, use

Shade $(0, x^2, 1, 3, 5)$

The 0 and 1 are standard for shading under one curve with standard resolution.

8.2 RANDOM VARIABLES, EXPECTED VALUE, AND VARIANCE

The letter x has been used to represent the length of time a light bulb will burn and the time at which an overnight delivery will arrive. The value that x might take on in any particular instance depends on chance. It is a matter of chance whether a light bulb will burn for 210 hours or 302 hours. Accordingly, the variable x that is used to represent that outcome is called a **random variable.**

A random variable can be discrete or continuous. A **discrete random variable** is one that can take on only a finite number of values. When two dice are rolled, the sum that shows is an integer between 2 and 12, inclusive. Here the random variable x can take on only the values 2, 3, 4, 5, . . . , 12. By contrast, a **continuous random variable** can take on an infinite number of values—any number in an interval of real numbers. In the overnight delivery example of Section 8.1, the random variable x could be any time in the interval [9, 16]—that is, *any* time from 9 a.m. to 4 p.m., inclusive. The exercises of Section 8.1 provide other examples of continuous random variables: the wait in a line, the total time a light bulb will burn, and the length of a telephone call.

Our emphasis will be on the use of continuous random variables, because they lend themselves to calculus methods. Problems involving discrete random variables will appear only as needed to develop a concept, as in the discussion that follows.

Suppose a banker makes an investment that is just as likely to return $400 as it is to return $500. What is the average she can expect as a return, if she makes similar investments over a period of time?

Intuitively, the average return from such an investment is

$$\frac{\$400 + \$500}{2}$$

which is $450.

Using a probability perspective, we could write this instead as

$$\frac{1}{2} \cdot \$400 + \frac{1}{2} \cdot \$500$$

and note that each 1/2 is the probability of that particular value of random variable x (say, $x_1 = \$400$ and $x_2 = \$500$).

Suppose now that the banker makes an investment having probability 1/4 of returning $200 and 3/4 of returning $300. If she makes similar investments over a period of time, how much can she expect to make on the average?

On the average, she can expect to make

$$\frac{1}{4} \cdot \$200 + \frac{3}{4} \cdot \$300$$

which is $275. In this example, the random variable x has two values—$x_1 = \$200$ and $x_2 = \$300$. The corresponding probabilities are $p_1 = 1/4$ and $p_2 = 3/4$.

Thus, the average value can be determined as

$$\text{average} = x_1 p_1 + x_2 p_2$$

$$= \$200 \cdot \frac{1}{4} + \$300 \cdot \frac{3}{4}$$

$$= \$275$$

The result $275 is called the *expected value* or *mean* of the random variable. The notation used is $E(x)$ for expected value of x and μ (the Greek letter "mu") for mean of x.

For discrete random variables, we make the following definition.

Expected Value—Discrete Case

If a discrete random variable x takes on the values $x_1, x_2, x_3, \ldots x_n$ with probabilities $p_1, p_2, p_3, \ldots, p_n$, respectively, then the **mean** or **expected value** of the random variable is

$$\mu = E(x) = x_1 p_1 + x_2 p_2 + x_3 p_3 + \cdots + x_n p_n = \sum_{i=1}^{n} x_i p_i$$

The extension of this definition to continuous random variables is straightforward. Let x be a continuous random variable and f a probability density function defined on the interval $[a, b]$. The interval can be divided into n subintervals, each of width $\Delta x = (b - a)/n$. The n intervals are $[x_0, x_1], [x_1, x_2], [x_2, x_3], \ldots, [x_{n-1}, x_n]$. The probabilities are as follows: p_1 is the probability that x is in the (first) interval $[x_0, x_1]$; p_2 is the probability that x is in the (second) interval $[x_1, x_2]$; and so on. It follows that p_1 is the area under the graph of f from $x = x_0$ to $x = x_1$, p_2 is the area under the graph of f from $x = x_1$ to $x = x_2$, and so on. Each of the n areas can be approximated by a rectangle of length $f(x_i)$ and width Δx. Figure 4 shows the area of the second rectangle to be $f(x_2)\Delta x$.

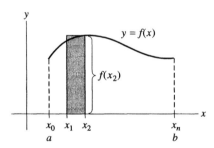

Figure 4 Area approximation for p_2

It follows that $p_1 = f(x_1)\Delta x$, $p_2 = f(x_2)\Delta x$, and so on. Thus,

$$E(x) \approx x_1 p_1 + x_2 p_2 + x_3 p_3 + \cdots + x_n p_n$$

$$\approx x_1 \cdot f(x_1)\Delta x + x_2 \cdot f(x_2)\Delta x + x_3 \cdot f(x_3)\Delta x + \cdots + x_n \cdot f(x_n)\Delta x$$

$$= \sum_{i=1}^{n} x_i f(x_i)\Delta x$$

The limit of this sum as $\Delta x \to 0$ yields the exact value of $E(x)$, which is expressed as a definite integral. In view of this, we have the following definition.

Expected Value

Let x be a continuous random variable and let f be a probability density function defined on $[a, b]$. The **expected value** of x is

$$\mu = E(x) = \int_a^b x f(x)\, dx$$

Visually, the mean or expected value is the x value at the center or balance point. Figure 5 illustrates this interpretation.

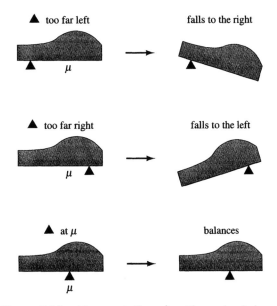

Figure 5 Visual interpretation of μ. The region balances when the fulcrum (▲) is at μ.

APPLIED

EXAMPLE 1 *AVERAGE WAIT IN A LINE*

The wait in line for tickets to a popular concert is described by the probability density function

$$f(x) = .0002x \qquad 0 \le x \le 100$$

where x is in minutes. Determine the time of the average wait.

SOLUTION The expected value of x is the average wait time.

$$E(x) = \int_a^b x\, f(x)\, dx = \int_0^{100} x(.0002x)\, dx = \int_0^{100} .0002x^2\, dx$$

$$= \left[\frac{.0002x^3}{3}\right]_0^{100} \approx \left[.000067x^3\right]_0^{100} = 67$$

The average wait is 67 minutes. ◆

The amount by which the values of x vary from the mean (or expected value) is measured by the **variance** of the distribution. Geometrically, the smaller the variance, the greater the area near the mean. The larger the variance, the larger the area away from the mean. From a probability perspective, the smaller the variance, the greater the probability that a randomly chosen x value is near the mean. Figure 6 shows a comparison of small and large variances.

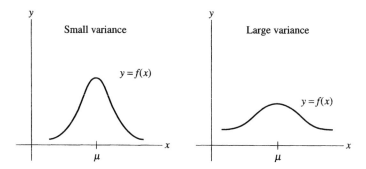

Figure 6 Small variance versus large variance

For a discrete random variable x, any individual x value x_i differs (varies) from the mean by the amount $x_i - \mu$. Because $x_i - \mu$ can be negative or positive, we use the square $(x_i - \mu)^2$ to avoid having the negatives and positives cancel out when we form the sum of all the $x_i - \mu$. Next, each $(x_i - \mu)^2$ is multiplied by the probability of x_i, which is p_i. The products are then added to compute the variance, denoted Var(x), of the discrete random variable x.

$$\text{Var}(x) = \sum_{i=1}^{n} (x_i - \mu)^2\, p_i \qquad \text{discrete case}$$

Earlier, when the definition of expected value was extended from discrete to continuous random variables, we obtained $f(x_i)\,\Delta x$ as the probability that x is in the ith interval of width Δx. (f is a probability density function.) Using a similar approach, we can obtain Var(x) for a continuous random variable x.

$$\text{Var}(x) = \lim_{\Delta x \to 0} \sum_{i=1}^{n} (x_i - \mu)^2\, f(x_i)\, \Delta x = \int_a^b (x - \mu)^2\, f(x)\, dx$$

Thus, we have the following definition.

Variance

Let x be a continuous random variable and let f be a probability density function defined on $[a, b]$. The **variance** of x is

$$\text{Var}(x) = \int_a^b (x - \mu)^2 f(x)\, dx$$

The integral formula provided by the definition of variance is not designed for easy calculation. In view of this, we now derive an alternative formula, one that is usually easier to work with.

$$\text{Var}(x) = \int_a^b (x - \mu)^2 f(x)\, dx = \int_a^b (x^2 - 2\mu x + \mu^2) f(x)\, dx$$

$$= \int_a^b [x^2 f(x) - 2\mu x f(x) + \mu^2 f(x)]\, dx$$

$$= \int_a^b x^2 f(x)\, dx - \int_a^b 2\mu x f(x)\, dx + \int_a^b \mu^2 f(x)\, dx$$

$$= \int_a^b x^2 f(x)\, dx - 2\mu \int_a^b x f(x)\, dx + \mu^2 \int_a^b f(x)\, dx$$

The second and third integrals can be simplified considerably.

$$\int_a^b x f(x)\, dx = \mu$$

and because f is a probability density function, it follows that

$$\int_a^b f(x)\, dx = 1$$

Consequently, we have

$$\text{Var}(x) = \int_a^b x^2 f(x)\, dx - 2\mu \cdot \mu + \mu^2 \cdot 1 = \int_a^b x^2 f(x)\, dx - \mu^2$$

Variance (for Calculation)

Let x be a continuous random variable and let f be a probability density function defined on $[a, b]$. Then

$$\text{Var}(x) = \int_a^b x^2 f(x)\, dx - \mu^2$$

A related measure called the **standard deviation** is used frequently. It provides an alternative measure of the amount by which the values of x vary from the mean μ. The standard deviation is denoted by σ (lower-case Greek "sigma") and is defined as the square root of the variance.

Standard Deviation

$$\sigma = \sqrt{\mathrm{Var}(x)}$$

EXAMPLE 2   *LIFE EXPECTANCY OF A WATER HEATER*

APPLIED

Suppose that the life expectancy of a water heater is given by the probability density function

$$f(x) = .1 - .005x \qquad 0 \le x \le 20$$

where x is in years.

(a) Determine the expected value, which is the average life expectancy of these water heaters.

(b) Determine the variance.

(c) Determine the standard deviation.

SOLUTION   **(a)** The expected value is

$$E(x) = \int_a^b x f(x)\, dx = \int_0^{20} x(.1 - .005x)\, dx$$

$$= \int_0^{20} (.1x - .005x^2)\, dx \approx \left[.05x^2 - .0017x^3 \right]_0^{20} = 6.4$$

The average life expectancy of these water heaters is 6.4 years.

(b) The variance is

$$\mathrm{Var}(x) = \int_a^b x^2 f(x)\, dx - \mu^2 = \int_0^{20} x^2(.1 - .005x)\, dx - (6.4)^2$$

$$= \int_0^{20} (.1x^2 - .005x^3)\, dx - 40.96$$

$$\approx \left[.03333x^3 - .00125x^4 \right]_0^{20} - 40.96$$

$$= 266.64 - 200 - 40.96$$

$$= 25.68$$

(c) The standard deviation is

$$\sigma = \sqrt{\mathrm{Var}(x)} = \sqrt{25.68} \approx 5.07$$

Because the values found here for $E(x)$, $\text{Var}(x)$, and σ are approximate, we decided (arbitrarily) to keep two decimal places for $\text{Var}(x)$ and σ. ◆

8.2   Exercises

In Exercises 1–10, determine the expected value associated with the given probability density function. Round the final result to two decimal places.

1. $f(x) = \dfrac{1}{2}$, $6 \le x \le 8$

2. $f(x) = \dfrac{2}{3}$, $1 \le x \le 2.5$

3. $f(x) = \dfrac{1}{18}x$, $0 \le x \le 6$

4. $f(x) = \dfrac{1}{2}x$, $0 \le x \le 2$

5. $f(x) = \dfrac{1}{21}x^2$, $1 \le x \le 4$

6. $f(x) = \dfrac{1}{9}x^2$, $0 \le x \le 3$

7. $f(x) = \dfrac{1}{6\sqrt{x}}$, $1 \le x \le 16$

8. $f(x) = \dfrac{1}{7}\left(1 + \dfrac{1}{\sqrt{x}}\right)$, $4 \le x \le 9$

9. $f(x) = \dfrac{6 - 3\sqrt{x}}{8}$, $0 \le x \le 4$

10. $f(x) = \dfrac{3}{16}\sqrt{x}$, $0 \le x \le 4$

In Exercises 11–16, determine visually whether the approximate location of μ is at c, d, e, or f. Recall that the region will balance if placed at μ.

11.
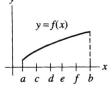

12.
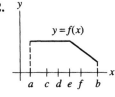

13.
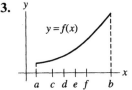

14.
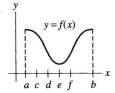

15.
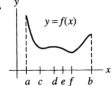

16.
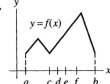

 In Exercises 17–24, probability density functions are given. Find the expected value, variance, and standard deviation in each case. Round final results to two decimal places. *A calculator is needed to determine σ.*

17. $f(x) = \dfrac{1}{6}$, $4 \le x \le 10$

18. $f(x) = \dfrac{1}{10}$, $1 \le x \le 11$

19. $f(x) = \dfrac{2x}{15}$, $1 \le x \le 4$

20. $f(x) = \dfrac{1}{30}x$, $2 \le x \le 8$

21. $f(x) = \dfrac{1}{8}(4 - x)$, $0 \le x \le 4$

22. $f(x) = \dfrac{3\sqrt{x}}{52}$, $1 \le x \le 9$

23. $f(x) = \dfrac{1}{2\sqrt{x}}$, $9 \le x \le 16$

24. $f(x) = \dfrac{3}{64}x^2$, $0 \le x \le 4$

25. (WAITING IN LINE) The wait in line during registration is described by the probability density function

$$f(x) = .005x \qquad 0 \le x \le 20$$

where x is in minutes. Determine the length of the average wait.

26. (TRAFFIC LIGHT) A traffic light that you pass on the way home is timed to turn yellow in your direction every 90 seconds. The probability density function is

$$f(x) = \dfrac{1}{90} \qquad 0 \le x \le 90$$

where x is the number of seconds before the next yellow light. If you were to look at the traffic light at randomly chosen times, how long would you expect to wait (on the average) before you saw a yellow light?

27. (LIFE EXPECTANCY) Suppose that the life expectancy of an air conditioning unit is given by the probability density function

$$f(x) = .2 - .02x \qquad 0 \le x \le 10$$

where x is in years.

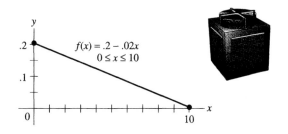

(a) Determine the average life expectancy (the mean or expected value).

(b) Determine the variance.

28. (JOB-TRAINING GRANTS) Because of a state revenue short-fall, recipients of job-training grants believe the funding of their grants will end within the next 4 years according to the probability density function

$$f(x) = \dfrac{1}{8}\left(3 - \dfrac{x}{2}\right) \qquad 0 \le x \le 4$$

(a) On the basis of this function, find the average time that a grant will remain funded.

(b) Determine the variance and standard deviation.

29. (TREE LIFE) A particular type of tree lives no more than 10 years. The probability density function

$$f(x) = .125 - .00075x^2 \qquad 0 \le x \le 10$$

describes the probability that the tree will die at any time x (in years).

(a) Find the expected value.

W (b) Explain the meaning of the number obtained in part (a).

(c) Determine the variance and standard deviation.

30. (USEFUL LIFE) The probability density function

$$f(x) = \dfrac{1}{300}(2 + .8x) \qquad 0 \le x \le 25$$

describes the number of months x of useful service of a car's windshield wipers.

(a) On the basis of this function, find the average life expectancy of a car's windshield wipers.

(b) Determine the standard deviation.

TECHNOLOGY *EXERCISES*

In Exercises 1–3, graph the probability density function on the given interval and then approximate μ to the nearest integer.

1. $f(x) = \dfrac{3}{68}(3 + 4x - x^2)$ on $[0, 4]$. Use y in $[-.02, .5]$.

2. $f(x) = \dfrac{1}{2.5} e^{-(x-6)^2/2}$ on [3, 9]. Use y in [-1, 1].

3. $f(x) = \dfrac{1}{5} - \dfrac{1}{50}x$ on [0, 10]. Use y in [$-.1$, .3].

8.3 | *UNIFORM AND EXPONENTIAL RANDOM VARIABLES*

When the probability density function is a constant function, it is called the **uniform probability density function.** The random variable x associated with the uniform probability density function is said to be *uniformly distributed*, and we speak of the *uniform distribution*.

The exercises of Section 8.1 provided two examples of uniform probability density functions.

1. A smoke detector flashes every 30 seconds to show that it is operational. The probability density function is

$$f(x) = \frac{1}{30} \qquad 0 \le x \le 30$$

where x is the number of seconds before the next flash.

2. The wait (x minutes) for a bus is described by the probability density function

$$f(x) = \frac{1}{25} \qquad 0 \le x \le 25$$

With this background, we now define the uniform distribution.

The Uniform Distribution

Random variable x has the **uniform distribution** if its probability density function is defined by

$$f(x) = \frac{1}{b-a} \qquad a \le x \le b$$

We say that x is a *uniformly distributed random variable* or that x is *uniformly distributed*. See Figure 7.

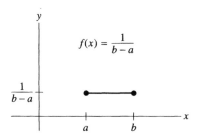

Figure 7 The uniform probability density function

EXAMPLE 1   **LENGTH OF WAIT FOR A BUS**

A shuttle bus comes every 15 minutes. Consequently, a wait at the bus stop will be between 0 and 15 minutes. If random variable x represents the length of the wait, then the (uniform) probability density function is

$$f(x) = \frac{1}{15} \qquad 0 \leq x \leq 15$$

What is the probability that the shuttle bus will come within the first 6 minutes after you arrive?

SOLUTION   We seek $P(0 \leq x \leq 6)$.

$$p(0 \leq x \leq 6) = \int_0^6 \frac{1}{15}\, dx = \left[\frac{1}{15}x\right]_0^6 = \frac{1}{15} \cdot 6 - \frac{1}{15} \cdot 0 = \frac{2}{5} = .4$$

The probability that the shuttle bus will come within the first 6 minutes is .4.   ◆

In Section 8.1, Example 2 provided the probability density function

$$f(x) = .002e^{-.002x} \qquad x \geq 0$$

where x is the total number of hours that a light bulb will burn. Function f is an example of an **exponential probability density function.** The random variable x associated with an exponential probability density function is said to be *exponentially distributed*, and we speak of the *exponential distribution*.

The Exponential Distribution

A random variable x has the **exponential distribution** if its probability density function is defined by

$$f(x) = ae^{-ax} \qquad x \geq 0 \qquad \text{constant } a \geq 0$$

We say that x is an *exponentially distributed random variable* or that x is *exponentially distributed*.

APPLIED

EXAMPLE 2 **LENGTH OF A PHONE CALL**

A phone company has determined that the length of a phone call (x minutes) has the exponential probability density function

$$f(x) = .2e^{-.2x} \qquad x \geq 0$$

What is the probability that a phone call will last no more than 10 minutes?

SOLUTION We seek $P(0 \leq x \leq 10)$.

$$P(0 \leq x \leq 10) = \int_0^{10} .2e^{-.2x}\, dx = .2\int_0^{10} e^{-.2x}\, dx = -\left[e^{-.2x}\right]_0^{10}$$

$$= -\left[e^{-2} - e^0\right] = -e^{-2} + 1 \approx -.1353 + 1$$

$$= .8647$$

The probability that a phone call will last no more than 10 minutes is .8647. ◆

8.3   Exercises

1. (SMOKE DETECTOR) A smoke detector flashes every 20 seconds to show that it is operational. Let x be the number of seconds before the next flash. Then random variable x has the uniform distribution given by

$$f(x) = \frac{1}{20} \qquad 0 \leq x \leq 20$$

What is the probability that you will see a flash within 5 seconds of looking at the smoke detector?

2. (FLIGHT DEPARTURE) At a particular airport the planes never leave early, and flights are routinely delayed by as much as 30 minutes. The uniform distribution is given by

$$f(x) = \frac{1}{30} \qquad 0 \leq x \leq 30$$

Here random variable x is the number of minutes a given flight is delayed. What is the probability that your flight will leave within 12 minutes of when it is scheduled to depart?

3. (FLOWER SIZE) The diameter of the flowers on a particular

rose bush can be between 5 cm and 8 cm. Using x to represent the diameter of a randomly selected rose, assume that the probability density function is

$$f(x) = \frac{1}{3} \qquad 5 \leq x \leq 8$$

(a) Verify that f is a probability density function.
(b) Determine $P(5 \leq x \leq 6)$.
W (c) What word describes the distribution of random variable x?

4. (WAITING FOR A TRAIN) The wait (x minutes) for a subway train is described by the probability density function

$$f(x) = \frac{1}{12} \qquad 0 \leq x \leq 12$$

(a) Verify that f is a probability density function.
(b) What is the probability that you will have to wait at least 3 minutes?
(c) What is the longest wait you should anticipate?
W (d) What word describes the distribution of the random variable?

5. (*SMOKE DETECTOR*) Rewrite the probability density function of Exercise 1, assuming the smoke detector flashes every 25 seconds.

6. (*FLIGHT DEPARTURE*) Rewrite the probability density function of Exercise 2, assuming that planes are routinely delayed by as much as 40 minutes.

7. (*FLOWER SIZE*) Rewrite the probability density function of Exercise 3, assuming that the diameter of a rose can be between 4 cm and 10 cm.

8. (*WAITING FOR A TRAIN*) Rewrite the probability density function of Exercise 4, assuming that the wait for a subway train can be no more than 10 minutes.

9. (*LIGHT BULB LIFE*) Suppose the total hours x that a light bulb will burn is given by the exponential probability density function

$$f(x) = .0015e^{-.0015x} \qquad x \geq 0$$

(a) What is the probability that a light bulb will burn 400 hours or less?

(b) What is the probability that a light bulb will burn between 100 and 600 hours?

10. (*PHONE CALL LENGTH*) A local telephone company finds that the probability density function for the length of time (x minutes) of a phone call is

$$f(x) = .25e^{-.25x} \qquad x \geq 0$$

(a) What is the probability that a phone call will last no more than 8 minutes?

(b) What is the probability that a phone call will last between 4 and 12 minutes?

11. (*LEARNING EXPERIMENT*) Psychologists have determined that the time it takes a rat to find its way through a maze is exponentially distributed. Let x be the time in seconds, and for a particular maze,

$$f(x) = .025e^{-.025x} \qquad x \geq 0$$

is the probability density function.

(a) What is the probability that a rat can find its way through the maze in 20 seconds or less?

(b) What is the probability that a rat will take between 30 seconds and a minute to get through the maze?

(c) Determine the probability that a rat will take at least 80 seconds to find its way through the maze.

12. (*COMPUTER CHIP LIFE*) The useful life of a computer chip is described by an exponential random variable. If x

represents the chip's life expectancy in years, then the probability density function is given by

$$f(x) = .2e^{-.2x} \qquad x \geq 0$$

(a) Find the probability that a chip will break within the first year.

(b) What is the probability that a chip will break between the first and second years?

(c) Determine the probability that a chip will last at least 4 years.

13. (*BEETLE FLIGHT*) Each summer, Japanese beetles crawl out of the ground and fly to nearby trees and bushes on which they feed. The distance x (in feet) that a beetle flies before reaching a tree or bush is an exponential random variable. For one particular suburban neighborhood, the probability density function is

$$f(x) = .04e^{-.04x} \qquad x \geq 0$$

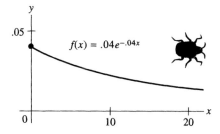

Determine the probability that a Japanese beetle will fly 100 feet or less to reach a bush or tree.

The following result is needed for Exercises 14–17.

Integration by parts can be used to show that the expected value of the exponential distribution

$$f(x) = ae^{-ax} \qquad x \geq 0$$

is

$$\mu = \frac{1}{a}$$

14. (*LIGHT BULB LIFE*) Refer to Exercise 9. To the nearest hour, what is the average (mean) life expectancy of such light bulbs?

15. **(PHONE CALL LENGTH)** Refer to Example 2.
    (a) What is the average (mean) length of a phone call?
    (b) How would you redefine the probability density function if it must still be exponential, *but* the mean length of a phone call is 8 minutes?

16. **(LEARNING EXPERIMENT)** Define a probability density function f for a rat maze (see Exercise 11) in which the mean time for a rat to get through the maze is 25 seconds.

17. **(COMPUTER CHIP LIFE)** Define a probability density function f for computer chips (see Exercise 12) if the mean life expectancy is 4 years.

18. Show that the uniform probability density function defined by

$$f(x) = \frac{1}{b - a} \qquad a \le x \le b$$

is indeed a probability density function.

19. Show that the mean of the uniform probability density function is $\frac{1}{2}(a + b)$.

20. Show that the exponential probability density function defined by

$$f(x) = ae^{-ax} \qquad x \ge 0, \, a \ge 0$$

is indeed a probability density function.

W 21. Is

$$f(x) = .2e^{-.4x} \qquad x \ge 0$$

a probability density function? Explain.

8.4 | *THE NORMAL DISTRIBUTION*

The **normal distribution** is the best known and most widely used probability distribution. Many natural occurrences are normally distributed. Adult heights and weights, blood pressure, and cholesterol level tend to be normally distributed. Scores on IQ (Intelligence Quotient) tests and other standardized tests have a normal distribution. In statistics, many problems are solved by working with the normal probability density function.

> ### The Normal Distribution
>
> A random variable x has the **normal distribution** if its probability density function is defined by
>
> $$f(x) = \frac{1}{\sigma\sqrt{2\pi}} e^{-(x-\mu)^2/(2\sigma^2)} \qquad \text{for } -\infty < x < \infty$$
>
> where the mean is μ, the variance is σ^2, and the standard deviation is σ. We say that x is a *normally distributed random variable*, that x is *normally distributed*, or that x is a *normal random variable*.

The graph of a normal probability density function is a bell-shaped curve. Such curves are often called **normal curves.** A normal curve is symmetric about the line $x = \mu$; that is, the curve to the left of the line $x = \mu$ is the mirror image of the curve to the right of the line

$x = \mu$. The x axis is a horizontal asymptote for the graph of any normal probability density function. Figure 8 shows a normal curve.

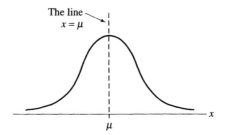

Figure 8 A normal curve

Applications of the normal distribution usually involve the **standard normal distribution,** which is the normal distribution in which $\mu = 0$ and $\sigma = 1$. The standard normal probability density function is given by

$$f(x) = \frac{1}{\sqrt{2\pi}} e^{-x^2/2} \qquad -\infty < x < \infty$$

The corresponding graph, the **standard normal curve,** is shown in Figure 9.

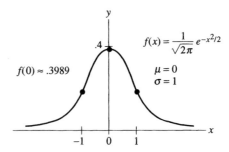

Figure 9 The standard normal curve

If x is a standard normal random variable, then the probability that x is between a and b is given by

$$P(a \le x \le b) = \int_a^b \frac{1}{\sqrt{2\pi}} e^{-x^2/2} \, dx$$

Although we are unable to evaluate this integral by elementary methods, numerical methods can be used to obtain good approximations. Table 6 in the Appendix gives probabilities for the standard normal distribution.

Normal distributions other than the *standard* normal distribution are presented later in the section. There you will see how a normal random variable x is converted to the standard normal random variable. To distinguish the two variables (normal and standard normal), we introduce the letter z to represent the **standard normal random variable.**

The Standard Normal Random Variable

The letter z is used for the standard normal random variable.

Each Table 6 entry is the probability that the standard normal random variable is between zero and some specific positive value of z. Geometrically, each table entry is the area under the standard normal curve from 0 to that specific positive value of z. Although most of the table entries are approximations, we will use the notation $=$ rather than $\approx$ and not belabor the point.

Examples 1 to 5, which follow, *begin* with a standard normal random variable. Consequently, the letter z (rather than x) appears immediately in those examples. Examples 6 and 7 demonstrate the conversion from x to z.

EXAMPLE 1 Assume that z is the standard normal random variable. Find $P(0 \leq z \leq .62)$.

SOLUTION From Table 6 (a portion of which is shown in Figure 10), we obtain

$$P(0 \leq z \leq .62) = .2324$$

To locate this probability in Table 6, look for the entry that corresponds to .62. In other words, go down the z column (far left) until you come to .6. Then proceed to the right until you are under the .02 column. The entry there is $P(0 \leq z \leq .62)$. Figure 11 shows the graph that illustrates this situation.

z	.00	.01	.02	.03	.04	.05	.06	.07	.08	.09
.0	.0000	.0040	.0080	.0120	.0160	.0199	.0239	.0279	.0319	.0359
.1	.0398	.0438	.0478	.0517	.0557	.0596	.0636	.0675	.0714	.0753
.2	.0793	.0832	.0871	.0910	.0948	.0987	.1026	.1064	.1103	.1141
.3	.1179	.1217	.1255	.1293	.1331	.1368	.1406	.1443	.1480	.1517
.4	.1554	.1591	.1628	.1664	.1700	.1736	.1772	.1808	.1844	.1879
.5	.1915	.1950	.1985	.2019	.2054	.2088	.2123	.2157	.2190	.2224
.6	.2257	.2291	.2324	.2357	.2389	.2422	.2454	.2486	.2517	.2549
.7	.2580	.2611	.2642	.2673	.2704	.2734	.2764	.2794	.2823	.2852
.8	.2881	.2910	.2939	.2967	.2995	.3023	.3051	.3078	.3106	.3133
.9	.3159	.3186	.3212	.3238	.3264	.3289	.3315	.3340	.3365	.3389
1.0	.3413	.3438		.485	.3508	.3531	.3554	.3577	.3599	.3621
	.3643								.3810	.3830

Figure 10 Using Table 6 to determine $P(0 \leq z \leq .62)$

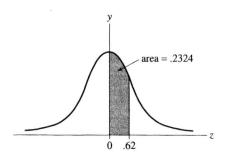

Figure 11 $P(0 \le z \le .62) = .2324$ ◆

EXAMPLE 2   Assume that z is the standard normal random variable. Find $P(z \le .62)$.

SOLUTION   From the preceding example, we know that the area between 0 and .62 is .2324. The area to the left of 0 is .5, because it is half of the entire area under the curve—half of 1. (Recall that the normal distribution is defined by a probability density function, which means that the area under the curve must be 1.) Thus, the area we seek is the sum of .2324 and .5. (See Figure 12.)

$$P(z \le .62) = P(z \le 0) + P(0 \le z \le .62)$$
$$= .5 + .2324$$
$$= .7324$$

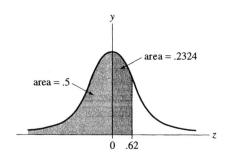

Figure 12 $P(z \le .62) = .7324$ ◆

EXAMPLE 3   Assume that z is the standard normal random variable. Find $P(z \ge .62)$.

SOLUTION   From the previous example, we know that $P(z \le .62) = .7324$. Also, the area under the entire curve is 1. Thus,

$$P(z \ge .62) + P(z \le .62) = 1$$

or

$$P(z \ge .62) = 1 - P(z \le .62)$$
$$= 1 - .7324$$
$$= .2676$$

If we had not already known the value of $P(z \leq .62)$, then we would have needed to obtain it. Figure 13 should help you to see that we must obtain $P(z \geq .62)$ indirectly as $1 - P(z \leq .62)$.

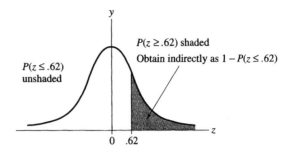

$P(z \leq .62)$
unshaded

$P(z \geq .62)$ shaded
Obtain indirectly as $1 - P(z \leq .62)$

0 .62

Figure 13 $P(z \geq .62) = .2676$ ◆

EXAMPLE 4 Assume that z is the standard normal random variable. Find $P(-.83 \leq z \leq 1.2)$.

SOLUTION The desired area is shown shaded in Figure 14.

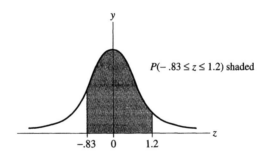

$P(-.83 \leq z \leq 1.2)$ shaded

-.83 0 1.2

Figure 14

The area can be considered as the sum of two areas: the area between $-.83$ and 0 plus the area between 0 and 1.2. Furthermore, by the symmetry of the normal curve, the area from $-.83$ to 0 is the same as the area from 0 to $.83$. Thus, with the aid of Table 6, we find that

$$P(-.83 \leq z \leq 1.2) = P(-.83 \leq z \leq 0) + P(0 \leq z \leq 1.2)$$
$$= P(0 \leq z \leq .83) + P(0 \leq z \leq 1.2)$$
$$= .2967 + .3849$$
$$= .6816$$ ◆

EXAMPLE 5 Assume that z is the standard normal random variable. Find $P(1.3 \leq z \leq 2)$.

SOLUTION The desired area is shown shaded in Figure 15.

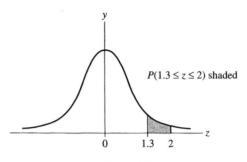

Figure 15

The desired area is the area under the curve from 0 to 2 *minus* the area from 0 to 1.3. Thus,

$$P(1.3 \leq z \leq 2) = P(0 \leq z \leq 2) - P(0 \leq z \leq 1.3)$$
$$= .4772 - .4032$$
$$= .0740 \qquad \qquad \blacklozenge$$

Other Normal Distributions

The examples and table we have been using assume the *standard* normal distribution, which has mean 0 and standard deviation 1. If the normal distribution under consideration does not have mean 0 and standard deviation 1, then it can be converted to the standard normal distribution by using the following **standardizing formula.**

Standardizing Formula

$$z = \frac{x - \mu}{\sigma}$$

where μ is the mean of the normal distribution, σ is the standard deviation of the normal distribution, and x is any value of the normally distributed random variable. Numbers that result from using this formula are often called z **scores.**

Intuitively, we can justify this conversion formula as follows. First, it converts the mean μ of the distribution to 0, which is the mean of the standard normal distribution. To see this, replace x by μ in the formula, and $z = 0$ results. Second, the numbers on the horizontal axis of the standard normal distribution measure standard deviations—1 means 1 standard deviation; 1.2 means 1.2 standard deviations. Subtracting μ from x gives the distance of x from the mean. Then, dividing by σ converts that distance into the number of standard deviations from the mean.

EXAMPLE 6   A normal distribution has mean 53 and standard deviation 5. Find the probability that random variable x has a value less than 60.

SOLUTION   The problem of finding $P(x \leq 60)$ for the given normal distribution can be changed to a problem involving the standard normal distribution. Here

$$z = \frac{x - \mu}{\sigma} = \frac{60 - 53}{5} = 1.4$$

The problem has been changed to finding $P(z \leq 1.4)$, where z is the standard normal random variable. The problem now resembles that of Example 2.

$$P(z \leq 1.4) = P(z \leq 0) + P(0 \leq z \leq 1.4)$$
$$= .5 + .4192$$
$$= .9192$$

Thus, the probability that x has a value less than 60 is .9192.   ◆

APPLIED

EXAMPLE 7   **IQ TEST SCORES**

An IQ test is designed so that scores are normally distributed with mean 100 and standard deviation 15. If a tested person is chosen at random, what is the probability that his or her IQ is between 100 and 124?

SOLUTION   We seek $P(100 \leq x \leq 124)$ for a normally distributed random variable. Using $x = 100$ and $x = 124$ in the standardizing formula will yield the z scores. (Note that $\mu = 100$ and $\sigma = 15$.)

$$z = \frac{100 - 100}{15} = 0 \qquad\qquad z = \frac{124 - 100}{15} = 1.6$$

We now seek $P(0 \leq z \leq 1.6)$. From Table 6, we have immediately

$$P(0 \leq z \leq 1.6) = .4452$$

Thus, the probability that the person's IQ is between 100 and 124 is .4452.   ◆

Note

Probabilities have been computed as decimal numbers. They can be converted to *percent* in the usual way. In Example 7, the probability .4452 is the same as 44.52%.

8.4   Exercises

In Exercises 1–28, find the requested probability. Assume that z is the standard normal random variable. Use Table 6 in the Appendix as needed.

1. $P(0 \le z \le 1.1)$ **2.** $P(0 \le z \le 1.7)$

3. $P(0 \le z \le .73)$ **4.** $P(0 \le z \le .46)$

5. $P(z \le .42)$ **6.** $P(z \le .67)$

7. $P(z \le 1.45)$ **8.** $P(z \le 1.52)$

9. $P(-1.6 \le z \le 0)$ **10.** $P(-1.1 \le z \le 0)$

11. $P(-2.1 \le z \le 0)$ **12.** $P(-.92 \le z \le 0)$

13. $P(z \ge .84)$ **14.** $P(z \ge .53)$

15. $P(z \ge 1.72)$ **16.** $P(z \ge 2.11)$

17. $P(-.95 \le z \le 1.3)$ **18.** $P(-.75 \le z \le 1.45)$

19. $P(-.8 \le z \le 2.15)$ **20.** $P(-1.1 \le z \le .95)$

21. $P(.25 \le z \le 1)$ **22.** $P(1.35 \le z \le 2)$

23. $P(1.3 \le z \le 2.45)$ **24.** $P(.87 \le z \le 1.74)$

25. $P(z \le -.82)$ **26.** $P(z \le -.45)$

27. $P(z \le -1.2)$ **28.** $P(z \le -.9)$

In Exercises 29–36, determine the probability. In each case, x is a normal random variable that has the given mean μ and standard deviation σ.

29. $P(x \le 17)$, $\mu = 14$, $\sigma = 2$

30. $P(x \le 23)$, $\mu = 20$, $\sigma = 4$

31. $P(x \ge 14)$, $\mu = 20$, $\sigma = 4$

32. $P(x \ge 43)$, $\mu = 45$, $\sigma = 2$

33. $P(11 \le x \le 14)$, $\mu = 10$, $\sigma = 5$

34. $P(15 \le x \le 18)$, $\mu = 12$, $\sigma = 5$

35. $P(18 \le x \le 25)$, $\mu = 20$, $\sigma = 4$

36. $P(20 \le x \le 31)$, $\mu = 25$, $\sigma = 4$

Exercises 37–44 are based on an IQ test with normally distributed scores, a mean of 100, and standard deviation 15. Find the probability that a randomly chosen person has the listed IQ score.

37. Between 100 and 130   **38.** Greater than 100

39. Greater than 115   **40.** Between 85 and 115

41. Less than 100   **42.** Between 85 and 100

43. Between 90 and 100   **44.** Less than 105

45. (*LEAF SIZE*) The lengths of the leaves on a particular type of oak tree are normally distributed with mean 4 inches and standard deviation .5 inch. What percentage of the leaves on such a tree are at least 3.5 inches long?

46. (*NAIL LENGTH*) The lengths of nails made by a machine are normally distributed with mean 1 inch and standard deviation .05 inch. What is the probability that a nail chosen at random is between .95 and 1.05 inches long?

47. (*ANNUAL SNOWFALL*) Records of a city's annual snowfall show it to be normally distributed with mean 24 inches and standard deviation 4 inches.
   (a) What is the probability that an annual snowfall is more than 30 inches?
   (b) What is the probability that an annual snowfall is less than 20 inches?

48. (*BOTTLING SODA*) The machine in a bottling facility fills quart (32-ounce) bottles with soda. The amount poured into the bottles is normally distributed with mean 32.5 ounces and standard deviation .75 ounce. What is the probability that the machine puts at least 32 ounces in a bottle?

49. (*SAT SCORES*) A highly competitive engineering college will consider only applicants with SAT math scores of 680 or greater. Assuming that SAT scores are normally distributed with mean 500 and standard deviation 100, what percent of those taking the SAT test will meet the SAT math requirement established by this college?

50. (*SAT SCORES*) The students at a southern college have combined SAT scores that are normally distributed with mean 1200 and standard deviation 200. What percent of the college's student population has combined SAT scores of at least 1100?

51. (*BLOOD PRESSURE*) For adults, systolic blood pressure is normally distributed with mean 130 and standard deviation 20. What is the probability that a randomly chosen adult will have systolic blood pressure that is between 118 and 144?

52. (*BATTERY LIFE*) A manufacturer offers an automobile battery that is supposed to last 6 years. Experience shows the lifetime of the batteries to be normally distributed with a mean of 4.6 years and a standard deviation of 1.2 years. Based on experience, what percent of the batteries actually last at least 6 years?

53. Begin with the normal probability density function and let $\mu = 0$ and $\sigma = 1$. Show that this leads to the standard normal density function,

$$f(x) = \frac{1}{\sqrt{2\pi}}\, e^{-x^2/2}$$

 54. *Use a calculator* to show that if f is the standard normal probability density function, then $f(0) \approx .3989$.

W 55. Let z be the standard normal random variable. What must be the value of $P(-\infty < z < \infty)$? Explain your answer.

W 56. Let x be a normally distributed random variable. Determine $P(x \geq \mu)$ and explain your answer.

W 57. The standard normal probability density function is given by

$$f(x) = \frac{1}{\sqrt{2\pi}}\, e^{-x^2/2} \qquad -\infty < x < \infty$$

(a) What must be the value of the integral

$$\int_{-\infty}^{\infty} \frac{1}{\sqrt{2\pi}}\, e^{-x^2/2}\, dx$$

Explain.

(b) It is known that

$$\int_{-\infty}^{\infty} e^{-x^2/2}\, dx = \sqrt{2\pi}$$

Explain, then, why the standard normal probability density function is given by

$$f(x) = \frac{1}{\sqrt{2\pi}}\, e^{-x^2/2}$$

rather than simply

$$f(x) = e^{-x^2/2}$$

TECHNOLOGY *EXERCISES*

1. You can obtain a nice graph of the standard normal probability density function

$$f(x) = \frac{1}{\sqrt{2\pi}}\, e^{-x^2/2}$$

by using the interval $[-4, 4]$ for x and $[-.2, .6]$ for y.

(a) From the graph, what is the approximate value, to the nearest hundredth, of $f(1)$?

(b) Similarly, determine the approximate value of $f(2)$.

W 2. Consider the probability density function associated with normal distributions. (It is given in the box at the beginning of the section.)

(a) Graph the standard normal curve ($\mu = 0$, $\sigma = 1$) and the normal curve with $\mu = 1$ and $\sigma = 1$. Use $[-4, 4]$ for x and $[-.2, .6]$ for y. How do the curves differ? Explain the effect of changing the mean from 0 to 1.

(b) Graph the standard normal curve ($\mu = 0$, $\sigma = 1$) and the normal curve with $\mu = 0$ and $\sigma = 2$. Use $[-4, 4]$ for x and $[-.2, .6]$ for y. How do the curves differ? Explain the effect of changing the standard deviation from 1 to 2.

Note When we are considering the standard normal probability density function, the probability that a random variable is between two numbers a and b is given by

$$\int_{a}^{b} \frac{1}{\sqrt{2\pi}}\, e^{-x^2/2}\, dx \qquad\qquad (continued)$$

Computer algebra systems can evaluate definite integrals of this form. If you have access to such a system, try doing Example 1 and Example 4 in this manner.

Key Terms and Ideas

probability density function
random variable
discrete random variable
continuous random variable
expected value
mean
variance

standard deviation
uniform probability density function
uniform distribution
exponential probability density function
exponential distribution
normal distribution

normal curve
standard normal distribution
standard normal curve
standard normal random variable (z)
standardizing formula
z scores

Review Exercises for Chapter 8

1. Show that $f(x) = \frac{1}{42}x$ on [4, 10] is a probability density function.

2. Show that $f(x) = \frac{1}{51}(3x^2 - 10)$ on [4, 5] is a probability density function.

3. Given probability density function $f(x) = x^3/4$ on [0, 2], determine $P(1 \le x \le 2)$.

4. Given probability density function $f(x) = 2x/15$ on [1, 4], determine $P(2 \le x \le 3)$.

5. *(WAITING IN LINE)* The wait in line (x minutes) to get tickets for a rock concert is given by the probability density function

$$f(x) = .00005x \qquad 0 \le x \le 200$$

(a) Find the probability that the wait will be 30 minutes or less.
(b) Find the probability that the wait will be at least an hour.

6. *(WAITING IN LINE)* What is the time of the average wait in line for the rock concert tickets of Exercise 5?

7. *(TICKET SALES)* The probability density function for the number of lottery tickets x that a convenience store will sell in a day is

$$f(x) = .0002x \qquad 0 \le x \le 100$$

What is the probability that the store will sell at least 70 lottery tickets today?

8. *(BEACON LIGHT)* A rotating beacon light shines on a post every 18 seconds. Let x represent the number of seconds before the next time the light shines on the post. Write the probability density function for this uniform distribution, including the domain.

9. Determine the expected value associated with probability density function $f(x) = .1x$ on [4, 6].

10. Determine the expected value associated with probability density function $f(x) = x/16$ on [2, 6].

11. Determine the expected value, variance, and standard deviation associated with probability density function $f(x) = \frac{1}{9}x^2$ on [0, 3].

12. Determine the expected value, variance, and standard deviation associated with probability density function $f(x) = 1 - .5x$ on [0, 2].

13. *(WAITING FOR A BUS)* The wait (x minutes) for the airport shuttle bus is described by the probability density function

$$f(x) = \frac{1}{10} \qquad 0 \le x \le 10$$

How long is the average wait for the bus?

14. Verify that

$$f(x) = .4e^{-.4x} \qquad x \geq 0$$

is a probability density function.

15. **(PHONE CALL LENGTH)** Suppose your local telephone company says that the probability density function for the length of time (x minutes) of a phone call is

$$f(x) = .3e^{-.3x} \qquad x \geq 0$$

   (a) What is the probability that a phone call will last no more than 5 minutes?
   (b) What is the probability that a phone call will last at least 10 minutes?

In Exercises 16–21, determine the requested probability. Assume that z is the standard normal random variable.

16. $P(0 \leq z \leq .81)$ **17.** $P(0 \leq z \leq .57)$

18. $P(-.2 \leq z \leq 1)$ **19.** $P(-1.8 \leq z \leq 2.14)$

20. $P(z \geq 1.87)$ **21.** $P(.72 \leq z \leq 2.83)$

In Exercises 22–25, determine the probability. Here x is a normal random variable that has the given mean μ and standard deviation σ.

22. $P(0 \leq x \leq 30)$, $\mu = 25$, $\sigma = 4$

23. $P(x \geq 19)$, $\mu = 12$, $\sigma = 5$

24. $P(x \leq 106)$, $\mu = 100$, $\sigma = 10$

25. $P(51 \leq x \leq 59)$, $\mu = 50$, $\sigma = 4$

26. **(IQ SCORES)** Based on an IQ test with normally distributed scores, a mean of 100, and standard deviation 15, what is the probability that a randomly chosen person has a genius-level IQ score of more than 140?

27. **(BOTTLING SODA)** A machine fills 12-ounce cans with ginger ale. The amount of ginger ale poured into the cans is normally distributed with mean 12.15 ounces and standard deviation .05 ounce. What is the probability that the machine puts at least 12 ounces in a can?

28. **(PACKAGING CEREAL)** A machine fills boxes with cereal. The label on the box says 18 ounces. The amount of cereal put into the boxes is normally distributed with mean 18.1 ounces and standard deviation .1 ounce. What is the probability that the machine puts at least 17.9 ounces in a box?

W 29. Let f be a probability density function defined on the interval $[0, 8]$ and let

$$\int_3^8 f(x)\, dx = .75$$

Determine the value of

$$\int_0^3 f(x)\, dx$$

and explain how you know its value.

W 30. Let f be defined on the interval $[0, 12]$ and let $f(x) \geq 0$ for all x in the interval. Also, suppose that

$$\int_0^{10} f(x)\, dx = 1$$

Can f be a probability density function? Explain.

Chapter Projects and Essays

Many of the projects and essays lend themselves to group activity, although most can be completed by individual effort.

1. HISTORY OF PROBABILITY

BACKGROUND   The mathematical study of probability began in 1654, when Blaise Pascal and Pierre de Fermat studied games of chance. Other mathematicians soon extended the study beyond games and gambling.

THE PROJECT Given next are the names of several mathematicians who established and developed the field of probability. Write an essay about one or more of these mathematicians' contributions to the development of probability. Most books on the history of mathematics contain information about these mathematicians.

Blaise Pascal	Thomas Bayes
Pierre de Fermat	Daniel Bernouilli
Christian Huygens	Leonhard Euler
Jakob Bernoulli	Joseph Louis Lagrange
Abraham DeMoivre	Pierre Simon de Laplace

2. IS PROBABILITY OR STATISTICS IN YOUR FUTURE?

BACKGROUND You may well encounter probability, or the closely related study of statistics, in college or at work.

(a) As an undergraduate student, you may be required to take a course in statistics. In graduate school, you will take special statistics courses if you will be doing research that must be supported by statistics.

(b) Probability and statistics are fields of applied mathematics that offer many employment opportunities.

THE PROJECT **(a)** If your field of study requires statistics, find out what types of courses are required and what they include. Investigate why statistics is required; that is, determine how it will be applied in your field of study. Write a paper on your findings.

(b) Investigate career opportunities in probability and statistics, and write a paper describing them. Listed next are some sources of information.

The Career Planning and Placement Office on your campus

People you might know who work in the field

The Society of Actuaries

The Operations Research Society of America

The American Statistical Association

The Mathematical Association of America

DIFFERENTIAL EQUATIONS

9

After an early cold snap, the outlook for fall apple harvests can look dismal. How much apple prices will rise—and how farmers' incomes will fare—is influenced by a fundamental economic concept, "elasticity of demand." The concept of demand elasticities is a common application of differential equations.

*I*nterpreting the derivative as a rate of change has led to a variety of applications, including

1. Marginal cost, marginal revenue, and marginal profit

2. Velocity and acceleration

3. Rate of growth of bacteria, a city's population, or investments.

4. Increasing and decreasing functions

5. Tests for concavity and relative extrema

Because many applications involve rates of change, it is not surprising that many equations describe rates of change. These equations contain derivatives, since rates of change are described by derivatives.

9.1 | *INTRODUCTION TO DIFFERENTIAL EQUATIONS*

An equation that contains one or more derivatives of some function is called a **differential equation.** The following are two examples of differential equations.

$$\frac{dy}{dx} + 2xy = x^3 \qquad\qquad y'' - 3y' - 4y = 0$$

A **solution** of a differential equation is any function $y = f(x)$ that satisfies the differential equation.

EXAMPLE 1   Show that $y = x^2$ is a solution of the differential equation

$$xy' = 2y$$

SOLUTION $y = x^2$ is a solution if it satisfies the differential equation. In other words, if x^2 is substituted for y and $2x$ for y' in the given equation $xy' = 2y$, an identity (an equation that is always true) will result. To begin,

$$xy' = 2y$$

After substitution of x^2 for y and $2x$ for y', we have

$$x \cdot 2x = 2 \cdot x^2$$

Upon simplification, we obtain an obvious identity.

$$2x^2 = 2x^2$$

Thus, $y = x^2$ is indeed a solution.   ◆

Example 1 can be continued by noting that $y = x^2$ is not the only solution of $xy' = 2y$. Specifically, $y = 3x^2$ and $y = 10x^2$ are also solutions. (You may want to verify this.) In fact, $y = cx^2$ is a solution for any real number c. We call $y = cx^2$ the **general solution** and a solution such as $y = x^2$ or $y = 3x^2$ a **particular solution.** Figure 1 shows graphs of some particular solutions of $xy' = 2y$.

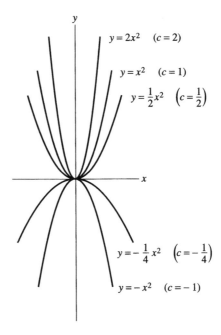

Figure 1 Some particular solutions, $y = cx^2$

It is interesting to note that the solutions of differential equations are themselves equations. Solving a differential equation amounts to finding all functions that satisfy the differential equation.

Sometimes a differential equation is presented in a form that enables us to solve it simply by antidifferentiating, as shown in the next example.

EXAMPLE 2   Solve the differential equation $y' = 4x + 1$.

SOLUTION   Since the derivative of the desired function is $4x + 1$, the function we seek is the antiderivative of $4x + 1$. That is, because

$$\frac{dy}{dx} = 4x + 1$$

it follows that

$$y = \int (4x + 1)\, dx = 2x^2 + x + C$$

The general solution of the differential equation is $y = 2x^2 + x + C$.   ◆

In practice, when you solve a differential equation, the solution you obtain will be a general solution. *Then* there may be additional conditions that the function and its derivative(s) must satisfy. When such **initial conditions** are given, a particular solution can be obtained.

If Example 2 had included initial conditions, then a specific value could have been determined for C and a particular solution would have been obtained. Suppose, for example, that we had known that $y = 7$ when $x = 0$. Then in

$$y = 2x^2 + x + C$$

we would have

$$7 = 2(0)^2 + 0 + C \qquad \text{or} \qquad C = 7$$

The particular solution would then be

$$y = 2x^2 + x + 7$$

An initial condition such as $y = 7$ when $x = 0$ is usually written in the function-like notation $y(0) = 7$.

EXAMPLE 3 Find the particular solution of the differential equation $y' = 12x^2 - 8$, with initial condition $y(1) = 6$.

SOLUTION This differential equation can be solved directly by antidifferentiation.

$$y' = 12x^2 - 8$$
$$y = 4x^3 - 8x + C$$

Since $y(1) = 6$, it follows that

$$6 = 4(1)^3 - 8(1) + C \qquad \text{or} \qquad 6 = 4 - 8 + C$$

Clearly $C = 10$, and we have the particular solution

$$y = 4x^3 - 8x + 10 \qquad\qquad \blacklozenge$$

In the sections that follow, you will be seeing differential equations that are associated with various applications. Here is a list of some of them.

1. Bacteria growth: $\dfrac{dA}{dt} = .12A$

2. Continuous compounding: $\dfrac{dA}{dt} = .05A + 400$

3. Elasticity of demand: $.05p = -\dfrac{p}{x} \cdot \dfrac{dx}{dp}$

4. Newton's law of cooling: $\dfrac{dT}{dt} = k(T - 20)$

5. Logistic growth: $\dfrac{dy}{dt} = ky(N - y)$

9.1   Exercises

In Exercises 1–10, show that the specified function is a solution of the given differential equation.

1. $xy' = 2y; \quad y = 5x^2$

2. $y' + y = (x + 1)^2; \quad y = 1 + x^2$

3. $y' - 4y = 0; \quad y = e^{4x}$

4. $y' + 2y = 0; \quad y = e^{-2x}$

5. $xy' - 1.5y = 3; \quad y = 4x^{3/2} - 2$

6. $3xy' - 4y = 0; \quad y = 3x^{4/3}$

7. $y'' - 3y' + y = x^2; \quad y = x^2 + 6x + 16$

8. $xy'' - y' = 5; \quad y = 3x^2 - 5x$

9. $(y')^2 - 4y - 8x = 0; \quad y = 1 - 2x$

10. $x(y')^2 - 4y + 4 = 0; \quad y = 4x + 1$

In Exercises 11–20, determine the general solution of each differential equation.

11. $y' = 6x + 19$

12. $y' = 12x^3 - 18x + 1$

13. $y' = e^x + 1$

14. $y' = \dfrac{1}{\sqrt{x}}$

15. $f'(x) = 2 + \sqrt{x}$

16. $f'(x) = e^{.01x}$

17. $\dfrac{dy}{dt} = e^{-2t}$

18. $\dfrac{dy}{dt} = 4t^{1/3}$

19. $f'(t) = 1 + \dfrac{3}{t}$

20. $f'(t) = t + 6\sqrt{t}$

In Exercises 21–30, determine the particular solution of each differential equation.

21. $y' = 6x^2 - 2x; \quad y(0) = 5$

22. $y' = 1 - 4x; \quad y(0) = 1$

23. $f'(x) = x^7 + 3; \quad f(0) = 14$

24. $g'(x) = \sqrt[3]{x}; \quad g(0) = 3$

25. $\dfrac{dy}{dx} = 10x - e^x; \quad y(0) = 0$

26. $\dfrac{dy}{dx} = 2e^{.01x}; \quad y(0) = 250$

27. $\dfrac{dy}{dx} = 3\sqrt{x}; \quad y(4) = 11$

28. $\dfrac{dy}{dx} = 1 + x^{-.5}; \quad y(1) = 7$

29. $\dfrac{dy}{dt} = \dfrac{8}{t}; \quad y(1) = 3$

30. $\dfrac{dy}{dt} = \dfrac{1}{2}\left(1 + \dfrac{1}{t}\right); \quad y(1) = 5/2$

Differential equations may describe marginal cost, marginal revenue, and marginal profit. In Exercises 31–36, solve the differential equation to find the requested cost, revenue, or profit.

31. *(COST)* $C'(x) = 50 - .06x, \; C(0) = 150.$ Find $C(x)$.

32. *(COST)* $C'(x) = \dfrac{20}{\sqrt{x}}, \; C(0) = 35.$ Find $C(x)$.

33. *(REVENUE)* $R'(x) = 5 + .0002x, \; R(0) = 0.$ Find $R(x)$.

34. *(REVENUE)* $R'(x) = 70 - .4x, \; R(0) = 0.$ Find $R(x)$.

35. *(PROFIT)* $P'(x) = 80 - .3\sqrt{x}, \; P(0) = -50.$ Find $P(x)$.

36. *(PROFIT)* $P'(x) = 200 + .6x - .08x^2, \; P(0) = 0.$ Find $P(x)$.

W 37. Could $y = 3$ be a solution of a differential equation? Explain.

W 38. How many solutions are there for the differential equation $y' = 6x$? Explain.

39. Consider a curve that has slope $3x^2$ and passes through the point (2, 11).
 (a) Write the differential equation that describes the situation. Include the initial condition.
 (b) Solve the differential equation in order to obtain the equation of the curve.

40. Let the rate of growth of x with respect to t be constant k.
 (a) Write the differential equation that describes this situation.
 (b) Solve the differential equation, assuming that $x(0) = c$.

41. (a) Obtain a differential equation that has the general solution $y^2 - x^2 = c$.
 W (b) What special differentiation process did you use in part (a)?

TECHNOLOGY *EXERCISES*

1. (a) Determine the general solution of the differential equation $y' = 2x$.

W (b) Graph the particular solutions that correspond to $C = 0$, $C = 3$, and $C = -2$. Explain how the graphs are related and how the choice of C influences them.

2. (a) Determine the general solution of the differential equation $y' = 1/\sqrt{x}$.

W (b) Graph the particular solutions that correspond to $C = 0$, $C = 2$, and $C = -3$. Explain how the graphs are related and how the choice of C influences them.

3. (a) Determine the general solution of the differential equation $y' = 3x^2$.

(b) Graph the particular solutions that correspond to $C = 0$, $C = 4$, and $C = -5$ and comment.

W 4. Graph the particular solution of $y' = 1/x$ for $C = 0$ and graph $y = \ln x$. Explain how the graphs differ and why.

9.2	***SEPARATION OF VARIABLES***

In order to solve differential equations, it is often useful to separate the derivative dy/dx into the two differentials dy and dx. (Hence the name "differential" equations.) In Example 2 of Section 9.1, we had

$$\frac{dy}{dx} = 4x + 1$$

which may be written as

$$dy = (4x + 1)\, dx$$

Integration can then be performed on each side:

$$\int dy = \int (4x + 1)\, dx$$

The result is

$$y = 2x^2 + x + C$$

> *Note*
>
> Technically, a constant is produced on each side (by each integration)—say C_1 on the left and C_2 on the right. We combine them into one constant C on the right.

EXAMPLE 1   Solve the differential equation.

$$\frac{dy}{dx} = \frac{x^2}{y^3}$$

SOLUTION   In this case it is *necessary* to use differential form because we cannot antidifferentiate x^2/y^3 with respect to x. The y^3 poses a problem. However, using differential form, we can write

$$dy = \frac{x^2}{y^3}\, dx$$

Then we can remove the y^3 from the $x^2\, dx$ by multiplying both sides by y^3.

$$y^3 dy = x^2\, dx$$

The variables are now separated—y^3 is with dy and x^2 is with dx. Integration is now possible.

$$\int y^3\, dy = \int x^2\, dx$$

$$\frac{y^4}{4} = \frac{x^3}{3} + C \qquad \text{solution}$$ ◆

The method used to separate the variables and solve the equation in Example 1 is called **separation of variables.** Two additional examples follow.

EXAMPLE 2   Solve $y' = 2ty^2 + 3y^2$.

SOLUTION   The variables are t and y, so in this setting y' means dy/dt. The equation to be solved is then

$$\frac{dy}{dt} = 2ty^2 + 3y^2$$

To separate the variables, begin by factoring out y^2.

$$\frac{dy}{dt} = y^2(2t + 3)$$

Now multiply both sides by dt and divide both sides by y^2. The result is

$$\frac{dy}{y^2} = (2t + 3)\, dt$$

We continue by integrating both sides.

$$\int \frac{1}{y^2} \, dy = \int (2t + 3) \, dt$$

$$\int y^{-2} \, dy = \int (2t + 3) \, dt$$

$$-\frac{1}{y} = t^2 + 3t + C \qquad \text{solution}$$

The solution can also be written in any of these forms:

$$y(t^2 + 3t + C) = -1$$
$$t^2 y + 3ty + Cy = -1$$
$$t^2 y + 3ty + Cy + 1 = 0$$
$$y = \frac{-1}{t^2 + 3t + C}$$

You may prefer the last form, because it shows y *explicitly* in terms of t, whereas the others show y as a function of t implicitly. Unfortunately, you will not always be able to solve for y explicitly, as demonstrated in the next example.   ◆

EXAMPLE 3 Solve $y' = \dfrac{x + 1}{3y^2 + 2y}; \quad y(0) = 1.$

SOLUTION To begin, consider y' as dy/dx.

$$\frac{dy}{dx} = \frac{x + 1}{3y^2 + 2y}$$

Multiplying both sides by dx and by $3y^2 + 2y$ will separate the variables.

$$(3y^2 + 2y) \, dy = (x + 1) \, dx$$

$$\int (3y^2 + 2y) \, dy = \int (x + 1) \, dx$$

$$y^3 + y^2 = \frac{x^2}{2} + x + C$$

To determine C, we use the initial condition $y(0) = 1$; $y = 1$ when $x = 0$.

$$1^3 + 1^2 = 0 + 0 + C \qquad \text{or} \qquad C = 2$$

Thus, the solution is

$$y^3 + y^2 = \frac{x^2}{2} + x + 2 \qquad \text{solution}$$

If desired, you can multiply all terms on both sides by 2. This will eliminate the fraction.

$$2y^3 + 2y^2 = x^2 + 2x + 4$$

or

$$2y^3 + 2y^2 - x^2 - 2x - 4 = 0 \qquad \text{alternative solution}$$

The form of the answer is often based on personal preference, especially in cases where you cannot express y *explicitly* as a function of x. ◆

The next example shows how a differential equation that describes a rate of growth leads to a familiar type of exponential growth formula.

APPLIED

EXAMPLE 4 **BACTERIA GROWTH**

Suppose the rate of growth of bacteria in a culture is 12% per hour. Let A represent the amount of bacteria present at any time t (in hours). Then we can say that the rate of change of A with respect to t is .12 times A, or

$$\frac{dA}{dt} = .12A$$

To solve this equation for A, we begin by writing it in differential form.

$$dA = .12A \; dt$$

$$\frac{dA}{A} = .12 \; dt \qquad \text{Separate the variables.}$$

$$\int \frac{dA}{A} = \int .12 \; dt \qquad \text{Integrate.}$$

$$\ln |A| = .12t + C_1$$

$$\ln A = .12t + C_1 \qquad \text{since } A > 0$$

Changing the equation from logarithmic to exponential form will yield A:

$$A = e^{.12t + C_1}$$

The right-hand side can be simplified. To begin,

$$A = e^{.12t} e^{C_1} \qquad \text{using a law of exponents}$$

Now, because both e and C_1 are constants, it follows that e^{C_1} is a constant. Call it C. Then we have

$$A = Ce^{.12t}$$

Notice that we have derived the exponential growth formula $A = Ce^{kt}$ (from Chapter 5) for the specific case where k is .12. ◆

> *Note*
>
> Recall from Chapter 5 that exponential growth occurs when the rate of increase of A is proportional to the amount present A. We began with $dA/dt = .12A$, which says that the rate of change of A is equal to $.12$ times A. In other words, the rate of change of A is proportional to A.

Keep in mind that the method of separation of variables can be applied only if the variables can indeed be separated. Unfortunately, it is not always possible to accomplish the separation. Many techniques must be learned in order to solve the varieties of differential equations that exist. In fact, there are entire courses and sequences of courses devoted to the methods of solving differential equations.

9.2 Exercises

In Exercises 1–20, solve each differential equation by using separation of variables.

1. $\dfrac{dy}{dx} = 2x$

2. $\dfrac{dy}{dx} = 1 + \sqrt{x}$

3. $\dfrac{dy}{dx} = xy$

4. $\dfrac{dy}{dx} = \dfrac{x}{y}$

5. $\dfrac{dy}{dt} = te^{-y}$

6. $\dfrac{dy}{dt} = ye^{t}$

7. $y' = 6xy^2 + 5y^2$

8. $y' = x^2y - y$

9. $x\,dy + y\,dx = 0$

10. $t\,dy - 2y^2\,dt = 0$

11. $\dfrac{dy}{e^x} = \dfrac{dx}{e^y}$

12. $dy = \dfrac{dx}{\sqrt{y}}$

13. $x^2\dfrac{dy}{dx} - 1 = 0$

14. $\dfrac{dy}{t^3} = \dfrac{dt}{\sqrt{2y+1}}$

15. $2t\,dy - y^3\,dt = 0$

16. $4\,dy + 3\,dx = 0$

17. $x^2\,dx = (1 + x^3)y^4\,dy$

18. $x\sqrt{3+y^2}\,dx - y\sqrt{2+x^2}\,dy = 0$

19. $y' - 2xy = 0 \quad (y > 0)$ **20.** $e^x\,dx - e^y\,dy = 0$

In Exercises 21–30, solve each differential equation by separation of variables. Use the given initial conditions to determine the particular solution.

21. $y' = \dfrac{x}{y}; \quad y(0) = 4$

22. $y' = \dfrac{x+1}{4y}; \quad y(0) = 3$

23. $y' = 2xy; \quad y(0) = 2$

24. $y' = 3\sqrt{xy}; \quad y(0) = 1$

25. $\dfrac{dy}{dx} = 4xe^{-y}; \quad y(0) = 0$ **26.** $\dfrac{dy}{dx} = \dfrac{2x}{e^y}; \quad y(1) = 0$

27. $\dfrac{dy}{dx} = \dfrac{y}{x}; \quad y(1) = e$ **28.** $\dfrac{dy}{dx} = \dfrac{2x-5}{3y^2}; \quad y(0) = 2$

29. $3\dfrac{dy}{dx} = 4x; \quad y(0) = 1$ **30.** $2y\dfrac{dy}{dx} = 1; \quad y(4) = 3$

In Exercises 31–36, write the differential equation that describes the situation. *Do not solve* the equation. Use t for time, unless the situation indicates otherwise.

31. The rate of change of y with respect to x is 3 less than x.

32. The rate of change of y with respect to x is a constant times the product of x and y.

33. (**BACTERIAL INFECTION**) A bacterial infection is growing at the rate of 5% per hour. Let B be the number of bacteria in the infection.

34. (FUNGUS GROWTH) The rate of growth of a fungus is 3% per hour. Let F be the size of the fungus.

35. (RADIOACTIVITY) A mass of radioactive substance *loses* its radioactivity at the rate of 2% per year. Let M be the amount that is radioactive.

36. The value of x is *decreasing* at the rate of twice the square root of x per second.

37. (BACTERIA GROWTH) Suppose the rate of growth of bacteria in a culture is 9% per hour. Let A represent the amount of bacteria present at any time t (in hours). Following Example 4,
   (a) Establish a differential equation that describes the number of bacteria present at any time t.
   (b) Solve the differential equation for A.
   (c) Determine the value of C, assuming there are 3000 bacteria at the beginning.

38. (INTEREST) The amount of money M in an account is increasing at the rate of 9% per year.
   (a) Write a differential equation that describes the amount at any time t.
   (b) Solve the differential equation for A. Assume that the account began with $2000 in it.

39. (GDP GROWTH) Suppose the gross domestic product (GDP) of a small country is $100,000,000, and it increases at the rate of 3% per year.
   (a) Establish a differential equation that describes the amount A of the GDP at any time t.
   (b) Solve the differential equation for A.

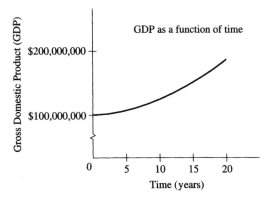

GDP as a function of time

A graph of the solution of the differential equation

40. (INVESTMENT LOSS) An investment is losing value at the rate of 4% per year. Let A be the amount of the investment,

and let t be the time in years. The investment was worth $5000 originally.
   (a) Write a differential equation that describes the value of the investment at any time t.
   (b) Solve the differential equation for A.

41. (DRUG CONCENTRATION) A patient is given 10 milligrams of a drug intravenously, after which the amount present in the bloodstream decreases at the rate of 8% per hour. Let A represent the amount of the drug present at any time t (in hours).
   (a) Establish a differential equation that describes the number of milligrams of the drug in the bloodstream at any time t.
   (b) Solve the differential equation for A. Use the given initial condition to determine the constant.

42. (STIMULUS AND RESPONSE) The Weber-Fechner law (in psychology) offers a relationship between stimulus (S) and response (R).

$$\frac{dR}{dS} = k \cdot \frac{1}{S} \qquad k = \text{constant}$$

   (a) Determine R by solving the differential equation.
   (b) Solve for the added constant C by using the initial condition that response R is 0 for some small stimulus s.
   (c) Use your knowledge of algebra to rewrite the solution from part (b) as

$$R = k \ln \frac{S}{s}$$

43. (INFLATION) If inflation causes the value of money to decline by 5% a year, what will be the value of a dollar in 10 years?

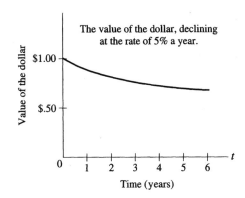

The value of the dollar, declining at the rate of 5% a year.

44. (**INFLATION**) A retired couple have life savings of $200,000. If inflation causes the value of money to decline by 6% a year, how many years will it take to erode the real value of their life savings to $150,000?

45. (**MEDICAL TRACER**) Iodine-131 is used medically as a radioactive tracer to monitor thyroid problems and brain tumors. The rate of decay for iodine-131 is approximately 8.1% per day.
   (a) Establish a differential equation that describes the relationship between the amount of iodine-131 present (A) and the time in days (t).
   (b) Solve the differential equation.
   (c) Determine the half-life of iodine-131. Round your answer to the nearest tenth of a day. (Recall the presentation of *half-life* in Section 5.2. Examples 11 and 12.)

46. (**NUCLEAR TESTING**) As a consequence of testing nuclear weapons in the atmosphere, strontium-90 is now present in our food and water. The rate of decay for strontium-90 is approximately 2.5% per year.
   (a) Establish a differential equation that describes the relationship between the amount of strontium-90 present (A) and the time in years (t).
   (b) Solve the differential equation.
   (c) Determine the half-life of strontium-90. Round your answer to the nearest year.

W 47. Explain in words how an initial condition enables us to determine the value of C. Base your explanation on the assumption that a differential equation contains dy/dx and that the solution is an equation involving x, y, and C.

48. Solve the differential equation

$$\frac{dy}{dx} = y$$

to show that $y = ce^x$ is the only function (or kind of function) that is its own derivative.

49. Determine the equation of a curve if the slope of the tangent line at any point (x, y) is $-4x/9y$ and the curve passes through the point $(0, 2)$.

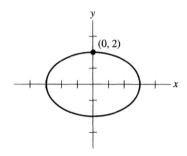

50. Solve the differential equation

$$\frac{dy}{dx} = ky$$

in order to obtain

$$y = Ce^{kx}$$

where $C = e^{C_1}$. This will show that if the rate of change is proportional to the amount present, then the amount at any time is given by an exponential expression.

TECHNOLOGY *EXERCISES*

1. (a) Show that the solution to Exercise 25, namely $e^y = 2x^2 + 1$, can be written as $y = \ln(2x^2 + 1)$.

   (b) Graph the function $y = \ln(2x^2 + 1)$. Is the function defined for all real numbers x?

   (c) Does the derivative exist at $x = 0$? If so, what is its value there?

2. (a) Solve the two differential equations

$$y' = 2xy, \; y(0) = 2 \qquad y' = 1.5xy, \; y(0) = 2$$

   Write each solution in the form $y = Ce^u$, where u is a function of x and C is a constant.

W **(b)** Consider the graphs of the solutions, using $[-4, 4]$ for x and $[0, 25]$ for y. Anticipate and describe the graph of the solution of the following differential equation.

$$y' = 4xy, \; y(0) = 2$$

3. Suppose that inflation causes the value of money to decline by 4% a year. Let y be the value of a dollar at any time x in years.

   (a) Write a differential equation that describes the effect of inflation on the value of a dollar.

   (b) State the initial condition.

   (c) Solve the differential equation and write the solution in $y = f(x)$ form.

   (d) Graph $y = f(x)$ in order to determine when a dollar will be worth only 77¢. Use the windows $[0, 10]$ for x and $[-.5, 1.5]$ for y.

Note   Computer algebra systems can be used to solve differential equations. However, it is not always as simple or straightforward as graphing or determining limits, derivatives, or integrals. *Mathematica* has a **Dsolve** command for this purpose, and *Maple* has a **dsolve** command to solve certain differential equations.

9.3 | *ADDITIONAL APPLICATIONS*

Section 9.2 concluded with an application in which the rate of growth of bacteria was described by a differential equation. The solution was an equation describing exponential growth. The exercises included differential equation settings that led to exponential growth and decay equations, including some that resemble the continuous compounding of interest presented in Chapter 5. Now we will consider an interesting variation on the standard continuous compounding situations.

APPLIED

EXAMPLE 1 **CONTINUOUS COMPOUNDING**

A couple opens a savings account with $2000 and plans to add $400 to the account at the end of each year. The money will earn 5% annual interest compounded continuously.

   (a) Write a differential equation that describes this situation. Let A be the amount in the account at any time t in years.

   (b) Solve the differential equation.

   (c) Determine the amount in the account after 6 years.

SOLUTION   **(a)** The rate of change of A with respect to t is .05 times A *plus* 400. Thus, we have the following differential equation.

$$\frac{dA}{dt} = .05A + 400$$

(b) The differential equation can be solved by separation of variables.

$$dA = (.05A + 400) \, dt$$

$$\frac{dA}{.05A + 400} = dt$$

$$\int \frac{dA}{.05A + 400} = \int dt$$

It follows that

$$\frac{1}{.05} \ln |.05A + 400| = t + C_1$$

$$\ln (.05A + 400) = .05t + .05C_1$$

$$.05A + 400 = e^{.05t + .05C_1} \qquad \text{exponential form}$$

$$.05A + 400 = e^{.05t} e^{.05C_1}$$

The number $e^{.05C_1}$ is a constant. Call it C_2.

$$.05A + 400 = C_2 e^{.05t}$$

$$.05A = C_2 e^{.05t} - 400 \qquad \text{isolating the } A \text{ term}$$

$$A = 20C_2 e^{.05t} - 8000 \qquad \text{solving for } A$$

We can replace the constant $20C_2$ by the simple constant C.

$$A = C e^{.05t} - 8000$$

The value of C can be determined by noting that the account is opened with a $2000 deposit. This means $A = 2000$ when $t = 0$.

$$2000 = C e^{.05(0)} - 8000 \qquad \text{or} \qquad C = 10,000$$

Finally, we have the solution of the differential equation.

$$A = 10,000 e^{.05t} - 8000$$

The graph of the solution is shown in Figure 2.

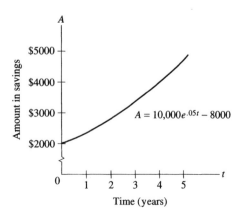

$$A = 10,000 e^{.05t} - 8000$$

Figure 2 The graph of the solution of the differential equation

(c) After 6 years, the balance in the account will be

$$A = 10,000e^{.05(6)} - 8000 \approx 10,000(1.3499) - 8000 = 5499$$

The account balance will be $5499 after 6 years. ◆

Elasticity of demand was presented in Section 4.6. Recall that

$$E = -\frac{p}{x} \cdot \frac{dx}{dp}$$

where E = elasticity of demand, x = demand (quantity), and p = price per unit. When the demand equation was given, we were able to calculate the elasticity for any desired price. The next example shows how the demand can be determined when the elasticity is known.

APPLIED

EXAMPLE 2 **ELASTICITY OF DEMAND**

For a pharmaceutical preparation, the elasticity of demand E is equal to $.05p$. Assume $p = \$60$ when $x = 1$ pint.

(a) Determine price p as a function of quantity demanded x.

(b) Determine quantity demanded x as a function of price p.

SOLUTION **(a)** To begin, the elasticity equation is

$$E = -\frac{p}{x} \cdot \frac{dx}{dp}$$

We can replace E by $.05p$, since it is given in the statement of the example.

$$.05p = -\frac{p}{x} \cdot \frac{dx}{dp}$$

To separate the variables, we begin by multiplying both sides by dp.

$$.05p \, dp = -\frac{p}{x} \, dx$$

$$.05 \, dp = -\frac{dx}{x} \qquad \text{dividing by } p$$

$$\int .05 \, dp = -\int \frac{dx}{x} \qquad \text{integrating}$$

$$.05p = -\ln x + C$$

We can find C by using the condition that $p = 60$ when $x = 1$.

$$.05(60) = -\ln(1) + C$$

$$3 = 0 + C$$

$$C = 3$$

Thus, we have

$$.05p = -\ln x + 3$$
$$.05p = 3 - \ln x$$

Multiplying both sides by 20 will yield the desired form:

$$p = 60 - 20 \ln x$$

See Figure 3 for the graph of the solution.

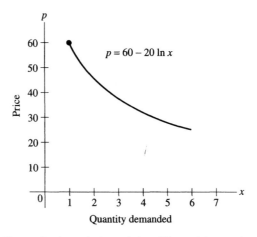

Figure 3 The solution of the differential equation

(b) To express x as a function of p, we need only solve the equation

$$p = 60 - 20 \ln x$$

for x in terms of p. In steps, we have

$$p - 60 = -20 \ln x$$
$$20 \ln x = 60 - p$$
$$\ln x = 3 - .05p$$
$$x = e^{3-.05p}$$

which is the desired result. If we prefer, an alternative form can be obtained. Consider

$$x = e^3 \cdot e^{-.05p} \quad \text{or} \quad x = 20.1e^{-.05p} \qquad \text{using } e^3 \approx 20.1 \qquad \blacklozenge$$

When a warm object is put into cooler surroundings, it cools according to **Newton's law of cooling.**

> **Newton's Law of Cooling**
>
> The rate of change of the temperature of an object is proportional to the difference in temperature between the object and the surrounding environment.

APPLIED

EXAMPLE 3 *NEWTON'S LAW OF COOLING*

An ice cube tray filled with water at room temperature (70°F) is placed into a 20°F freezer. Let T be the temperature of the water after it has been in the freezer for t minutes.

(a) Write a differential equation that applies Newton's law of cooling to this situation.

(b) Solve the differential equation. Consider that after 15 minutes the temperature of the water is 45°.

(c) What will be the temperature of the water after 25 minutes?

(d) From the time the tray is placed into the freezer, how long does it take for the water to reach 32° (freezing temperature)?

SOLUTION **(a)** The rate of change of the temperature of the water is dT/dt. The difference in temperature between the object $(T°)$ and the surrounding environment $(20°)$ is $T - 20°$. Newton's law of cooling says, in this instance, that dT/dt is proportional to $T - 20°$. Thus, for some constant k,

$$\frac{dT}{dt} = k(T - 20)$$

(b) The differential equation can be solved by separating the variables, as

$$\frac{dT}{T - 20} = k\, dt$$

$$\int \frac{dT}{T - 20} = \int k\, dt \qquad \text{integrating}$$

$$\ln |T - 20| = kt + C_1$$

$$T - 20 = e^{kt+C_1}$$

$$T = e^{kt}e^{C_1} + 20$$

Replacing the constant e^{C_1} by C yields

$$T = Ce^{kt} + 20$$

At the beginning, $T = 70°$. In other words, when $t = 0$, $T = 70$. This information can be used to determine C as follows:

$$70 = Ce^0 + 20 \qquad \text{or} \qquad C = 50$$

Replacing C by 50 in the equation gives

$$T = 50e^{kt} + 20$$

The value of k can be determined by noting that after 15 minutes the temperature of the water is $45°$; that is, when $t = 15$, $T = 45$. We have

$$45 = 50e^{k(15)} + 20$$
$$25 = 50e^{15k}$$
$$.5 = e^{15k}$$
$$15k = \ln .5$$
$$k = \frac{\ln .5}{15} \approx \frac{-.6931}{15} \approx -.046$$

Replacing k by $-.046$ in

$$T = 50e^{kt} + 20$$

yields the solution of the differential equation, namely

$$T = 50e^{-.046t} + 20$$

(c) To find the temperature T of the water after 25 minutes, let $t = 25$.

$$T = 50e^{-.046(25)} + 20$$
$$= 50e^{-1.15} + 20$$
$$\approx 50(.3166) + 20$$
$$= 35.83$$

To the nearest degree, the temperature of the water will be $36°$.

(d) The water will reach $32°$ when $T = 32$. Accordingly, we will let $T = 32$ and determine the corresponding t value.

$$32 = 50e^{-.046t} + 20$$
$$12 = 50e^{-.046t}$$
$$.24 = e^{-.046t}$$
$$\ln .24 = -.046t$$
$$-.046t = \ln .24$$
$$t = \frac{\ln .24}{-.046} \approx \frac{-1.427}{-.046} \approx 31.02$$

The water will reach $32°$ in approximately 31 minutes.   ◆

It is interesting to note that coroners use tables obtained by Newton's law of cooling to determine the time of death.

The concept of **logistic growth** was introduced in Section 5.1, where situations were presented in which the environment inhibits what would otherwise be unrestricted exponential growth. The growth of a fish population in a breeding lake was presented in that section.

In logistic growth, the rate of growth is proportional to both the population size and the remaining room for possible growth.

The general form of the differential equation that defines logistic growth is shown next. The presentation that follows shows how a formula for logistic growth can be derived from the differential equation.

Logistic Growth (*Differential Equation*)

$$\frac{dy}{dt} = ky(N - y)$$

y = population t = time

k = a positive constant

N = maximum population possible

Notice that $N - y$ is the remaining room for possible growth.

Because solving differential equations of this type requires considerably more work than usual, we shall solve the general equation in order to obtain a formula to use when logistic growth situations arise.

$$\frac{dy}{dt} = ky(N - y)$$

can be written with variables separated, as

$$\frac{dy}{y(N - y)} = k\,dt$$

which leads to

$$\int \frac{1}{y(N - y)}\,dy = \int k\,dt$$

The form of the integrand on the left side of the equation must be modified before the integration can be performed. The algebra used to rewrite the integrand is called *partial fractions,* and it is beyond the scope of this book. However, we will use the following result that is obtained by using partial fractions. (You can verify the result by adding the fractions on the right side of the equation.)

$$\frac{1}{y(N-y)} = \frac{1}{N}\left(\frac{1}{y} + \frac{1}{N-y}\right)$$

Replacing the integrand on the left by the form above yields

$$\int \frac{1}{N}\left(\frac{1}{y} + \frac{1}{N-y}\right) dy = \int k \, dt$$

Multiplying both sides of the equation by N leads to

$$\int \left(\frac{1}{y} + \frac{1}{N-y}\right) dy = N \int k \, dt$$

$$\int \frac{dy}{y} + \int \frac{dy}{N-y} = Nk \int dt$$

The two integrals on the left yield natural logarithms, and since $y > 0$ and $N - y > 0$, the absolute value symbols are not needed. We have

$$\ln y - \ln (N - y) = Nkt + C_1$$

$$\ln \frac{y}{N-y} = Nkt + C_1$$

$$\frac{y}{N-y} = e^{Nkt+C_1}$$

$$\frac{y}{N-y} = e^{Nkt} \cdot e^{C_1}$$

Replacing the constant e^{C_1} by C yields

$$\frac{y}{N-y} = Ce^{Nkt}$$

Now we can solve for y.

$$y = (N - y)Ce^{Nkt}$$
$$y = NCe^{Nkt} - yCe^{Nkt}$$
$$y + yCe^{Nkt} = NCe^{Nkt}$$
$$(1 + Ce^{Nkt})y = NCe^{Nkt}$$

$$y = \frac{NCe^{Nkt}}{Ce^{Nkt} + 1}$$

If we divide the numerator and denominator (all three terms) by Ce^{Nkt}, we obtain the simpler result shown next (in which $1/C$ is renamed C).

> ### Logistic Growth (*Solution*)
>
> $$y = \frac{N}{1 + Ce^{-Nkt}}$$
>
> y = population $\qquad t$ = time
> k, C = positive constants
> N = maximum population possible

APPLIED

EXAMPLE 4 **LOGISTIC GROWTH OF A FISH POPULATION**

50 fish are placed into a breeding lake that can support at most 2000 fish. After 10 months, it is estimated that the fish population has risen to 400. Assume that the rate at which the fish population grows is proportional to both the population and the remaining room for population growth. Obtain a formula that gives the fish population y at any time t.

SOLUTION The statement of the example makes it clear that this is a logistic growth situation. Time t will be measured in months. Here $N = 2000$ and

$$y = \frac{N}{1 + Ce^{-Nkt}}$$

$$y = \frac{2000}{1 + Ce^{-2000kt}} \qquad \text{using 2000 for } N$$

There are 50 fish in the lake initially. This means $y = 50$ when $t = 0$. Using these values in the equation will enable us to determine C.

$$50 = \frac{2000}{1 + Ce^{-2000(k)(0)}}$$

$$50 = \frac{2000}{1 + C \cdot 1}$$

$$50 + 50C = 2000$$

$$50C = 1950$$

$$C = 39$$

Thus far we have

$$y = \frac{2000}{1 + 39e^{-2000kt}}$$

To determine k, use the given condition that when $t = 10$, $y = 400$.

$$400 = \frac{2000}{1 + 39e^{-2000(k)(10)}}$$

$$400 = \frac{2000}{1 + 39e^{-20,000k}}$$

$$400 + 15,600e^{-20,000k} = 2000$$

$$e^{-20,000k} \approx .1026$$

$$-20,000k \approx \ln .1026$$

$$k \approx .00011$$

We can now conclude that the logistic growth equation that describes the fish population growth is

$$y = \frac{2000}{1 + 39e^{-.22t}}$$

A graph of the equation is shown in Figure 4.

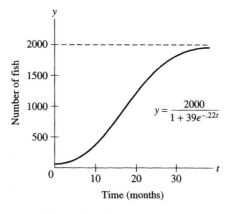

Figure 4 The graph of a logistic growth function ◆

9.3   Exercises

1. (SAVINGS ACCOUNT) Juanita opens a savings account with $3000 and plans to add $500 to the account at the end of each year. The money will earn 8% annual interest compounded continuously.
   (a) Establish a differential equation and solve it. Let A be the amount in the account at time t years.

(b) Find the amount in the account after 9 years.

2. (ANNUITY) Robert creates an annuity by placing $40,000 into a bank account. The bank pays 8% annual interest compounded continuously on the balance in the account.

At the end of each year, the bank withdraws $5000 from his account and sends him a check for $5000.

(a) Write a differential equation that describes this situation. Let A be the balance in the account at any time t (in years).

(b) Solve the differential equation.

(c) How much is in the account after 7 years?

3. *(NATIONAL DEBT)* Suppose a country has a national debt of $10,000,000 and must pay interest on that debt at the rate of 5% per year compounded continuously. Also, at the end of each year, the country is able to pay off $200,000 of the debt.

(a) Write a differential equation that describes this situation. Let A be the amount of debt at any time t in years.

(b) Solve the differential equation.

(c) What is the country's debt after 4 years?

W (d) Comment on your answer to part (c).

4. *(NATIONAL DEBT)* Redo all parts of Exercise 3 assuming instead that the country decides to pay off $1,000,000 of the debt each year.

5. *(NATIONAL DEBT)* Redo parts (a) through (c) of Exercise 3 assuming that instead of paying off $200,000 of the debt each year, the country increases its debt by $200,000 each year.

6. *(ELASTICITY OF DEMAND)* Assume that the elasticity of demand E is $.04p$ and that $p = 100$ when $x = 1$. Determine price p as a function of quantity demanded x.

7. *(ELASTICITY OF DEMAND)* For a commodity, the elasticity of demand E is equal to $.1p$. Assume that $p = 20$ when $x = 1$. Determine price p as a function of quantity demanded x.

8. *(COFFEE TEMPERATURE)* A restaurant serves you 200°F coffee. After 1 minute, it is 190° (still too hot to drink). If you wait another 5 minutes, how hot will it be then? Assume that the temperature inside the restaurant is 75°.

9. *(MELTING ICE)* Suppose the ice cube tray of Example 3 has been in the 20°F freezer for a month and is removed and placed in a 70° room. *Newton's law of cooling applies to such a "warming" situation as well.*

(a) Write a differential equation to describe this situation.

(b) Solve the differential equation, assuming that the temperature of the tray is 40° after 10 minutes.

10. *(COOKING A ROAST)* A raw brisket of beef has been stored in a 40°F refrigerator. It is removed and placed in a 350° oven. After 40 minutes, the temperature of the meat is 100°. How many minutes does it take to cook the roast until it is done (that is, 160°)?

11. *(COOLING)* In an experiment, a glass beaker has been heated to a temperature of 400°F. The heat is removed and the beaker is allowed to cool in the 70° air of the laboratory. If the beaker's temperature is 300° after 1 minute, how long does it take the 400° beaker to cool down to 100°?

12. *(FISH POPULATION)* Consider Example 4.

(a) What is the fish population after 18 months?

(b) If the lake can, instead, support 4000 fish, what is the fish population after 18 months?

13. *(SPREAD OF FLU)* Flu is spreading through a city at a rate proportional to the product of the number of people who have the flu and the number of people who do not. There are 40,000 people in the city. At the beginning of the outbreak, 200 people had the flu. Five days later, 400 people had the flu.

(a) Obtain an equation that will indicate the number of people who have been infected y after any number of days t.

(b) How long will it take to infect 5000 people?

14. *(FRUIT FLY POPULATION)* The rate at which a contained fruit fly colony is growing is proportional to both the population and the remaining room for population growth. The colony began with 4 flies. A week later there were 10. If the environment can support at most 80 flies, how many flies will there be after 3 weeks?

15. *(SPREAD OF A RUMOR)* A rumor spreads through a school at a rate proportional to the product of the number of students who have heard it and the number who have not yet heard it. Suppose 4 students start a rumor, and after two days 30 students have heard it. If there are 2000 students in the school, how long will it take before half the school has heard the rumor?

W 16. In Example 2, part (a), we had the integration

$$-\int \frac{dx}{x} = -\ln x + C$$

Explain why the right-hand side is not $-\ln |x| + C$. In other words, why is the absolute value symbol not written here?

~~TECHNOLOGY~~ *E X E R C I S E S*

1. Beginning with x in $[0, 25]$ and y in $[0, 35]$, graph the logistic growth function

$$y = \frac{30}{1 + 12e^{-.4x}}$$

   (a) Is the curve concave up or concave down on $(50, \infty)$?

   (b) Is the following inequality true or false?

$$\frac{d^2y}{dx^2} < 0 \quad \text{for } x \text{ in } (3, \infty)$$

2. Graph the logistic growth function

$$y = \frac{14}{1 + 3e^{-.22x}}$$

   Also graph the line $y = 14$. Begin with x in $[0, 30]$ and y in $[3, 15]$.

   (a) Examine the graphs for large values of x. What is the relationship between the logistic curve and the line?

   (b) Which of the following statements are true for this logistic growth function?

   (i) $\dfrac{dy}{dx} > 0$ for $x > 0$ **(ii)** $\dfrac{d^2y}{dx^2} > 0$ for $x > 0$

   (iii) $\dfrac{dy}{dx} = 0$ for large values of x **(iv)** $\dfrac{d^2y}{dx^2} < 0$ for $x > 17$

W 3. Graph the price function obtained in Exercise 6, namely $p = 100 - 25 \ln x$. Use x in $[1, 75]$ and p in $[-20, 90]$.

   (a) From the graph, can the quantity x be any positive number? Explain.

   (b) The graph shows that as the price decreases, the quantity demanded _____.

   (c) The graph shows that as the price increases, the quantity demanded _____.

4. In Example 3, we found that the temperature T of water in a 20°F freezer for t minutes was given by $T = 50e^{-.046t} + 20$. Graph the temperature function for t in $[0, 60]$ and T in $[-20, 80]$.

   (a) From the graph, determine the temperature of the water (ice) when it has been in the freezer for 40 minutes.

   (b) From the graph, determine when the water has reached a temperature of 38°.

W (c) If you follow the graph out far enough, will it fall below the line $T = 20$? Explain how the mathematics is consistent with the statement of the problem.

5. In Example 4, we found that the number of fish y in a breeding lake at any time t months is

$$y = \frac{2000}{1 + 39e^{-.22t}}$$

Graph the function using t in $[0, 50]$ and y in $[0, 2200]$.

(a) From the graph, determine the number of fish in the lake at $t = 21$ months.

(b) From the graph, determine when the fish population reaches 1815.

9.4 A NUMERICAL METHOD

In Chapter 7, numerical methods of integration were introduced to approximate the value of definite integrals that could not be evaluated by ordinary methods of integration. Similar situations arise with differential equations, because many differential equations cannot be solved by any method, even methods studied in advanced courses in differential equations.

The numerical method chosen for use here is called **Euler's method,** named for the Swiss mathematician Leonhard Euler. The method is used to solve (by approximation) one particular form of differential equation, namely the form $y' = g(x,y)$, where $g(x,y)$ represents an expression involving both x and y. The procedure is relatively simple to use and understand. Although other methods may provide greater accuracy, they are beyond the scope of this book.

Numerical approximations to the solution of a differential equation have one particularly interesting aspect. Whereas the exact equation is a function defined for all x in an interval, the approximate solution consists of specific y values obtained for several specific x values x_1, x_2, x_3, and so on, in an interval.

The exact solution of the differential equation $y' = g(x,y)$ having initial condition $f(x_0) = y_0$ is $y = f(x)$. The problem of solving the differential equation subject to a condition such as $f(x_0) = y_0$ is called an **initial value problem.** A typical solution might have a graph such as the one shown in Figure 5.

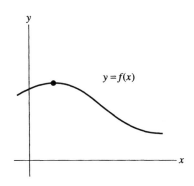

Figure 5 Graph of a solution

Euler's method approximates the graph of the exact solution by using a series of connected line segments. The first line segment is tangent to the graph of $y = f(x)$ at the point (x_0, y_0). It begins at the point (x_0, y_0) and ends at the point (x_1, y_1). As shown in Figure 6, y_1 is not the exact solution corresponding to the x value x_1; it is merely an approximation. The second line segment begins at point (x_1, y_1) and has the same slope as the graph of $y = f(x)$ at $x = x_1$. The segment ends at (x_2, y_2). See Figure 7. Approximations may be improved by making Δx smaller—that is, reducing the width of the intervals from x_0 to x_1, from x_1 to x_2, and so on.

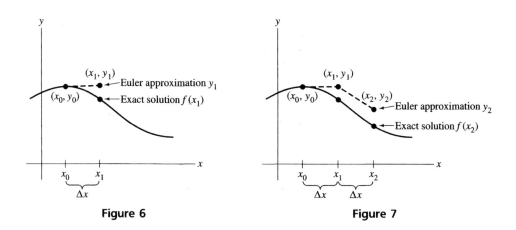

Figure 6   **Figure 7**

The slope of the first line segment is $f'(x_0)$. Furthermore, the equation $y' = g(x, y)$ can be considered as $f'(x) = g(x, y)$. This means that the slope of the first line segment is $g(x_0, y_0)$. Since that line passes through the points (x_0, y_0) and (x_1, y_1), we have

$$g(x_0, y_0) = \frac{y_1 - y_0}{x_1 - x_0}$$

This equation can be rewritten as follows.

$$y_1 = y_0 + g(x_0, y_0)(x_1 - x_0)$$

or

$$y_1 = y_0 + g(x_0, y_0)\, \Delta x$$

where y_1 is an approximation to $f(x_1)$.

Similarly, the second line segment, which connects (x_1, y_1) and (x_2, y_2), gives us

$$y_2 = y_1 + g(x_1, y_1)\, \Delta x$$

In general,

$$y_{i+1} = y_i + g(x_i, y_i)\, \Delta x$$

Euler's Method

The differential equation

$$y' = g(x, y), \qquad y(x_0) = y_0$$

has the approximate solution

$$y_{i+1} = y_i + g(x_i, y_i)\, \Delta x$$

where $i = 0, 1, 2, 3, \ldots, n-1$

$$\Delta x = \frac{x_n - x_0}{n} \quad \text{on } [x_0, x_n]$$

$$x_{i+1} = x_i + \Delta x$$

Note

In previous sections, the solution (the *exact* solution) was an equation. The numerical approximation we obtain here will be a specific y corresponding to a specific x or several specific y values in an interval.

Recall the notation used for initial conditions—that $y(0)$ is the value of y when $x = 0$, and $y(1)$ is the value of y when $x = 1$. We will extend the use of this notation to any x value used in Euler's method, whether for initial conditions or otherwise. Thus, $y(.4)$ is the y value when $x = .4$.

EXAMPLE 1 Consider the initial value problem

$$y' = 2xy \qquad y(0) = 1$$

Use Euler's method with $\Delta x = .1$ to obtain an approximate value of $y(.6)$. Round results to four decimal places (when they contain more than four decimal digits).

SOLUTION The differential equation $y' = 2xy$ fits the form $y' = g(x, y)$. Here we have

$$g(x, y) = 2xy \qquad \Delta x = .1 \qquad x_0 = 0 \qquad y_0 = 1$$

and

$$y_{i+1} = y_i + g(x_i, y_i)\, \Delta x$$

Since $x_0 = 0$ and $\Delta x = .1$, it follows that $x_1 = .1$, $x_2 = .2$, $x_3 = .3$, $x_4 = .4$, $x_5 = .5$, and $x_6 = .6$. In order to obtain $y(.6)$, we must first obtain $y(.1)$, $y(.2)$, $y(.3)$, $y(.4)$, and $y(.5)$.

To begin, let $i = 0$. Then we have

$$y_1 = y_0 + g(x_0, y_0)\, \Delta x$$
$$= y_0 + 2x_0 y_0\, \Delta x$$
$$= 1 + 2(0)(1)(.1) = 1$$

Since y_1 is $y(.1)$, we have $y(.1) = 1$. Similarly,

$$y_2 = y_1 + 2x_1 y_1\, \Delta x$$
$$= 1 + 2(.1)(1)(.1) = 1.02$$

or $y_2 = y(.2) = 1.02$. Continuing,

$$y_3 = y_2 + 2x_2 y_2\, \Delta x$$
$$= 1.02 + 2(.2)(1.02)(.1) = 1.0608$$

or $y_3 = y(.3) = 1.0608$.

The other results are as follows. For practice, you may want to verify them.

$$y_4 = y(.4) = 1.1244$$
$$y_5 = y(.5) = 1.2144$$
$$y_6 = y(.6) = 1.3358$$

The approximate value of $y(.6)$ is 1.3358.   ♦

The differential equation of Example 1 can be solved by separation of variables. One result, rounded to four decimal places, is $y(.6) = 1.4333$. (Exercise 29 requests that you verify this result.)

The table below compares the approximations we have obtained with the exact values (rounded to four decimal places) that can be determined, since this differential equation is one we can solve.

x_i	approximate y_i	exact y_i
.1	1.0000	1.0101
.2	1.0200	1.0408
.3	1.0608	1.0942
.4	1.1244	1.1735
.5	1.2144	1.2840
.6	1.3358	1.4333

Figure 8 provides a visual comparison of the approximations with the exact solutions. Two graphs are shown—one passing through the approximations we have obtained and the other passing through the exact solutions.

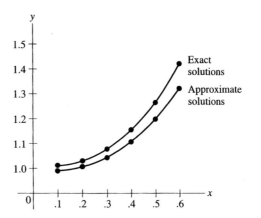

Figure 8 Exact and approximate solutions

The approximations obtained by using Euler's method in Example 1 can be improved by using a smaller value for Δx—say .05. By contrast, the approximations would be worse if a larger Δx (say .2) had been used. The table below shows y_i obtained using $\Delta x = .05$ and $\Delta x = .2$, as well as $\Delta x = .1$ and the exact y_i values.

x_i	**Example 1** $y_i(\Delta x = .1)$	**better** $y_i (\Delta x = .05)$	**worse** $y_i (\Delta x = .2)$	**exact** y_i
.2	1.0200	1.0303	1.0000	1.0408
.4	1.1244	1.1483	1.0800	1.1735
.6	1.3358	1.3824	1.2528	1.4333

In the next example, we apply Euler's method to an equation that cannot be solved by separation of variables.

EXAMPLE 2   Use Euler's method with $\Delta x = .05$ to obtain the approximate solution to the initial value problem

$$y' = x - y^2 \qquad y(1) = 0$$

for all x_i in the interval $[1, 1.2]$. Round results to four decimal places (when they contain more than four decimal digits).

SOLUTION   The differential equation $y' = x - y^2$ fits the form $y' = g(x, y)$. We have

$$g(x, y) = x - y^2 \qquad \Delta x = .05 \qquad x_0 = 1 \qquad y_0 = 0$$

and

$$y_{i+1} = y_i + g(x_i, y_i) \, \Delta x$$

Since $x_0 = 1$ and $\Delta x = .05$, it follows that $x_1 = 1.05$, $x_2 = 1.10$, $x_3 = 1.15$, and $x_4 = 1.20$. We will use Euler's method to obtain $y(1.05)$, $y(1.10)$, $y(1.15)$, and $y(1.20)$.

Keep in mind the notation: $y_1 = y(1.05)$, $y_2 = y(1.10)$, $y_3 = y(1.15)$, and $y_4 = y(1.20)$.

$$y_1 = y_0 + g(x_0, y_0)\,\Delta x$$
$$= 0 + [1 - (0)^2](.05) = .05$$

Thus, $y(1.05) = .05$. Similarly,

$$y_2 = y_1 + g(x_1, y_1)\,\Delta x$$
$$= .05 + [1.05 - (.05)^2](.05)$$
$$= .05 + (1.0475)(.05) = .1024$$

$$y_3 = y_2 + g(x_2, y_2)\,\Delta x$$
$$= .1024 + [1.10 - (.1024)^2](.05)$$
$$= .1024 + (1.0895)(.05) = .1569$$

and (you can verify that)

$$y_4 = .2132$$

Thus, we have the approximate solutions

$$y(1.05) = .05$$
$$y(1.10) = .1024$$
$$y(1.15) = .1569$$
$$y(1.20) = .2132$$ ◆

9.4   Exercises

In Exercises 1–10, use Euler's method to obtain the requested approximation. Round results to four decimal places.

1. $y' = 4xy$, $y(1) = 2$, $\Delta x = .1$. Find $y(1.3)$.

2. $y' = \dfrac{y}{x}$, $y(1) = 3$, $\Delta x = .1$. Find $y(1.3)$.

3. $y' = x + y$, $y(0) = 1$, $\Delta x = .1$. Find $y(.4)$.

4. $y' = x - y$, $y(0) = -3$, $\Delta x = .1$. Find $y(.4)$.

5. $y' = x^2 + y^2$, $y(0) = 1$, $\Delta x = .1$. Find $y(.5)$.

6. $y' = x\sqrt{y}$, $y(0) = 0$, $\Delta x = .1$. Find $y(.5)$.

7. $y' = 2xy - y$, $y(1) = 2$, $\Delta x = .05$. Find $y(1.2)$.

8. $y' = xy + x$, $y(0) = 4$, $\Delta x = .05$. Find $y(.2)$.

9. $y' = 1 + e^x$, $y(0) = 1$, $\Delta x = .05$. Find $y(.3)$.

10. $y' = 5 - 2e^x$, $y(0) = 4$, $\Delta x = .05$. Find $y(.3)$.

11. In Exercise 9 you obtained $y(.3)$. Now obtain the exact solution, $f(.3)$, by solving the differential equation and then using the fact that $f(0) = 1$. Compare the results.

12. In Exercise 2 you obtained $y(1.3)$. Now obtain the exact solution, $f(1.3)$, by solving the differential equation and then using the fact that $f(1) = 3$. Compare the results.

13. In Exercise 7 you obtained $y(1.2)$. Now obtain the exact solution, $f(1.2)$, by solving the differential equation and then using the fact that $f(1) = 2$. Compare the results.

14. In Exercise 6, you obtained $y(.5)$. Now obtain the exact solution, $f(.5)$, by solving the differential equation and then using the fact that $f(0) = 0$. Compare the results.

In Exercises 15–22, use Euler's method to obtain the approximate solution for all x_i in the given interval. Round results to four decimal places.

15. $y' = xy + x$, $y(0) = 1$, $[0, .5]$, $\Delta x = .1$

16. $y' = \dfrac{2x}{y}$, $y(1) = 1$, $[1, 1.5]$, $\Delta x = .1$

17. $y' = x - y$, $y(0) = 3$, $[0, .3]$, $\Delta x = .05$

18. $y' = x^2 + y^2$, $y(0) = 1$, $[0, .3]$, $\Delta x = .05$

19. $y' = 6 - 2y$, $y(0) = 2$, $[0, .6]$, $\Delta x = .1$

20. $y' = 2xy + 4x$, $y(0) = 1$, $[0, .6]$, $\Delta x = .1$

21. $y' = 2xy - y$, $y(1) = 1$, $[1, 1.5]$, $\Delta x = .1$

22. $y' = 3x^2y + 2xy$, $y(1) = 1$, $[1, 1.5]$, $\Delta x = .1$

23. (*ANIMAL POPULATION*) An animal population is changing according to $dn/dt = g(t, n)$, where n is the number of animals and t is the time in months. At the beginning there are 357 animals. State the initial condition using the appropriate notation.

24. (*CORPORATION DEBT*) A corporation's debt is changing according to $dx/dt = g(t, x)$, where x is the debt in dollars and t is the time in weeks. After 4 weeks, the corporation's debt is $15,700. State this condition using the notation of the section.

W **25.** (*MOLD GROWTH*) Suppose a mold is growing at the rate of $dy/dt = g(t, y)$ milligrams per hour. Explain the meaning of $y(3) = 40$ using words and units of measure.

W **26.** (*PRINTER SALES*) A laser printer manufacturer finds that sales are changing according to $dy/dt = g(t, y)$ printers per week. Explain the meaning of $y(5) = 210$ using words and units of measure.

27. (*SPREAD OF A RUMOR*) Suppose a rumor spreads through a high school at the rate dn/dt given by

$$n' = \frac{dn}{dt} = .1(1000 - n)\sqrt{n}$$

where n is the number of students who have heard the rumor at time t (hours). Originally, 10 students heard (or started) the rumor; that is, $n(0) = 10$. Use Euler's method with $\Delta t = .25$ to determine the approximate number of students who have heard the rumor after 1 hour.

28. (*POLITICS*) A politician who is not well known uses various media in an attempt to become better known in her political district. As a result, she becomes known at the rate dn/dt given by

$$n' = \frac{dn}{dt} = .001(30{,}000 - n)\sqrt{n}$$

where n is the number of people who are familiar with her political beliefs at time t (days). After 10 days, 2400 people know her views; that is, $n(10) = 2400$. Use Euler's method with $\Delta t = 1$ to determine the approximate number of people who know her views after 2 weeks.

29. Solve the differential equation of Example 1 by using separation of variables. Then use the solution to show that $f(.6) = 1.4333$, correct to four decimal places.

TECHNOLOGY *EXERCISES*

In Exercises 1–6, use program 4 (Euler's method) to obtain the requested approximations. You will need to edit one line of the program in order to introduce the $g(x, y)$ for the specific differential equation. The program shown here (for the TI–81 and TI-82) contains $g(x, y) = 2xy$,

```
Prgm4:EULER
:Disp "DELTA X"
:Input D
:Disp "X0"
:Input X
:Disp "Y0"
:Input Y
:Disp "N"
:Input N
:1→I
:Lb1 1
:2*X*Y→G
:I+1→I
:Y+G*D→Y
:X+D→X
:Disp Y
:If I≤N
:Goto 1
:End
```

The expression for $g(x,y)$ must be edited into the program each time, to correspond to the particular differential equation being solved. Here $g(x, y) = 2xy$, the function of Example 1.

which fits Example 1. When executing, the program will request Δx, x_0, y_0, and the number N of approximations you seek. For Example 1, be ready to respond with .1 for Δx, 0 for x_0, 1 for y_0, and 6 for N. Your output will be the (six) values for y_1, y_2, y_3, y_4, y_5, and y_6.

1. Do Example 1 and continue it to obtain y_1 through y_7.

2. Do Example 2 and continue it to obtain y_1 through y_7.

3. Do Exercise 15 to obtain y_1 through y_5.

4. Do Exercise 16 to obtain y_1 through y_5.

5. Do Exercise 19 to obtain y_1 through y_6.

6. Do Exercise 20 to obtain y_1 through y_6.

Note You may have access to computer software or a calculator capable of using another method of approximation. If so, you may want to try it on Exercises 5, 7, 19, and 21.

Key Terms and Ideas

differential equation	particular solution	logistic growth
solution	initial conditions	Euler's method
general solution	separation of variables	initial value problem

Review Exercises for Chapter 9

1. Show that $y = 1 - 6x^2$ is a solution of the differential equation $xy' = 2y - 2$.

2. Show that $y = \ln x$ is a solution of the differential equation $5x^2y' + x^3y'' = 4x$.

Solve each differential equation in Exercises 3–10.

3. $y' = 1 - x^3$

4. $y' = 5 - e^{3x}$

5. $x^3 \, dy = dx$

6. $y' = 3xy$

7. $y \, dx - x \, dy = 0$

8. $e^{-x} \, dy = e^{-y} \, dx$

9. $\dfrac{dy}{t} - \dfrac{dt}{y} = 0$

10. $5 \, dt + 4 \, dy = 0$

Solve each differential equation in Exercises 11–14.

11. $y' = \dfrac{2}{\sqrt{x}}$; $y(1) = 5$

12. $y' = 4e^{.02x}$; $y(0) = 280$

13. $dy = x\sqrt{y} \, dx$; $y(0) = 9$

14. $xy\dfrac{dy}{dx} = 1$; $y(1) = 4$

15. (*BACTERIA GROWTH*) Suppose bacteria are growing at a

rate of 8% per hour, and let A represent the number of bacteria present at any time t (in hours).

(a) Establish a differential equation that describes this situation.

(b) Solve the differential equation for A.

(c) Determine the constant C if there were 2000 bacteria present at the beginning.

16. **(INTEREST ON SAVINGS)** Let A be the amount of money (dollars) in a savings account, and suppose the interest rate on the money is 6% per year.

(a) Establish a differential equation that describes this situation.

(b) Solve the differential equation for A.

(c) Determine the constant C if there was $1500 in the account at the beginning.

17. **(REVENUE)** Solve the differential equation in order to find the revenue function.

$$R'(x) = 12 + .04x; \quad R(0) = 0$$

18. **(LOGISTIC GROWTH)** The rate of change of the fish population in a lake is given by the logistic growth differential equation

$$\frac{dy}{dt} = .0002y(3000 - y); \quad y(0) = 60$$

Use the logistic growth solution formula to solve for y, the number of fish in the lake at any time t.

19. **(ELASTICITY OF DEMAND)** The elasticity of demand is $.02p$, and $p = 50$ when $x = 1$. Determine price p as a function of quantity demanded x.

20. **(LAW OF COOLING)** From Newton's law of cooling, we get the differential equation

$$\frac{dT}{dt} = k(T - T_F)$$

Follow the approach of Section 9.3, Example 3, part (b), to show in steps that the general solution is

$$T = (T_0 - T_F)e^{kt} + T_F$$

where T_0 is the initial temperature of the water and T_F is the temperature of the freezer.

In Exercises 21–22, use Euler's method to obtain the approximate solution for all x_i in the given interval. Round the results to four decimal places.

21. $y' = 4xy^2$, $y(0) = 1$, $[0, .5]$, $\Delta x = .1$

22. $y' = 3x^2y$, $y(0) = 0$, $[0, .5]$, $\Delta x = .1$

23. **(ANIMAL POPULATION)** Let N be the number of animals in a population at any time t. Also, the birth and death rates are the constants b and d, respectively. Then

$$\frac{dN}{dt} = bN - dN$$

W (a) Explain in words what the differential equation says.

(b) Solve the differential equation to obtain

$$N = N_0 e^{(b-d)t}$$

where N_0 is the initial population e^C for some constant C.

W (c) What happens to the population if $b < d$?

W (d) What happens to the population if $b > d$?

Chapter Projects and Essays

Many of the projects and essays lend themselves to group activity, although most can be completed by individual effort.

1. APPLICATIONS OF DIFFERENTIAL EQUATIONS

BACKGROUND This chapter includes a variety of applications of differential equations, but only those that can be readily solved by the separation of variables. There are many other kinds of differential equations and associated applications.

THE PROJECT   Select one of the following fields of study:

  1. Economics   **2.** Psychology/sociology

  3. Biology/medicine **4.** Chemistry/physical science

Seek out books, journals, faculty members, or fellow students in order to obtain a list of differential equations that are applied in that field. Indicate what each equation describes or represents, and include the meaning of all variables in the equation. Do not solve the differential equations.

2. THE BERNOULLI FAMILY

BACKGROUND   The Bernoulli brothers, Jakob and Johann, worked extensively in the study of differential equations and other areas of mathematics. They were the first generation of a Swiss family that produced a total of eight talented mathematicians.

THE PROJECT   Using books on the history of mathematics and other sources, write an essay on one of the following topics.

  1. Johann Bernoulli—his accomplishments and his jealous quarrels with other mathematicians

  2. The accomplishments of Jakob Bernoulli and Daniel Bernoulli.

  3. The Bernoulli family—three generations of mathematicians and scientists

MULTIVARIABLE CALCULUS

10

A variety of ingredients goes into manufacturing consumer goods like frozen dinners. Along with the basic cost of food, costs like packaging, machinery maintenance and labor must be considered when assessing the overall profitability of a frozen-food venture. Cost functions for such goods involve two or more variables, and can be used to obtain vital economic information.

Up to this point we have worked exclusively with functions of one variable. Yet there are many applications of functions of two or more variables. For example, costs, revenues, and profits often depend on more than one variable.

After we introduce functions, graphs, and their applications, we will consider the calculus of functions of two or more variables. The presentation will include differentiation, maximum/minimum concepts, differentials, integrals, and other ideas and applications.

10.1 | *FUNCTIONS OF SEVERAL VARIABLES*

The notation $f(x)$ used for functions of one variable can be extended to $f(x, y)$ for **functions of two variables** and $f(x, y, z)$ for **functions of three variables.** Functions of four or more variables will not be used in this text.

Let us consider an example of a function $z = f(x, y)$ of two variables. The equation that defines the function can be written in either of the forms shown next.

$$z = x^2 + 5xy \qquad \text{or} \qquad f(x, y) = x^2 + 5xy$$

For every x and y supplied, there is a corresponding $f(x, y)$ value (or z value). If $x = 2$ and $y = 4$, then

$$z = (2)^2 + 5(2)(4) = 44 \qquad \text{or} \qquad f(2, 4) = 44$$

EXAMPLE 1   Let $f(x, y) = 10xy + 3$. Find $f(4, 9)$.

SOLUTION $f(4, 9)$ is the number obtained when 4 is used for x and 9 is used for y in the equation that defines the function. If

$$f(x, y) = 10xy + 3$$

then

$$f(4, 9) = 10(4)(9) + 3 = 363 \qquad \blacklozenge$$

EXAMPLE 2   Let $z = 5e^{xy}$. Find z when $x = 4$ and $y = 0$.

SOLUTION   Using 4 for x and 0 for y yields

$$z = 5e^{xy} = 5e^{(4)(0)} = 5e^0 = 5 \cdot 1 = 5 \qquad \blacklozenge$$

EXAMPLE 3   VOLUME OF A CONE

Consider the volume V of a cone as a function of two variables.

SOLUTION The volume of a cone is $\frac{1}{3}\pi r^2 h$, where r is the radius of the base of the cone and h is its height. Clearly, volume V is a function of two variables, r and h. The function can be given either as $V = \frac{1}{3}\pi r^2 h$ or as $V(r, h) = \frac{1}{3}\pi r^2 h$. Notice that π is a constant; $\pi \approx 3.14$. (See Figure 1.)

Figure 1

◆

EXAMPLE 4   COST OF MAKING CHAIRS

A furniture manufacturer makes chairs from oak and from maple. If the oak chairs cost \$75 each to make and the maple chairs cost \$50 each, determine the cost function for x oak chairs and y maple chairs.

SOLUTION Since it costs \$75 to make each oak chair, it will cost $75x$ dollars to make x oak chairs. Similarly, it costs $50y$ dollars to make y maple chairs. Thus, it costs $75x + 50y$ dollars to make all the chairs. Using C as the cost function, we have

$$C(x, y) = 75x + 50y$$

◆

EXAMPLE 5   CEPHALIC INDEX

Anthropologists use head shape as one means of classifying humans. The *cephalic index C* is given by

$$C(w, l) = 100\frac{w}{l}$$

where w is the width and l is the length of the person's head. (Both measurements are made across the top of the head.)

(a) Find the cephalic index of a person whose head has width 6 inches and length 8 inches.

(b) Find $C(16, 20)$, where the measurements are in centimeters.

SOLUTION **(a)** We seek $C(6, 8)$.

$$C(6, 8) = 100 \cdot \frac{6}{8} = 75$$

The cephalic index is 75.

(b) We calculate $C(16, 20)$.

$$C(16, 20) = 100 \cdot \frac{16}{20} = 80$$

The cephalic index is 80.

◆

The Cobb-Douglas Production Function

In economics, the **Cobb-Douglas production function** specifies how the number of units of a product manufactured depends upon the amounts spent on labor and capital. "Capital" means buildings, machinery, and other things needed in the production process. If x represents the number of units of labor and y represents the number of units of capital, then the number of units produced, $f(x, y)$, is given by

$$f(x, y) = Cx^a y^{1-a}$$

The number C is a positive constant, and a is a positive number less than 1. The exponents are a and $1 - a$, which means the sum of the exponents is 1. Here are two examples of Cobb-Douglas production functions.

$$f(x, y) = 20x^{.4}y^{.6} \qquad f(x, y) = x^{2/3}y^{1/3}$$

Ordinarily, units of labor are "person hours" and units of capital are "dollars," "hundreds of dollars," or the like.

EXAMPLE 6   *COBB-DOUGLAS PRODUCTION FUNCTION*

Given the Cobb-Douglas production function $f(x, y) = 20x^{.4}y^{.6}$, determine the number of units produced using 1200 units of labor and 2000 units of capital.

SOLUTION   The number of units produced is $f(1200, 2000)$.

$$f(1200, 2000) = 20(1200)^{.4}(2000)^{.6} \approx 20(17.05)(95.64) \approx 32{,}613 \text{ units} \qquad \blacklozenge$$

Graphs

A function $z = f(x, y)$ can be graphed in a **three-dimensional rectangular coordinate system.** When an x value and a y value are supplied, a corresponding z value is determined. The points are of the form (x, y, z). Because for every x-y pair there is a corresponding z value, the collection of all the points (x, y, z) of $z = f(x, y)$ forms a surface. An example of such a surface is shown in Figure 2, graphed in a three-dimensional rectangular coordinate system.

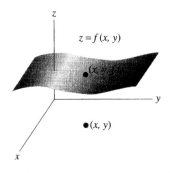

Figure 2 The graph of a surface, $z = f(x, y)$

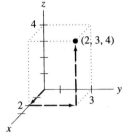

Figure 3
Plotting the point (2, 3, 4)

Next, we will plot two points in order to provide some feeling for three-dimensional plotting and graphing. First, consider the point (2, 3, 4). To plot the point, begin at the origin (where the x, y, and z axes meet). Go 2 units along the x axis, then go 3 units parallel to the y axis, and finally go up 4 units parallel to the z axis. See Figure 3.

Only the positive coordinate axes are shown in Figure 3. The positive z axis goes upward and is perpendicular to the plane formed by the x and y axes. (The negative z axis is an extension of the z axis below the xy plane. The negative y axis is a leftward extension of the y axis. The negative x axis is an extension of the x axis back through the plane created by the y and z axes.) As a second example, consider the point $(3, 4, -2)$, which is plotted in Figure 4.

Although we will not pursue three-dimensional graphing, computer-generated graphs of the functions $z = \ln(x^2 + y^2)$ and $z = y^2 - x^2$ are shown in Figure 5.

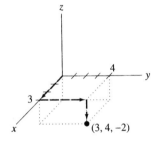

Figure 4
Plotting the point $(3, 4, -2)$

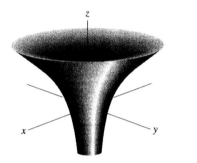
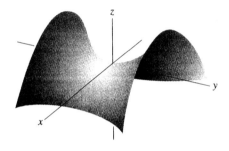

Figure 5 The graphs of functions of two variables

Domain

The **domain** of a function $z = f(x, y)$ is the set of all ordered pairs of real numbers (x, y) for which $f(x, y)$ is defined.

EXAMPLE 7 Determine the domain of each function.

(a) $z = \dfrac{3x}{2y - 16}$ **(b)** $f(x, y) = \sqrt{y - 5x}$ **(c)** $z = x^2 - y^2 + 10$

SOLUTION **(a)** The function

$$z = \frac{3x}{2y - 16}$$

is defined for all (x, y) except those that result in division by zero. Thus, $2y - 16$ cannot be zero, which means $y \neq 8$. The domain of this function consists of all ordered pairs of real numbers (x, y) except those for which $y = 8$.

(b) The function

$$f(x, y) = \sqrt{y - 5x}$$

Notes within the Technology Exercises suggest *Mathematica* as one of the choices among computer algebra systems which can evaluate limits, derivatives, and integrals. *Mathematica* can also be used to produce graphs in two and three dimensions, to serve as a programming language, to create documents, and to run software applications packages.

Mathematica was produced by Wolfram Research, Inc., a company formed by Stephen Wolfram. In fact, it was Dr. Wolfram who led the design and development of *Mathematica*. Soon after earning a Ph.D. in theoretical physics (1979), Dr. Wolfram pioneered the development of a basic computer algebra system. He followed that several years later with the more complex and powerful computer software system known as *Mathematica*.

is defined for all (x, y) except those that give the square root of a negative number. Thus, $y - 5x$ must be nonnegative:

$$y - 5x \geq 0$$

This is better expressed by solving for y in terms of x:

$$y \geq 5x$$

The domain is all ordered pairs of real numbers (x, y) in which $y \geq 5x$.

(c) The function

$$z = x^2 - y^2 + 10$$

is defined for all (x, y). No choices of x or y will lead to division by zero or to the square root (or other even root) of a negative number. Thus, the domain consists of all ordered pairs of real numbers (x, y).   ◆

Level Curves

You have probably seen *topographic maps* of mountainous regions. In such maps, the rugged three-dimensional surface is represented by a series of two-dimensional curves. Each curve represents a horizontal slice of the mountain's surface at a particular level of elevation. The topographic map gives (abstractly) a "bird's-eye view" of the mountain. In Figure 6, c is the elevation in feet.

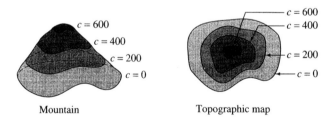

Mountain   Topographic map

Figure 6 A topographic map of a mountain

The topographic map is intended as an introductory example. In general, the graph of a three-dimensional surface $z = f(x, y)$ can be described by a collection of two-dimensional curves called **level curves.** The level curves are obtained by letting $f(x, y)$ be equal to "height" c and then selecting values for c.

EXAMPLE 8   Sketch some level curves of the function $f(x, y) = 9 - x^2 - y^2$. Specifically, let $c = 0, 2, 4, 6,$ and 8.

SOLUTION   Although a three-dimensional graph of the function is neither requested nor needed, it is given in Figure 7 as a visual aid.

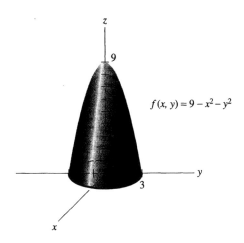

$f(x, y) = 9 - x^2 - y^2$

Figure 7

To obtain level curves for $f(x, y) = 9 - x^2 - y^2$, we will use the equation $9 - x^2 - y^2 = c$ with various c values. Specifically, we will use $c = 0, 2, 4, 6$, and 8 (the arbitrary choices in the statement of the example). The results are displayed in the table below.

c	intermediate result	level curve
0	$9 - x^2 - y^2 = 0$	$x^2 + y^2 = 9$
2	$9 - x^2 - y^2 = 2$	$x^2 + y^2 = 7$
4	$9 - x^2 - y^2 = 4$	$x^2 + y^2 = 5$
6	$9 - x^2 - y^2 = 6$	$x^2 + y^2 = 3$
8	$9 - x^2 - y^2 = 8$	$x^2 + y^2 = 1$

Note
The graph of $x^2 + y^2 = r^2$ is a *circle* centered at the origin and having radius r.

The graph of $x^2 + y^2 = 9$ is a circle centered at the origin and having radius 3. The graph of $x^2 + y^2 = 7$ is a circle with center at $(0, 0)$ and radius $\sqrt{7}$. Figure 8 (at the top of the next page) shows the level curves together with the three-dimensional graph of the original function $f(x, y) = 9 - x^2 - y^2$.

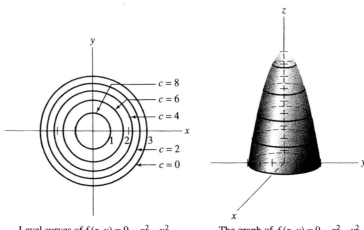

Level curves of $f(x, y) = 9 - x^2 - y^2$ The graph of $f(x, y) = 9 - x^2 - y^2$

Figure 8 The level curves and graph of the function
$f(x, y) = 9 - x^2 - y^2$ ◆

EXAMPLE 9   Sketch level curves of the function $f(x, y) = x^2 - y$. Use $c = 0, 1, 2,$ and 3.

SOLUTION

c	intermediate result	level curve
0	$x^2 - y = 0$	$y = x^2$
1	$x^2 - y = 1$	$y = x^2 - 1$
2	$x^2 - y = 2$	$y = x^2 - 2$
3	$x^2 - y = 3$	$y = x^2 - 3$

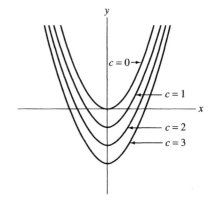

Figure 9 Level curves of $f(x, y) = x^2 - y$

Each of these level curves is a parabola, as shown in Figure 9.   ◆

If f is a production function, then the points (x, y) of each level curve are points at which the production level is constant. Such curves are called **isoquants** ("equal quantities"). Let us consider the Cobb-Douglas production function $f(x, y) = 20x^{2/3}y^{1/3}$ and the associated level curve (isoquant) $20x^{2/3}y^{1/3} = 300$. This level curve contains all points (x, y) for which the production level is 300. The points of the isoquant are all the combinations of labor x and capital y that will yield 300 as a production level. See Figure 10.

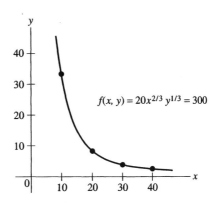

Figure 10 An isoquant (level curve) associated with a Cobb-Douglas production function

10.1   Exercises

For each function given in Exercises 1–10, compute $f(4, 2)$, $f(-1, 6)$, $f(0, 2)$, $f(1, 0)$, and $f(0, 1)$.

1. $f(x, y) = x^2 + y^2$ **2.** $f(x, y) = x^2 - y^2 + 1$

3. $f(x, y) = \dfrac{x}{x + y}$ **4.** $f(x, y) = \sqrt{x^2 + y^2}$

5. $f(x, y) = 1 - x - y$ **6.** $f(x, y) = -x^2 + y^2$

7. $f(x, y) = 3x^2 - 7y$ **8.** $f(x, y) = 3y - 7x$

9. $f(x, y) = \sqrt{5 + x^2 + y^2}$ **10.** $f(x, y) = (x + y)^2$

In Exercises 11–14, compute $g(1, 4)$ and $g(e, 0)$ for each function.

11. $g(x, y) = y \ln x$ **12.** $g(x, y) = xe^y$

13. $g(x, y) = y + x \ln x$ **14.** $g(x, y) = xy \ln x^2$

Compute $f(0, 1, 2)$ for each function in Exercises 15–18.

15. $f(x, y, z) = x^2 + y^2 - z^2 + 7$

16. $f(x, y, z) = \sqrt{xyz + 1}$ **17.** $f(x, y, z) = \dfrac{x + y}{2y}$

18. $f(x, y, z) = e^x + 5 \ln y - 3z$

19. *(COMPOUND INTEREST)* If an amount p dollars (principal) is invested at annual interest rate $r\%$ compounded continuously for t years, the total amount accumulated is given by the function

$$f(p, r, t) = pe^{.01rt}$$

The factor .01 is placed in the exponent in order to convert the percent ($r\%$) to a decimal form.
(a) Determine $f(1000, 8, 2)$.
(b) How much money will accumulate if the account begins with \$3000, the interest rate is 10%, and the money is left in the account for 7 years?

20. *(COMPOUND INTEREST)* Using $f(p, r, t) = pe^{.01rt}$, find

(a) $f(100, 6, 5)$ **(b)** $f(2000, 9, 3)$

21. *(PRODUCTION FUNCTION)* Given the Cobb-Douglas production function $f(x, y) = 20x^{.4}y^{.6}$, determine the number of units produced when 2400 units of labor and 4000 units of capital are used.

22. *(PRODUCTION FUNCTION)* Given the Cobb-Douglas production function $f(x, y) = 4x^{1/3}y^{2/3}$, determine the number of units produced when 60 units of labor and 150 units of capital are used.

23. *(IQ)* A person's IQ is defined as

$$f(a, m) = 100 \cdot \frac{m}{a}$$

where a is the person's actual age in years and m is the mental age (based on test results) in years.

(a) What is the IQ of a 10-year-old child whose test score suggests a mental age of 13?

(b) What is the IQ of a 10-year-old child whose test score yields a mental age of 8?

W (c) According to the function defined here, what is the meaning of an IQ of 100?

24. *(POINTS IN FOOTBALL)* The number of points scored by a kicker in football depends on the number of field goals (3 points each) and points after touchdown (1 point each) made by the kicker. Determine the total point function $P(x, y)$ for a player who makes x field goals and y point-after-touchdown kicks.

25. *(POINTS IN BASKETBALL)* The number of points scored by a basketball player depends on the number of free throws (1 point each), regular field goals (2 points each), and "long" field goals (3 points each) made by the player. Determine the total point function $P(x, y, z)$ for a player who makes x free throws, y regular field goals, and z long field goals.

26. *(CEPHALIC INDEX)* Refer to Example 5. What is the cephalic index of a person whose head width is the same as its length?

27. *(POISEUILLE'S LAW)* When Poiseuille's law is applied to the flow of blood in capillaries, the resistance to blood flow is given by

$$R(l, r) = k \cdot \frac{l}{r^4}$$

where k is a constant, l is the length of the capillary, and r is its radius (see the figure).

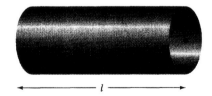

(a) Compute $R(64, 2)$ and $R(64, 1)$.

W (b) What happens to the resistance when the radius is reduced to half its original size?

28. *(FLAG COST)* A producer makes two sizes of flags. Large flags cost $4 each to produce, and Small flags cost $3 each to produce. Determine the cost function $C(x, y)$ for making x large flags and y small flags.

29. *(FLAG PROFIT)* The producer in Exercise 28 sells large flags for $6.50 each and small ones for $5 each.

(a) Determine the revenue function.

(b) Determine the profit function.

30. *(VOLUME)* The volume of a cylinder is $\pi r^2 h$, where r is the radius and h is the height (see the figure). We can write $V(r, h) = \pi r^2 h$.

(a) Compute $V(10, 3)$.

W (b) Explain in words the meaning of $V(10, 3)$.

(c) If the radius and height are known to be the same (that is, $r = h$) express the volume of the cylinder as a function of one variable. In other words, determine a function $V(r)$ or $V(h)$.

31. *(VOLUME OF A BOX)* The volume of a rectangular box is computed as length times width times height.

(a) If a rectangular box has length x, width y, and height z, obtain the function $V(x, y, z)$ that gives its volume (see the figure).

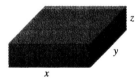

(b) If height z of the box is twice width y, obtain the function $V(x, y)$ that expresses the volume of the box in terms of variables x and y only.

32. *(COST OF A BOX)* If the box in Exercise 31 has a top, the surface area of the box (that is, the *area* of all four sides plus the top and bottom) is

$$S(x, y, z) = 2xy + 2xz + 2yz$$

If it costs 5¢ per square unit to make the sides and 7¢ per square unit for the top and bottom, determine $C(x, y, z)$, the cost of making such a box.

In Exercises 33–48, determine the domain of each function.

33. $f(x, y) = x + y$ **34.** $f(x, y) = 5x - 2y + 3$

35. $f(x, y) = x^2 + y^2 - 9$ **36.** $f(x, y) = 20 - x^2 + y^2$

37. $z = \sqrt{y - x}$ **38.** $z = \sqrt{3x - y}$

39. $z = \dfrac{x}{1 - y}$ **40.** $z = \dfrac{2y + 9}{3x}$

41. $g(x, y) = \dfrac{x^2 + y^2}{x - y}$ **42.** $g(x, y) = x\sqrt{y - 4}$

43. $f(x, y) = \dfrac{\sqrt{5x}}{2y + 3}$ **44.** $f(x, y) = \dfrac{\sqrt{y}}{1 - 9x}$

45. $z = 5xe^y$ **46.** $z = e^{x - y}$

47. $z = y \ln (x - 1)$ **48.** $z = 3x \ln (y + 2)$

49. Using $c = 1, 3, 5$, and 7, obtain level curves for the function $f(x, y) = 9 - x^2 - y^2$ of Example 8.

W 50. Describe the level "curve" obtained for the function $f(x, y) = 9 - x^2 - y^2$ if $c = 9$ is used.

In Exercises 51–64, sketch the level curves of the given function for the specific c values listed.

51. $f(x, y) = 16 - x^2 - y^2$; $c = 0, 7, 12, 15$

52. $f(x, y) = 10 - x^2 - y^2$; $c = 1, 6, 9$

53. $f(x, y) = x^2 - y + 1$; $c = 0, 1, 2$

54. $f(x, y) = x^2 - y - 1$; $c = 0, 1, 2, 3$

55. $f(x, y) = x - y + 2$; $c = 0, 2, 4, 6$

56. $f(x, y) = x + y$; $c = -2, 0, 2, 4$

57. $f(x, y) = 1 - x - y$; $c = 1, 3, 5, 7$

58. $f(x, y) = 3 - x - y$; $c = 0, 1, 2, 3$

59. $f(x, y) = \dfrac{y}{x}$; $c = 1, 2, 3, 4$

60. $f(x, y) = -\dfrac{y}{x}$; $c = 1, 2, 3, 4$

61. $f(x, y) = e^x - y$; $c = -3, -2, -1, 0$

62. $f(x, y) = e^x + y$; $c = 0, 1, 2, 3$

63. $f(x, y) = \ln x - y$; $c = -2, -1, 0, 1$

64. $f(x, y) = \ln x + y$; $c = -1, 0, 1, 2$

65. *(P/E RATIO)* The price-to-earnings (P/E) ratio of a stock is given by

$$f(P, E) = \dfrac{P}{E}$$

(a) If a stock is selling at \$42 a share, what must be the company's earnings in order for the P/E ratio to be 15?

(b) If the price of a stock increases while the earnings remain unchanged, what happens to the P/E ratio of the stock?

66. *(LIMITS)* Extend the notion of limit in an intuitive manner to determine each limit given here.

(a) The limit of $x^2 + 3y$ as x approaches 5 and y approaches 2

(b) The limit of $\sqrt{x^2 - y^2}$ as x approaches 13 and y approaches 5

(c) The limit of

$$\dfrac{3xy}{x + y}$$

as x approaches 0 and y approaches -7

W 67. *(LIMITS)* Based on the table, write a sentence about the limit of $f(x, y)$ as x and y approach particular numbers. (Assume that approaches from the left would yield similar results.)

x	y	$f(x, y)$
.1	.9	2.4
.01	.99	2.45
.001	.999	2.481
.0001	.9999	2.4988
.00001	.99999	2.4998
.000001	.999999	2.49999

W 68. Can a *negative* number c be used to obtain level curves? Explain. You may want to consider Example 8.

TECHNOLOGY *EXERCISES*

1. Consider the function

$$f(x, y) = x^2 - y$$

Graph the level curve for $c = -2$. Also graph the lines $y = x + 2$, $y = 6$, and $y = 1 - 2x$. Which line is tangent to the level curve?

2. Consider the function

$$f(x, y) = 2\sqrt{x} - y$$

Graph the level curve for $c = -3$. Also graph the lines $y = 2x + 3$, $y = x + 4$, and $y = 6 - x$. Which line is tangent to the level curve?

3. Consider the Cobb-Douglas production function

$$f(x, y) = 4x^{2/3}y^{1/3}$$

Three associated isoquants are

(i) $4x^{2/3}y^{1/3} = 12$ **(ii)** $4x^{2/3}y^{1/3} = 16$ **(iii)** $4x^{2/3}y^{1/3} = 20$

Each of these three equations can be manipulated into a form more suitable for graphing, namely

(i) $y_1 = \dfrac{27}{x^2}$ **(ii)** $y_2 = \dfrac{64}{x^2}$ **(iii)** $y_3 = \dfrac{125}{x^2}$

Graph the three functions for $x > 0$ and answer the questions that follow.

(a) Which function (y_1, y_2, or y_3) will have the smallest y value for any particular x value?

(b) Of the three functions (y_1, y_2, and y_3), which one is associated with the largest production level?

Note *Maple* and *Mathematica* can produce three-dimensional graphs of functions of the form $z = f(x, y)$. The function

$$z = \ln (x^2 + y^2 + 1)$$

can be graphed as follows.

Mathematica: `Plot3D[log[x^2 + y^2 + 1], {x, -5, 5}, {y, -5, 5}]`

Maple: `plot3d(ln (x^2 + y^2 + 1), x = -5..5, y = -5..5);`

If you have access to such a system, graph the following functions.

(a) $z = 6 - x^2 - y^2$ **(b)** $z = xy$ **(c)** $z = x^2y^4$

10.2 | *PARTIAL DERIVATIVES*

We have covered a variety of interpretations and applications of the derivative of functions of one variable. One interpretation is that the derivative of f is the rate of change of $f(x)$ compared with the change in the variable x. Recall the definition of the derivative of $f(x)$ with respect to x:

$$f'(x) = \lim_{\Delta x \to 0} \frac{f(x + \Delta x) - f(x)}{\Delta x}$$

To extend the rate of change interpretation to a function $f(x, y)$ of two variables, we consider how the function values change as x changes (that is, with y held constant) and how the function values change as y changes (that is, with x held constant). Consequently, there are two separate derivatives, called **partial derivatives.** First, consider informal definitions.

Partial Derivatives—Informal Definitions

1. The **partial derivative of $f(x, y)$ with respect to x** is obtained by differentiating $f(x, y)$ with respect to x, treating y as a constant. The notation for this partial derivative is f_x or $\partial f/\partial x$.

2. The **partial derivative of $f(x, y)$ with respect to y** is obtained by differentiating $f(x, y)$ with respect to y, treating x as a constant. The notation for this partial derivative is f_y or $\partial f/\partial y$.

Next we give the formal definitions.

Partial Derivatives—Formal Definitions

1. The **partial derivative of $f(x, y)$ with respect to x** is

$$\frac{\partial f}{\partial x} = \lim_{\Delta x \to 0} \frac{f(x + \Delta x, y) - f(x, y)}{\Delta x}$$

In $\partial f/\partial x$, y is held constant, so there is no change in y and no Δy appears. The change (Δx) is in x only.

2. The **partial derivative of $f(x, y)$ with respect to y** is

$$\frac{\partial f}{\partial y} = \lim_{\Delta y \to 0} \frac{f(x, y + \Delta y) - f(x, y)}{\Delta y}$$

In $\partial f/\partial y$, x is held constant, so there is no change in x and no Δx appears. The change (Δy) is in y only.

EXAMPLE 1 Use the formal definition to determine $\partial f/\partial x$ for $f(x, y) = x^2 y$.

SOLUTION

$$\frac{\partial f}{\partial x} = \lim_{\Delta x \to 0} \frac{f(x + \Delta x, y) - f(x, y)}{\Delta x}$$

$$= \lim_{\Delta x \to 0} \frac{(x + \Delta x)^2 y - x^2 y}{\Delta x}$$

$$= \lim_{\Delta x \to 0} \frac{[x^2 + 2x(\Delta x) + (\Delta x)^2] y - x^2 y}{\Delta x}$$

$$= \lim_{\Delta x \to 0} \frac{x^2 y + 2x(\Delta x) y + (\Delta x)^2 y - x^2 y}{\Delta x}$$

$$= \lim_{\Delta x \to 0} \frac{2x(\Delta x) y + (\Delta x)^2 y}{\Delta x}$$

$$= \lim_{\Delta x \to 0} \frac{\Delta x [2xy + (\Delta x) y]}{\Delta x}$$

$$= \lim_{\Delta x \to 0} [2xy + (\Delta x) y]$$

$$= 2xy \qquad \blacklozenge$$

Note

We do not need to use the formal definition to determine partial derivatives. Since we already know the rules for ordinary differentiation, all we need to do is keep in mind which variable is being treated as a constant.

The derivative determined in Example 1 can be obtained using the informal definition, as demonstrated in the next example.

EXAMPLE 2   If $f(x, y) = x^2 y$, determine $\partial f / \partial x$.

SOLUTION   Because we seek the partial derivative of $f(x, y)$ with respect to x, consider y to be a constant. Then

$$\frac{\partial}{\partial x} (x^2 y) = 2x \cdot y = 2xy \qquad \text{answer}$$

Since y is treated as a constant, the derivative of $x^2 y$ is y times the derivative of x^2, or y times $2x$. As an alternative, you may prefer to factor out the "constant" y, placing it in front of the $\partial / \partial x$ before continuing the differentiation.

$$\frac{\partial}{\partial x} (x^2 y) = y \cdot \frac{\partial}{\partial x} x^2 = y \cdot 2x = 2xy \qquad \blacklozenge$$

EXAMPLE 3   If $f(x, y) = x^2 y$, determine $\partial f / \partial y$.

SOLUTION Here x is treated as a constant. This means x^2 is a constant. Thus we are differentiating a constant times y.

$$\frac{\partial f}{\partial y} = \frac{\partial}{\partial y} (x^2 y) = x^2 \cdot 1 = x^2 \qquad \blacklozenge$$

The next example uses the notation f_x and f_y for the partial derivatives.

EXAMPLE 4 Let $f(x, y) = x^3 + x^2 y^4$.   Find **(a)** f_x **(b)** f_y

SOLUTION **(a)** $f_x = 3x^2 + 2x \cdot y^4 = 3x^2 + 2xy^4$ treating y as a constant

(b) $f_y = 0 + x^2 \cdot 4y^3 = 4x^2 y^3$ treating x as a constant $\blacklozenge$

EXAMPLE 5 Determine $\partial f / \partial x$ and $\partial f / \partial y$ for each function.

(a) $f(x, y) = xe^y$ **(b)** $f(x, y) = \ln x$

SOLUTION **(a)** $\dfrac{\partial}{\partial x} (xe^y) = e^y \quad \dfrac{\partial}{\partial y} (xe^y) = xe^y$ **(b)** $\dfrac{\partial}{\partial x} (\ln x) = \dfrac{1}{x} \quad \dfrac{\partial}{\partial y} (\ln x) = 0 \qquad \blacklozenge$

Geometric Interpretation of the Partial Derivative

The geometric interpretation of partial derivatives resembles the original geometric interpretation of the derivative of a function (presented in Section 3.1). For $z = f(x, y)$, $\partial f / \partial y$ is the derivative of $f(x, y)$ with respect to y, treating x as a constant. Thus, $\partial f / \partial y$ is the slope of a line tangent to the graph of the surface $z = f(x, y)$. Since x is held constant, the tangent line lies in a plane parallel to the yz plane. See Figure 11. Similarly, $\partial f / \partial x$ is the slope of a line tangent to the graph of $z = f(x, y)$. In this case y is held constant, so the tangent line lies in a plane parallel to the xz plane. See Figure 12.

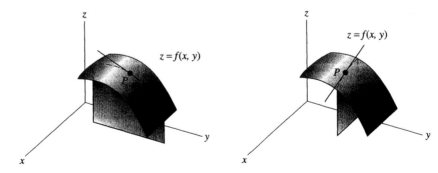

Figure 11 The slope at point P is $\partial f / \partial y$ at P **Figure 12** The slope at point P is $\partial f / \partial x$ at P

Evaluating a Partial Derivative

Sometimes it is necessary to evaluate a partial derivative of $f(x, y)$ at a point (a, b), just as we have previously evaluated ordinary derivatives of $f(x)$ at a number a. The partial derivatives of $f(x, y)$ evaluated at (a, b) are written as

$$\frac{\partial f}{\partial x}(a, b) \quad \text{or} \quad f_x(a, b) \qquad\qquad \frac{\partial f}{\partial y}(a, b) \quad \text{or} \quad f_y(a, b)$$

EXAMPLE 6   For $f(x, y) = x^2 + 3xy + y + 7$, determine $f_x(5, 8)$ and $f_y(5, 8)$.

SOLUTION $f_x = 2x + 3y$, which means $f_x(5, 8) = 2(5) + 3(8) = 34$

$f_y = 3x + 1$,   which means $f_y(5, 8) = 3(5) + 1 = 16$ ◆

With the use of partial differentiation, information analogous to marginal cost and marginal revenue can be obtained from cost functions $C(x, y)$ and revenue functions $R(x, y)$.

EXAMPLE 7   **REVENUE**

Suppose that revenue from the sale of x model A10 stereo speakers and y model A20 stereo speakers is given by

$$R(x, y) = 100x + 150y - .03x^2 - .02y^2 \quad \text{dollars}$$

Determine the rate at which revenue will change with respect to the change in the number of model A10 speakers sold, when 50 model A10 speakers and 40 model A20 speakers have been sold.

SOLUTION   The rate of change we seek is

$$\frac{\partial R}{\partial x}(50, 40)$$

Since

$$R(x, y) = 100x + 150y - .03x^2 - .02y^2$$

it follows that

$$\frac{\partial R}{\partial x} = 100 - .06x$$

$$\frac{\partial R}{\partial x}(50, 40) = 100 - .06(50) = 97 \qquad \text{answer}$$

The answer (97) means that the additional revenue that will be obtained from the sale of the next A10 speaker is approximately \$97, assuming that 50 A10 speakers and 40 A20 speakers have been sold.   ◆

A function $f(x, y, z)$ of three variables has partial derivatives f_x, f_y, and f_z. The partial derivative f_x is determined by treating both y and z as constants. In general, to determine the partial derivative with respect to any one of the variables, consider the other two variables as constants.

EXAMPLE 8   Let $f(x, y, z) = x^2y^3z + x \ln z + y$. Determine

   (a) f_x **(b)** f_y **(c)** f_z

SOLUTION   **(a)** $f_x = 2x \cdot y^3 z + 1 \cdot \ln z + 0 = 2xy^3 z + \ln z$

(b) $f_y = x^2 z \cdot 3y^2 + 0 + 1 = 3x^2 y^2 z + 1$

(c) $f_z = x^2 y^3 \cdot 1 + x \cdot \dfrac{1}{z} + 0 = x^2 y^3 + \dfrac{x}{z}$ ◆

Higher-Order Partial Derivatives

Just as there are higher-order ordinary derivatives, there are higher-order partial derivatives. We will now consider second partial derivatives of a function $f(x, y)$ of two variables.

To begin, there are two first partial derivatives, $\partial f/\partial x$ and $\partial f/\partial y$. (or f_x and f_y.) Each of these two derivatives can be differentiated with respect to either x or y to obtain a second partial derivative. This means there are four **second partial derivatives,** as shown below.

Second Partial Derivatives

$$\frac{\partial}{\partial x}\left(\frac{\partial f}{\partial x}\right) = \frac{\partial^2 f}{\partial x^2} = f_{xx} \qquad\qquad \frac{\partial}{\partial x}\left(\frac{\partial f}{\partial y}\right) = \frac{\partial^2 f}{\partial x \partial y} = f_{yx}$$

$$\frac{\partial}{\partial y}\left(\frac{\partial f}{\partial y}\right) = \frac{\partial^2 f}{\partial y^2} = f_{yy} \qquad\qquad \frac{\partial}{\partial y}\left(\frac{\partial f}{\partial x}\right) = \frac{\partial^2 f}{\partial y \partial x} = f_{xy}$$

Notice a possible source of confusion with the so-called "mixed partials" f_{yx} and f_{xy}.

f_{yx} means that f is differentiated *first* with respect to y and *then* with respect to x. This notation follows from $(f_y)_x = f_{yx}$.

$\dfrac{\partial^2 f}{\partial x \partial y}$ means that f is differentiated *first* with respect to y and *then* with respect to x.

$$f_{yx} = \frac{\partial^2 f}{\partial x \partial y} \qquad \text{and} \qquad f_{xy} = \frac{\partial^2 f}{\partial y \partial x}$$

EXAMPLE 9   Let $f(x, y) = x^3 + 4xy^2 + 15$. Find all four second partials.

SOLUTION

$$\frac{\partial f}{\partial x} = 3x^2 + 4y^2 \qquad \text{and} \qquad \frac{\partial f}{\partial y} = 8xy$$

Now,

$$f_{xx} = \frac{\partial^2 f}{\partial x^2} = \frac{\partial}{\partial x}\left(\frac{\partial f}{\partial x}\right) = \frac{\partial}{\partial x}(3x^2 + 4y^2) = 6x$$

$$f_{yy} = \frac{\partial^2 f}{\partial y^2} = \frac{\partial}{\partial y}\left(\frac{\partial f}{\partial y}\right) = \frac{\partial}{\partial y}(8xy) = 8x$$

$$f_{yx} = \frac{\partial^2 f}{\partial x \partial y} = \frac{\partial}{\partial x}\left(\frac{\partial f}{\partial y}\right) = \frac{\partial}{\partial x}(8xy) = 8y$$

$$f_{xy} = \frac{\partial^2 f}{\partial y \partial x} = \frac{\partial}{\partial y}\left(\frac{\partial f}{\partial x}\right) = \frac{\partial}{\partial y}(3x^2 + 4y^2) = 8y$$ ◆

Notice that $f_{yx} = f_{xy}$ in Example 9. As a matter of fact, for all functions $z = f(x, y)$ used in this book, it will be true that $f_{yx} = f_{xy}$.

10.2 Exercises

Determine both $\partial f/\partial x$ and $\partial f/\partial y$ for each function in Exercises 1–16. Use the informal definition (as we did in Examples 2–5).

1. $f(x, y) = 2x + 5y$ **2.** $f(x, y) = 2xy$

3. $f(x, y) = x^3 - 4y^2$ **4.** $f(x, y) = x - x^2y^2 + y^3$

5. $f(x, y) = \dfrac{x}{y}$ **6.** $f(x, y) = \dfrac{y^3}{x^2}$

7. $f(x, y) = y \ln x$ **8.** $f(x, y) = e^x \ln y$

9. $f(x, y) = e^{3xy}$ **10.** $f(x, y) = 1 - e^{-xy}$

11. $f(x, y) = x\sqrt{y}$ **12.** $f(x, y) = \sqrt{xy}$

13. $f(x, y) = \sqrt{x^2 + y^2}$ **14.** $f(x, y) = x^2\sqrt{1 + y^2}$

15. $f(x, y) = \dfrac{x}{x + y}$ **16.** $f(x, y) = \dfrac{xy}{x + y}$

Determine f_x and f_y for each function in Exercises 17–22. Use the informal definition.

17. $f(x, y) = x^3y^5$ **18.** $f(x, y) = 5x^2 - 2y^3$

19. $f(x, y) = \ln(x^2 + y^2)$ **20.** $f(x, y) = e^{x^2 + y^2}$

21. $f(x, y) = xe^{-y}$ **22.** $f(x, y) = y\sqrt{x}$

In Exercises 23–30, use the *formal definition* of the partial derivative to determine $\partial f/\partial x$ for each function. Refer to Example 1.

23. $f(x, y) = xy$ **24.** $f(x, y) = xy^2$

25. $f(x, y) = x^2$ **26.** $f(x, y) = y^2$

27. $f(x, y) = 3y$ **28.** $f(x, y) = 5x$

29. $f(x, y) = x^2y^2$ **30.** $f(x, y) = x^2y^2 + 1$

31–38. Use the functions of Exercises 23–30, but determine $\partial f/\partial y$ instead. Again, use the *formal definition* of partial derivative.

39. Let $f(x, y) = x^2y^2 - 3x + 2y$. Determine
(a) $f_x(5, 4)$ (b) $f_y(-1, 8)$

(c) $\dfrac{\partial f}{\partial x}(1, -5)$ (d) $\dfrac{\partial f}{\partial y}(0, 9)$

40. Let $f(x, y) = xe^y + x^3y$. Determine
(a) $f_x(4, 3)$ (b) $f_y(3, 0)$

(c) $\dfrac{\partial f}{\partial x}(-1, 6)$ (d) $\dfrac{\partial f}{\partial y}(2, 1)$

41. Let $g(x, y) = x \ln y + xy$. Determine
(a) $g_y(8, 2)$ (b) $g_x(3, 1)$

(c) $\dfrac{\partial g}{\partial x}(4, e)$ (d) $\dfrac{\partial g}{\partial y}(2e, e)$

42. Let $g(x, y) = y^2 \ln x$. Determine
(a) $g_y(e, 3)$ (b) $g_x(2, 10)$

(c) $\dfrac{\partial g}{\partial x}(1, e)$ (d) $\dfrac{\partial g}{\partial y}(1, e)$

For each function in Exercises 43–50, find f_x, f_y, and f_z.

43. $f(x,y,z) = x^2 + y^2 + z^2$ **44.** $f(x,y,z) = x^2y^2z^2$

45. $f(x,y,z) = xyz - x + y$ **46.** $f(x,y,z) = \dfrac{\ln x}{y} + z$

47. $f(x,y,z) = xye^z$

48. $f(x,y,z) = xz\sqrt{y}$

49. $f(x,y,z) = \dfrac{x}{y+z}$

50. $f(x,y,z) = \dfrac{xy}{z^2}$

For each function in Exercises 51–60, find all four second partials.

51. $f(x,y) = x^2 + xy + y^2$

52. $f(x,y) = x^3 + x^2y^2 - 10$

53. $f(x,y) = y \ln x$

54. $f(x,y) = x^2 + \ln y$

55. $g(x,y) = 3xe^y$

56. $g(x,y) = e^{xy}$

57. $h(x,y) = x^2 \ln y$

58. $h(x,y) = \dfrac{x}{y}$

59. $f(x,y) = \ln(x + y^2)$

60. $f(x,y) = \sqrt{x - y}$

61. (REVENUE) Refer to Example 7.
  (a) Determine the approximate additional revenue obtained from the sale of the next A20 speaker, assuming that 50 A10 speakers and 40 A20 speakers have been sold.
  (b) Determine the approximate additional revenue obtained from the sale of the next A10 speaker, assuming that 60 A10 speakers and 38 A20 speakers have been sold.

62. (COST) Suppose that the cost of producing x amplifiers and y receivers is given by

$$C(x, y) = .1x^2 + .2y^2 + 90x + 140y$$

30 amplifiers and 70 receivers have been produced.
  (a) What is the approximate cost of producing the 31st amplifier, assuming that the production of receivers remains at 70?
  (b) What is the approximate cost of producing the 71st receiver, assuming that the production of amplifiers remains at 30?

63. (PRODUCTION FUNCTION) Consider the Cobb-Douglas production function $f(x, y) = 2x^{.4}y^{.6}$, where x is the number of units of labor and y is the number of units of capital. (See Example 6 in Section 10.1, if needed.)
  (a) Determine $\partial f/\partial x$, the *marginal productivity of labor*.
  (b) Determine the *marginal productivity of capital*.

64. (PRODUCTION FUNCTION) Redo Exercise 63 using $f(x, y) = 20x^{2/3}y^{1/3}$.

65. (PRODUCTION FUNCTION) Consider $f(x,y) = 20x^{1/4}y^{3/4}$, where x is the number of units of labor, y is the number of units of capital, and $f(x, y)$ is the number of units produced. Assume that the current production level uses

256 units of labor and 81 units of capital. If the number of units of capital is held fixed and labor is increased by 1 unit, determine the approximate increase in the number of units produced—the *marginal productivity of labor*.

66. (PRODUCTION FUNCTION) Refer to Exercise 65. If the number of units of labor is held fixed and the number of units of capital is increased by 1, determine the approximate increase in the number of units produced—the *marginal productivity of capital*.

67. (TEMPERATURE VARIATION) A thin metal plate is being heated in such a way that the temperature T at any point (x, y) on the surface of the plate is given by

$$T(x, y) = 350 - x^2 - y^2 \qquad \text{degrees}$$

x and y are measured in centimeters (see the figure).

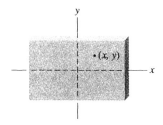

  (a) What is the temperature at the origin?
  W (b) On the basis of the function T, why will the temperature be greatest at the origin?
  (c) Determine the rate of change of temperature with respect to distance at the point $(10, 6)$, assuming x can vary and y is held constant.
  (d) Determine the rate of change of temperature with respect to distance at the point $(10, 6)$, assuming y can vary and x is held constant.
  W (e) Explain why the rates of change in parts (c) and (d) are negative.

68. (COST) Suppose the cost of making a product is given by $C(x, y) = 15 + 3x + xy + 8y$, where x is the number of units of labor and y is the number of units of capital.
  (a) Determine the rate of change of cost with respect to labor when $x = 5$. Assume the number of units of capital is kept constant at $y = 3$.
  (b) Determine the rate of change of cost with respect to capital when $y = 3$. Assume the number of units of labor is kept constant at $x = 5$.

69. (VOLUME) Determine the instantaneous rate of change of the volume of a cylinder with respect to its height if the radius remains constant ($V = \pi r^2 h$).

70. *(VOLUME)* Determine the instantaneous rate of change of the volume of a cone with respect to its radius if the height remains constant ($V = \frac{1}{3}\pi r^2 h$).

71. *(GAS LAW)* The ideal gas law states that

$$P = k \cdot \frac{T}{V}$$

where P is the pressure exerted by the gas, T is the temperature of the gas, and V is the volume of the gas. The number k is a constant.
(a) Find the rate of change of pressure with respect to temperature, if the volume is kept constant.
(b) Determine $\partial P/\partial V$.
W **(c)** Tell in words what $\partial P/\partial V$ represents.

72. *(OHM'S LAW)* Ohm's law gives the relationship of electric current I (in amperes), resistance R (in ohms), and voltage V (in volts) in an electric circuit.

$$I = \frac{V}{R}$$

(a) Find the rate of change of current with respect to voltage when resistance is held constant.
(b) Find the rate of change of current with respect to resistance when voltage is kept constant.
(c) Find the rate of change of voltage with respect to resistance when current is kept constant.

 73. *(PHYSIOLOGY)* Concern about body heat loss led to the development of a formula for measuring the surface area S of a person's body on the basis of the individual's weight w in kilograms and height h in centimeters.

$$S(w, h) = .0072w^{.425}h^{.725} \text{ square meters}$$

(a) Determine $S(80, 178)$.
(b) Find $S_w(w, h)$ and $S_h(w, h)$.
(c) Find $S_w(80, 178)$ and $S_h(80, 178)$.
W **(d)** Explain the meaning of S_w and S_h.

W **74.** *(POISEUILLE'S LAW)* The resistance R to blood flow in capillaries is given by

$$R(l, r) = \frac{kl}{r^4}$$

where k is a constant, l is the length of the capillary, and r is the radius of the capillary.
(a) Obtain $\partial R/\partial l$ and explain what information it provides.
(b) Obtain $\partial R/\partial r$ and explain what information it provides.

75. *(ELECTRICITY)* When two resistors R_1 and R_2 are connected in parallel, the total resistance R that results is given by

$$\frac{1}{R} = \frac{1}{R_1} + \frac{1}{R_2}$$

Determine $\partial R/\partial R_1$ when R_1 is 10 ohms and R_2 is 15 ohms.

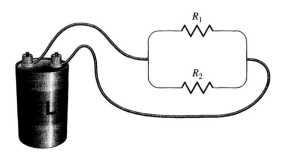

TECHNOLOGY *EXERCISES*

Note   Both *Mathematica* and *Maple* can perform partial differentiation. The partial derivative of

$$f(x, y) = x^2 + 7y$$

with respect to x and with respect to y can be determined as follows.

Mathematica: `D[x^2 + 7y, x]`   `D[x^2 + 7y, y]`

Maple: `diff(x^2 + 7*y, x);`   `diff(x^2 + 7*y, y);`

If you have access to one of these systems, use it to determine the partial derivatives requested in Exercises 3, 13, and 15.

10.3 | *MAXIMUM AND MINIMUM*

Since the graph of $z = f(x, y)$ is a surface in three dimensions, a **relative maximum point** stands out as a peak at the top of a hill. A **relative minimum point** stands out as the bottom of a valley. See Figure 13.

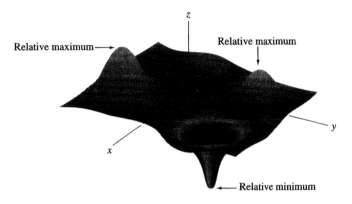

Figure 13 Relative maximum and relative minimum points of a surface $z = f(x, y)$

In Chapter 4 we began the search for relative extrema of functions of one variable by finding critical numbers. Now, with functions of two variables, we will seek *critical points* (a, b), since we want the x and y values needed to maximize or minimize a function $z = f(x, y)$. Note how the definition given next is an extension of the definition of critical number given in Section 4.1.

Critical Point

Let $z = f(x, y)$ be defined at point (a, b). Then (a, b) is a **critical point** of $f(x, y)$ if $f_x(a, b) = 0$ and $f_y(a, b) = 0$.

[Also, (a, b) is a critical point if either $f_x(a, b)$ or $f_y(a, b)$ fails to exist. However, we will not study such situations.]

With functions of one variable, the derivative is the slope of the tangent line. With functions of two variables, there are two tangent lines to consider. The partial derivatives f_x and f_y are the slopes of these two tangent lines. For (a, b) to be a critical point, we insist that $f_x(x, y)$ and $f_y(x, y)$ both be zero at (a, b). There must be two horizontal tangent lines at (a, b), as shown in Figure 14.

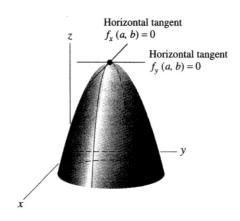

Figure 14 A critical point

EXAMPLE 1   Find the critical points of $f(x, y) = 8x + 2y - x^2 + 2y^2$.

SOLUTION   First, find the partial derivatives.

$$f_x(x, y) = 8 - 2x$$
$$f_y(x, y) = 2 + 4y$$

Next, solve the system of equations created by setting each partial derivative equal to zero. In other words, solve the system

$$\begin{cases} 8 - 2x = 0 \\ 2 + 4y = 0 \end{cases}$$

Since each equation contains only one variable, the solution is readily obtained. From $8 - 2x = 0$, we get $x = 4$. From $2 + 4y = 0$, we get $y = -1/2$. The solution is

$$x = 4, \ y = -\frac{1}{2}$$

Thus, the critical point is $(4, -1/2)$.   ◆

EXAMPLE 2   Find the critical points of $f(x, y) = x^2 - xy + y^2 + 4x - 23y$.

SOLUTION   First, find the partial derivatives.

$$f_x(x, y) = 2x - y + 4 \qquad \text{and} \qquad f_y(x, y) = -x + 2y - 23$$

Next, solve the system

$$\begin{cases} 2x - y + 4 = 0 \\ 2y - x - 23 = 0 \end{cases}$$

We can write the first equation as $y = 2x + 4$ and then substitute $2x + 4$ for y in the second equation.

$$2(2x + 4) - x - 23 = 0$$
$$4x + 8 - x - 23 = 0$$
$$3x - 15 = 0$$
$$x = 5$$

Because $y = 2x + 4$, we know that

$$y = 2(5) + 4 = 14$$

Thus, $(5, 14)$ is a critical point, the only critical point of this function. ◆

Just as with functions of one variable, critical points do not always lead to relative extrema. Figure 15 shows the graph of a function f such that $f_x(a, b) = 0$ and $f_y(a, b) = 0$. Yet the point $(a, b, f(a, b))$ is not a relative maximum or minimum. The point is called a **saddle point.** The saddle-shaped surface is produced if there is a minimum when approaching from one direction and a maximum when approaching from another direction.

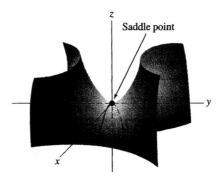

Figure 15 A saddle point

There is a second derivative test to determine whether critical point (a, b) is associated with a relative maximum, a relative minimum, or neither.

Second Partials Test

For $z = f(x, y)$, if $f_x(a, b) = 0$ and $f_y(a, b) = 0$, then consider

$$D = (f_{xx})(f_{yy}) - (f_{xy})^2 \quad \text{evaluated at } (a, b)$$

1. If $D > 0$ and $f_{xx} > 0$, then f has a *relative minimum* at (a, b).

2. If $D > 0$ and $f_{xx} < 0$, then f has a *relative maximum* at (a, b).

3. If $D < 0$, then f has a *saddle point* at (a, b).

4. If $D = 0$, then no conclusion can be drawn.

Note

As an aid in remembering the second partials test, consider that when $D > 0$, the test for relative maximum or relative minimum comes down to whether $f_{xx} > 0$ (minimum) or $f_{xx} < 0$ (maximum), which resembles the second derivative test for functions of one variable.

EXAMPLE 3   Determine the relative extrema of $f(x, y) = 3x^3 + y^2 - 9x - 6y + 1$.

SOLUTION   First, determine the critical points—points (x, y) for which both $f_x = 0$ and $f_y = 0$. Here $f_x = 9x^2 - 9$ and $f_y = 2y - 6$. Next, solve the system

$$\begin{cases} 9x^2 - 9 = 0 \\ 2y - 6 = 0 \end{cases}$$

Solving the system yields $x = \pm 1$ and $y = 3$. Thus, the critical points are $(1, 3)$ and $(-1, 3)$.

To apply the second partials test, we must evaluate D for the points $(1, 3)$ and $(-1, 3)$. Here $f_{xx} = 18x$, $f_{yy} = 2$, and $f_{xy} = 0$.

$$D = (f_{xx})(f_{yy}) - (f_{xy})^2$$

For (1, 3), we have

$$D = f_{xx}(1, 3) \cdot f_{yy}(1, 3) - [f_{xy}(1, 3)]^2 = 18(1) \cdot 2 - 0 = 36$$

Thus, $D > 0$ and $f_{xx}(1, 3) = 18 > 0$. Therefore, $f(1, 3)$ is a relative minimum (by case 1 of the four cases given in the second partials test). The actual relative minimum functional value is -14, determined by using 1 for x and 3 for y in the original function.

$$f(1, 3) = 3(1)^3 + (3)^2 - 9(1) - 6(3) + 1 = -14$$

For (−1, 3), we have

$$D = f_{xx}(-1, 3) \cdot f_{yy}(-1, 3) - [f_{xy}(-1, 3)]^2 = 18(-1) \cdot 2 - 0 = -36$$

Thus, $D < 0$. By case 3 of the second partials test, this means that $f(-1, 3)$ is neither a relative maximum nor a relative minimum. Rather, there is a saddle point at $(-1, 3, -2)$, with -2 being the value of $f(-1, 3)$.   ◆

The next examples apply the ideas that have been presented.

APPLIED

EXAMPLE 4   MAXIMUM PROFIT

A company makes two kinds of umbrellas. One kind sells for $8, and the other sells for $12. The revenue (in hundreds of dollars) from the sale of x hundred $8 umbrellas and y hundred $12 umbrellas is $R = 8x + 12y$. The cost of making the umbrellas is $C = x^2 - xy + y^2 - 4x + 6y + 2$ hundred dollars. How many of each kind should be made in order to maximize profit?

SOLUTION   Because profit = revenue − cost, we have

$$P(x, y) = (8x + 12y) - (x^2 - xy + y^2 - 4x + 6y + 2)$$
$$P(x, y) = -x^2 + xy - y^2 + 12x + 6y - 2 \qquad \text{when simplified}$$

To determine the critical points of function P, obtain the partial derivatives.

$$P_x = -2x + y + 12$$
$$P_y = x - 2y + 6$$

Solving the equations $P_x = 0$ and $P_y = 0$,

$$\begin{cases} -2x + y + 12 = 0 \\ x - 2y + 6 = 0 \end{cases}$$

yields $x = 10$ and $y = 8$. Thus, $(10, 8)$ is the only critical point. We now test it to be sure it produces a maximum value for P. To evaluate D, first determine the values of P_{xx}, P_{yy}, and P_{xy} at $(10, 8)$.

$$P_{xx}(10, 8) = -2 \qquad P_{yy}(10, 8) = -2 \qquad P_{xy}(10, 8) = 1$$

Then

$$D = P_{xx}(10, 8) \cdot P_{yy}(10, 8) - [P_{xy}(10, 8)]^2 = (-2)(-2) - (1)^2 = 3$$

Since $D > 0$ and $P_{xx}(10, 8) < 0$, P does indeed have a *maximum* value when $x = 10$ and $y = 8$. Keeping in mind that the numbers 10 and 8 represent *hundreds* of umbrellas, we conclude that the company should make 1000 of the $8 umbrellas and 800 of the $12 umbrellas in order to maximize its profit.   ♦

> **Note**
>
> In the applied problems of this section, the relative maximum or minimum will always be the absolute maximum or minimum as well. You will not have to check further. It is beyond the scope of this book to present such methods of verification.

APPLIED

EXAMPLE 5   *MINIMUM COST*

A manufacturer of aquariums wants to make a large rectangular box-shaped aquarium that will hold 64 cubic feet of water. If the material for the base costs $20 per square foot and the material for the sides costs $10 per square foot, find the dimensions for which the cost of the materials will be the least.

SOLUTION   Let the length, width, and height of the aquarium be x feet, y feet, and z feet, respectively. (See Figure 16.)

Figure 16

The area of the base is $x \cdot y$ square feet, and the cost per square foot is \$20. This means the cost of the base is $20xy$ dollars. Similarly, there are two sides of area xz square feet and two sides of area yz square feet, so the total area of all four sides is $2xz + 2yz$. Because their cost per square foot is \$10, the cost of all four sides is $10(2xz + 2yz)$ dollars. The total cost of materials is therefore

$$C(x, y, z) = 20xy + 10(2xz + 2yz)$$
$$C(x, y, z) = 20xy + 20xz + 20yz \qquad \text{when simplified}$$

This function of three variables can be changed to a function of two variables by using the fact that the volume $(x \cdot y \cdot z)$ must be 64 cubic feet.

$$xyz = 64 \qquad \text{or} \qquad z = \frac{64}{xy}$$

Replacing z by $64/xy$ in the cost function creates a function of two variables x and y.

$$C(x, y) = 20xy + 20x \cdot \frac{64}{xy} + 20y \cdot \frac{64}{xy}$$

$$C(x, y) = 20xy + \frac{1280}{y} + \frac{1280}{x} \qquad \text{when simplified}$$

We can proceed to minimize this function by getting $\partial C/\partial x = 0$ and $\partial C/\partial y = 0$.

$$\begin{cases} \dfrac{\partial C}{\partial x} = 20y - \dfrac{1280}{x^2} = 0 \\[2mm] \dfrac{\partial C}{\partial y} = 20x - \dfrac{1280}{y^2} = 0 \end{cases}$$

The first equation yields $y = 64/x^2$. Substituting $64/x^2$ for y in the second equation produces

$$20x - \frac{1280}{\left(\dfrac{64}{x^2}\right)^2} = 0 \qquad \text{or} \qquad 20x - \frac{20x^4}{64} = 0 \qquad \text{or} \qquad x - \frac{x^4}{64} = 0$$

After factoring out an x, we have

$$(x)\left(1 - \frac{x^3}{64}\right) = 0$$

The product is zero if $x = 0$ (which we reject as an impossible dimension for an aquarium) or if the other factor, $1 - x^3/64$, is zero. Continuing,

$$1 - \frac{x^3}{64} = 0$$

$$\frac{x^3}{64} = 1$$

$$x^3 = 64$$

$$x = 4$$

To obtain y, return to either of the original equations ($\partial C/\partial x = 0$ or $\partial C/\partial y = 0$) involving x and y and use 4 for x. We shall use the equation

$$20y - \frac{1280}{x^2} = 0$$

$$20y - \frac{1280}{16} = 0 \qquad \text{using 4 for } x$$

$$20y - 80 = 0$$

$$20y = 80$$

$$y = 4$$

Finally, because volume xyz is 64, we have $xyz = 64$, or $(4)(4)z = 64$. This yields $z = 4$.

Thus, the cost of the aquarium will be minimized if we make the length, width, and height all 4 feet. In Exercise 30, you will have the opportunity to verify that these dimensions do indeed minimize the cost (rather than maximize it). In Exercise 37, you will have a chance to comment on the shape. ◆

10.3 Exercises

In Exercises 1–14, find the critical points of each function.

1. $f(x, y) = x^2 + y^2 - 6x + 2y$

2. $f(x, y) = x^2 - 2y^2 - 5x + 4y - 9$

3. $f(x, y) = 3x^3 + y^2 - 36x - 10y + 7$

4. $f(x, y) = x^3 + 3y^2 - 48x + 3y - 2$

5. $g(x, y) = 2x^3 + 3x^2 + y^2 - 8y + 5$

6. $g(x, y) = 4x^3 - 6x^2 + 3y^2 - 12y - 1$

7. $f(x, y) = x^3 + y^3 - 3x - 27y + 4$

8. $g(x, y) = -x^2 - y^2 + 4x + 4y - 8$

9. $h(x, y) = x^2 + 6xy + 2y^2 - 6x + 10y + 1$

10. $f(x, y) = x^2 + xy + y^2 + 3x - 3y + 16$

11. $f(x, y) = x^3 + y^3 - 3x^2 - 3y^2 - 9x + 3$

12. $f(x, y) = x^2 + xy + 3x + 2y$

13. $f(x, y) = \frac{1}{3}x^3 - xy + \frac{1}{2}y^2 - 3$

14. $f(x, y) = x^2 + 4xy + y^2 + 2$

In Exercises 15–25, find the relative maximum and minimum values of each function, if there are any.

15. $f(x, y) = x^2 + y^2 + 8x - 2y + 5$

16. $f(x, y) = x^2 + y^2 + 6$

17. $f(x, y) = 1 + 4x - 6y - x^2 - y^2$

18. $f(x, y) = x^2 + 6xy - y^2 + 9$

19. $f(x, y) = -x^2 + xy - y^2 - 2x - 2y + 3$

20. $g(x, y) = 4x^3 - 6x^2 + 3y^2 - 12y - 1$

21. $f(x, y) = x^2 - 4xy + y^3 + 4y - 7$

22. $f(x, y) = x^2 + xy + y^2 + 3x - 3y$

23. $f(x, y) = x^3 + y^3 - 3x^2 - 3y^2 - 9x + 4$

24. $g(x, y) = 4x^3 + y^3 - 12x - 3y + 5$

25. $f(x, y) = x^2 + 3xy - y^2 + 4y - 6x + 1$

W 26. (REVENUE) Attempt to maximize the revenue function

$$R(x, y) = 2xy - \frac{1}{2}x^2 - y^2 - 3x - 4y + 20$$

What is your conclusion?

27. (PROFIT) A local company advertises on the radio and in the newspaper. Let x and y represent the amounts (in thousands of dollars) spent on radio and newspaper advertising, respectively. The company's profit based on this advertising has been determined to be (in thousands of dollars)

$$P(x, y) = -2x^2 - xy - y^2 + 8x + 9y + 10$$

How much money should the company spend on each type of advertising in order to maximize its profit?

28. (REVENUE) A manufacturer makes x thousand radios and y thousand tape recorders. The resulting revenue (in thousands of dollars) is

$$R(x, y) = xy - 2x^2 - y^2 + 30x - 4y + 20$$

How many of each product should the manufacturer make in order to have maximum revenue? Also, how much is that maximum revenue?

29. (PROFIT) A company makes two kinds of personal computers. One sells for $1200, the other sells for $1500. If the company sells x of the $1200 computers and y of the $1500 computers, the revenue (in hundreds of dollars) is $R = 12x + 15y$. The cost of making the computers is $C = x^2 + y^2 - xy$ hundred dollars. How many of each kind of computer should be made in order to maximize *profit*?

30. (COST) Use $C(x, y)$ and the second partials test to show that the values $x = 4$ and $y = 4$ do indeed minimize (rather than maximize) the cost function of Example 5.

31. Find three positive numbers that satisfy both of these conditions:
  (i) Their sum is 27.
  (ii) The sum of the squares of the numbers is as small as possible.
  Hint: Call the numbers x, y, and z. Obtain an equation from condition (i) and a function from condition (ii). Then use the equation to substitute for z in the function. Finally, proceed to minimize the resulting function of x and y.

32. (MINIMUM MATERIAL) A rectangular cardboard box (with a top) is being made to contain a volume of 27 cubic feet. Find the dimensions that will minimize the amount of material used to make the box.

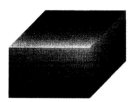

33. (USPS PACKAGE SIZE) The United States Postal Service (USPS) insists that the length plus girth of a package to be mailed cannot exceed 84 inches. The *girth* is the distance around the middle. The package shown here is taped along the girth, which is $2x + 2z$ inches. Determine the dimensions (x, y, and z) of the largest volume package that can be mailed (see the figure). The length of the package is y.

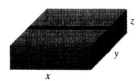

34. (*STORAGE FACILITY*) A farmers' cooperative plans to construct a rectangular storage facility for grain. The building will contain a volume of 16,000 cubic feet. The cost for the roof and the floor is $10 per square foot. The cost for the sides is $5 per square foot.

    (a) What should be the dimensions of the storage facility in order to minimize the cost of materials?

    (b) What is the cost of materials for a storage facility built to the specifications determined in part (a)?

35. (*MINIMUM COST*) A manufacturer of large boxes will use two different materials to make a closed rectangular box with a volume of 128 cubic feet. Material for the top and bottom costs 20¢ per square foot. Material for the sides costs 10¢ per square foot. Determine the dimensions that will minimize the cost of materials.

36. (*HARDY-WEINBERG LAW*) Alleles named A, B, and O determine the four blood types—A (AA or AO), B (BB or BO), O (OO), and AB. The Hardy-Weinberg law states that the proportion P of people in any population who have two different alleles is given by

$$P = 2pq + 2pr + 2rq$$

where p, q, and r are the proportions of alleles A, B, and O, respectively, in the population. Show that the largest P can be is 2/3. (*Hint:* Use the fact that $p + q + r = 1$ to eliminate r from the equation for P.)

W 37. (*MINIMUM COST*) Though it is often very important for a manufacturer to minimize the cost of making a product, sometimes other considerations can override this concern. Use the aquarium example (Example 5) and give reasons why you may not want to produce the shape indicated by the lowest-cost approach.

10.4 | *LAGRANGE MULTIPLIERS*

Figure 17
Joseph Louis Lagrange
(1736–1813)

Some applied problems require that we maximize or minimize a function subject to some additional condition or **constraint.** In Example 3 of Section 4.5, a family wanted to determine the dimensions that would maximize the area of their patio. The *constraint* was that they had only 120 feet of fence to enclose the patio. We solved that problem and other applied maximum/minimum problems by inserting the constraint information into the function to be maximized or minimized—either by immediate substitution or by manipulating a constraint equation and then substituting. Unfortunately, such equation manipulation cannot always be done easily, and sometimes it can produce an expression that is difficult to work with.

The French-Italian mathematician Joseph Louis Lagrange (1736–1813) developed a method that uses partial derivatives to solve such constrained maximum/minimum problems. In his method, called **Lagrange multipliers,** the constraint is stated as a function and is multiplied by a new variable called a Lagrange multiplier.

Suppose we wish to maximize a function $z = f(x, y)$. Its graph is a surface in three dimensions. The constraint, being an equation involving x and y (only), is a curve in the xy plane. Finding the maximum of the function subject to the constraint means finding the highest point on the surface that lies directly above the graph of the constraint equation. See Figure 18.

We now state the method of Lagrange multipliers for functions of two variables. The number λ (the Greek letter lambda) is the Lagrange multiplier.

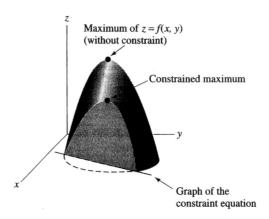

Figure 18 The maximum value of $z = f(x, y)$, subject to a constraint

---

The Method of Lagrange Multipliers

The relative extrema of $z = f(x, y)$ subject to the constraint $g(x, y) = 0$ are found from the new function

$$F(x, y, \lambda) = f(x, y) + \lambda \cdot g(x, y)$$

by solving the system

$$\begin{cases} F_x(x, y, \lambda) = 0 \\ F_y(x, y, \lambda) = 0 \\ F_\lambda(x, y, \lambda) = 0 \end{cases}$$

for λ and then for points (x, y). The relative extrema are included among the solution points (x, y) obtained.

The method of Lagrange multipliers does not specify whether the point obtained is a maximum, a minimum, or neither. Advanced techniques are needed to make the distinction. For problems given in this book, however, assume that the point obtained is the extremum requested. If more than one point is obtained, functional values can be calculated to determine which is the desired maximum or minimum.

The proof for this method requires advanced calculus. However, a geometric illustration using level curves offers justification for the method. Consider various level curves $f(x, y) = c$ of the function $z = f(x, y)$. If the level curves are graphed in the xy plane along with the graph of the constraint equation $g(x, y) = 0$, then the desired constrained extremum will occur at the point where the constraint curve is tangent to a level curve. (In the case of a maximum, it will be the highest level curve that intersects the constraint curve.) The method of Lagrange multipliers selects this point from among all points of intersection of the constraint curve and the level curves. Figure 19 shows the level curves of a function similar to the one graphed in Figure 18. The line is the constraint curve. The coordinates of the point of tangency will yield the constrained maximum. Looking at both Figure 19 and Figure 18 should help you to see this idea.

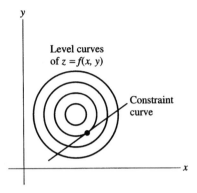

Figure 19 The coordinates of the point of tangency (big dot) will yield the constrained maximum.

EXAMPLE 1 Determine the minimum value of $f(x, y) = 2x^2 + y^2 + 7$ subject to the constraint $x + y = 18$.

SOLUTION Here $f(x, y) = 2x^2 + y^2 + 7$. The constraint $x + y = 18$ must be written in the form $g(x, y) = 0$. Thus we have

$$f(x, y) = 2x^2 + y^2 + 7 \qquad g(x, y) = x + y - 18$$

Now we can easily construct the function $F(x, y, \lambda) = f(x, y) + \lambda \cdot g(x, y)$.

$$F(x, y, \lambda) = (2x^2 + y^2 + 7) + \lambda \cdot (x + y - 18)$$
$$F(x, y, \lambda) = 2x^2 + y^2 + 7 + \lambda x + \lambda y - 18\lambda \qquad \text{when simplified}$$

It follows that the three partial derivatives are

$$F_x(x, y, \lambda) = 4x + \lambda$$
$$F_y(x, y, \lambda) = 2y + \lambda$$
$$F_\lambda(x, y, \lambda) = x + y - 18$$

The system we must solve is

$$\begin{cases} 4x + \lambda = 0 \\ 2y + \lambda = 0 \\ x + y - 18 = 0 \end{cases}$$

From the first two equations, we obtain $\lambda = -4x$ and $\lambda = -2y$. Then, $-4x = -2y$, or $y = 2x$. And since we now know that $y = 2x$, we can substitute $2x$ for y in the third equation, $x + y - 18 = 0$. As a result, we obtain the equation $x + 2x - 18 = 0$, or $3x = 18$. It follows readily that

$$x = 6 \qquad y = 12$$

In this example only one point (x, y) is produced, namely $(6, 12)$. Consequently, the minimum value of $f(x, y) = 2x^2 + y^2 + 7$ comes from $(6, 12)$. Specifically,

$$f(6, 12) = 2 \cdot 6^2 + 12^2 + 7 = 223$$

We conclude that the minimum value of $f(x, y) = 2x^2 + y^2 + 7$, subject to the given constraint $x + y = 18$, is 223. ◆

APPLIED

EXAMPLE 2   **COBB-DOUGLAS PRODUCTION FUNCTION**

Suppose that for a particular product the number of units manufactured is given by the Cobb-Douglas production function

$$f(x, y) = 600x^{2/3}y^{1/3}$$

where x is the number of units of labor and y is the number of units of capital. The cost of labor is \$400 per unit, and the cost of capital is \$200 per unit. The company wants to make 54,000 units of this product at the lowest cost.

(a) Determine the number of units of labor and the number of units of capital it should use to minimize its cost.

(b) Find the actual minimum cost of producing the 54,000 units.

SOLUTION   **(a)** Because x units of labor cost \$400 each and y units of capital cost \$200 each, the combined cost of labor and capital is

$$C(x, y) = 400x + 200y$$

And *this* is the function that we want to minimize. The *constraint* is that the production $600x^{2/3}y^{1/3}$ be 54,000 units. Thus, we seek to minimize $C(x, y)$ subject to $600x^{2/3}y^{1/3} = 54,000$. Here is a brief summary.

$$\textit{Minimize:} \quad C(x, y) = 400x + 200y$$
$$\textit{Subject to:} \quad g(x, y) = 600x^{2/3}y^{1/3} - 54,000 = 0$$

It follows that

$$F(x, y, \lambda) = 400x + 200y + \lambda \cdot (600x^{2/3}y^{1/3} - 54,000)$$

or

$$F(x, y, \lambda) = 400x + 200y + 600\lambda x^{2/3}y^{1/3} - 54,000\lambda$$

Obtaining partial derivatives, we have

$$\begin{cases} F_x = 400 + 400\lambda x^{-1/3}y^{1/3} = 0 \\ F_y = 200 + 200\lambda x^{2/3}y^{-2/3} = 0 \\ F_\lambda = 600x^{2/3}y^{1/3} - 54,000 = 0 \end{cases}$$

Solving the $F_x = 0$ equation for λ yields

$$\lambda = \frac{-400x^{1/3}}{400y^{1/3}}$$

Similarly, solving $F_y = 0$ for λ yields

$$\lambda = \frac{-200y^{2/3}}{200x^{2/3}}$$

The two expressions that are equal to λ can be set equal to each other.

$$\frac{-400x^{1/3}}{400y^{1/3}} = \frac{-200y^{2/3}}{200x^{2/3}} \qquad \text{or} \qquad \frac{x^{1/3}}{y^{1/3}} = \frac{y^{2/3}}{x^{2/3}}$$

Multiplying both sides by common denominator $x^{2/3}y^{1/3}$ produces

$$x = y$$

We can now substitute x for y in the third equation, $600x^{2/3}y^{1/3} - 54{,}000 = 0$. The result is the following equation in one unknown, x:

$$600x^{2/3}x^{1/3} - 54{,}000 = 0 \qquad \text{or} \qquad 600x - 54{,}000 = 0$$

This equation leads to $x = 90$. Then, since $x = y$, $y = 90$ also. The producer should use 90 units of labor and 90 units of capital in order to minimize the cost of making 54,000 units.

(b) The actual cost of making 54,000 units is $C(x, y)$ when $x = 90$ and $y = 90$. Because $C(x, y) = 400x + 200y$, we have

$$C(90, 90) = 400 \cdot 90 + 200 \cdot 90 = 36{,}000 + 18{,}000 = 54{,}000$$

The minimum cost of making 54,000 units is \$54,000. ◆

10.4 Exercises

Use Lagrange multipliers to find the requested maximum or minimum in each exercise of this section.

1. Maximize: $f(x, y) = xy$
Subject to: $x + y = 10$.

2. Maximize: $f(x, y) = 4xy$
Subject to: $x + 2y = 16$.

3. Minimize: $f(x, y) = x^2 + y^2 + 3$
Subject to: $2x + y = 5$.

4. Minimize: $f(x, y) = x^2 + y^2 - 7$
Subject to: $x + 2y = 10$.

5. Maximize: $f(x, y) = 4 - x^2 - y^2$
Subject to: $2x + y = 10$.

6. Minimize: $f(x, y) = x + y^2 + 1$
Subject to: $x + 4y = 6$.

7. Minimize: $f(x, y) = x^2 + 2y^2 - xy$
Subject to: $2x - y = 4$.

8. Minimize: $f(x, y) = 2x^2 + y^2 - xy$
Subject to: $x + y = 8$.

9. Maximize: $f(x, y) = 2xy - 4x$
Subject to: $x + y = 12$.

10. Minimize: $f(x, y) = 8y - 2xy$
Subject to: $x + 2y = 12$.

11. Minimize: $f(x, y) = x^2 + xy + y^2$
Subject to: $x + y = 20$.

12. Find two numbers (x and y) whose sum is 90 and whose product is maximum.

13. Find two numbers whose sum is 1000 and whose product is maximum.

14. *(GARDEN AREA)* If the area of a rectangular garden must be 1000 square feet, what should be its length and width in order to minimize the amount of fencing needed to enclose it? (See the figure.)

Garden area

y

x

15. *(FARMING)* A farmer has 200 meters of fencing. Determine the largest rectangular area he can enclose as a pig pen.

16. *(FARMING)* Assume that the pig pen of Exercise 15 is constructed using a wall of the barn as one side, so that only three sides need to be fenced in. Determine the largest area possible.

17. *(PRODUCTION FUNCTION)* Redo Example 2 (the Cobb-Douglas production function) using instead the function $f(x, y) = 300x^{2/3}y^{1/3}$. Assume the cost of labor is \$200 per unit and the cost of capital is \$100 per unit. The manufacturer wants to make 21,000 units.

18. *(PRODUCTION FUNCTION)* Redo Example 2 (the Cobb-Douglas production function) using instead the function $f(x, y) = 90x^{1/3}y^{2/3}$. Assume the cost of labor is \$50 per unit and the cost of capital is \$100 per unit. The manufacturer wants to make 6300 units.

19. *(PRODUCTION FUNCTION)* Determine the minimum cost of producing 24,000 units of a product, assuming that the cost is $20x + 80y$ and the production function is given by $f(x, y) = 200x^{1/2}y^{1/2}$, where x is the number of units of labor and y is the number of units of capital.

20. *(PRODUCTION FUNCTION)* Determine the minimum cost of producing 1000 units of a product, assuming that the cost is $20x + 60y$ and the production function is given by $f(x, y) = 40x^{1/4}y^{3/4}$, where x is the number of units of labor and y is the number of units of capital.

21. *(PRODUCTION FUNCTION)* Suppose the production function is given by $f(x, y) = 600x^{2/3}y^{1/3}$ and the cost constraint is $400x + 200y = 30,000$ dollars. How many units of labor (x) and how many units of capital (y) should be used in order to maximize production?

22. *(PROFIT)* Suppose a producer's profit on the sale of x radios and y tape recorders is

$$P(x, y) = 60x + 80y - x^2 - y^2$$

Assuming that the producer must make a total of 40 units, how many of each should be made in order to maximize profit, and what is that maximum profit?

23. *(CONTAINER SIZE)* A potato chip company needs cylindrical tin containers that hold 200 cubic inches. What should be the radius and the height of the container if the company wishes to use the least amount of material to make it? The total surface area of the can is $2\pi xy + 2\pi x^2$, where x is the radius and y is the height.

24. *(CARPET AREA)* Professor Konnick has a house with an entrance foyer in the shape of an ellipse. The equation $2x^2 + y^2 = 64$ defines the elliptical border of the floor (x and y are in feet). Find the dimensions of the largest (area) rectangular rug that can be placed in the foyer (see the figure). Note that the area of the rug is not xy.

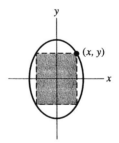

y

(x, y)

x

10.5 | *THE METHOD OF LEAST SQUARES*

Up until now we have solved a variety of problems by performing calculus operations on functions that were provided. However, in some situations we may only have *points* that describe a relationship between two variables. The problem, then, is to construct a function that represents the points, at least approximately.

The points themselves usually come from data that have been collected. For example, a study of people may show the following heights (in inches) and corresponding average weights (in pounds).

height (x)	weight (y)		(x, y)
62	110	$\longrightarrow$	(62, 110)
64	130		(64, 130)
68	140		(68, 140)
70	160		(70, 160)
72	170		(72, 170)

When the points are plotted, the resulting graph is called a **scatter diagram.** Figure 20 shows a scatter diagram of our data points. Although the points do not lie on a straight line, a straight line can be drawn that will be near these points. In other words, a line fits the data reasonably well. See Figure 21.

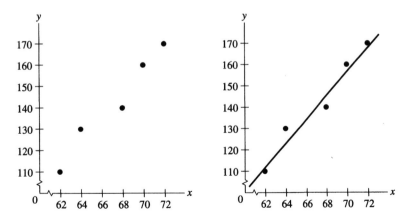

Figure 20 A scatter diagram   **Figure 21** A straight line fits the data reasonably well

Other lines can be drawn that also fit this data fairly well. The straight line that is considered to be the "best" is the one that minimizes the sum of the squares of the vertical distances from each point to that line. The line is called the **least squares line** or the **regression line.** See Figure 22.

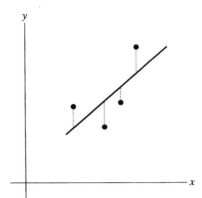

Figure 22 The least squares line minimizes the sum of the squares of the vertical distances from each point to that line.

Now let us proceed to determine the least squares line $y = mx + b$ for any set of points (x_1, y_1), (x_2, y_2), . . . , (x_n, y_n). The distance from each point to the line is measured vertically. This means that the distance is the difference in the y coordinates. Thus the distances are $y_1 - (mx_1 + b)$, $y_2 - (mx_2 + b)$, . . . , $y_n - (mx_n + b)$. The sum of the squares of these distances is

$$[y_1 - (mx_1 + b)]^2 + [y_2 - (mx_2 + b)]^2 + \cdots + [y_n - (mx_n + b)]^2$$

which we can simplify to

$$(y_1 - mx_1 - b)^2 + (y_2 - mx_2 - b)^2 + \cdots + (y_n - mx_n - b)^2$$

Since we seek the values of m and b that minimize this sum, we will call the sum $f(m, b)$, obtain $\partial f/\partial m = 0$ and $\partial f/\partial b = 0$, and then solve for m and b. This is the method used in Section 10.3 to minimize functions.

$$f(m, b) = (y_1 - mx_1 - b)^2 + (y_2 - mx_2 - b)^2 + \cdots + (y_n - mx_n - b)^2$$

$$\frac{\partial f}{\partial m} = -2x_1(y_1 - mx_1 - b) - 2x_2(y_2 - mx_2 - b) - \cdots - 2x_n(y_n - mx_n - b) = 0$$

$$\frac{\partial f}{\partial b} = -2(y_1 - mx_1 - b) - 2(y_2 - mx_2 - b) - \cdots - 2(y_n - mx_n - b) = 0$$

With some effort, we can obtain m and b. The result is

$$m = \frac{n(x_1 y_1 + x_2 y_2 + \cdots + x_n y_n) - (x_1 + x_2 + \cdots + x_n)(y_1 + y_2 + \cdots + y_n)}{n(x_1^2 + x_2^2 + \cdots + x_n^2) - (x_1 + x_2 + \cdots + x_n)^2}$$

$$b = \frac{(y_1 + y_2 + \cdots + y_n) - m(x_1 + x_2 + \cdots + x_n)}{n}$$

These formulas for m and b can be condensed by using summation notation. The result is shown next.

Least Squares Line

The **least squares line** for the n points (x_1, y_1), $(x_2, y_2), \ldots, (x_n, y_n)$ is

$$y = mx + b$$

where

$$m = \frac{n \cdot \Sigma x_i y_i - (\Sigma x_i)(\Sigma y_i)}{n \cdot \Sigma x_i^2 - (\Sigma x_i)^2} \qquad b = \frac{\Sigma y_i - m \cdot \Sigma x_i}{n}$$

Note

Once the equation of the least squares line is determined, predictions can be made by considering other x values and the y values that will correspond based on the equation. Keep in mind that such predictions are only approximations or good guesses, because the data points used to obtain the equation of the line are only near the line rather than on it.

EXAMPLE 1 Determine the equation of the least squares line for the data given below *and* estimate the y value when x is 6.

x	2	3	4	7	8
y	5	7	9	8	12

SOLUTION To obtain the least squares line $y = mx + b$, we use the boxed formulas to determine m and b. In this example, n is 5, because there are 5 data points. We proceed then to determine the values of the various sums that must be substituted into the formulas for m and b.

$$\Sigma x_i = 2 + 3 + 4 + 7 + 8 = 24$$

$$\Sigma y_i = 5 + 7 + 9 + 8 + 12 = 41$$

$$\Sigma x_i y_i = 2 \cdot 5 + 3 \cdot 7 + 4 \cdot 9 + 7 \cdot 8 + 8 \cdot 12 = 219$$

$$\Sigma x_i^2 = 2^2 + 3^2 + 4^2 + 7^2 + 8^2 = 142$$

$$(\Sigma x_i)^2 = (24)^2 = 576$$

Substituting these numbers into the formulas yields

$$m = \frac{5 \cdot 219 - 24 \cdot 41}{5 \cdot 142 - 576} \approx .83 \qquad b = \frac{41 - .83(24)}{5} \approx 4.22$$

Thus, the least squares line for this data is

$$y = .83x + 4.22 \qquad \text{answer}$$

Also, when $x = 6$,

$$y = .83(6) + 4.22 = 9.2$$

Thus, y is approximately 9.2 when x is 6. ◆

> **Note**
> It is usually not advisable to use a least squares line for *extrapolation*—that is, for estimating y values that correspond to x values outside the range of the x values in the given data. The flaw in the reasoning is not always obvious, but in some cases it is strikingly clear. In our section-opening example that used heights and weights, would it be reasonable to obtain the least squares line and then use it to estimate the weight of a baby who is 2 feet long? Consider data on the depreciation of automobiles. Would it be reasonable to look at the values of cars that are 1, 2 or 3 years old and then use the least squares line to estimate the value of an 8-year-old car? The least squares line will not predict the fact that the depreciation eventually slows down or stops. Extrapolation may even produce a negative value for an automobile!

The **method of least squares** was developed by Adrien-Marie Legendre to determine the "best" or "most probable" result of many observations by astronomers of a particular astronomical event. Legendre published his method in 1805.

10.5 Exercises

In Exercises 1–12, determine the equation of the least squares line for each collection of data points.

3.

x	8	9	10	12
y	0	3	5	6

1.

x	3	5	6
y	8	11	12

2.

x	1	4	7
y	2	9	13

4.

x	6	8	10	12
y	3	5	6	10

5.

x	0	1	2	3	4
y	3	4	6	6	8

6.

x	0	3	4	5	6
y	15	9	8	6	2

7.

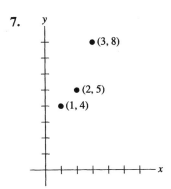

8.

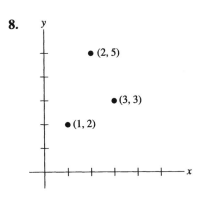

9. (0, 4), (1, 5), (2, 6), (4, 10)

10. (1, 0), (3, 4), (4, 4), (5, 7)

11. (1, 5), (2, 6), (3, 3), (4, 1), (5, 0)

12. (1, 5), (2, 5), (3, 4), (4, 2), (5, 1)

13. Consider the data given.

x	2	3	4	6
y	7	6	6	2

(a) Determine the equation of the least squares line.
(b) Estimate y for x = 5.
(c) Estimate x for y = 4.

14. Consider the data given.

x	6	8	9	10
y	1	5	6	8

(a) Determine the equation of the least squares line.
(b) Estimate y for x = 7.
(c) Estimate x for y = 3.

15. *(ACT AND GPA)* A college advisor is comparing the pre-college ACT scores of five students with the grade point average (GPA) they obtained in college. The data:

ACT (x)	GPA (y)
15	2.0
18	2.4
20	2.6
21	2.8
24	3.2

(a) Find the equation of the least squares line.
(b) On the basis of this study, what GPA might you expect of a student with an ACT score of 23?

16. *(ADVERTISING AND REVENUE)* The table given next shows the amount x (in thousands of dollars) that a company spent monthly on advertising and the corresponding amount y (in thousands of dollars) that the company grossed in revenue that month. Determine the least squares line.

advertising	revenue
3	80
4	100
5	110
6	140
8	170

17. (*CHEMISTRY EXPERIMENT*) A student in chemistry lab conducted an experiment in which he was able to dissolve different amounts (y) of a compound in water by varying the temperature (x) of the water. (The amount of water used was constant.) His data:

temperature (°C)	10	20	30	40	50	60
grams dissolved	61	65	72	77	85	90

(a) Determine the equation of the least squares line.

(b) Use the equation obtained to estimate how many grams of the compound will dissolve at 35°C.

(c) Estimate what temperature is needed to dissolve 80 grams of the compound.

18. (*HEIGHT AND WEIGHT*) Find the equation of the least squares line for the height and weight data given at the beginning of this section, namely:

height (x)	weight (y)
62	110
64	130
68	140
70	160
72	170

19. Show, in steps, how the least squares formula for b (in $y = mx + b$) can be written as $b = \bar{y} - m\bar{x}$.

W 20. The note at the end of the section warns of the danger of extrapolation. Unrealistic heights and negative values for automobiles were cited. Think of another example in which extrapolation may lead to absurd results, and write a brief explanation of it.

W 21. (*SERVER'S TIPS*) The waiters and waitresses at a restaurant have collected data on the amount of the tips left by customers compared with the amount of their bills. What could a least squares line tell them?

TECHNOLOGY *EXERCISES*

Note   A graphing calculator can be used to plot points. In the next two exercises, you will be displaying the data points and the least squares line. For the TI-81 and TI-82, you can proceed as follows. Graph the line first. Then **CLEAR** the graph. Use **DRAW** with **PT-on(** to plot a point. After a point is plotted, use CLEAR and DRAW PT-on(to plot the next point. (The TI-85 has a comparable **DRAW PTON** feature.)

1. In Example 1, the least squares line for the points (2, 5), (3, 7), (4, 9), (7, 8), and (8, 12) was determined to be $y = .83x + 4.22$. First, graph the least squares line using the window $[-1, 14]$ for x and y. Then plot the five given points.

  (a) From the graph, which point is closest (vertically) to the line?

  (b) From the graph, which point is furthest (vertically) from the line?

2. Redo Exercise 1 using instead the points (2, 7), (3, 6), (4, 6), and (6, 2) and the least squares line $y = -1.23x + 9.86$ (from Exercise 13).

Note Graphing calculators can be used to determine the least squares line for a set of data points. For the TI-81, use **STAT DATA Edit** to enter data points (x_1, y_1), (x_2, y_2), and so on. Then use **STAT CALC LinReg** to obtain the values of a and b for the least squares line $y = a + bx$. When finished, use **STAT DATA ClrStat** and Enter to clear out the old data. For the TI-82, use **STAT EDIT** and then **STAT CALC LinReg.** For the TI-85, use **STAT EDIT** to enter the data points and then **STAT CALC LINR** to obtain the a and b values.

In Exercises 3–6, use a graphing calculator to obtain the least squares line for the given data points.

3. Data from Example 1

4. Data from Exercise 9

5. Data from Exercise 15

6. Data from Exercise 17

10.6 | TOTAL DIFFERENTIALS

Section 3.10 presented the concept of the differential of a function of one variable. For $y = f(x)$, the differential dy was defined as

$$dy = f'(x)\, dx$$

with $dx = \Delta x$ and $dy \approx \Delta y$. The differential dy was used to approximate Δy for small values of dx. We estimated such things as the change in revenue associated with small changes in advertising expenditures and the change in price that would cause a small change in demand.

The differential concept can be extended to functions of two variables by the following definition.

Total Differential

Let $z = f(x, y)$. The **total differential** dz is

$$dz = f_x(x, y) \cdot dx + f_y(x, y) \cdot dy$$

where $dx = \Delta x$, $dy = \Delta y$, and $dz \approx \Delta z$ and

$$\Delta z = f(x + \Delta x, y + \Delta y) - f(x, y)$$

EXAMPLE 1 Let $z = f(x, y) = x^2y + 3x - 7y$. Determine dz.

SOLUTION $$dz = f_x(x, y) \cdot dx + f_y(x, y) \cdot dy = (2xy + 3)\, dx + (x^2 - 7)\, dy \qquad \blacklozenge$$

Since $dz \approx \Delta z$, the total differential dz gives an approximation to the change in z (that is, Δz) corresponding to small changes in x and y. Here are two examples.

EXAMPLE 2   Let $z = f(x, y) = xy^2 + 7x - 1$.

(a) Use differentials to find dz (the approximate change in z) when x changes from 4 to 4.01 and y changes from 5 to 5.03.

(b) Determine the exact change in z (that is, Δz) when x changes from 4 to 4.01 and y changes from 5 to 5.03.

SOLUTION   (a) First, obtain the differential.

$$dz = f_x(x, y)\,dx + f_y(x, y)\,dy$$
$$dz = (y^2 + 7)\,dx + 2xy\,dy$$

The x value begins at 4 and changes to 4.01. This means that $x = 4$ and $dx = .01$. Similarly, because y begins at 5 and changes to 5.03, we have $y = 5$ and $dy = .03$. Using these values of x, dx, y, and dy, we find

$$dz = (5^2 + 7)(.01) + 2(4)(5)(.03) = .32 + 1.20 = 1.52$$

The change in z is approximately 1.52.

(b) The exact change Δz is $f(4.01, 5.03) - f(4, 5)$.

$$\Delta z = [(4.01)(5.03)^2 + 7(4.01) - 1] - [(4)(5)^2 + 7(4) - 1]$$
$$= 128.5266 - 127 = 1.5266$$

The total differential provides a good, quick approximation—1.52 versus 1.5266.   ◆

EXAMPLE 3   ***REVENUE INCREASE ASSOCIATED WITH ADVERTISING***

A company advertises on radio and in the newspaper. The function

$$R(x, y) = -.25x^2 + 22x - .5y^2 + 18y + 300$$

gives the revenue in thousands of dollars that is associated with an expenditure of x hundred dollars on radio advertising and y hundred dollars on newspaper advertising. If the amount being spent on advertising now stands at \$2000 for radio and \$1200 for newspapers, use the total differential to determine the approximate increase in revenue associated with a \$150 increase in radio advertising and a \$100 increase in newspaper advertising.

SOLUTION   The approximate increase in revenue will be the value of the total differential dR for $x = 20$, $y = 12$, $dx = 1.5$, and $dy = 1$.

$$dR = R_x(x, y) \cdot dx + R_y(x, y) \cdot dy$$
$$= (-.5x + 22)\,dx + (-1.0y + 18)\,dy$$
$$= [-.5(20) + 22](1.5) + [-1.0(12) + 18](1) = 24$$

The approximate increase in revenue associated with a \$150 increase in radio advertising and a \$100 increase in newspaper advertising is \$24,000.

Exercise 25 asks you to show that the exact increase in revenue is \$22,937.50.   ◆

10.6 Exercises

In Exercises 1–10, determine dz.

1. $z = f(x, y) = x^2 + y^2 + 10$

2. $z = f(x, y) = 3x^2 - 8y^2 + 5$

3. $z = f(x, y) = xy^2 + 3x^2 - 2y^2$

4. $z = f(x, y) = 5x^2 + 3x^2y - 8y$

5. $z = f(x, y) = xe^y + ye^x + 1$

6. $z = f(x, y) = 4e^{xy} - 12$

7. $z = f(x, y) = \dfrac{y}{x} - 8x + 3y$

8. $z = f(x, y) = \dfrac{x}{y} + 4xy + 5$

9. $z = f(x, y) = x \ln y - x^2$

10. $z = f(x, y) = y \ln x + y^3$

In Exercises 11–16, determine dz for the given values of $x, dx, y,$ and dy.

11. $z = f(x, y) = 4x^2y^3$; $x = 5$, $dx = .01$, $y = 9$, $dy = .02$

12. $z = f(x, y) = 3xy + y$; $\quad x = 12$, $\quad dx = .03$, $\quad y = 17$, $dy = .01$

13. $z = f(x, y) = 6x^{1/3}y^{2/3}$; $\quad x = 1$, $\quad dx = .02$, $\quad y = 8$, $dy = .03$

14. $z = f(x, y) = 4x^{1/2}y^{1/3}$; $\quad x = 9$, $\quad dx = .001$, $\quad y = 8$, $dy = .015$

15. $z = f(x, y) = x\sqrt{y}$; $\quad x = 12$, $\quad dx = .015$, $\quad y = 64$, $dy = .01$

16. $z = f(x, y) = y + \sqrt{x}$; $\quad x = 100$, $\quad dx = .8$, $\quad y = 5$, $dy = .01$

In Exercises 17–22, use the total differential to approximate the change in f corresponding to the given changes in x and y.

17. $f(x, y) = 5x^3y^2 + y$; x changes from 4 to 4.01, y changes from 6 to 6.02.

18. $f(x, y) = x + x^2y^2$; x changes from 3 to 3.02, y changes from 10 to 10.01.

19. $f(x, y) = x \ln y$; x changes from 10 to 10.1, y changes from 1 to 1.2.

20. $f(x, y) = 3y \ln (x - 1)$; x changes from 2 to 2.01, y changes from 20 to 20.5.

21. $f(x, y) = 12x^{2/3}y^{1/3}$; x changes from 8 to 9, y changes from 27 to 29.

22. $f(x, y) = 10x^{1/2}y^{1/2}$; x changes from 16 to 17, y changes from 25 to 28.

23. (*REVENUE AND ADVERTISING*) Redo Example 3 assuming that the amount spent on radio advertising will be increased from \$1800 to \$2000 and that the amount spent on newspaper advertising will be increased from \$1400 to \$1500.

24. (*REVENUE AND ADVERTISING*) Find the *exact* increase in revenue for the situation described in Exercise 23.

25. (*REVENUE AND ADVERTISING*) Show that the *exact* increase in revenue for the situation described in Example 3 is \$22,937.50.

26. (*VOLUME CHANGE*) A manufacturer of paper drinking cups decides to make its standard cup slightly smaller than before. The cups are conical and hold volume $V = \frac{1}{3}\pi r^2 h$, where r is the radius of the top and h is the height (see figure). The radius will be changed from 1.5 inches to 1.4 inches, and the height will be changed from 4 inches to 3.9 inches. Use differentials to approximate the reduction in volume that results from these changes.

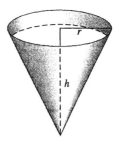

27. (*VOLUME REDUCTION*) A juice drink producer decides to reduce the size of the cylindrical can used to package the product for sale to the public. The volume of a can is $V = \pi r^2 h$, where r is the radius of the base and h is the height. The radius will be reduced from 2 inches to 1.9 inches, and the height will be reduced from 9 inches to 8.8 inches. Use differentials to approximate the reduction in volume as a result of these changes.

28. *(INCREASING PRODUCTION)* The cost of producing x units of one product (product M) and y units of another product (product N) is given by

$$C(x, y) = 500 + 30x + 60y - .1x^2 - .3y^2 \text{ dollars}$$

Use differentials to determine the approximate cost of raising the production levels 1 unit each—from 80 to 81 units of product M and from 93 to 94 units of product N.

29. *(INCREASING PRODUCTION)* The cost of producing x units of one product (product A) and y units of another product (product B) is given by

$$C(x, y) = 900 + 80x + 45y - .02xy \text{ dollars}$$

Use differentials to determine the approximate cost of raising the production levels 1 unit each—from 120 to 121 units of product A and from 200 to 201 units of product B.

30. *(PRODUCTION FUNCTION)* Consider the Cobb-Douglas production function

$$f(x, y) = 40x^{1/3}y^{2/3}$$

where x is the number of units of labor, y is the number of units of capital, and $f(x, y)$ is the number of units produced. Use differentials to estimate the change in production if the number of units of labor is increased from 27 to 28 and the number of units of capital is increased from 64 to 66.

31. *(PRODUCTION FUNCTION)* Consider the Cobb-Douglas production function

$$f(x, y) = 24x^{1/2}y^{1/2}$$

where x is the number of units of labor, y is the number of units of capital, and $f(x, y)$ is the number of units

produced. Use differentials to estimate the change in production if the number of units of labor is increased from 25 to 26 and capital is increased from 36 to 39 units.

32. *(AREA CHANGE)* The area of a rectangle having length x and width y is given by

$$A(x, y) = xy$$

(a) Use differentials to approximate the increase in area dA if the length is increased from 50 meters to 50.03 meters and the width is increased from 40 to 40.15 meters.

(b) Determine the exact increase in area suggested by the increases given in part (a).

(c) Show by using calculations that the difference between the exact increase in area [part (b)] and the approximate increase in area [part (a)] is $(dx)(dy)$. The drawing illustrates this idea.

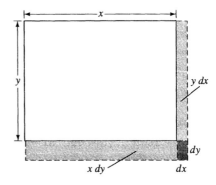

W 33. You have seen the use of differentials to find dz, an approximation to Δz. Are differentials used this way because the exact change Δz cannot be determined? Explain.

10.7 | DOUBLE INTEGRALS

After studying partial differentiation earlier in the chapter, it is natural to wonder if there is a corresponding process for integration (antidifferentiation). Indeed there is a process called **partial integration,** in which we perform the integration with respect to one variable while treating the other variable(s) as constant. Here are two examples of such integration, using definite integrals.

EXAMPLE 1 Evaluate $\displaystyle\int_1^2 6x^2y\,dx$.

SOLUTION The dx indicates that the integration is with respect to x, treating y as a constant.

$$\int_1^2 6x^2y\,dx = \left[2x^3y\right]_{x=1}^{x=2} = (16y) - (2y) = 14y$$ ◆

EXAMPLE 2 Evaluate $\displaystyle\int_0^4 6x^2y\,dy$.

SOLUTION The dy indicates that the integration is with respect to y, treating x as a constant.

$$\int_0^4 6x^2y\,dy = \left[3x^2y^2\right]_{y=0}^{y=4} = (48x^2) - (0) = 48x^2$$ ◆

In Example 1, integrating with respect to x produced a function of y.

$$\int_a^b f(x,\,y)\,dx \qquad \text{is a function of } y$$

The integral yields a function of y, so it can be integrated again—this time with respect to y. Similarly, the integral of Example 2 yields a function of x, which could be integrated again—this time with respect to x. With all of this in mind, we proceed to perform two such integrations.

EXAMPLE 3 Evaluate. **(a)** $\displaystyle\int_0^4\left[\int_1^2 6x^2y\,dx\right]dy$ **(b)** $\displaystyle\int_1^2\left[\int_0^4 6x^2y\,dy\right]dx$

SOLUTION **(a)**

$$\int_0^4\left[\int_1^2 6x^2y\,dx\right]dy = \int_0^4\left[14y\right]dy \qquad \text{done in Example 1}$$
$$= \left[7y^2\right]_0^4 = 112$$

(b)

$$\int_1^2\left[\int_0^4 6x^2y\,dy\right]dx = \int_1^2\left[48x^2\right]dx \qquad \text{done in Example 2}$$
$$= \left[16x^3\right]_1^2 = 112$$ ◆

The two integrals of Example 3 yield the same result. That is,

$$\int_1^2\left[\int_0^4 6x^2y\,dy\right]dx = \int_0^4\left[\int_1^2 6x^2y\,dx\right]dy$$

This equality is an example of the following important result.

Order of Integration

Double integrations such as those of Example 3 can be performed with respect to either variable first. The order of integration will not matter. That is,

$$\int_a^b \left[\int_c^d f(x, y)\, dy \right] dx = \int_c^d \left[\int_a^b f(x, y)\, dx \right] dy$$

The brackets can be removed, in which case we have

$$\int_a^b \int_c^d f(x, y)\, dy\, dx = \int_c^d \int_a^b f(x, y)\, dx\, dy$$

It is understood that the inner integration is done first.

We shall see next that the limits of integration lead to inequalities that define a rectangular region. We have

$$a \le x \le b \qquad \text{and} \qquad c \le y \le d$$

The region that includes all x between a and b and all y between c and d is rectangular, as illustrated in Figure 23. We will call such a region R.

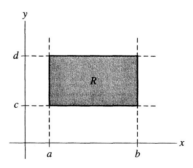

Figure 23 A rectangular region R

A definition of the double integral can now be given.

Double Integral

The **double integral** of $f(x, y)$ over the rectangular region R defined by $a \leq x \leq b$ and $c \leq y \leq d$ is given by

$$\iint_R f(x, y) \, dy \, dx \qquad \text{or} \qquad \iint_R f(x, y) \, dx \, dy$$

and is the same as

$$\int_a^b \int_c^d f(x, y) \, dy \, dx \qquad \text{or} \qquad \int_c^d \int_a^b f(x, y) \, dx \, dy$$

This definition is less formal than one you might find in an advanced mathematics text. It gives us the means to evaluate a variety of double integrals.

EXAMPLE 4   Evaluate the double integral $\displaystyle\int_3^4 \int_0^6 (3x + 2y) \, dx \, dy$.

SOLUTION   The inner integration (with respect to x) is done first.

$$\int_3^4 \int_0^6 (3x + 2y) \, dx \, dy = \int_3^4 \left[\frac{3x^2}{2} + 2xy \right]_{x=0}^{x=6} dy$$

$$= \int_3^4 [(54 + 12y) - (0 + 0)] \, dy$$

$$= \int_3^4 (54 + 12y) \, dy = \left[54y + 6y^2 \right]_3^4$$

$$= (216 + 96) - (162 + 54) = 96 \qquad \blacklozenge$$

EXAMPLE 5   Evaluate $\displaystyle\int_0^7 \int_1^2 4xy \, dy \, dx$.

SOLUTION   The inner integration (with respect to y) is done first.

$$\int_0^7 \int_1^2 4xy \, dy \, dx = \int_0^7 \left[2xy^2 \right]_{y=1}^{y=2} dx = \int_0^7 (8x - 2x) \, dx$$

$$= \int_0^7 6x \, dx = \left[3x^2 \right]_0^7 = 147 \qquad \blacklozenge$$

Volume

The double integral has a geometric interpretation. Recall that with functions of one variable, the definite integral represents the area under the curve when the function is nonnegative. Specifically,

$$\int_a^b f(x)\,dx$$

is the area under the graph of $y = f(x)$ between $x = a$ and $x = b$, when $f(x) \geq 0$. Furthermore, the integral notation represents the limit of the sum of the areas of approximating rectangles that have length $f(x_i)$ and width Δx.

$$\int_a^b f(x)\,dx = \lim_{\Delta x \to 0} \sum_{i=1}^{n} f(x_i)\,\Delta x$$

Note

If you would like to review the concept, drawing, and development of the area under a curve as the definite integral, refer to Section 6.3.

With functions of two variables, the graph is a surface. Consider $z = f(x, y)$ over the region R defined by $a \leq x \leq b$ and $c \leq y \leq d$, and assume that $f(x, y) \geq 0$ for all (x, y) in region R. See Figure 24. The rectangular region can be subdivided into small rectangles having length Δx and width Δy. The area of each rectangle is then $\Delta x \cdot \Delta y$. See Figure 25. Select some point (x_i, y_i) in the rectangular region. Then form a box by using as the base the Δx by Δy subregion containing (x_i, y_i) and using $f(x_i, y_i)$ as the height. The box will reach upward as far as the graph of the surface. Its volume will be $f(x_i, y_i)\,\Delta x\,\Delta y$—height times length times width. See Figure 26.

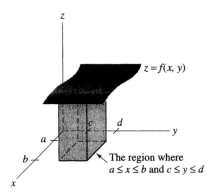

Figure 24 Considering the volume under a surface

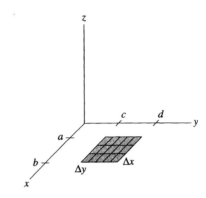

Figure 25 The subdivided rectangular region

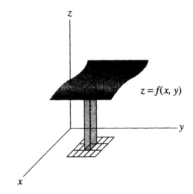

Figure 26 A box that reaches upward to the surface

Thus, $f(x_i, y_i) \, \Delta x \, \Delta y$ is the approximate volume between the surface $z = f(x, y)$ and one small region Δx by Δy in the xy plane. But there are many such small regions—based on, say, $n \, \Delta x$'s and $m \, \Delta y$'s. If you sum up all such box volumes involving all the subregions Δx by Δy, the volume is

$$V_{\text{boxes}} = \sum_{j=1}^{m} \sum_{i=1}^{n} f(x_i, y_j) \, \Delta x \, \Delta y$$

This is *approximately* the volume under the surface. The exact volume under the surface is the limit of this sum as $\Delta x \to 0$ and $\Delta y \to 0$. Using integral notation as in Sections 6.3–6.5, we have the following result.

Volume Under a Surface

Let $z = f(x, y)$ be nonnegative for all (x, y) in the region R defined by $a \leq x \leq b$ and $c \leq y \leq d$. Then the **volume** between the surface $z = f(x, y)$ and the region R is given by

$$V = \int_c^d \int_a^b f(x, y)\, dx\, dy$$

EXAMPLE 6 Determine the volume between the surface $f(x, y) = x^3 + xy$ and the region R defined by $0 \leq x \leq 2$ and $1 \leq y \leq 4$.

SOLUTION Since x goes from 0 to 2 and y goes from 1 to 4, the volume is

$$V = \int_1^4 \int_0^2 (x^3 + xy)\, dx\, dy = \int_1^4 \left[\frac{x^4}{4} + \frac{x^2 y}{2}\right]_{x=0}^{x=2} dy$$

$$= \int_1^4 [(4 + 2y) - (0 + 0)]\, dy = \int_1^4 (4 + 2y)\, dy$$

$$= \left[4y + y^2\right]_1^4 = (16 + 16) - (4 + 1) = 27 \text{ cubic units} \qquad \blacklozenge$$

Average Value

In Section 6.5 the average value of a function f of one variable x over an interval $a \leq x \leq b$ was found to be

$$\frac{1}{b - a} \int_a^b f(x)\, dx$$

The average value of a function $f(x, y)$ of two variables over the region R has a comparable formula.

Average Value of a Function

The **average value of $f(x, y)$** over the region R defined by $a \leq x \leq b$ and $c \leq y \leq d$ is

$$\frac{1}{\text{area of } R} \cdot \int_c^d \int_a^b f(x, y)\, dx\, dy$$

Since the length of the region is $b - a$ and the width is $d - c$, the *area of the region R* is $(b - a)(d - c)$.

EXAMPLE 7   Determine the average value of the function $f(x, y) = 2x + 3y$ over the region defined by $1 \leq x \leq 4$ and $0 \leq y \leq 5$.

SOLUTION   The area of the region is $(4 - 1)(5 - 0) = 15$. The average value is then

$$\frac{1}{15} \int_0^5 \int_1^4 (2x + 3y)\, dx\, dy = \frac{1}{15} \int_0^5 \left[x^2 + 3xy\right]_{x=1}^{x=4} dy$$

$$= \frac{1}{15} \int_0^5 [(16 + 12y) - (1 + 3y)]\, dy$$

$$= \frac{1}{15} \int_0^5 (15 + 9y)\, dy = \frac{1}{15} \left[15y + \frac{9y^2}{2}\right]_0^5$$

$$= \frac{1}{15} \left[\left(75 + \frac{225}{2}\right) - (0 + 0)\right]$$

$$= \frac{1}{15} \cdot \frac{375}{2} = \frac{25}{2} \quad \text{or} \quad 12.5 \qquad \blacklozenge$$

Nonrectangular Regions

Thus far, double integrals have been defined over rectangular regions where $a \leq x \leq b$ and $c \leq y \leq d$. In such instances all four limits of integration are constants. On the other hand, if either or both of the inner limits of integration were made to be variables (or functions of a variable), then the region R over which we are integrating would no longer be a rectangle. See Figure 27. The next example illustrates how the evaluation of such integrals resembles that of others already presented.

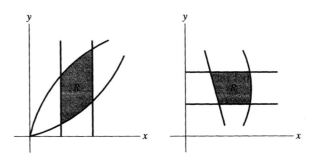

Figure 27 Two nonrectangular regions

EXAMPLE 8   Evaluate $\displaystyle\int_1^2 \int_0^x (2y + 3)\, dy\, dx.$

SOLUTION
$$\int_1^2 \int_0^x (2y + 3)\, dy\, dx = \int_1^2 \left[y^2 + 3y\right]_{y=0}^{y=x} dx = \int_1^2 [(x^2 + 3x) - (0 + 0)]\, dx$$

$$= \int_1^2 (x^2 + 3x)\, dx = \left[\frac{x^3}{3} + \frac{3x^2}{2}\right]_1^2 = \frac{41}{6}$$

Figure 28 illustrates the region over which the integration was done. It is the region bounded by $y = 0$, $y = x$, $x = 1$, and $x = 2$.

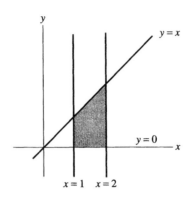

Figure 28 The region over which we are integrating   ◆

EXAMPLE 9 Evaluate $\displaystyle\int_0^1 \int_{\sqrt{y}}^{y^2} 2x \, dx \, dy.$

SOLUTION $\displaystyle\int_0^1 \int_{\sqrt{y}}^{y^2} 2x \, dx \, dy = \int_0^1 \left[x^2 \right]_{x=\sqrt{y}}^{x=y^2} dy = \int_0^1 (y^4 - y) \, dy = \left[\frac{y^5}{5} - \frac{y^2}{2} \right]_0^1 = -\frac{3}{10}$ ◆

10.7 Exercises

In Exercises 1–10, use partial integration to evaluate each integral.

1. $\displaystyle\int_1^3 12x^2y \, dx$

2. $\displaystyle\int_0^2 12x^2y \, dy$

3. $\displaystyle\int_0^3 8xy \, dy$

4. $\displaystyle\int_1^2 8xy^2 \, dx$

5. $\displaystyle\int_4^7 (1 + 3x) \, dy$

6. $\displaystyle\int_4^7 (1 + 3x) \, dx$

7. $\displaystyle\int_2^5 (2x + 2y) \, dx$

8. $\displaystyle\int_1^6 (2x + 2y) \, dy$

9. $\displaystyle\int_2^4 (x^2 + y) \, dy$

10. $\displaystyle\int_0^3 (x^2 + y) \, dx$

Evaluate each double integral in Exercises 11–24.

11. $\displaystyle\int_1^3 \int_0^2 (2x + 6y) \, dx \, dy$

12. $\displaystyle\int_1^4 \int_0^2 3x^2 \, dx \, dy$

13. $\displaystyle\int_0^2 \int_1^4 8xy \, dy \, dx$

14. $\displaystyle\int_2^3 \int_1^4 (1 + 2xy) \, dy \, dx$

15. $\displaystyle\int_1^4 \int_0^1 6xy^2 \, dx \, dy$

16. $\displaystyle\int_1^3 \int_0^2 6x^2y \, dx \, dy$

17. $\displaystyle\int_0^1 \int_0^2 (x^2 + y^2) \, dy \, dx$

18. $\displaystyle\int_0^4 \int_0^1 (x^3 + y^3) \, dx \, dy$

19. $\displaystyle\int_3^8 \int_0^6 \sqrt{1 + x} \, dy \, dx$

20. $\displaystyle\int_0^6 \int_3^8 \sqrt{1 + x} \, dx \, dy$

21. $\displaystyle\int_0^2 \int_0^1 e^{x+y} \, dx \, dy$

22. $\displaystyle\int_0^1 \int_2^7 e^y \, dx \, dy$

23. $\displaystyle\int_0^8 \int_1^e \frac{y}{x}\, dx\, dy$ **24.** $\displaystyle\int_1^e \int_0^8 \frac{y}{x}\, dy\, dx$

25. As you know, when all four limits of integration are constants (that is, when we are integrating over a rectangular region), the order of integration can be reversed. Reverse the order of integration in Exercise 11, and show that the result is the same as the original.

26. Do the same as in Exercise 25, except use the integrals of Exercises 13, 15, and 21.

27. Determine the limits of integration and then evaluate the double integral below over the rectangular region R whose vertices are $(2, 1)$, $(4, 1)$, $(2, 3)$, and $(4, 3)$. A drawing of the region may be helpful.

$$\iint_R (x + 2y)\, dx\, dy$$

28. Use the same integral as in Exercise 27, but let the vertices of the rectangular region be $(0, 2)$, $(8, 2)$, $(0, 5)$, and $(8, 5)$.

In Exercises 29–36, determine the volume between the given surface $z = f(x, y)$ and the rectangular region R defined in each case.

29. $f(x, y) = x + y$; R: $0 \le x \le 2$, $1 \le y \le 3$

30. $f(x, y) = 6x^2y$; R: $1 \le x \le 4$, $0 \le y \le 2$

31. $f(x, y) = x^2 + y^2$; R: $0 \le x \le 2$, $1 \le y \le 2$

32. $f(x, y) = x^2 + y^2 + 1$; R: $0 \le x \le 3$, $0 \le y \le 3$

33. $f(x, y) = 1 + x^2$; R: $1 \le x \le 2$, $0 \le y \le 4$

34. $f(x, y) = y^2 + 2$; R: $0 \le x \le 5$, $0 \le y \le 4$

35. $f(x, y) = \dfrac{1}{y}$; R: $1 \le x \le 10$, $1 \le y \le e$

36. $f(x, y) = e^x$; R: $0 \le x \le 1$, $1 \le y \le 5$

In Exercises 37–42, determine the average value of the function $f(x, y)$ over the rectangular region defined.

37. $f(x, y) = 4x + 3y$; R: $2 \le x \le 5$, $0 \le y \le 4$

38. $f(x, y) = x + y + 1$; R: $1 \le x \le 3$, $2 \le y \le 5$

39. $f(x, y) = 3x^2y$; R: $2 \le x \le 5$, $1 \le y \le 4$

40. $f(x, y) = 12xy^2$; R: $0 \le x \le 4$, $1 \le y \le 4$

41. $f(x, y) = x^2 + y^2$; R: $0 \le x \le 2$, $1 \le y \le 3$

42. $f(x, y) = \sqrt{1 + x}$; R: $1 \le x \le 6$, $0 \le y \le 4$

In Exercises 43–46, determine the limits of integration and *set up the integral* of $f(x, y) = 3xy$ over the region R. *Do not perform the integration.*

43.
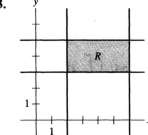

44.
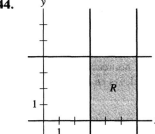

45.
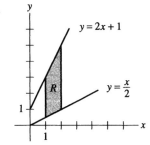

46.
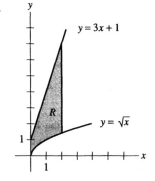

Evaluate each double integral in Exercises 47–60.

47. $\int_0^1 \int_0^y e^x \, dx \, dy$

48. $\int_1^2 \int_0^{y-1} y^2 \, dx \, dy$

49. $\int_2^3 \int_1^{x^2} 4x \, dy \, dx$

50. $\int_1^2 \int_1^{y^2} y \, dx \, dy$

51. $\int_0^2 \int_x^{x^2+1} xy \, dy \, dx$

52. $\int_2^4 \int_{x/2}^{\sqrt{x}} xy \, dy \, dx$

53. $\int_0^2 \int_0^{2x} e^{x^2} \, dy \, dx$

54. $\int_0^2 \int_{x-1}^0 (1 - x + y) \, dy \, dx$

55. $\int_1^2 \int_{-y}^{2y} 3x^2 y \, dx \, dy$

 56. $\int_0^{1/4} \int_{y^2}^{y/2} (x + y) \, dx \, dy$

57. $\int_0^1 \int_y^{\sqrt{y}} 2xy \, dx \, dy$

58. $\int_0^1 \int_{x^2}^x xy \, dy \, dx$

59. $\int_0^1 \int_x^{x^3} 2y \, dy \, dx$

60. $\int_0^2 \int_x^{x^2+1} (3x + 2y) \, dy \, dx$

In Exercises 61–66, draw the nonrectangular region over which integration was performed. As an example, the region for Exercise 60 is drawn here.

61. The region in Exercise 49

62. The region in Exercise 51

63. The region in Exercise 52

64. The region in Exercise 53

65. The region in Exercise 54

66. The region in Exercise 58

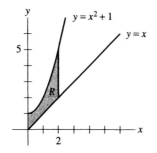

67. (*AVERAGE TEMPERATURE*) A thin, rectangular metal plate, 6 centimeters wide and 4 centimeters high, is being heated so that the temperature T at any point (x, y) on the surface of the plate is given by

$$T(x, y) = 350 - x^2 - y^2$$

T is measured in degrees Fahrenheit and x and y are measured in centimeters (see the figure).

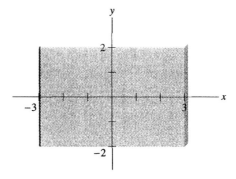

Determine, to the nearest degree, the average temperature of the surface of the plate.

68. (*AVERAGE HEIGHT*) Suppose $H(x, y)$ gives the height, in feet, above sea level of a hilly region. Write the integral that gives the average height above sea level of the region in the figure.

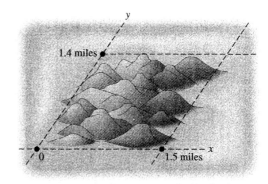

TECHNOLOGY EXERCISES

1. Refer to the Note in the Technology Exercises for Section 6.7. Apply the DRAW Shade instruction to the region of Example 8. You may want to use Shade (0, x, 1, 1, 2). Begin with windows of $[-1, 4]$ for x and y. Use Zoom Square before entering the Shade instruction.

2. Shade the region of Exercise 45. Begin with windows of $[-1, 3]$ for x and $[-1, 8]$ for y. Use Zoom Square before entering the Shade instruction.

3. Shade the region of Exercise 46. Begin with windows of $[-1, 4]$ for x and $[-1, 8]$ for y. Use Zoom Square before entering the Shade instruction.

Note *Mathematica* and *Maple* can evaluate double integrals. The double integral

$$\int_1^4 \int_0^1 6xy^2\, dx\, dy$$

can be evaluated as follows.

Mathematica: `Integrate[6*x*y^2,{x, 0, 1}, {y, 1, 4}]`

Maple: `int(int(6*x*y^2, x = 0..1), y = 1..4);`

If such software is available, use it to evaluate the integrals of Exercises 11, 23, 47, 49, and 57.

Key Terms and Ideas

function of two variables	second partial derivatives	scatter diagram
function of three variables	critical point	least squares line
Cobb-Douglas production function	relative maximum point	regression line
three-dimensional rectangular coordinate system	relative minimum point	total differential
	saddle point	partial integration
domain of $z = f(x, y)$	second partials test	double integral
level curves	Lagrange multipliers	volume under a surface
isoquants	constraint	average value of a function
partial derivative	method of least squares	

Review Exercises for Chapter 10

1. Let $f(x, y) = \dfrac{x^2 + y^2}{2x}$. Compute $f(4, 8)$ and $f(-6, 0)$.

2. Let $f(x, y) = \dfrac{2y + 9}{1 + 5x}$. Compute $f(5, 2)$ and $f(0, 0)$.

3. Determine the domain of $f(x, y) = \dfrac{y - 3}{x - 1}$.

4. Determine the domain of $f(x, y) = \sqrt{2x + y}$.

In Exercises 5–8, sketch the level curves of the given function for the specific c values listed.

5. $f(x, y) = x^2 - y + 2$; $\quad c = -2, 0, 1$

6. $f(x, y) = x^2 + y + 4$; $\quad c = 2, 3, 4$

7. $f(x, y) = 2x - y$; $\quad c = 1, 3, 5$

8. $f(x, y) = 2x + y$; $\quad c = -3, -2, -1, 0$

Determine f_x and f_y for each function in Exercises 9–12.

9. $f(x, y) = x^4 + x^2y^2 - y^4$ **10.** $f(x, y) = x(1 + y)^6$

11. $f(x, y) = e^{3x} + x \ln y$ **12.** $f(x, y) = \dfrac{2y}{3x}$

13. For $f(x, y, z) = xe^y + 3z^5$, find $f_x, f_y,$ and f_z.

14. For $f(x, y, z) = 5xy^2z^3 - 1$, find $f_x, f_y,$ and f_z.

15. Find all four second partials of the function defined by $f(x, y) = 5x^2 - xy + y^3$.

16. Find all four second partials of $f(x, y) = ye^{2x}$.

17. Find the critical points of the function defined by $f(x, y) = x^2 + 2xy - y^2 + 8x - 16y$.

18. Find the critical points of $f(x, y) = 4x^2 - y^2 + 17$.

19. Find the relative maximum or minimum value (if any) of $f(x, y) = 2x^2 + 12xy - 2y^2 - 11$.

20. Find the relative maximum or minimum value (if any) of $f(x, y) = 2x^2 + y^2 - xy - 5y - x + 6$.

21. *(BASEBALL, ERA)* In baseball, a pitcher's earned run average (ERA) is given by

$$E(r, i) = \frac{9r}{i}$$

where r is the number of earned runs scored during the number of innings i that he or she pitched.
(a) Matt pitched 4 innings and gave up 1 earned run. What is his ERA?
(b) Tanya pitched 12 innings and gave up no earned runs. What is her ERA?

22. *(SURFACE OF BOX)* The surface area of an open box (a box with no top) having length x, width y, and height z is

$$S(x, y, z) = xy + 2xz + 2yz$$

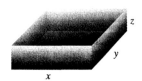

(a) Compute the value of $S(3, 5, 2)$.
W (b) Explain in words exactly what you determined in part (a). In your explanation, *do not use* the letters x, y, z, or S or the notation $S(3, 5, 2)$.

23. *(REVENUE)* A microwave oven producer makes x hundred of its regular model and y hundred of its deluxe model. Their revenue (in hundreds of dollars) is

$$R(x, y) = xy - x^2 - 2y^2 - x + 25y$$

How many of each model should be made in order to maximize revenue?

24. Use Lagrange multipliers to maximize the function $f(x, y) = 4xy - 8x$ subject to $x + y = 30$.

25. Use Lagrange multipliers to minimize the function $f(x, y) = x^2 + 2y^2 - 2x + 5$ subject to $x + 2y = 10$.

26. *(CHOLESTEROL LEVEL)* Blood cholesterol level is known to increase as one gets older. Find the equation of the least squares line for the data given here from a random sample of 7 men.

age (x)	23	28	31	46	47	53	61
cholesterol (y)	164	201	180	235	220	305	260

27. *(ASSESSMENT TESTING)* The college gives all students an assessment test before they begin studying calculus. At the end of the calculus course, the instructor notes each student's final exam score (percent). Given the following data for 8 students, find the equation of the least squares line.

assessment score (x)	20	21	23	25	26	27	28	30
calculus exam (y)	72	90	76	87	80	98	85	92

28. *(PRODUCTION FUNCTION)* Given the Cobb-Douglas production function

$$f(x, y) = 50x^{1/4}y^{3/4}$$

use differentials to estimate the change in production if the number of units of labor (x) is decreased from 26 to 25 and the number of units of capital (y) is decreased from 40 to 38.

29. *(VOLUME INCREASE)* The volume of a box with a square base is given by

$$V(x, y) = x^2y$$

where the length and width of the box are both x and the

height is y. Use differentials to approximate the increase in volume obtained by increasing both length and width from 120 centimeters to 124 centimeters and increasing the height from 70 centimeters to 73 centimeters.

30. **(MINIMUM MATERIAL)** An open rectangular box is being made to contain a volume of 108 cubic feet. Find the dimensions that will minimize the amount of material used to make the box.

31. **(MAXIMUM CARPET)** Use Lagrange multipliers to determine the dimensions of the rectangular carpet of largest area that can be placed inside a circular foyer defined by $x^2 + y^2 = 4$. (x and y are in feet.)

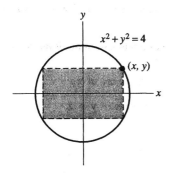

Evaluate each double integral in Exercises 32–41.

32. $\displaystyle\int_4^{10}\int_2^3 12xy\,dx\,dy$

33. $\displaystyle\int_2^8\int_1^3 (4x-3y)\,dx\,dy$

34. $\displaystyle\int_{-4}^9\int_1^e \frac{1}{y}\,dy\,dx$

35. $\displaystyle\int_0^5\int_0^{1/2} 4e^{2x}\,dx\,dy$

36. $\displaystyle\int_2^5\int_1^6 \sqrt{y+3}\,dy\,dx$

37. $\displaystyle\int_{-2}^1\int_1^4 8\,dy\,dx$

38. $\displaystyle\int_{-3}^1\int_2^{2y} (x-y)\,dx\,dy$

39. $\displaystyle\int_0^6\int_0^{\sqrt{y}} (2x+4x^3)\,dx\,dy$

40. $\displaystyle\int_{-1}^0\int_0^{x+1} e^y\,dy\,dx$

41. $\displaystyle\int_0^1\int_x^{x^2} 4y\,dy\,dx$

W **42.** If level curves were used to describe a lake, what would the different curves represent?

Chapter Projects and Essays

Many of the projects and essays lend themselves to group activity, although most can be completed by individual effort.

1. LEVEL CURVES

BACKGROUND   Level curves were introduced in Section 10.1. This project offers an opportunity to continue the study in specific application areas.

THE PROJECT   Select at least one of the following five subjects. Locate drawings or other information related to the associated level curves. Prepare a report about the applications, and include drawings of level curves.

Economics: isocosts and isoprofits based on cost and profit functions. For reference, use economics texts.

Meteorology: isotherms and isobars on weather maps. For reference, use newspapers and meteorology texts.

Geography: topographic maps for mountains, valleys, lakes, etc. For reference, make use of geography texts.

Demographics: distribution of population in a state or country. For reference, use almanacs and encyclopedias.

Energy consumption: levels of usage of fuels (electricity, natural gas, heating oil) for heating in various parts of the United States. For reference, contact local utility companies.

2. PARTIAL DIFFERENTIAL EQUATIONS

BACKGROUND   Just as ordinary differential equations contain derivatives, partial differential equations contain partial derivatives.

THE PROJECT   **Step 1.** In (a) through (c), show that the given function u is a solution of the partial differential equation.

    (a) $u_x + u_y = 2xe^y + x^2e^y + 7;$ $u = x^2e^y + 4x + 3y$

    (b) $u_{xy} = 6x^2 - 12y;$ $u = 2x^3y - 6xy^2 + 7x - y + 8$

    (c) $u_{xx} = 14y;$ $u = 7x^2y + x \ln y + y^3$

Step 2. Using books on differential equations or the history of mathematics,

    (a) Report on the partial differential equation known as *Laplace's equation* (in two dimensions, using u for the function and x and y for the variables).

    (b) Show that $u = xy^3 - yx^3 + x^2 - y^2 + 8x + 1$ is a solution of Laplace's equation.

    (c) Describe some applications that involve Laplace's equation.

Step 3. List at least five mathematicians who developed partial differential equations, and indicate when they were active in that field.

APPENDIX TABLES

APPENDIX TABLE 1

Powers of e

x	e^x	e^{-x}	x	e^x	e^{-x}	x	e^x	e^{-x}
.00	1.0000	1.0000	.21	1.2337	.8106	.42	1.5220	.6570
.01	1.0101	.9900	.22	1.2461	.8025	.43	1.5373	.6505
.02	1.0202	.9802	.23	1.2586	.7945	.44	1.5527	.6440
.03	1.0305	.9704	.24	1.2712	.7866	.45	1.5683	.6376
.04	1.0408	.9608	.25	1.2840	.7788	.46	1.5841	.6313
.05	1.0513	.9512	.26	1.2969	.7711	.47	1.6000	.6250
.06	1.0618	.9418	.27	1.3100	.7634	.48	1.6161	.6188
.07	1.0725	.9324	.28	1.3231	.7558	.49	1.6323	.6126
.08	1.0833	.9231	.29	1.3364	.7483	.50	1.6487	.6065
.09	1.0942	.9139	.30	1.3499	.7408	.51	1.6653	.6005
.10	1.1052	.9048	.31	1.3634	.7334	.52	1.6820	.5945
.11	1.1163	.8958	.32	1.3771	.7261	.53	1.6989	.5886
.12	1.1275	.8869	.33	1.3910	.7189	.54	1.7160	.5827
.13	1.1388	.8781	.34	1.4049	.7118	.55	1.7333	.5769
.14	1.1503	.8694	.35	1.4191	.7047	.56	1.7507	.5712
.15	1.1618	.8607	.36	1.4333	.6977	.57	1.7683	.5655
.16	1.1735	.8521	.37	1.4477	.6907	.58	1.7860	.5599
.17	1.1853	.8437	.38	1.4623	.6839	.59	1.8040	.5543
.18	1.1972	.8353	.39	1.4770	.6771	.60	1.8221	.5488
.19	1.2092	.8270	.40	1.4918	.6703	.61	1.8404	.5434
.20	1.2214	.8187	.41	1.5068	.6637	.62	1.8589	.5379

APPENDIX TABLE 1 *(Continued)*

Powers of **e**

x	e^x	e^{-x}	x	e^x	e^{-x}	x	e^x	e^{-x}
.63	1.8776	.5326	.84	2.3164	.4317	1.05	2.8577	.3499
.64	1.8965	.5273	.85	2.3396	.4274	1.06	2.8864	.3465
.65	1.9155	.5220	.86	2.3632	.4232	1.07	2.9154	.3430
.66	1.9348	.5169	.87	2.3869	.4190	1.08	2.9447	.3396
.67	1.9542	.5117	.88	2.4109	.4148	1.09	2.9743	.3362
.68	1.9739	.5066	.89	2.4351	.4107	1.10	3.0042	.3329
.69	1.9937	.5016	.90	2.4596	.4066	1.11	3.0344	.3296
.70	2.0138	.4966	.91	2.4843	.4025	1.12	3.0649	.3263
.71	2.0340	.4916	.92	2.5093	.3985	1.13	3.0957	.3230
.72	2.0544	.4868	.93	2.5345	.3946	1.14	3.1268	.3198
.73	2.0751	.4819	.94	2.5600	.3906	1.15	3.1582	.3166
.74	2.0959	.4771	.95	2.5857	.3867	1.16	3.1899	.3135
.75	2.1170	.4724	.96	2.6117	.3829	1.17	3.2220	.3104
.76	2.1383	.4677	.97	2.6379	.3791	1.18	3.2544	.3073
.77	2.1598	.4630	.98	2.6645	.3753	1.19	3.2871	.3042
.78	2.1815	.4584	.99	2.6912	.3716	1.20	3.3201	.3012
.79	2.2034	.4538	1.00	2.7183	.3679	1.21	3.3535	.2982
.80	2.2255	.4493	1.01	2.7456	.3642	1.22	3.3872	.2952
.81	2.2479	.4449	1.02	2.7732	.3606	1.23	3.4212	.2923
.82	2.2705	.4404	1.03	2.8011	.3570	1.24	3.4556	.2894
.83	2.2933	.4360	1.04	2.8292	.3535	1.25	3.4903	.2865

APPENDIX TABLE 1 *(Continued)*

Powers of **e**

x	e^x	e^{-x}	x	e^x	e^{-x}	x	e^x	e^{-x}
1.26	3.5254	.2837	1.47	4.3492	.2299	1.68	5.3656	.1864
1.27	3.5609	.2808	1.48	4.3929	.2276	1.69	5.4195	.1845
1.28	3.5966	.2780	1.49	4.4371	.2254	1.70	5.4739	.1827
1.29	3.6328	.2753	1.50	4.4817	.2231	1.71	5.5290	.1809
1.30	3.6693	.2725	1.51	4.5267	.2209	1.72	5.5845	.1791
1.31	3.7062	.2698	1.52	4.5722	.2187	1.73	5.6407	.1773
1.32	3.7434	.2671	1.53	4.6182	.2165	1.74	5.6973	.1755
1.33	3.7810	.2645	1.54	4.6646	.2144	1.75	5.7546	.1738
1.34	3.8190	.2618	1.55	4.7115	.2122	1.76	5.8124	.1720
1.35	3.8574	.2592	1.56	4.7588	.2101	1.77	5.8709	.1703
1.36	3.8962	.2567	1.57	4.8066	.2080	1.78	5.9299	.1686
1.37	3.9354	.2541	1.58	4.8550	.2060	1.79	5.9895	.1670
1.38	3.9749	.2516	1.59	4.9037	.2039	1.80	6.0496	.1653
1.39	4.0149	.2491	1.60	4.9530	.2019	1.81	6.1104	.1637
1.40	4.0552	.2466	1.61	5.0028	.1999	1.82	6.1719	.1620
1.41	4.0960	.2441	1.62	5.0531	.1979	1.83	6.2339	.1604
1.42	4.1371	.2417	1.63	5.1039	.1959	1.84	6.2965	.1588
1.43	4.1787	.2393	1.64	5.1552	.1940	1.85	6.3598	.1572
1.44	4.2207	.2369	1.65	5.2070	.1920	1.86	6.4237	.1557
1.45	4.2631	.2346	1.66	5.2593	.1901	1.87	6.4883	.1541
1.46	4.3060	.2322	1.67	5.3122	.1882	1.88	6.5535	.1526

APPENDIX TABLE 1 *(Continued)*

Powers of **e**

x	e^x	e^{-x}	x	e^x	e^{-x}	x	e^x	e^{-x}
1.89	6.6194	.1511	3.00	20.0855	.0498	5.10	164.022	.0061
1.90	6.6859	.1496	3.10	22.1980	.0450	5.20	181.272	.0055
1.91	6.7531	.1481	3.20	24.5325	.0408	5.30	200.337	.0050
1.92	6.8210	.1466	3.30	27.1126	.0369	5.40	221.406	.0045
1.93	6.8895	.1451	3.40	29.9641	.0334	5.50	244.692	.0041
1.94	6.9588	.1437	3.50	33.1155	.0302	5.60	270.426	.0037
1.95	7.0287	.1423	3.60	36.5982	.0273	5.70	298.867	.0033
1.96	7.0993	.1409	3.70	40.4473	.0247	5.80	330.300	.0030
1.97	7.1707	.1395	3.80	44.7012	.0224	5.90	365.038	.0027
1.98	7.2427	.1381	3.90	49.4024	.0202	6.00	403.429	.0025
1.99	7.3155	.1367	4.00	54.5982	.0183	6.10	445.858	.0022
2.00	7.3891	.1353	4.10	60.3403	.0166	6.20	492.749	.0020
2.10	8.1662	.1225	4.20	66.6863	.0150	6.30	544.572	.0018
2.20	9.0250	.1108	4.30	73.6998	.0136	6.40	601.845	.0017
2.30	9.9742	.1003	4.40	81.4509	.0123	6.50	665.142	.0015
2.40	11.0232	.0907	4.50	90.0171	.0111	6.60	735.095	.0014
2.50	12.1825	.0821	4.60	99.4843	.0101	6.70	812.406	.0012
2.60	13.4637	.0743	4.70	109.9472	.0091	6.80	897.847	.0011
2.70	14.8797	.0672	4.80	121.5104	.0082	6.90	992.275	.0010
2.80	16.4446	.0608	4.90	134.2898	.0074	7.00	1096.63	.00091
2.90	18.1741	.0550	5.00	148.413	.0067	7.10	1211.97	.00083

APPENDIX TABLE 1 *(Continued)*

Powers of *e*

x	e^x	e^{-x}	x	e^x	e^{-x}	x	e^x	e^{-x}
7.20	1339.43	.00075	8.20	3640.95	.00027	9.20	9897.13	.00010
7.30	1480.30	.00068	8.30	4023.87	.00025	9.30	10938.02	.00009
7.40	1635.98	.00061	8.40	4447.07	.00022	9.40	12088.38	.00008
7.50	1808.04	.00055	8.50	4914.77	.00020	9.50	13359.73	.00007
7.60	1998.20	.00050	8.60	5431.66	.00018	9.60	14764.78	.00007
7.70	2208.35	.00045	8.70	6002.91	.00017	9.70	16317.61	.00006
7.80	2440.60	.00041	8.80	6634.24	.00015	9.80	18033.74	.00006
7.90	2697.28	.00037	8.90	7331.97	.00014	9.90	19930.37	.00005
8.00	2980.96	.00034	9.00	8103.08	.00012			
8.10	3294.47	.00030	9.10	8955.29	.00011			

APPENDIX TABLE 2

Natural Logarithms

x	ln x	x	ln x	x	ln x	x	ln x	x	ln x
.01	−4.6052	.22	−1.5141	.43	−.8440	.64	−.4463	.85	−.1625
.02	−3.9120	.23	−1.4697	.44	−.8210	.65	−.4308	.86	−.1508
.03	−3.5066	.24	−1.4271	.45	−.7985	.66	−.4155	.87	−.1393
.04	−3.2189	.25	−1.3863	.46	−.7765	.67	−.4005	.88	−.1278
.05	−2.9957	.26	−1.3471	.47	−.7550	.68	−.3857	.89	−.1165
.06	−2.8134	.27	−1.3093	.48	−.7340	.69	−.3711	.90	−.1054
.07	−2.6593	.28	−1.2730	.49	−.7133	.70	−.3567	.91	−.0943
.08	−2.5257	.29	−1.2379	.50	−.6931	.71	−.3425	.92	−.0834
.09	−2.4079	.30	−1.2040	.51	−.6733	.72	−.3285	.93	−.0726
.10	−2.3026	.31	−1.1712	.52	−.6539	.73	−.3147	.94	−.0619
.11	−2.2073	.32	−1.1394	.53	−.6349	.74	−.3011	.95	−.0513
.12	−2.1203	.33	−1.1087	.54	−.6162	.75	−.2877	.96	−.0408
.13	−2.0402	.34	−1.0788	.55	−.5978	.76	−.2744	.97	−.0305
.14	−1.9661	.35	−1.0498	.56	−.5798	.77	−.2614	.98	−.0202
.15	−1.8971	.36	−1.0217	.57	−.5621	.78	−.2485	.99	−.0101
.16	−1.8326	.37	−.9943	.58	−.5447	.79	−.2357	1.00	.0000
.17	−1.7720	.38	−.9676	.59	−.5276	.80	−.2231	1.01	.0100
.18	−1.7148	.39	−.9416	.60	−.5108	.81	−.2107	1.02	.0198
.19	−1.6607	.40	−.9163	.61	−.4943	.82	−.1985	1.03	.0296
.20	−1.6094	.41	−.8916	.62	−.4780	.83	−.1863	1.04	.0392
.21	−1.5606	.42	−.8675	.63	−.4620	.84	−.1744	1.05	.0488

APPENDIX TABLE 2 *(Continued)*
Natural Logarithms

x	$\ln x$	x	$\ln x$	x	$\ln x$	x	$\ln x$	x	$\ln x$
1.06	.0583	1.27	.2390	1.48	.3920	1.69	.5247	1.90	.6419
1.07	.0677	1.28	.2469	1.49	.3988	1.70	.5306	1.91	.6471
1.08	.0770	1.29	.2546	1.50	.4055	1.71	.5365	1.92	.6523
1.09	.0862	1.30	.2624	1.51	.4121	1.72	.5423	1.93	.6575
1.10	.0953	1.31	.2700	1.52	.4187	1.73	.5481	1.94	.6627
1.11	.1044	1.32	.2776	1.53	.4253	1.74	.5539	1.95	.6678
1.12	.1133	1.33	.2852	1.54	.4318	1.75	.5596	1.96	.6729
1.13	.1222	1.34	.2927	1.55	.4383	1.76	.5653	1.97	.6780
1.14	.1310	1.35	.3001	1.56	.4447	1.77	.5710	1.98	.6831
1.15	.1398	1.36	.3075	1.57	.4511	1.78	.5766	1.99	.6881
1.16	.1484	1.37	.3148	1.58	.4574	1.79	.5822	2.00	.6931
1.17	.1570	1.38	.3221	1.59	.4637	1.80	.5878	2.05	.7178
1.18	.1655	1.39	.3293	1.60	.4700	1.81	.5933	2.10	.7419
1.19	.1740	1.40	.3365	1.61	.4762	1.82	.5988	2.15	.7655
1.20	.1823	1.41	.3436	1.62	.4824	1.83	.6043	2.20	.7885
1.21	.1906	1.42	.3507	1.63	.4886	1.84	.6098	2.25	.8109
1.22	.1989	1.43	.3577	1.64	.4947	1.85	.6152	2.30	.8329
1.23	.2070	1.44	.3646	1.65	.5008	1.86	.6206	2.35	.8544
1.24	.2151	1.45	.3716	1.66	.5068	1.87	.6259	2.40	.8755
1.25	.2231	1.46	.3784	1.67	.5128	1.88	.6313	2.45	.8961
1.26	.2311	1.47	.3853	1.68	.5188	1.89	.6366	2.50	.9163

APPENDIX TABLE 2 *(Continued)*

Natural Logarithms

x	$\ln x$	x	$\ln x$	x	$\ln x$	x	$\ln x$	x	$\ln x$	x	$\ln x$
2.55	.9361	3.60	1.2809	4.65	1.5369	5.70	1.7405	6.75	1.9095		
2.60	.9555	3.65	1.2947	4.70	1.5476	5.75	1.7492	6.80	1.9169		
2.65	.9746	3.70	1.3083	4.75	1.5581	5.80	1.7579	6.85	1.9242		
2.70	.9933	3.75	1.3218	4.80	1.5686	5.85	1.7664	6.90	1.9315		
2.75	1.0116	3.80	1.3350	4.85	1.5790	5.90	1.7750	6.95	1.9387		
2.80	1.0296	3.85	1.3481	4.90	1.5892	5.95	1.7834	7.00	1.9459		
2.85	1.0473	3.90	1.3610	4.95	1.5994	6.00	1.7918	7.05	1.9530		
2.90	1.0647	3.95	1.3737	5.00	1.6094	6.05	1.8001	7.10	1.9601		
2.95	1.0818	4.00	1.3863	5.05	1.6194	6.10	1.8083	7.15	1.9671		
3.00	1.0986	4.05	1.3987	5.10	1.6292	6.15	1.8165	7.20	1.9741		
3.05	1.1151	4.10	1.4110	5.15	1.6390	6.20	1.8245	7.25	1.9810		
3.10	1.1314	4.15	1.4231	5.20	1.6487	6.25	1.8326	7.30	1.9879		
3.15	1.1474	4.20	1.4351	5.25	1.6582	6.30	1.8405	7.35	1.9947		
3.20	1.1632	4.25	1.4469	5.30	1.6677	6.35	1.8485	7.40	2.0015		
3.25	1.1787	4.30	1.4586	5.35	1.6771	6.40	1.8563	7.45	2.0082		
3.30	1.1939	4.35	1.4702	5.40	1.6864	6.45	1.8641	7.50	2.0149		
3.35	1.2090	4.40	1.4816	5.45	1.6956	6.50	1.8718	7.55	2.0215		
3.40	1.2238	4.45	1.4929	5.50	1.7047	6.55	1.8795	7.60	2.0281		
3.45	1.2384	4.50	1.5041	5.55	1.7138	6.60	1.8871	7.65	2.0347		
3.50	1.2528	4.55	1.5151	5.60	1.7228	6.65	1.8946	7.70	2.0412		
3.55	1.2669	4.60	1.5261	5.65	1.7317	6.70	1.9021	7.75	2.0477		

APPENDIX TABLE 2 *(Continued)*

Natural Logarithms

x	ln x	x	ln x	x	ln x	x	ln x	x	ln x
7.80	2.0541	9.70	2.2721	19.0	2.9444	39.0	3.6636	60.0	4.0943
7.85	2.0605	9.80	2.2824	19.5	2.9704	40.0	3.6889	61.0	4.1109
7.90	2.0669	9.90	2.2925	20.0	2.9957	41.0	3.7136	62.0	4.1271
7.95	2.0732	10.0	2.3026	21.0	3.0445	42.0	3.7377	63.0	4.1431
8.00	2.0794	10.5	2.3514	22.0	3.0910	43.0	3.7612	64.0	4.1589
8.10	2.0919	11.0	2.3979	23.0	3.1355	44.0	3.7842	65.0	4.1744
8.20	2.1041	11.5	2.4423	24.0	3.1781	45.0	3.8067	66.0	4.1897
8.30	2.1163	12.0	2.4849	25.0	3.2189	46.0	3.8286	67.0	4.2047
8.40	2.1282	12.5	2.5257	26.0	3.2581	47.0	3.8501	68.0	4.2195
8.50	2.1401	13.0	2.5649	27.0	3.2958	48.0	3.8712	69.0	4.2341
8.60	2.1518	13.5	2.6027	28.0	3.3322	49.0	3.8918	70.0	4.2485
8.70	2.1633	14.0	2.6391	29.0	3.3673	50.0	3.9120	71.0	4.2627
8.80	2.1748	14.5	2.6741	30.0	3.4012	51.0	3.9318	72.0	4.2767
8.90	2.1861	15.0	2.7081	31.0	3.4340	52.0	3.9512	73.0	4.2905
9.00	2.1972	15.5	2.7408	32.0	3.4657	53.0	3.9703	74.0	4.3041
9.10	2.2083	16.0	2.7726	33.0	3.4965	54.0	3.9890	75.0	4.3175
9.20	2.2192	16.5	2.8034	34.0	3.5264	55.0	4.0073	76.0	4.3307
9.30	2.2300	17.0	2.8332	35.0	3.5553	56.0	4.0254	77.0	4.3438
9.40	2.2407	17.5	2.8622	36.0	3.5835	57.0	4.0431	78.0	4.3567
9.50	2.2513	18.0	2.8904	37.0	3.6109	58.0	4.0604	79.0	4.3694
9.60	2.2618	18.5	2.9178	38.0	3.6338	59.0	4.0775	80.0	4.3820

APPENDIX TABLE 2 *(Continued)*

Natural Logarithms

x	ln x	x	ln x	x	ln x	x	ln x	x	ln x
81.0	4.3944	120.	4.7875	330.	5.7991	540.	6.2916	750.	6.6201
82.0	4.4067	130.	4.8675	340.	5.8289	550.	6.3099	760.	6.6333
83.0	4.4188	140.	4.9416	350.	5.8579	560.	6.3279	770.	6.6464
84.0	4.4308	150.	5.0106	360.	5.8861	570.	6.3456	780.	6.6593
85.0	4.4427	160.	5.0752	370.	5.9135	580.	6.3630	790.	6.6720
86.0	4.4543	170.	5.1358	380.	5.9402	590.	6.3801	800.	6.6846
87.0	4.4659	180.	5.1930	390.	5.9661	600.	6.3969	810.	6.6970
88.0	4.4773	190.	5.2470	400.	5.9915	610.	6.4135	820.	6.7093
89.0	4.4886	200.	5.2983	410.	6.0162	620.	6.4297	830.	6.7214
90.0	4.4998	210.	5.3471	420.	6.0403	630.	6.4457	840.	6.7334
91.0	4.5109	220.	5.3936	430.	6.0638	640.	6.4615	850.	6.7452
92.0	4.5218	230.	5.4381	440.	6.0868	650.	6.4770	860.	6.7569
93.0	4.5326	240.	5.4806	450.	6.1092	660.	6.4922	870.	6.7685
94.0	4.5433	250.	5.5215	460.	6.1312	670.	6.5073	880.	6.7799
95.0	4.5539	260.	5.5607	470.	6.1527	680.	6.5221	890.	6.7912
96.0	4.5643	270.	5.5984	480.	6.1738	690.	6.5367	900.	6.8024
97.0	4.5747	280.	5.6348	490.	6.1944	700.	6.5511	910.	6.8134
98.0	4.5850	290.	5.6699	500.	6.2146	710.	6.5653	920.	6.8244
99.0	4.5951	300.	5.7038	510.	6.2344	720.	6.5793	930.	6.8352
100.	4.6052	310.	5.7366	520.	6.2538	730.	6.5930	940.	6.8459
110.	4.7005	320.	5.7683	530.	6.2729	740.	6.6067	950.	6.8565

APPENDIX TABLE 2 *(Continued)*

Natural Logarithms

x	$\ln x$	x	$\ln x$	x	$\ln x$	x	$\ln x$	x	$\ln x$
960.	6.8669	1200.	7.0901	1800.	7.4955	4000.	8.2940	7000.	8.8537
970.	6.8773	1300.	7.1701	1900.	7.5496	4500.	8.4118	7500.	8.9227
980.	6.8876	1400.	7.2442	2000.	7.6009	5000.	8.5172	8000.	8.9872
990.	6.8977	1500.	7.3132	2500.	7.8240	5500.	8.6125	8500.	9.0478
1000.	6.9078	1600.	7.3778	3000.	8.0064	6000.	8.6995	9000.	9.1050
1100.	7.0031	1700.	7.4384	3500.	8.1605	6500.	8.7796	9500.	9.1590

APPENDIX TABLE 3

Trigonometric Functions—Degrees

θ	sin θ	cos θ	tan θ	θ	sin θ	cos θ	tan θ	θ	sin θ	cos θ	tan θ
0°	.0000	1.0000	.0000	21°	.3584	.9336	.3839	42°	.6691	.7431	.9004
1°	.0175	.9998	.0175	22°	.3746	.9272	.4040	43°	.6820	.7314	.9325
2°	.0349	.9994	.0349	23°	.3907	.9205	.4245	44°	.6947	.7193	.9657
3°	.0523	.9986	.0524	24°	.4067	.9135	.4452	45°	.7071	.7071	1.0000
4°	.0698	.9976	.0699	25°	.4226	.9063	.4663	46°	.7193	.6947	1.0355
5°	.0872	.9962	.0875	26°	.4384	.8988	.4877	47°	.7314	.6820	1.0724
6°	.1045	.9945	.1051	27°	.4540	.8910	.5095	48°	.7431	.6691	1.1106
7°	.1219	.9925	.1228	28°	.4695	.8829	.5317	49°	.7547	.6561	1.1504
8°	.1392	.9903	.1405	29°	.4848	.8746	.5543	50°	.7660	.6428	1.1918
9°	.1564	.9877	.1584	30°	.5000	.8660	.5774	51°	.7771	.6293	1.2349
10°	.1736	.9848	.1763	31°	.5150	.8572	.6009	52°	.7880	.6157	1.2799
11°	.1908	.9816	.1944	32°	.5299	.8480	.6249	53°	.7986	.6018	1.3270
12°	.2079	.9781	.2126	33°	.5446	.8387	.6494	54°	.8090	.5878	1.3764
13°	.2250	.9744	.2309	34°	.5592	.8290	.6745	55°	.8192	.5736	1.4281
14°	.2419	.9703	.2493	35°	.5736	.8192	.7002	56°	.8290	.5592	1.4826
15°	.2588	.9659	.2679	36°	.5878	.8090	.7265	57°	.8387	.5446	1.5399
16°	.2756	.9613	.2867	37°	.6018	.7986	.7536	58°	.8480	.5299	1.6003
17°	.2924	.9563	.3057	38°	.6157	.7880	.7813	59°	.8572	.5150	1.6643
18°	.3090	.9511	.3249	39°	.6293	.7771	.8098	60°	.8660	.5000	1.7321
19°	.3256	.9455	.3443	40°	.6428	.7660	.8391	61°	.8746	.4848	1.8040
20°	.3420	.9397	.3640	41°	.6561	.7547	.8693	62°	.8829	.4695	1.8807

APPENDIX TABLE 3 *(Continued)*

Trigonometric Functions—Degrees

θ	$\sin \theta$	$\cos \theta$	$\tan \theta$	θ	$\sin \theta$	$\cos \theta$	$\tan \theta$	θ	$\sin \theta$	$\cos \theta$	$\tan \theta$
63°	.8910	.4540	1.9626	73°	.9563	.2924	3.2709	83°	.9925	.1219	8.1443
64°	.8988	.4384	2.0503	74°	.9613	.2756	3.4874	84°	.9945	.1045	9.5144
65°	.9063	.4226	2.1445	75°	.9659	.2588	3.7321	85°	.9962	.0872	11.4301
66°	.9135	.4067	2.2460	76°	.9703	.2419	4.0108	86°	.9976	.0698	14.3007
67°	.9205	.3907	2.3559	77°	.9744	.2250	4.3315	87°	.9986	.0523	19.0811
68°	.9272	.3746	2.4751	78°	.9781	.2079	4.7046	88°	.9994	.0349	28.6363
69°	.9336	.3584	2.6051	79°	.9816	.1908	5.1446	89°	.9998	.0175	57.2900
70°	.9397	.3420	2.7475	80°	.9848	.1736	5.6713	90°	1.0000	.0000	—
71°	.9455	.3256	2.9042	81°	.9877	.1564	6.3138				
72°	.9511	.3090	3.0777	82°	.9903	.1392	7.1154				

APPENDIX TABLE 4

Trigonometric Functions—Radians

t	sin t	cos t	tan t	t	sin t	cos t	tan t	t	sin t	cos t	tan t
.00	.0000	1.0000	.0000	.21	.2085	.9780	.2131	.42	.4078	.9131	.4466
.01	.0100	1.0000	.0100	.22	.2182	.9759	.2236	.43	.4169	.9090	.4586
.02	.0200	.9998	.0200	.23	.2280	.9737	.2341	.44	.4259	.9048	.4708
.03	.0300	.9996	.0300	.24	.2377	.9713	.2447	.45	.4350	.9004	.4831
.04	.0400	.9992	.0400	.25	.2474	.9689	.2553	.46	.4439	.8961	.4954
.05	.0500	.9988	.0500	.26	.2571	.9664	.2660	.47	.4529	.8916	.5080
.06	.0600	.9982	.0601	.27	.2667	.9638	.2768	.48	.4618	.8870	.5206
.07	.0699	.9976	.0701	.28	.2764	.9611	.2876	.49	.4706	.8823	.5334
.08	.0799	.9968	.0802	.29	.2860	.9582	.2984	.50	.4794	.8776	.5463
.09	.0899	.9960	.0902	.30	.2955	.9553	.3093	.51	.4882	.8727	.5594
.10	.0998	.9950	.1003	.31	.3051	.9523	.3203	.52	.4969	.8678	.5726
.11	.1098	.9940	.1104	.32	.3146	.9492	.3314	.53	.5055	.8628	.5859
.12	.1197	.9928	.1206	.33	.3240	.9460	.3425	.54	.5141	.8577	.5994
.13	.1296	.9916	.1307	.34	.3335	.9428	.3537	.55	.5227	.8525	.6131
.14	.1395	.9902	.1409	.35	.3429	.9394	.3650	.56	.5312	.8473	.6269
.15	.1494	.9888	.1511	.36	.3523	.9359	.3764	.57	.5396	.8419	.6310
.16	.1593	.9872	.1614	.37	.3616	.9323	.3879	.58	.5480	.8365	.6552
.17	.1692	.9856	.1717	.38	.3709	.9287	.3994	.59	.5564	.8309	.6696
.18	.1790	.9838	.1820	.39	.3802	.9249	.4111	.60	.5646	.8253	.6841
.19	.1889	.9820	.1923	.40	.3894	.9211	.4228	.61	.5729	.8196	.6989
.20	.1987	.9801	.2027	.41	.3986	.9171	.4346	.62	.5810	.8139	.7139

APPENDIX TABLE 4 *(Continued)*

Trigonometric Functions—Radians

t	$\sin t$	$\cos t$	$\tan t$	t	$\sin t$	$\cos t$	$\tan t$	t	$\sin t$	$\cos t$	$\tan t$
.63	.5891	.8080	.7291	.84	.7446	.6675	1.1156	1.05	.8674	.4976	1.7433
.64	.5972	.8021	.7445	.85	.7513	.6600	1.1383	1.06	.8724	.4889	1.7844
.65	.6052	.7961	.7602	.86	.7578	.6524	1.1616	1.07	.8772	.4801	1.8270
.66	.6131	.7900	.7761	.87	.7643	.6448	1.1853	1.08	.8820	.4713	1.8712
.67	.6210	.7838	.7923	.88	.7707	.6372	1.2097	1.09	.8866	.4625	1.9171
.68	.6288	.7776	.8087	.89	.7771	.6294	1.2346	1.10	.8912	.4536	1.9648
.69	.6365	.7712	.8253	.90	.7833	.6216	1.2602	1.11	.8957	.4447	2.0143
.70	.6442	.7648	.8423	.91	.7895	.6137	1.2864	1.12	.9001	.4357	2.0660
.71	.6518	.7584	.8595	.92	.7956	.6058	1.3133	1.13	.9044	.4267	2.1198
.72	.6594	.7518	.8771	.93	.8016	.5978	1.3409	1.14	.9086	.4176	2.1759
.73	.6669	.7452	.8949	.94	.8076	.5898	1.3692	1.15	.9128	.4085	2.2345
.74	.6743	.7358	.9131	.95	.8134	.5817	1.3984	1.16	.9168	.3993	2.2958
.75	.6816	.7317	.9316	.96	.8192	.5735	1.4284	1.17	.9208	.3902	2.3600
.76	.6889	.7248	.9505	.97	.8249	.5653	1.4592	1.18	.9246	.3809	2.4273
.77	.6961	.7179	.9697	.98	.8305	.5570	1.4910	1.19	.9284	.3717	2.4979
.78	.7033	.7109	.9893	.99	.8360	.5487	1.5237	1.20	.9320	.3624	2.5722
.79	.7104	.7038	1.0092	1.00	.8415	.5403	1.5574	1.21	.9356	.3530	2.6503
.80	.7174	.6967	1.0296	1.01	.8468	.5319	1.5922	1.22	.9391	.3436	2.7328
.81	.7243	.6895	1.0505	1.02	.8521	.5234	1.6281	1.23	.9425	.3342	2.8198
.82	.7311	.6822	1.0717	1.03	.8573	.5148	1.6652	1.24	.9458	.3248	2.9119
.83	.7379	.6749	1.0934	1.04	.8624	.5062	1.7036	1.25	.9490	.3153	3.0096

APPENDIX TABLE 4 *(Continued)*

Trigonometric Functions—Radians

t	$\sin t$	$\cos t$	$\tan t$	t	$\sin t$	$\cos t$	$\tan t$	t	$\sin t$	$\cos t$	$\tan t$
1.26	.9521	.3058	3.1133	1.37	.9799	.1994	4.9131	1.48	.9959	.0907	10.9834
1.27	.9551	.2963	3.2236	1.38	.9819	.1896	5.1774	1.49	.9967	.0807	12.3499
1.28	.9580	.2867	3.3413	1.39	.9837	.1798	5.4707	1.50	.9975	.0707	14.1014
1.29	.9608	.2771	3.4672	1.40	.9854	.1700	5.7979	1.51	.9982	.0608	16.4281
1.30	.9636	.2675	3.6021	1.41	.9871	.1601	6.1654	1.52	.9987	.0508	19.6695
1.31	.9662	.2579	3.7471	1.42	.9887	.1502	6.5811	1.53	.9992	.0408	24.4984
1.32	.9687	.2482	3.9033	1.43	.9901	.1403	7.0555	1.54	.9995	.0308	32.4611
1.33	.9711	.2385	4.0723	1.44	.9915	.1304	7.6018	1.55	.9998	.0208	48.0785
1.34	.9735	.2288	4.2556	1.45	.9927	.1205	8.2381	1.56	.9999	.0108	92.6205
1.35	.9757	.2190	4.4552	1.46	.9939	.1106	8.9886	1.57	1.0000	.0008	1255.7656
1.36	.9779	.2092	4.6734	1.47	.9949	.1006	9.8874				

APPENDIX TABLE 5

Table of Integrals

Familiar Formulas

1. $\int u^n \, du = \dfrac{u^{n+1}}{n+1} + C$

2. $\int k \, du = ku + C$

3. $\int \dfrac{1}{u} \, du = \ln |u| + C$

4. $\int e^u \, du = e^u + C$

New Formulas (Note that $a > 0$ in formulas involving a^2.)

5. $\int \dfrac{u \, du}{a + bu} = \dfrac{1}{b^2} (bu - a \ln |a + bu|) + C$

6. $\int \dfrac{du}{u(a + bu)} = \dfrac{1}{a} \ln \left| \dfrac{u}{a + bu} \right| + C$

7. $\int \dfrac{u \, du}{\sqrt{a + bu}} = \dfrac{2(bu - 2a)}{3b^2} \sqrt{a + bu} + C$

8. $\int \sqrt{u^2 + a^2} \, du = \dfrac{u}{2} \sqrt{u^2 + a^2} + \dfrac{a^2}{2} \ln |u + \sqrt{u^2 + a^2}| + C$

9. $\int \dfrac{du}{\sqrt{u^2 + a^2}} = \ln |u + \sqrt{u^2 + a^2}| + C$

10. $\int \dfrac{du}{\sqrt{u^2 - a^2}} = \ln |u + \sqrt{u^2 - a^2}| + C$

11. $\int \dfrac{du}{u\sqrt{u^2 + a^2}} = -\dfrac{1}{a} \ln \left| \dfrac{a + \sqrt{u^2 + a^2}}{u} \right| + C$

12. $\int \dfrac{du}{u\sqrt{a^2 - u^2}} = -\dfrac{1}{a} \ln \left| \dfrac{a + \sqrt{a^2 - u^2}}{u} \right| + C$

13. $\int \dfrac{du}{u^2\sqrt{u^2 + a^2}} = -\dfrac{\sqrt{u^2 + a^2}}{a^2 u} + C$

14. $\int \dfrac{du}{u^2\sqrt{a^2 - u^2}} = -\dfrac{\sqrt{a^2 - u^2}}{a^2 u} + C$

APPENDIX TABLE 5 *(Continued)*

Table of Integrals

15. $\displaystyle\int \frac{\sqrt{a^2 - u^2}}{u}\,du = \sqrt{a^2 - u^2} - a \ln\left|\frac{a + \sqrt{a^2 - u^2}}{u}\right| + C$

16. $\displaystyle\int \frac{du}{u^2 - a^2} = \frac{1}{2a} \ln\left|\frac{u - a}{u + a}\right| + C$

17. $\displaystyle\int u^n \ln u\,du = \frac{u^{n+1}}{n + 1} \ln u - \frac{u^{n+1}}{(n + 1)^2} + C \qquad n \neq -1$

18. $\displaystyle\int \frac{du}{1 + e^u} = u - \ln(1 + e^u) + C$

Two Reduction Formulas

19. $\displaystyle\int (\ln u)^n\,du = u(\ln u)^n - n\int (\ln u)^{n-1}\,du$

20. $\displaystyle\int u^n e^u\,du = u^n e^u - n\int u^{n-1}e^u\,du$

Trigonometric Integrals

21. $\displaystyle\int \sin u\,du = -\cos u + C$

22. $\displaystyle\int \cos u\,du = \sin u + C$

23. $\displaystyle\int \sec^2 u\,du = \tan u + C$

24. $\displaystyle\int \csc^2 u\,du = -\cot u + C$

25. $\displaystyle\int \sec u \tan u\,du = \sec u + C$

26. $\displaystyle\int \csc u \cot u\,du = -\csc u + C$

27. $\displaystyle\int \tan u\,du = -\ln|\cos u| + C$

28. $\displaystyle\int \cot u\,du = \ln|\sin u| + C$

APPENDIX TABLE 6

Standard Normal Distribution

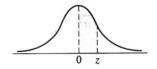

z	.00	.01	.02	.03	.04	.05	.06	.07	.08	.09
.0	.0000	.0040	.0080	.0120	.0160	.0199	.0239	.0279	.0319	.0359
.1	.0398	.0438	.0478	.0517	.0557	.0596	.0636	.0675	.0714	.0753
.2	.0793	.0832	.0871	.0910	.0948	.0987	.1026	.1064	.1103	.1141
.3	.1179	.1217	.1255	.1293	.1331	.1368	.1406	.1443	.1480	.1517
.4	.1554	.1591	.1628	.1664	.1700	.1736	.1772	.1808	.1844	.1879
.5	.1915	.1950	.1985	.2019	.2054	.2088	.2123	.2157	.2190	.2224
.6	.2257	.2291	.2324	.2357	.2389	.2422	.2454	.2486	.2517	.2549
.7	.2580	.2611	.2642	.2673	.2704	.2734	.2764	.2794	.2823	.2852
.8	.2881	.2910	.2939	.2967	.2995	.3023	.3051	.3078	.3106	.3133
.9	.3159	.3186	.3212	.3238	.3264	.3289	.3315	.3340	.3365	.3389
1.0	.3413	.3438	.3461	.3485	.3508	.3531	.3554	.3577	.3599	.3621
1.1	.3643	.3665	.3686	.3708	.3729	.3749	.3770	.3790	.3810	.3830
1.2	.3849	.3869	.3888	.3907	.3925	.3944	.3962	.3980	.3997	.4015
1.3	.4032	.4049	.4066	.4082	.4099	.4115	.4131	.4147	.4162	.4177
1.4	.4192	.4207	.4222	.4236	.4251	.4265	.4279	.4292	.4306	.4319
1.5	.4332	.4345	.4357	.4370	.4382	.4394	.4406	.4418	.4429	.4441
1.6	.4452	.4463	.4474	.4484	.4495	.4505	.4515	.4525	.4535	.4545
1.7	.4554	.4564	.4573	.4582	.4591	.4599	.4608	.4616	.4625	.4633

APPENDIX TABLE 6 *(Continued)*

Standard Normal Distribution

z	.00	.01	.02	.03	.04	.05	.06	.07	.08	.09
1.8	.4641	.4649	.4656	.4664	.4671	.4678	.4686	.4693	.4699	.4706
1.9	.4713	.4719	.4726	.4732	.4738	.4744	.4750	.4756	.4761	.4767
2.0	.4772	.4778	.4783	.4788	.4793	.4798	.4803	.4808	.4812	.4817
2.1	.4821	.4826	.4830	.4834	.4838	.4842	.4846	.4850	.4854	.4857
2.2	.4861	.4864	.4868	.4871	.4875	.4878	.4881	.4884	.4887	.4890
2.3	.4893	.4896	.4898	.4901	.4904	.4906	.4909	.4911	.4913	.4916
2.4	.4918	.4920	.4922	.4925	.4927	.4929	.4931	.4932	.4934	.4936
2.5	.4938	.4940	.4941	.4943	.4945	.4946	.4948	.4949	.4951	.4952
2.6	.4953	.4955	.4956	.4957	.4959	.4960	.4961	.4962	.4963	.4964
2.7	.4965	.4966	.4967	.4968	.4969	.4970	.4971	.4972	.4973	.4974
2.8	.4974	.4975	.4976	.4977	.4977	.4978	.4979	.4979	.4980	.4981
2.9	.4981	.4982	.4982	.4983	.4984	.4984	.4985	.4985	.4986	.4986
3.0	.4987	.4987	.4987	.4988	.4988	.4989	.4989	.4989	.4990	.4990

ANSWERS TO ODD-NUMBERED EXERCISES

SECTION 1.1   (page 10)

1. [5, 9]   **3.** [6, ∞)   **5.** (−∞, 0)   **7.** (−2, ∞)   **9.** (−∞, π)   **11.** $x \geq 0$ **13.** $1 \leq x \leq 75$ **15.** $x < -2$

17. $x > -5$ **19.** $\pi \leq x < 7$ **21.** $x \leq 6$ **23.** $x \geq 0$ **25.** $x \geq 1/8$ **27.** $y < 8/5$

29. The notation should be (3, ∞). It is an open interval. The symbol ∞ does not represent a number.   **31.** x^{17} **33.** b^{21}

35. x^6 **37.** 2   **39.** $1/x^3$ **41.** $7x^2$ **43.** 1/9   **45.** 7   **47.** 3   **49.** 1/4   **51.** 8   **53.** 9   **55.** 1/27   **57.** 11.3137

59. 1142.4502   **61.** 1.0601   **63.** $4\sqrt{3}/3$ **65.** $2\sqrt{5}/5$ **67.** $2\sqrt{3}$ **69.** ±8   **71.** 0, 9   **73.** −7, −2

75. −2, 4   **77.** −2, 5   **79.** −2/3, 4   **81.** −2, 3/2   **83.** $\dfrac{-3 \pm \sqrt{5}}{2}$ **85.** $1 \pm \sqrt{5}$ **87.** $2 \pm \sqrt{6}$

89. $\dfrac{-5 \pm 3\sqrt{5}}{4}$ **91.** $\dfrac{-3 \pm \sqrt{15}}{2}$ **93.** $x - 3$ **95.** $\dfrac{x}{x + 4}$ **97.** 2/3   **99.** $\dfrac{1}{x + 5}$ **101.** $\dfrac{11}{3x}$ **103.** $\dfrac{8x - 1}{x(x - 1)}$

105. $\dfrac{6 - 7x}{2x(x + 2)}$ **107.** $\dfrac{x}{x - 1}$ **109.** $5x/2$ **111.** $\dfrac{5}{x + 4}$ **113.** $\dfrac{4x^2}{x - 1}$ **115.** $\dfrac{3x}{2 - x}$ **117.** $\dfrac{3h + h^2 x}{hx^2 + x}$

119. 8   **121.** 3   **123.** **(a)** If $a = 0$, then the equation is linear ($bx + c = 0$) rather than quadratic.
    (b) If $a = 0$, then division by 0 is indicated. But we cannot divide by 0.

SECTION 1.2   (page 16)

1. $f(0) = 7, f(1) = 12, f(2) = 17, f(-1) = 2$ **3.** $f(0) = 1, f(1) = 5, f(2) = 11, f(-1) = -1$

5. $f(0) = 5, f(1) = 4, f(2) = 1, f(-1) = 4$ **7.** $f(0) = 6, f(1) = 6, f(2) = 6, f(-1) = 6$

9. $f(0) = 1, f(1) = \sqrt{2}, f(2) = \sqrt{3}, f(-1) = 0$ **11.** $f(x + 2) = x^2 + x + 5, f(x - 3) = x^2 - 9x + 25$

13. $f(x + 2) = 4x^2 + 25x + 34, f(x - 3) = 4x^2 - 15x + 9$ **15.** $f(x + 2) = \dfrac{x + 7}{x - 5}, f(x - 3) = \dfrac{x + 2}{x - 10}$

17. $f(x + h) = 3x + 3h - 4, f(x + h) - f(x) = 3h$ **19.** $f(x + h) = -9x - 9h + 2, f(x + h) - f(x) = -9h$

21. $f(.4) = .4376, f(.25) = .3734375, f(-1.8) = 20.7612$ **23.** $256   **25.** **(a)** 505°F **(b)** 65°F   **27.** $69,500

29. **(a)** 1021 **(b)** 1300 **(c)** $t = 0$; 1000 bacteria   **31.** **(a)** $D(c) = \dfrac{50(c + 1)}{3}$ **(b)** $D(8) = 150$

   (c) The dosage for an 8-year-old child is 150 milligrams.   **33.** all the real numbers   **35.** $x \geq 2$ **37.** $x \neq -3$

39. $x \neq 0, 1$ **41.** $x \geq 2/3$ **43.** $x \geq -1$ **45.** $x \neq 0$ **47.** −3   **49.** ±3   **51.** 4, 5   **53.** $\dfrac{-5 \pm \sqrt{33}}{2}$

55. $(f \circ g)(x) = 21x + 1$; $(g \circ f)(x) = 21x + 7$ **57.** $(f \circ g)(x) = x^2 - 1$; $(g \circ f)(x) = x^2 + 2x - 1$

59. $(f \circ g)(x) = \dfrac{1}{3x}$; $(g \circ f)(x) = \dfrac{3}{x}$

61. f is the *name* of the function, whereas $f(x)$ is the value of f that corresponds to a particular x value.

SECTION 1.3   (page 25)

1.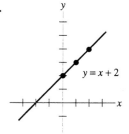

3.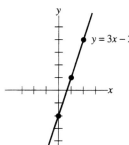

5.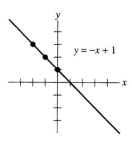

7.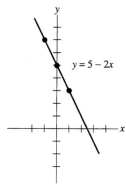

9.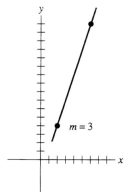

11.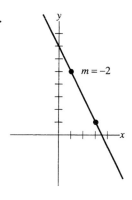

13.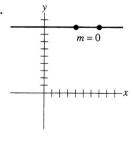

15. 4/5   **17.** -2 **19.** -1.953 **21.** slope $= 5$; y intercept $= (0, 3)$ or 3   **23.** slope $= 1$; y intercept $= (0, -9)$ or -9

25. slope $= -7$; y intercept $= (0, 1)$ or 1   **27.** slope $= 0$; y intercept $= (0, 3)$ or 3   **29.** slope $= 8$; y intercept $= (0, 6)$ or 6

31. $y = -2x + 4$ **33.** $y = 5x - 3$ **35.** $y = -1$ **37.** $y = \dfrac{2}{3}x + \dfrac{1}{2}$ **39.** $y = 1.8x + 2.4$ **41.** $y = 3x + 5$

43. $y = -2x + 7$ **45.** $y = -x - 3$ **47.** $y = 3x - 10$

49. (a) When the temperature is $60°$, a cricket will chirp at the rate of 80 chirps per minute.   **(b)** $y = 4x - 160$ (for $x \geq 40°$)

51. (a) $y = -200t + 3400$ **(b)** \$1800   **53. (a)** m represents the annual appreciation, which is \$100 in this case.

y represents the (appreciated) value after x years.   **(b)** $y = 100x + 2000$ **(c)** \$2700   **(d)** 12 years

55. The domain of the function is all of the real numbers. For every real number x there is a corresponding real number y.

(The y is computed as $2 \cdot x + 1$.)   **57.** u, because $\Delta y / \Delta t$ is nearly the same from point to point.

SECTION 1.4 (page 37)

1. (a) 8 **(b)** 6 **(c)** −4 **(d)** 2 **(e)** 2, 6   **3. (a)** 30   **(b)** 5   **(c)** 40   **(d)** $m = 1/2$, $b = 0$ **(e)** $0 \le t \le 60$

5. (a) $t = 0$ **(b)** $t > 0$ (could also be $0 < t \le 2$)
  (c) Memorized nonsense words are more readily forgotten than are the memorized words of a song.

7. (a) The northeastern city.
  (b) Yes. The point $(15, w(15))$ is above the point $(15, n(15))$, so $w(15)$ is greater than $n(15)$.

  (c) No. The point $(5, n(5))$ is above the point $(5, w(5))$, so $n(5) > w(5)$.   **9.** function   **11.** not a function   **13.** function

15.
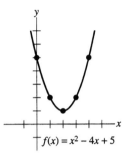

17.
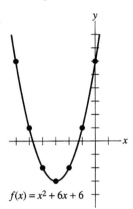

19.
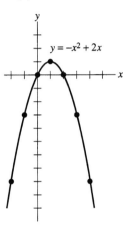

21.
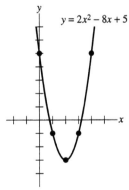

23.
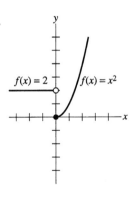

25.
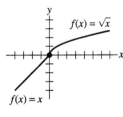

27.
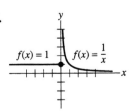

29.
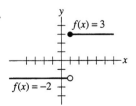

31. $W(x) = \begin{cases} 5x & 0 \le x \le 40 \\ 7.5x - 100 & x > 40 \end{cases}$ **33.** When x is 2, y is 8.

35. $P(6) - P(0)$ is the change in the insect population over the next 6 months—that is, the amount by which the insect population will increase or decrease over the next 6 months.

37. (a) A horizontal straight line segment from $t = 0$ to $t = 15$.
  (b) One horizontal straight line segment from $t = 0$ to $t = 4$ and another from $t = 4$ to $t = 15$. The second segment is 1 unit lower than the first.
  (c) One horizontal straight line segment from $t = 0$ to $t = 1$, another from $t = 1$ to $t = 3$, and a third from $t = 3$ to $t = 15$. The second segment is 1 unit higher than the first. The third segment is the same height as the first.

39.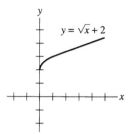

41.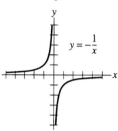

43.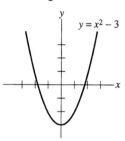

45.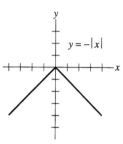

Technology Exercises   (page 40)

1. (a) 3 **(b)** -4 **3. (a)** none **(b)** $-.2$ **5.** $x < -3, 0 < x < 2$ **7.** 5.5   **9.** 2.8   **11.** -2.2 and 2.2

SECTION 1.5   (page 50)

1. (a) $397.50 **(b)** $9.90 **(c)** $210   **3.** 23   **5. (a)** $2600 **(b)** $25.01   **7. (a)** $P(x) = -.1x^2 + 130x - 1000$ **(b)** $5250

9. (a) $C(x) = 29x + .02x^2$ **(b)** $R(x) = 54x$ **(c)** $P(x) = 25x - .02x^2$ **11.** $P(x) = 9x - .02x^2$

13. (a) $170 **(b)** $210 **(c)** $4100   **15.** First, determine the profit function $P(x)$ (as revenue minus cost). Then evaluate $P(x)$ at 75 and at 74. Finally, subtract $P(74)$ from $P(75)$.   **17. (a)** No, because cost is greater than revenue.

  (b) $P(x_4)$, because $R(x) - C(x)$ is the greatest at x_4. **(c)** $P(x_1)$, because $R(x) - C(x)$ is the smallest at x_1.   **19.** 1900 units

21. $R(x) = 50x - .1x^2$, $1840   **23.** 160 units   **25. (a)** $C(x) = 24x + .4x^2$ **(b)** $640 **(c)** $31.60

27. (a) 30 **(b)** $11 **(c)** (30, 11)   **29. (a)** 480 **(b)** $52 **(c)** (480, 52)   **31. (a)** 200 **(b)** $7 **(c)** (200, 7)

33. 39; $121   **35.** 80; $29   **37.** Since the equilibrium quantity (x) is the quantity for which *supply and demand are equal*, it does not matter which equation (supply or demand) is used to compute the price that corresponds to the equilibrium quantity.

39. C_3, because $C_3(0)$ is larger than $C_1(0)$ and $C_2(0)$.

Technology Exercises   (page 52)

1. 17   **3.** There is no break-even point. Cost is always greater than revenue, which means the company will operate at a loss regardless of the quantity sold.   **5.** (14, 42)

REVIEW EXERCISES FOR CHAPTER 1   (page 53)

1. [1, 7)   **3.** $(-\infty, 11/4]$ **5.** $-1, 3/2$ **7.** $\dfrac{5 \pm \sqrt{17}}{2}$ **9.** $f(0) = 0; f(2) = 4; f(-2) = -12$

11. $f(4) = 2; f(7) = 4; f(8) = 2\sqrt{5}$ **13.** $f(x + 1) = 3x^2 + 6x + 3; f(x + h) = 3x^2 + 6xh + 3h^2$ **15.** $2xh + h^2$

17. $x \neq 1/2$ **19.** $x \geq -9$ **21.** ± 3 **23.** $(f \circ g)(x) = x^2 + 2x - 2$ **25.**

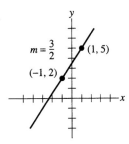

27. slope is 5; y intercept is $(0, -1)$ or -1 **29.** $y = 6x - 19$ **31.** $y = -3x + 6$

33.

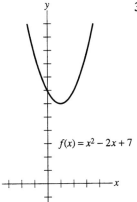

35.

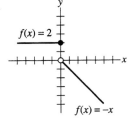

37.

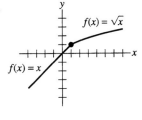

39. No, because there are two different y values for the same x value (3).   **41.** $y = .30x + 26$ (dollars)

43. **(a)** 300 **(b)** $n(5) = 385$. After 5 hours there will be 385 bacteria in the culture.   **45.** **(a)** $R(x) = 300x$

(b) $P(x) = -.1x^2 + 130x - 900$ **(c)** $P(5) = -252.50$. The manufacturer will lose \$252.50 on the production and sale of 5 stereo units. **(d)** \$2610 **(e)** \$171.90   **47.** $(200, 5)$ **49.** **(a)** $y = 2500t + 30,000$ **(b)** 7 years   **51.** 1982–1995

53. **(a)** $y = 1.2x + .2$ **(b)** 5 feet **(c)** 5.5 years

SECTION 2.1   (page 63)

1. -6 **3.** 20   **5.** 19   **7.** 9   **9.** 2/9   **11.** 3   **13.** -2 **15.** 7.5   **17.** cannot determine by substitution; 4

19. 0   **21.** cannot determine by substitution; -3 **23.** 0   **25.** **(a)** $p(x) = .50$ (dollars) *or* $p(x) = 50$ (cents)

(b) .50 (dollars) *or* 50 (cents)   **27.** $\lim\limits_{t \to 25} N = 0$ **29.** 0   **31.** **(a)** A **(b)** B

Technology Exercises   (page 65)

1. 2   **3.** .4   **5.** 2.7   **7.** 0

SECTION 2.2   (page 72)

1. 28   **3.** 37   **5.** 2/7   **7.** −1/5   **9.** 5   **11.** 7   **13.** 0   **15.** 0   **17.** 3/2

19. 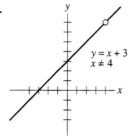   **21.**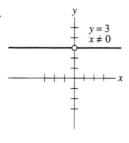

23. $\sqrt{-1}$ is not a real number.   **25.** Division by zero is not defined.   **27.** 3   **29.** 4

31. (a) At the beginning of each year, beginning in 1995.
(b) At the beginning of each year, new cases are added, so the workload is suddenly increased at that time.

33.

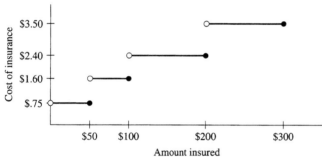

35. 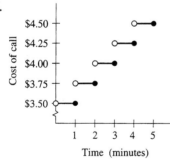   **37.**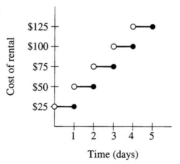

39. Not necessarily true. Only if f is continuous at 2 is it true that $f(2)$ is equal to the limit as x approaches 2.

41. Determine the limit of $f(x)$ as x approaches 4. Also, compute $f(4)$. If the limit is equal to $f(4)$, then the function is continuous at 4. If the limit is not equal to $f(4)$, then the function is not continuous at 4. (Of course, if the limit fails to exist or if f is not defined at 4, then the function is not continuous at 4.)

43. Usually the level of sound is very low and the graph appears as a horizontal line. When the person hiccups, the sound is immediately louder for a moment. Thus, the graph jumps up to a higher level and then falls down to the lower level. There is a discontinuity at each time the person hiccups.

45. continuous   **47.** discontinuous at 0   **49.** discontinuous at all numbers in the interval.   **51.** 1/2   **53.** −1/9

Technology Exercises   (page 74)

1. .7 and 4.3   **3.** 1.8   **5.** $(5, \infty)$ **7.** $(-\infty, 0)$

SECTION 2.3   (page 79)

1. (a) 2   **(b)** 1   **3. (a)** limit does not exist **(b)** 2   **5. (a)** −1 **(b)** −1

7. $\sqrt{2x}$ is not defined for $2x$ less than 0; that is, $f(x) = \sqrt{2x}$ is not defined for the values of x along the approach. As x approaches 0 from the left, $2x$ takes on negative values.

9. $\sqrt{1-x}$ is not defined for $1-x$ less than 0; that is, $f(x) = \sqrt{1-x}$ is not defined for the values of x along the approach. As x approaches 1 from the right, $1-x$ takes on negative values.

11. In order for $\lim_{x \to 0} \sqrt{3x}$ to exist, both the left-hand and right-hand limits must exist and be equal. Although the right-hand limit exists and is 0, that is, $\lim_{x \to 0^+} \sqrt{3x} = 0$, the left-hand limit fails to exist (for the same reason as in Exercise 7).

13. (a) 2 **(b)** −1   **15. (a)** −1 **(b)** −1   **17.** does not exist   **19.** −1

21. (a) $2.40 **(b)** $1.60 **(c)** $1.60 **(d)** $.75 **(e)** does not exist **(f)** no
   (g) Yes, because $\lim_{x \to 120} M(x) = M(120)$. Both the limit and the functional value are the same, 2.40.

23. (a) 10 **(b)** 10.5 **(c)** no **(d)** 9.5 **(e)** 10 **(f)** no

25. (a) 300 **(b)** approximately 500
   (c) At 3 hours, the patient receives 200 more milligrams of medicine, so there is a difference of approximately 200 milligrams just before and just after 3 hours.

27. f is continuous at 3 because $\lim_{x \to 3} f(x) = f(3)$; that is, $11 = 11$.

29. f is continuous at 2 because $\lim_{x \to 2} f(x) = f(2)$; that is, $5 = 5$.

31. f is not continuous at 2 because $\lim_{x \to 2} f(x) \neq f(2)$. Specifically, $\lim_{x \to 2} f(x)$ does not exist, because the left-hand limit is 11 and the right-hand limit is 16.

33. f is not continuous at 4 because $\lim_{x \to 4} f(x) \neq f(4)$. Specifically, $\lim_{x \to 4} f(x)$ does not exist, because the left-hand limit is 14 and the right-hand limit is 13.

35. No. Since $\lim_{x \to 3} f(x) = 5$, the left-hand and right-hand limits must be equal—and equal to 5. If $\lim_{x \to 3^+} f(x)$ were equal to 4, then $\lim_{x \to 3} f(x)$ would not exist.

Technology Exercises   (page 82)

1. (a) does not exist **(b)** does not exist **(c)** 1 **(d)** does not exist **(e)** 2.732 (approximately)   **3.** 1   **5.** discontinuous at 3.5

7. continuous

SECTION 2.4   (page 88)

1.

x	$\dfrac{x + 1}{x}$
100	1.01
1000	1.001
10,000	1.0001
1,000,000	1.000001

The limit is 1.

3.

x	$\dfrac{1 + 3x}{2x}$
-100	1.495
-1000	1.4995
$-10,000$	1.49995
$-1,000,000$	1.4999995

The limit is 1.5.

5. 0   **7.** 0   **9.** 0   **11.** 0   **13.** 3/5   **15.** 2   **17.** 1/2   **19.** $-1/2$ **21.** 0   **23.** $y = 2$ **25.** $y = -1$

27. $y = 0$ **29.** $y = 1/3$ **31. (a)** 0 **(b)** $y = 0$ **33.** $12   **35.** 5 feet

37. (a) 0

(b) After the drug is injected, the amount remaining in the bloodstream will eventually tend toward zero. In other words, eventually there will be no presence of the drug.

39. b

41. A limit as $x \to \infty$ is a left-hand limit, because the approach is through values less than ∞. A limit as $x \to -\infty$ is a right-hand limit, because the approach is through values greater than $-\infty$.

Technology Exercises   (page 90)

3. (a) 1 **(b)** 1   **5.** $y = 0$ **7.** $y = 2, y = -2$ **9.** $y = -3, y = 3$

SECTION 2.5   (page 96)

1. ∞ **3.** ∞ **5.** $-\infty$ **7.** $-\infty$ **9.** ∞ **11.** $-\infty$ **13.** ∞ **15.** ∞ **17.** $-\infty$

19. (a)

percent removed	cost
10	10,000
25	12,000
50	18,000
80	45,000
90	90,000
95	180,000
98	450,000

(b) No. Theoretically, it would cost an infinite amount of money to remove 100% of the pollutants, since $\lim\limits_{x \to 100^-} C(x) = \infty$.

21. $x = 5$ **23.** $x = 0$ **25.** $x = -2$ **27.** $x = 1$ **29.** ∞ **31.** ∞ **33.** 5/7   **35. (a)** 4.5 **(b)** $\lim\limits_{t \to 0^+} \dfrac{81}{t}$ **(c)** ∞

Technology Exercises   (page 97)

1. (a) $-\infty$ **(b)** ∞ **3. (a)** .2   **(b)** .2   **(c)** $-\infty$ **(d)** ∞ **5.** $x = 4$ **7.** $x = 2.6$

REVIEW EXERCISES FOR CHAPTER 2 (page 98)

1. 1/64 **3.** 5/13 **5.** 5 **7.** 0 **9.** 4 **11.** 0 **13.** 5/7 **15.** 0 **17.** $-\infty$ **19.** ∞ **21.** 6 **23.** does not exist

25. (a) no (b) yes (c) yes (d) no (e) no (f) no (g) yes (h) yes **27.** 4 minutes **29.** $8449.64

31. (a) $C(x) = 7x + 2300$ (b) $\overline{C}(x) = 7 + \dfrac{2300}{x}$ (c) $7 **33.** (a) $4.50 (b) $4.50 (c) does not exist

35. (a) 103.1°, 100.1°, 99.05° (b) 98.6° **37.** No. There would be a hole in the graph at $x = 1$.

39. Yes. If the limit did not exist, the function could not be continuous.

SECTION 3.1 (page 112)

1. $f'(x) = 5$ **3.** $f'(x) = 2x$ **5.** $f'(x) = 2x - 4$ **7.** $f'(x) = 6x + 7$ **9.** $f'(x) = 0$ **11.** $f'(x) = 3x^2$

13. $f'(x) = 3x^2 + 2x + 1$ **15.** $f'(x) = -\dfrac{2}{x^2}$ **17.** $f'(x) = 4x^3$ **19.** $f'(x) = 2x + 6; f'(2) = 10$

21. $f'(x) = 3x^2; f'(4) = 48$ **23.** $y = 10x - 4$

25. This is not division by zero. The number Δx is not zero. Even after the reduction, when the limit as $\Delta x \to 0$ is considered, Δx is very close to zero but still not equal to zero.

27. (a) b (b) The tangent line at $x = b$ has the smallest slope.

29. The graph of g is the graph of f translated vertically upward 1 unit.

Technology Exercises (page 113)

1. (a) positive (b) zero (c) positive (d) negative **3.** no **5.** 0 and 2 **7.** f

9. (a) negative (b) negative
(c) $f'(x)$ is the slope of the tangent line to the graph of f.
(d) Same as (a) through (c), except "positive."

SECTION 3.2 (page 119)

1. $f'(x) = 4x^3$ **3.** $f'(x) = -\dfrac{2}{x^3}$ **5.** $g'(x) = 0$ **7.** $y' = \dfrac{3}{2}x^{1/2}$ or $\dfrac{3\sqrt{x}}{2}$ **9.** $y' = -\dfrac{2}{3x^{5/3}}$ **11.** $f'(x) = \dfrac{-5}{x^6}$

13. $y' = \dfrac{1}{3x^{2/3}}$ **15.** $f'(x) = \dfrac{15}{\sqrt{x}}$ **17.** $y' = x^3$ **19.** $y' = \dfrac{-5}{t^{3/2}}$ **21.** $-3x^2$ **23.** $-\dfrac{1}{x^2}$ **25.** $\dfrac{1}{2\sqrt{x}}$

27. $\dfrac{dy}{dx} = 2x - 5$ **29.** $\dfrac{dy}{dx} = \dfrac{3}{2}\sqrt{x} + 8x$ **31.** $\dfrac{dy}{dx} = -\dfrac{1}{x^{3/2}}$ **33.** $D_xy = 18x^5 - 4x^3$ **35.** $D_xy = \dfrac{5}{x^6}$

37. $f'(x) = 3x^2 - 12x + 4$ **39.** $f'(x) = 14x^{3/4} + 10x^{2/3}$ **41.** $f'(x) = \dfrac{3}{2\sqrt{x}} + 10x$ **43.** 14 **45.** 34 **47.** 1/6

49. 1 **51.** -12 **53.** 2 **55.** $y = -32x - 48$ **57.** Here $f'(x) = \lim\limits_{\Delta x \to 0} \dfrac{c - c}{\Delta x} = \lim\limits_{\Delta x \to 0} \dfrac{0}{\Delta x} = \lim\limits_{\Delta x \to 0} (0) = 0$

59. The function is not defined at 0. Because the definition of $f'(x)$ includes $f(x)$ in its numerator, $f'(x)$ cannot exist if it includes an expression that is not defined.

61. Once the specific value (such as 3 or 1) is substituted, the expression becomes a constant. Differentiation at that point will always produce zero as a result.

63. (a) $f'(x_1)$ (b) $g'(x_2)$ (c) $g'(x_3)$ **65.** The limit is $2x$, the derivative of $x^2 + 7$.

Technology Exercises   (page 121)

1. $f'(3)$ **3.** $f'(5)$ **5.** 3

7. (a) They are the same. (b) Each is $3x^2 - 6x$. (c) f' and g' are the same, and since the derivative is the slope of the tangent line, the slopes of the tangent lines to f and g are the same, point for point. This can also be seen from the graphs of the functions.

SECTION 3.3   (page 127)

1. 1.5% per month   **3.** 2700 people per year   **5.** 54 points per day   **7.** 64 feet per second downward

9. 2   **11.** .54   **13.** 96 feet per second

15. *After 5 hours*: 300 bacteria per hour (A used) *versus* 100 bacteria per hour (B used). *After 10 hours*: 500 bacteria per hour (A used) *versus* 0 bacteria per hour (B used).

17. (a) 24,000 (b) 1600 people per day   **19.** $2kr$ **21.** (a) 40 tires per hour (b) at $t = 6$ hours   **23.** $2\pi r$

25. (a) $v(1) = 3$ feet per second; $v(5) = 11$ feet per second (b) after 4 seconds (c) 9 feet per second (d) after 11 seconds

27. (a) g_1 has the greater rate of increase. $g_1'(t_1) > g_2'(t_1)$; the slope of the tangent line is greater for g_1
(b) No; g_1 has the greater rate of increase for the same reason as in part (a).

29. (a) after 6 minutes; for 2 minutes (b) at or just before 2 minutes (c) between 2 and 4 minutes (d) after 4 minutes

31. (a) 14 inches of snow falls in 6 hours. (b) the number of inches of snow that falls in the 4th hour
(c) After 2 hours, snow is falling at the rate of 3 inches per hour.
(d) The rate at which snow is falling is greater after 4 hours than it is after 3 hours.

33. For any linear function, the instantaneous rate of change and the average rate of change are the same—in this case, 10.

Technology Exercises   (page 131)

1. (a) 2.3 seconds (b) 88 feet   **3.** (a) the first one (b) the second one

SECTION 3.4   (page 136)

1. $C'(x) = -.2x$ **3.** $C'(x) = 150 - 2x$ **5.** $C'(x) = 90 + .04x$

7. (a) $20 (b) $19
(c) MC(10), the marginal cost when 10 units have been produced, is the approximate cost of producing the 11th unit.

9. 20 chairs   **11.** 14 hats   **13.** $R'(x) = 50 + .4x$ **15.** $R'(x) = .002x + .7$

17. (a) $R(1) = \$399.99$, $R(10) = \$3999$, $R(100) = \$39,900$ (b) $MR(x) = 400 - .02x$
(c) $MR(1000) = \$380$. Once 1000 CD players have been sold, the revenue from the sale of the next CD player is approximately $380.

19. $P'(x) = .04x + 9$ **21.** $P'(x) = 40 - .02x$ **23. (a)** \$60 **(b)** \$108.75 **(c)** $P'(x) = .001x + 1$
25. $MP(x) = .02x + 85$ **27.** $MP(x) = 10$ **29.** 5000 **31.** 750 **33.** 500 **35.** 500
37. (a) $MP(x) = 26 - .02x$ **(b)** 1300 **39.** \$59.60 **41. (a)** $MR(x) = 1000 - .08x$ **(b)** \$394 **(c)** \$393.98
43. The tax rates are marginal in the sense that they are the rates at which the "next income" will be taxed. For example, once your taxable income reaches \$8000, any income above that amount will be taxed at 16%. Once your taxable income reaches \$20,000, any income above that amount will be taxed at 26%.

45. MC is greater at x_1. MC $= C'(x)$, the slope of the tangent line, and the slope of the tangent line is greater at x_1.

Technology Exercises   (page 138)

1. 26 **3. (a)** positive **(b)** negative

5. MR is greater at $x = 14$, because the slope of the tangent line to the graph of R is greater there.

SECTION 3.5   (page 144)

1. $\dfrac{dy}{dx} = 2x - 1$ **3.** $f'(x) = 20x - 1$ **5.** $\dfrac{dy}{dt} = 4t^3 + 14t$ **7.** $f'(x) = 16x^3 - 9x^2$ **9.** $y' = 4 - \dfrac{1}{x^2}$

11. $y' = -4x^3 + 3x^2 - 2$ **13.** $\dfrac{dy}{dx} = 2x - 3x^2 - 5x^4$ **15.** $\dfrac{dy}{dx} = \dfrac{1}{(1+x)^2}$ **17.** $f'(x) = \dfrac{2}{(3x+1)^2}$ **19.** $f'(t) = 0$

21. $s'(t) = \dfrac{12t^2 + 8t + 1}{(1 + 3t)^2}$ **23.** $\dfrac{dy}{dx} = \dfrac{x^2 + 8x + 23}{(x+4)^2}$ **25.** $\dfrac{dy}{dx} = \dfrac{2x^{3/2} - (4 + 2x)\frac{3}{2}x^{1/2}}{x^3}$, which simplifies to $-\dfrac{x+6}{x^{5/2}}$

27. $y' = -1 + \dfrac{3}{x^4}$ **29.** $f'(x) = 7 - \dfrac{2x}{3} - \dfrac{1}{x^2}$ **31.** $f'(t) = 5t^4 - 24t^2 + 2t$ **33.** $\dfrac{ds}{dt} = \dfrac{-t^2 + 2t + 8}{(1-t)^2}$

35. -4 **37.** 7/12 **39.** 0 **41.** 7 **43.** 3.9 inches per second

45. (a) $-$\$20, a *loss* of \$20 **(b)** \$0 **(c)** \$45.45 **(d)** $MP(x) = \dfrac{10x^2 + 20x - 50}{(x+1)^2}$

47. (a) 110 pounds; 50 pounds; 35 pounds **(b)** -10 pounds per year **(c)** decreasing

49. $\dfrac{d}{dx}\left(\dfrac{x^2}{9}\right) = \dfrac{(9)(2x) - (x^2)(0)}{(9)^2} = \dfrac{18x}{81} = \dfrac{2x}{9}$

51. Once the expression is written as x^{-2}, then the power rule can be used to obtain the derivative. Such an approach is much simpler than using the quotient rule. (Check it out if you aren't convinced.)

Technology Exercises   (page 146)

1. (a) negative **(b)** negative **(c)** negative **3.** 4

SECTION 3.6   (page 151)

1. $\dfrac{dy}{dx} = 10x(x^2 + 3)^4$ **3.** $\dfrac{dy}{dx} = 15(3x)^4$ **5.** $\dfrac{dy}{dx} = \dfrac{1}{(3x+4)^{2/3}}$ **7.** $\dfrac{ds}{dt} = \dfrac{24t^3}{(1-t^4)^7}$ **9.** $\dfrac{dy}{dx} = \dfrac{2}{\sqrt{4x+1}}$

11. $f'(x) = 8x(2x^2 + 1)(x^4 + x^2 + 1)^3$ **13.** $f'(t) = \dfrac{-12t}{(t^2 + 1)^7}$ **15.** $y' = \dfrac{-3}{(6x + 5)^{3/2}}$

17. $\dfrac{dy}{dx} = 20x^2(5x - 2)^3 + 2x(5x - 2)^4$, *or* $2x(5x - 2)^3(15x - 2)$

19. $\dfrac{dy}{dx} = 6(x + 3)(2x + 1)^2 + (2x + 1)^3$, *or* $(2x + 1)^2(8x + 19)$

21. $\dfrac{dy}{dx} = (x^2 + 1)^4 + 8x(x - 2)(x^2 + 1)^3$, *or* $(x^2 + 1)^3(9x^2 - 16x + 1)$

23. $\dfrac{dy}{dx} = 6x(5x - 2)^2(x^2 + 7)^2 + 10(x^2 + 7)^3(5x - 2)$, *or* $2(5x - 2)(x^2 + 7)^2(20x^2 - 6x + 35)$

25. $\dfrac{dy}{dt} = 3(2t + 3)^4(t - 7)^2 + 8(t - 7)^3(2t + 3)^3$, *or* $(2t + 3)^3(t - 7)^2(14t - 47)$

27. $\dfrac{dy}{dx} = \dfrac{3(x + 1)(x + 4)^2 - (x + 4)^3}{(x + 1)^2}$ *or* $\dfrac{(x + 4)^2(2x - 1)}{(x + 1)^2}$ **29.** $\dfrac{dy}{dt} = \dfrac{8(t - 2)(2t + 3)^3 - (2t + 3)^4}{(t - 2)^2}$ *or* $\dfrac{(2t + 3)^3(6t - 19)}{(t - 2)^2}$

31. $\dfrac{dy}{dx} = 3(2x - 5)(2x + 1)^{1/2} + 2(2x + 1)^{3/2}$, *or* $(2x + 1)^{1/2}(10x - 13)$

33. $\dfrac{dy}{dx} = 2x(2x + 1)^{-1/2} + 2(2x + 1)^{1/2}$, *or* $\dfrac{2(3x + 1)}{\sqrt{2x + 1}}$ **35.** $\dfrac{dy}{dx} = \dfrac{8(x - 1)^3}{(x + 1)^5}$

37. $\dfrac{dy}{dx} = \dfrac{1}{2}\left(\dfrac{2x + 1}{x - 1}\right)^{-1/2} \cdot \dfrac{-3}{(x - 1)^2}$, *or* $\dfrac{-3}{2(2x + 1)^{1/2}(x - 1)^{3/2}}$ **39.** -4 **41.** $2/3$ **43.** $1/2$ **45.** $MP(x) = \dfrac{100x}{\sqrt{x^2 - 1}}$

47. (a) $100\%, 95\%, 45\%$ **(b)** 0% per mile, -1.58% per mile, -13.4% per mile

49. The power rule, $D_x x^n = nx^{n-1}$, provides a rule for differentiating a power of a variable (say x) with respect to that variable. For example, $D_x x^3 = 3x^2$. But this power rule cannot be used to differentiate $(x^2 + 1)^3$ with respect to x, because the expression is not a power of x; it is a power of $x^2 + 1$. The chain rule is needed for such a differentiation.

51. $\dfrac{dy}{dx} = 16x(x + 1)^2(2x - 3)^5(x^2 + 1)^7 + 10(x + 1)^2(x^2 + 1)^8(2x - 3)^4 + 2(x + 1)(2x - 3)^5(x^2 + 1)^8$, *or*

$\quad 2(x + 1)(2x - 3)^4(x^2 + 1)^7(23x^3 - 6x^2 - 17x + 2)$

53. $\dfrac{dy}{dx} = \dfrac{2(2x + 7)(x^2 + 3)^5(x + 1) + 10x(2x + 7)(x + 1)^2(x^2 + 3)^4 - 2(x^2 + 3)^5(x + 1)^2}{(2x + 7)^2}$ *or*

$\quad \dfrac{2(x + 1)(x^2 + 3)^4(11x^3 + 51x^2 + 38x + 18)}{(2x + 7)^2}$

Technology Exercises (page 152)

1. positive **3. (a)** any x such that $x > 1.29$ **(b)** $x \approx 1.285$ **(c)** any x such that $0 < x < 1.28$

5. (a) $f'(x) = 3(x^2 + 4.6x + 7.1)^2(2x + 4.6)$ **(b)** -2.3 **7.** $1/2$

SECTION 3.7 (page 157)

1. $f''(x) = 12x^2 - 20$ **3.** $y''' = 6$ **5.** $f^{(4)}(x) = 24$ **7.** $D_x^3 y = -\dfrac{10}{27}x^{-4/3}$ *or* $\dfrac{-10}{27x^{4/3}}$ **9.** $y'' = 0$

11. $y'' = \dfrac{-2}{(1+x)^3}$ 13. $\dfrac{d^2y}{dx^2} = 180(3x-1)^3$ 15. $\dfrac{d^2s}{dt^2} = -32$ 17. $\dfrac{d^2y}{dt^2} = \dfrac{200}{t^6}$ 19. 14   21. 1/32   23. $-5/16$

25. $6x - 14$ 27. $-.25$ 29. $-.12$ 31. $-.005$ 33. $a = -32$

35. (a) $v = 2t - 2 - \dfrac{4}{t^2}$ (b) $a = 2 + \dfrac{8}{t^3}$ (c) 10 feet per second per second (d) 3 feet per second per second

37. $f''(x) = \dfrac{-2x^3 + 6x^2 + 6x - 2}{(x^2+1)^3}$ 39. $y'' = 15x(1+x^2)^{-1/2} - 5x^3(1+x^2)^{-3/2}$ or $\dfrac{5x(2x^2+3)}{(1+x^2)^{3/2}}$

41. (a) $v = -5.3t + 106$ (b) $a = -5.3$
   (c) Yes. On the moon there is less gravitational pull on the ball (-5.3 feet per second per second) than there is on the earth (-32 feet per second per second).
   (d) 40 seconds

43. $P''(x)$ is the rate of change of $P'(x)$, which means that $P''(x)$ is the rate of change of marginal profit.

45. It is the derivative of $f'(x)$, namely $f''(x)$.

47. Because $g'(x)$ has an additional factor of x, obtaining its derivative $g''(x)$ requires use of the product rule. Thus, $g''(x)$ is more difficult to determine.

Technology Exercises   (page 158)

1. (a) positive (b) undefined (c) positive
3. (a) $f'(x) = 18x^2 + 80x + 81$, $f''(x) = 36x + 80$ (b) $x > -2.22$

SECTION 3.8   (page 163)

1. $\dfrac{dy}{dx} = -\dfrac{x}{y}$ 3. $\dfrac{dy}{dx} = \dfrac{2x+6}{3y^2}$ 5. $\dfrac{dy}{dx} = -\dfrac{x^2}{y^2}$ 7. $\dfrac{dy}{dx} = \dfrac{2x+7}{2y}$ 9. $\dfrac{dy}{dx} = \dfrac{1-2x}{2y-3y^2}$ 11. $\dfrac{dy}{dx} = -\dfrac{x^{1/2}}{y^{1/2}}$

13. $\dfrac{dy}{dx} = \dfrac{1-2xy^2}{2x^2y-3}$ 15. $\dfrac{dy}{dx} = \dfrac{3-y^3}{3xy^2+5}$ 17. $\dfrac{dy}{dx} = \dfrac{-1-8y}{8x}$ 19. $\dfrac{dy}{dx} = \dfrac{-2x}{3y^2-1}$ or $\dfrac{2x}{1-3y^2}$; m at $(1, 2)$ is $-2/11$.

21. $\dfrac{dy}{dx} = \dfrac{-10y-1}{10x}$; m at $(5, -1)$ is 9/50.   23. $y = -\dfrac{3}{4}x + \dfrac{25}{4}$ 25. (a) $\dfrac{dy}{dx} = \dfrac{18x^2 - 4x^3}{18y}$ (b) 4.5

27. (a) For $(8, 1)$, show that $8^{2/3} + 1^{2/3} = 5$. (b) $\dfrac{dy}{dx} = -\dfrac{y^{1/3}}{x^{1/3}}$ (c) $-1/2$ (d) 2

29. $\dfrac{dy}{dx} = \dfrac{2(x+5)}{3(y-3)^2}$ 31. $\dfrac{dy}{dx} = \dfrac{1+2x-2xy^2}{2x^2y-1}$ 33. (a) no (b) yes (c) yes (d) no

35. This equation can be considered as $y = x^2 - 9x$, in which y is given *explicitly* in terms of x. Consequently, implicit differentiation is not needed.

Technology Exercises   (page 165)

1. $y = .75x + 6.25$

3.

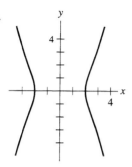

SECTION 3.9   (page 171)

1. 4.5π (≈ 14) square miles per year   **3.** $\dfrac{1}{4\pi}$ ($\approx .08$) meter per hour   **5.** 500π (≈ 1571) cubic millimeters per month

7. $\dfrac{1}{4\pi}$ ($\approx .08$) foot per minute   **9.** 144 square millimeters per second   **11.** $400 per day   **13.** $\dfrac{dy}{dt} = -2\dfrac{dx}{dt}$

15. (a) $R = 12x - .00015x^2$ **(b)** $22.50 per week   **17.** 1.5 feet per second

19. (a) $V = \dfrac{1}{3}\pi r^3$ **(b)** $\dfrac{2}{25\pi}$ ($\approx .025$) foot per minute   **21.** 12 units per second   **23.** 1920 miles per hour

25. (a) $\dfrac{dA}{dt}$ and $\dfrac{dr}{dt}$

  (b) the rate of change of the area with respect to time; the rate of change of the radius with respect to time

  (c) $\dfrac{dA}{dt} = 2\pi r\dfrac{dr}{dt}$

SECTION 3.10   (page 177)

1. $dy = 3x^2\, dx$ **3.** $dy = (2x + 5)\, dx$ **5.** $dy = 10x(x^2 - 3)^4\, dx$ **7.** $dy = -36(1 - 9x)^3\, dx$ **9.** .8

11. .008   **13.** .000125   **15.** .30   **17.** .0175   **19.** $-.045$ **21.** $12,750

23. Computing $R(16) - R(15)$ leads to 12.25, which is $12,250.   **25.** $-.02$ **27.** 3   **29.** 3.53 cubic inches

31. No; the exact change Δy can be calculated, but dy offers a good, fast approximation.

REVIEW EXERCISES FOR CHAPTER 3   (page 179)

1. $f'(x) = 0$ **3.** $f'(x) = x^6$ **5.** $f'(t) = \dfrac{-1}{8t^{3/2}}$ **7.** $\dfrac{dy}{dx} = \dfrac{4}{x^{1/3}} - 14$ **9.** $\dfrac{dy}{dx} = \dfrac{-1}{x^2}$ **11.** $D_x y = -\dfrac{1}{x^2} - \dfrac{9x^8}{7}$

13. $D_x y = \dfrac{-1}{x^{4/3}}$ **15.** $f'(x) = \dfrac{5}{3}x^{2/3}$ **17.** $y' = \dfrac{4}{\sqrt{8x}}$ **19.** $f'(t) = \dfrac{2t}{3(1 + t^2)^{2/3}}$ **21.** $y' = \dfrac{-x^2}{(1 + x^3)^{4/3}}$

23. $\dfrac{dy}{dx} = \dfrac{8(x^2 + 4)(2x - 1)^3 - 2x(2x - 1)^4}{(x^2 + 4)^2}$ *or* $\dfrac{2(2x - 1)^3(2x^2 + x + 16)}{(x^2 + 4)^2}$

25. $\dfrac{dy}{dx} = 4(x^2 + 7)^3(x - 5)^3 + 6x(x - 5)^4(x^2 + 7)^2$ or $2(x - 5)^3(x^2 + 7)^2(5x^2 - 15x + 14)$

27. 3/2   **29.** $y'' = \dfrac{-12}{(x + 3)^3}$ **31.** $\dfrac{dy}{dx} = \dfrac{-2x - y^4}{4xy^3 - 1}$ *or* $\dfrac{2x + y^4}{1 - 4xy^3}$ **33.** .0275   **35.** 972   **37.** 48° per second

39. (a) \$34.80 **(b)** \$34.79 **(c)** −\$.02 per item per item   **41.** MP(x) = −4 + .002x   **43.** 35 units

45. (a) Show that $(1 + 1)^2 - 4(-1)(-1) = 0$. **(b)** $\dfrac{dy}{dx} = \dfrac{4y - 4xy^2 - 4x^3}{4y^3 + 4x^2y - 4x}$ **(c)** −1   **47.** 1.26 cubic centimeters

49. (a) 6.27 seconds **(b)** 201 feet per second   **51.** 9.2 feet per second   **53.** 36π cubic centimeters per minute

55. 627.456

SECTION 4.1   (page 193)

1. increasing on $(-2, 3)$; decreasing on $[-5, -2)$ and $(3, 7]$ **3.** increasing on $(-3, 2)$; decreasing on $[-5, -3)$

5. never increasing; decreasing on $[-6, 0)$ and $(0, 6]$ **7.** increasing when $x > 3$, decreasing when $x < 3$

9. increasing when $x < 0$, decreasing when $x > 0$ **11.** increasing when $x < 5$, decreasing when $x > 5$

13. increasing when $x < 150$, decreasing when $x > 150$ **15.** never increasing; decreasing when $x < 0$ and when $x > 0$

17. never decreasing; increasing when $x > 0$ **19.** never decreasing; increasing when $x > 0$

21. never increasing; decreasing when $x < 0$ and when $x > 0$ **23.** After 16 seconds (when $x > 16$)

25. (a) During the first 25 seconds of the flight (when $0 < t < 25$) **(b)** After 50 seconds (when $t = 50$) **(c)** During the last 25 seconds of the flight (when $25 < t < 50$)

27. When the number of TV antennas produced is less than 900   **29.** decreasing   **31.** increasing

33. (a) $\overline{C}(x) = 36 - .02x$ **(b)** $\overline{C}(x)$ is decreasing for all $x > 0$. $(0 < x \le 1200)$.   **35.** increasing

37. (a) No. Because the graph of $y = B(t)$ is *below* the graph of $y = C(t)$ on $[0, 6]$, the $B(t)$ values are less than the $C(t)$ values on $[0, 6]$. **(b)** No. $B'(t)$ is the slope of the curve $y = B(t)$, and $C'(t)$ is the slope of the curve $y = C(t)$. From the graph we can see that the slope of $y = B(t)$ is not greater than the slope of $y = C(t)$ on $[0, 6]$. **(c)** Although crash dieting provides greater weight loss (and a faster rate of weight loss) early in the program, the crash dieter eventually gains back the lost weight. By contrast, the behavior modification dieter keeps the weight off.

39. (a) (i) increased (ii) stayed the same (iii) decreased **(b)** (i) increased (ii) increased (iii) increased

41. 8   **43.** −3/10   **45.** 0   **47.** −5/3, 1   **49.** $\pm\sqrt{2}$ **51.** $-2 \pm \sqrt{3}$ **53.** 0   **55.** none   **57.** $-1 \pm \sqrt{6}$

59. none   **61.** 0, 2   **63.** −3/2, 1/36   **65.** increasing for $x > 0$; decreasing for $x < 0$

67. increasing for $x > -3$ (but not at $x = 0$); decreasing for $x < -3$ **69.** 0, $-3 \pm \sqrt{7}$

71. (a) 2 **(b)** −1 **(c)** not defined

73. At a it is continuous and differentiable. At b it is continuous but not differentiable. At c it is continuous and differentiable. At d it is not continuous and not differentiable. At e it is not continuous and not differentiable.

75. Yes. If $f'(3) = 0$, then f must be defined at 3. (The derivative cannot exist at a number, such as 3, unless the function is defined there.)

77. Begin by finding the derivative of g. Then find all numbers for which g' is zero or undefined. Test those numbers to determine for which ones the function g is defined. The critical numbers of g are the numbers for which g' is zero or undefined *and* g is defined.

79. There are four possibilities for the derivative $f'(x)$. It can be positive, negative, zero, or undefined. When $f'(x)$ is positive, the function is increasing, so there can be no relative maximum or minimum point for any such x. When $f'(x)$ is negative, the function is decreasing, so there can be no relative maximum or minimum point for any such x. Thus, the only possible numbers that can lead to relative maximum or minimum points are numbers for which $f'(x)$ is zero or undefined (provided that f is defined)—that is, critical numbers.

81. The derivative of a difference is the difference of the derivatives.

Technology Exercises   (page 197)

   1. increasing on $(-\infty, 0)$; decreasing on $(0, \infty)$ **3.** increasing on $(0, 2)$; decreasing on $(-\infty, 0)$ and $(2, \infty)$

   5. increasing on $(-\infty, 0)$; decreasing on $(0, \infty)$ **7.** .4 and 4.9   **9.** -1.6 and 1.9

   11. (a) $f'(x) = \dfrac{4}{3x^{1/3}}$, which is undefined at $x = 0$.   **(b)** The tangent line is vertical at $x = 0$.

SECTION 4.2   (page 204)

   1. $(3, 24)$ relative maximum   **3.** $(10, -100)$ relative minimum   **5.** $(1, -4)$ relative minimum; $(-1, 0)$ relative maximum

   7. $(0, 0)$ relative maximum; $(4, -32)$ relative minimum   **9.** $(-3, 86)$ relative maximum; $(2, -39)$ relative minimum

   11.
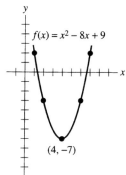

   13.
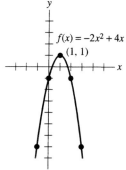

   15.
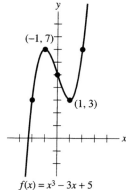

17.

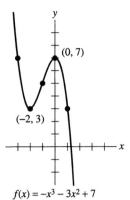

$(0, 7)$

$(-2, 3)$

$f(x) = -x^3 - 3x^2 + 7$

19. $f(x) = 2x^3 - 3x^2 - 12x + 8$

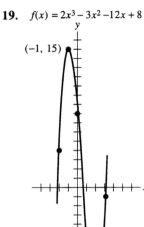

$(-1, 15)$

$(2, -12)$

21.

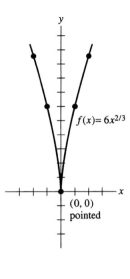

$f(x) = 6x^{2/3}$

$(0, 0)$
pointed

23.

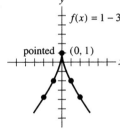

$f(x) = 1 - 3x^{2/3}$

pointed $(0, 1)$

25.

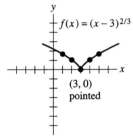

$f(x) = (x - 3)^{2/3}$

$(3, 0)$
pointed

27. none   **29.** (0, 10) relative maximum   **31.** none   **33.** none

35. $(-3, 0)$ relative maximum; $(-1, -16)$ relative minimum   **37.** (0, 0) relative minimum

39. $(-3, -170)$ relative minimum; (0, 19) relative maximum; (2, -45) relative minimum

41. $C'(x) = 3x^2 - 12x + 12$

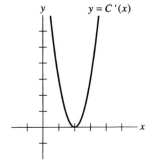

$y = C'(x)$

43. $f'(x_1)$ is zero; $f'(x_2)$ is negative; $f'(x_3)$ is zero; $f'(x_4)$ is undefined

45.

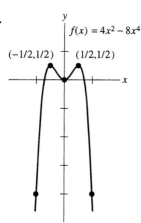

$f(x) = 4x^2 - 8x^4$

$(-1/2, 1/2)$　$(1/2, 1/2)$

47.

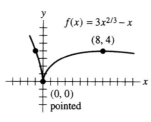

$f(x) = 3x^{2/3} - x$

$(8, 4)$

$(0, 0)$
pointed

49. (a) after 2 minutes **(b)** after 3 minutes; for 1 minute **(c)** 6 miles per hour **(d)** walking north at a constant rate of 3 miles per hour

51. A relative maximum function value is the largest value the function takes on (in some interval)—the largest y value. A relative maximum point is a *point*, the highest point (in some interval) of the graph of the function.

53. $f'(2) = 0$; 2 is a critical number. Also, $f'(x)$ is positive to the left of 2 and negative to the right of 2.

55. (a) horizontal **(b)** vertical

Technology Exercises　　(page 206)

1. $(-1, -3)$ relative minimum　　**3.** $(.6, 8.7)$ relative maximum; $(3.4, -2.7)$ relative minimum

5. -1 is the x coordinate of the relative maximum point; 3 is the x coordinate of the relative minimum point.

7. (a) 2 **(b)** The graph of f' crosses the x axis at the critical number of f, because $f'(x) = 0$ there. This will happen for any polynomial function that has a relative maximum or minimum point.

9. (a) 4 **(b)** negative **(c)** positive **(d)** relative minimum point

11. $-.7$, relative minimum; $.7$, relative maximum

SECTION 4.3　　(page 216)

1. concave up on $(0, 3)$; concave down on $(-4, 0)$　　**3.** concave up on $(-\infty, 0)$ and $(0, \infty)$　　**5.** concave up on $(-\infty, \infty)$

7. concave up on $(0, \infty)$; concave down on $(-\infty, 0)$　　**9.** concave up on $(-1, \infty)$; concave down on $(-\infty, -1)$

11. concave up on $(-\infty, 1/2)$; concave down on $(1/2, \infty)$　　**13.** concave up on $(0, \infty)$; concave down on $(-\infty, 0)$

15. $(-2, 9)$ relative maximum; $(0, 5)$ relative minimum　　**17.** $(-4, 130)$ relative maximum; $(4, -126)$ relative minimum

19. $(-4, -73)$ relative minimum; $(2, 35)$ relative maximum　　**21.** $(0, 0)$ relative maximum; $(5, -125)$ relative minimum

23. none　　**25.** $(0, 5)$ relative minimum

27. $\left(-\frac{1}{2}, 4\frac{11}{16}\right)$ relative minimum; $(0, 5)$ relative maximum; $(1, 3)$ relative minimum

29. $(0, -4)$　　**31.** $(-2, 4)$　　**33.** $(1, 2)$　　**35.** $\left(\frac{1}{2}, 3\frac{1}{2}\right)$

37.

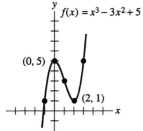

$f(x) = x^3 - 3x^2 + 5$

$(0, 5)$

$(2, 1)$

Point of inflection $(1, 3)$

39. $f(x) = x^3 - 3x^2 + 3x - 1$

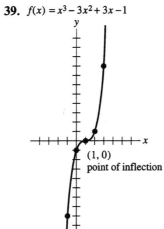

$(1, 0)$
point of inflection

41.

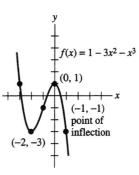

$f(x) = 1 - 3x^2 - x^3$

$(0, 1)$

$(-1, -1)$
point of
inflection

$(-2, -3)$

43.

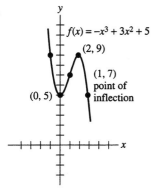

$f(x) = -x^3 + 3x^2 + 5$

$(2, 9)$

$(1, 7)$
point of
inflection

$(0, 5)$

45.

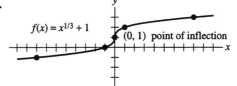

$f(x) = x^{1/3} + 1$

$(0, 1)$ point of inflection

47.

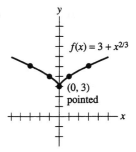

$f(x) = 3 + x^{2/3}$

$(0, 3)$
pointed

49.

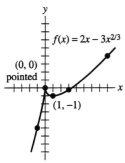

$f(x) = 2x - 3x^{2/3}$

$(0, 0)$
pointed

$(1, -1)$

51.

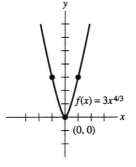

$f(x) = 3x^{4/3}$

$(0, 0)$

53.

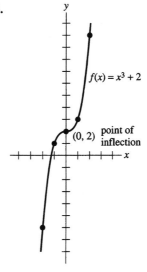

$f(x) = x^3 + 2$

$(0, 2)$ point of
inflection

55.

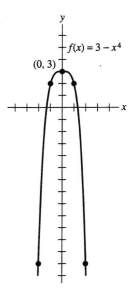

$f(x) = 3 - x^4$

$(0, 3)$

57.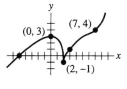

59.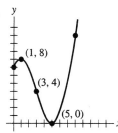

61.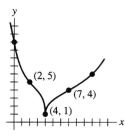

63. $f''(x) = -\dfrac{2}{9x^{4/3}}$. Since $x^{4/3} = (x^{1/3})^4$, $f''(x) < 0$ for $x > 0$ and for $x < 0$. Thus, it is concave down everywhere.

65. Each point $(a, f(a))$ and $(b, g(b))$ is both a relative extreme point *and* a point of inflection.

67. **(a)** zero **(b)** zero **(c)** negative **(d)** negative **(e)** negative **(f)** positive **(g)** positive **(h)** negative

69. No. The second derivative can be zero at a relative maximum or minimum point.

71. The function is not defined at $x = 0$; that is, there is no point $(0, f(0))$ on the graph of f.

73. f' is increasing; the slopes of the tangent lines are increasing. **75. (a)** up **(b)** positive **77.** up

79. The slope of the curve (the derivative of the revenue function) is the marginal revenue. For R_1, the slope of the curve (the marginal revenue) is decreasing.

81. -1

83.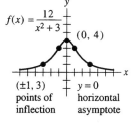

85.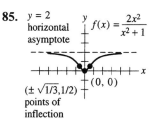

87.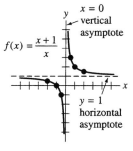

89.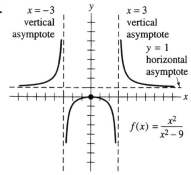

91.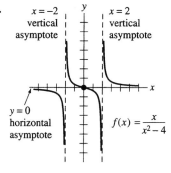

93. Choice (ii), because prices rise if there is *any* associated inflation.

Technology Exercises   (page 220)

1. concave up on $(-3, \infty)$; concave down on $(-\infty, -3)$ **3.** 1.6 to 1.8   **5.** one   **7.** two

9. **(a)** negative **(b)** positive **(c)** undefined **(d)** positive **(e)** positive

11. up for $x > 3$; down for $x < 3$; point of inflection at $x = 3$ **13.** -1.3

***SECTION* 4.4**   (page 222)

1. relative maximum 3; relative minimum 1; absolute maximum 5; absolute minimum 1

3. relative maximum 5; no relative minimum; absolute maximum 5; absolute minimum 1

5. relative maximum 6; relative minimum 5; absolute maximum 7; absolute minimum 2

7. absolute maximum 69; absolute minimum 5   **9.** absolute maximum -9; absolute minimum -41

11. absolute maximum 400; absolute minimum -32 **13.** absolute maximum 1344; absolute minimum -141

15. absolute maximum -34; absolute minimum -50 **17.** absolute maximum 205; absolute minimum 5

19. absolute maximum 109; absolute minimum -591

21. The only x values that can correspond to the absolute extrema of a function (on a closed interval) are the endpoints and any x values within the interval that correspond to relative extrema. The critical numbers are the only numbers that can possibly lead to relative extrema. Our concern here is *absolute* extrema, so it is faster simply to evaluate the function at all critical numbers in the interval (and at the endpoints) and see which numbers lead to absolute extrema. If some critical number does not correspond to a relative extremum, then it will not correspond to an absolute extremum, and we have tested it for nothing. Still, this is far more efficient than testing each critical number first to see if it corresponds to a relative extremum.

Technology Exercises   (page 223)

1. 9.5   **3.** **(a)** -1.8 **(b)** -7.0 **5.** **(a)** $[-4, 4]$ **(b)** $(2.8, 8.0)$ **(c)** $(-2.8, -8.0)$

***SECTION* 4.5**   (page 231)

1. 370°F   **3.** 151 feet   **5.** **(a)** 650 **(b)** \$422,500   **7.** 25   **9.** 1 hour after being swallowed   **11.** 50, 50

13. 400 feet by 400 feet   **15.** 120 feet   **17.** width 24 feet, length 72 feet

19. 60 inches long, 30 inches wide, 20 inches high   **21.** $6\frac{2}{3}$ centimeters   **23.** 7 centimeters   **25.** 62 meters per second

27. width 7 inches, length 14 inches   **29.** 22 trees   **31.** 48 feet (vertical sides) by 36 feet (horizontal sides)

33. 4 feet wide by 8 feet high   **35.** **(a)** 300 **(b)** 500   **37.** **(a)** 1050 **(b)** \$24.50   **39.** 80   **41.** d

43. **(a)** \$95 **(b)** 190 **(c)** \$18,050   **45.** $4b/5$ **47.** $\dfrac{200}{\pi + 4}$ centimeters

Technology Exercises   (page 236)

1. **(a)** 487°F **(b)** at 7 minutes and at 26 minutes **(c)** between 7 minutes and 26 minutes   **3.** 20,300 cubic centimeters

5. **(a)** \$304 billion **(b)** 24.7%

SECTION 4.6 (page 241)

1. 1.5   **3.** .125   **5.** $\dfrac{2p^2}{321 - p^2}$ **7.** 1   **9.** (a) 460,000 (b) 140,000 (c) .94   **11.** 25   **13.** .54% or .55%

15. $28   **17.** Raising the price will increase revenue, because demand is inelastic ($E = .315 < 1$).

19. The wholesaler should decrease the price in order to increase revenue, because demand is elastic ($E = 2.57 > 1$).

21. $1600   **23.** $5

Technology Exercises (page 242)

1. (a) 61,859 (b) $1.80

REVIEW EXERCISES FOR CHAPTER 4 (page 243)

1. increasing when $x < 0$; decreasing when $x > 0$ **3.** never increasing; decreasing when $x < 1$ and when $x > 1$

5. $-2, 6$ **7.** 0   **9.** $-1, 1$

11.

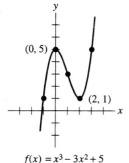

$f(x) = x^3 - 3x^2 + 5$

13.

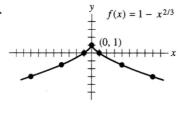

15. $(6, -415)$ relative minimum   **17.** none   **19.** concave up on $(0, \infty)$; concave down on $(-\infty, 0)$ **21.** $(4, -64)$

23. (a) negative (b) positive (c) negative (d) positive (e) negative (f) negative (g) negative (h) negative (i) positive (j) zero (k) positive (l) positive

25. absolute maximum 559; absolute minimum -305 **27.** 14 items   **29.** 60 feet by 60 feet   **31.** .25

33. (a) negative, because the function is decreasing (b) positive, because the curve is concave upward

35. Yes, this will happen when the graph is concave down (dy/dt decreasing) while the slope of the curve is positive (y increasing).

37. No, the graph is always concave up.   **39.** all real numbers x **41.** 3

43. portion c, because the curve must change concavity at the point of inflection.

45. The second derivative is negative from 1983 to 1986 and positive from 1986 to 1990. The CPI increased at a decreasing rate from 1983 to 1986 and increased at an increasing rate from 1986 to 1990.

47. $\dfrac{dS}{dW} = \dfrac{-a}{(W + b)^2} < 0$ **49.** 18 feet   **51.** $\dfrac{1}{2\pi}$ mile

SECTION 5.1   (page 258)

1.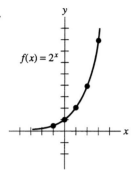

$f(x) = 2^x$

3.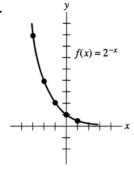

$f(x) = 2^{-x}$

5.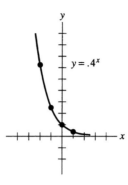

$y = .4^x$

7.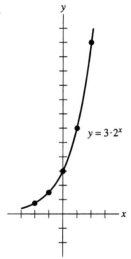

$y = 3 \cdot 2^x$

9.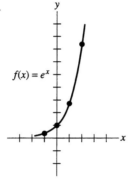

$f(x) = e^x$

11.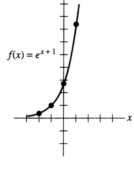

$f(x) = e^{x+1}$

13.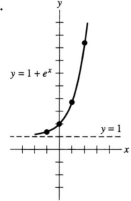

$y = 1 + e^x$

$y = 1$

15.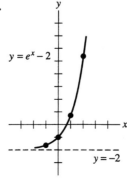

$y = e^x - 2$

$y = -2$

17. 4   **19.** −5   **21.** e^{2x-1} **23.** e^{3x+1} **25.** e^{6x} **27.** $1492   **29.** $8510   **31.** $29,447

33. (a) 50 **(b)** 305 **(c)** 1500   **35. (a)** 30 millimeters **(b)** 50 millimeters
    (c) Fruit growth is not unlimited; it increases toward a specific size.

37. (a) $y = 18(1 - e^{-.3(0)}) = 18(1 - e^0) = 18(1 - 1) = 18 \cdot 0 = 0$ **(b)** 5, 8, 11, 13, 14, 17 **(c)** 18

(d)

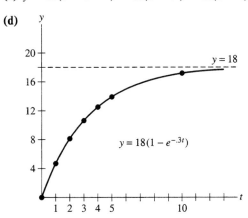

39. (a) $C(x) = 30xe^{-.02x}$ **(b)** \$136

41. 1985–1987 was a time of exponential growth; the index was increasing at an increasing rate. The increase from 1986 to 1987 was much greater than the increase from 1985 to 1986. (By contrast, the growth from 1983 to 1985 was linear.)

43.

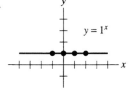

45. (a) The slopes of the tangent lines are increasing, which means that the function is always increasing.
    (b) The graph is always concave up.

47. (a) $y = 0$ for both **(b)** For $f(x) = 3^x$, $\lim_{x \to -\infty} 3^x = 0$. For $f(x) = .5^x$, $\lim_{x \to \infty} .5^x = 0$. **49.** logistic **51.** none

Technology Exercises (page 260)

1. (a) 8 **(b)** 22 **(c)** 12 **(d)** $y = 20$ **3.** 1.8 **5.** 0 **7. (a)** symmetric with respect to the y axis

   (b) The portion in the second quadrant is different because there are no negative exponents with $e^{|x|}$.

SECTION 5.2 (page 272)

1. $\log_2 32 = 5$ **3.** $\log_{10} 100 = 2$ **5.** $\ln 1 = 0$ **7.** $3^2 = 9$ **9.** $10^2 = 100$ **11.** $10^{-1} = .1$ **13.** $e^1 = e$

15. $\ln 3$ **17.** $\frac{1}{3} \ln 2$ **19.** $\frac{1}{5} \ln 14$ **21.** e^{-2} **23.** $\frac{1}{4}e^{30}$ **25.** 1/3 **27.** $\frac{1}{3}e^8$ **29.** 4 **31.** 10 **33.** 0 **35.** 7

37. 1/2 **39.** $\ln x + \ln y$ **41.** $1 + \ln x$ **43.** $\frac{1}{2} \ln x$ **45.** $\ln 2x$ **47.** $\ln \frac{4}{x}$ **49.** $\ln x^3$ **51.** $\ln 5x^2$ **53.** 9.9 years

55. 9.16%   **57. (a)** .06 **(b)** k is the annual rate at which the population will grow over the 5-year period. Here k = .06, or 6%.

59. 8.6 hours   **61. (a)** 19.87% **(b)** 1998   **63. (a)** 97,350 **(b)** $5\frac{1}{2}$ months from now   **65.** .6 gram   **67.** 800 years ago

69. (a) −.025 **(b)** 2056   **71. (a)** −.081 **(b)** 6%   **73. (a)** 15.06 units per volume **(b)** .41 units per volume

(c) 57.6 minutes   **75. (a)** $R(x) = \dfrac{50x}{\ln(x + 3)}$ **(b)** $429   **77. (a)** $D = 10^{a-b\log T}$ **(b)** $T = 10^{(a-\log D)/b}$ **79. (a)** $r = \dfrac{\ln 2}{t}$

(b) r = 13.9%, 11.6%, 9.9%, 8.7%, 7.7%, 6.9%, 6.3%, 5.8%   **81.** 6.50%   **83.** 5.94%   **85. (a)** increases **(b)** positive

(c) positive **(d)** increasing, increasing   **87. (a)** logistic growth **(b)** learning curve **(c)** exponential decay **(d)** logistic growth

(e) exponential growth **(f)** logistic growth **(g)** logistic growth **(h)** logistic growth **(i)** learning curve   **89. (a)** 315°

(b) −.0047 **(c)** between 81 and 82 minutes   **91.** When $t = 0$, $A = Ce^{k(0)} = Ce^0 = C \cdot 1 = C$.

93. Yes, c is an exponent when $\log_b a = c$ is written in the alternative form $a = b^c$.

95. (a) The tangent lines all have positive slopes, which shows that $f(x) = \ln x$ is increasing.
  (b) The graph is concave down everywhere.

97. $\ln(x - 2)$ is not defined for $x \le 2$, because the logarithm of a negative number or zero is not defined.

Technology Exercises   (page 277)

1. 5 days   **3. (a)** 1.6 **(b)** 1.6   **5.** 2.5   **7. (a)** 16 years **(b)** $1800   **9. (a)** 6.4% **(b)** 5.5%

SECTION 5.3   (page 284)

1. $y' = x^2 e^x + 2xe^x = xe^x(x + 2)$ **3.** $y' = 5e^x$ **5.** $f'(x) = 4e^x(e^x + 2)^3$ **7.** $y' = \dfrac{xe^x - e^x - 1}{x^2}$

9. $f'(x) = -\dfrac{3(e^x + 1)}{(e^x + x)^4}$ **11.** $f'(x) = \dfrac{e^x}{(e^x + 1)^2}$ **13.** $f'(x) = 6e^{6x-1}$ **15.** $f'(x) = -2xe^{-x^2}$ **17.** $f'(x) = \dfrac{e^{\sqrt{x}}}{2\sqrt{x}}$

19. $\dfrac{dy}{dx} = -4xe^{-5x^2}$ **21.** $y' = e^{-x} - xe^{-x} = (1 - x)e^{-x}$ **23.** $f'(x) = \dfrac{3xe^{3x} + 2e^{3x}}{(x + 1)^2}$ or $\dfrac{(3x + 2)e^{3x}}{(x + 1)^2}$

25. $y' = \dfrac{e^x - e^{-x}}{2}$ **27.** $f'(x) = \dfrac{5 - 5x}{e^x}$ **29.** $y' = 50e^{5x}(1 + e^{5x})^9$ **31.** $f''(x) = 9e^{3x}$

33. $f''(x) = xe^x + 2e^x = (x + 2)e^x$ **35.** increasing for all x; never decreasing   **37.** never increasing; decreasing for all x

39. increasing when $x > -1$; decreasing when $x < -1$ **41.** increasing when $x > 0$; decreasing when $x < 0$ **43. (a)** −2, 0

(b) relative maximum $\dfrac{4}{e^2}$ (when $x = -2$); relative minimum 0 (when $x = 0$)   **45. (a)** −2 **(b)** relative minimum $-\dfrac{2}{e}$

47. (a) 0, 2 **(b)** relative minimum 0 (when $x = 0$); relative maximum $\dfrac{4}{e^2}$ (when $x = 2$)   **49. (a)** −4/3 **(b)** relative minimum $-\dfrac{1}{3e^4}$

51. The exponential function has no critical numbers (the only numbers that can possibly correspond to relative extrema), since $f'(x) = e^x$, and e^x is never zero or undefined.

53.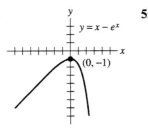

55.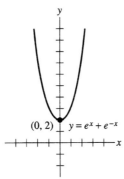

57. (a) $C(x) = 50xe^{-.04x}$ **(b)** $MC(x) = (1 - .04x)50e^{-.04x}$ **(c)** $C(10) = \$335.16$; $MC(10) = \$20.11$ **(d)** when $x = 25$

59. $MP(x) = 1.2xe^{.03x} + 40e^{.03x} + .8xe^{-.02x} - 40e^{-.02x}$ **61.** 10 units

63. (a) .001 gram per cubic centimeter (source), .000135 gram per cubic centimeter (1 mile downstream)
(b) $-.002e^{-2x}$ gram per cubic centimeter per mile

65. 4 **67.** $y = ex$ **69.** $\dfrac{dy}{dx} = \dfrac{-e^y - 1}{1 + xe^y}$ **71.** $\dfrac{dy}{dx} = \dfrac{e^y - ye^x}{1 + e^x - xe^y}$ or $\dfrac{ye^x - e^y}{xe^y - e^x - 1}$ **73.** $\dfrac{dy}{dx} = \dfrac{-2x - e^{x+y}}{2y + e^{x+y}}$

75. $\dfrac{dy}{dx} = \dfrac{ye^{xy} - 2}{1 - xe^{xy}}$ or $\dfrac{2 - ye^{xy}}{xe^{xy} - 1}$ **77.** $\dfrac{dy}{dx} = \dfrac{e^{y^2} + 2xe^y}{1 - x^2e^y - 2xye^{y^2}}$ **79.** $y' = 2^x \ln 2$ **81.** $y' = 7^{4x} \cdot 4 \ln 7$

83. $f'(x) = -3^{-x^2} \cdot 2x \ln 3$ **85.** $f'(x) = 9^{1+x^2} \cdot 4x \ln 9$ **87.** $y' = 2^{3x}(1 + 3x \ln 2)$ **89.** $y' = \dfrac{3^x(x \ln 3 - 1)}{2x^2}$

91. $f'(x) = \dfrac{10^{2x} - 1 - 10^{2x} \cdot 2x \ln 10}{3x^2}$ **93.** 0 **95.** e^2 **97.** $\dfrac{1}{1 + e}$ **99.** $(0, 1)$

101. No, $5e^{2x}$ is a constant (5) times a function (e^{2x}). There is no need to consider it as the product of two functions.

103. The slope of the tangent line, which is geometrically the derivative (or the growth rate), is greatest at the point of inflection.

Technology Exercises   (page 286)

1. (a) $(4.0, 3.0)$ **(b)** nowhere   **3. (a)** negative **(b)** positive **(c)** $y = 0$ **5.** $-.105$

SECTION 5.4   (page 295)

1. $y' = \dfrac{1}{x}$ **3.** $y' = 1 + \ln x$ **5.** $y' = \dfrac{1 - \ln x}{x^2}$ **7.** $y' = \dfrac{\ln x - 1 - \dfrac{1}{x}}{(\ln x)^2}$ or $\dfrac{x \ln x - x - 1}{x(\ln x)^2}$

9. $f'(x) = \dfrac{1}{2x\sqrt{\ln x}}$ **11.** $f'(x) = \dfrac{\ln x}{(1 + \ln x)^2}$ **13.** $y' = \dfrac{2x}{x^2 + 7}$ **15.** $y' = \dfrac{6}{2x + 1}$ **17.** $f'(x) = -\dfrac{1}{x}$

19. $f'(x) = \dfrac{1}{2x}$ **21.** $f'(x) = \dfrac{1}{x(x + 1)}$ **23.** $y' = \dfrac{x + 1}{x}$ **25.** $y = 3x - 3$ **27.** $f''(x) = \dfrac{1}{x}$ **29.** $f''(x) = \dfrac{2 - 2 \ln x}{x^2}$

31. $f''(x) = \dfrac{-3 + 2 \ln x}{x^3}$ **33. (a)** $MR(x) = 70 + \dfrac{100}{x}$ **(b)** \$75

35. (a) $C(x) = 3x \ln (x + 1)$ **(b)** $MC(x) = \dfrac{3x}{x + 1} + 3 \ln (x + 1)$

37. $c'(t) = .1 + \dfrac{1}{t + 1}$, which is positive for all t being considered. Thus, c is an increasing function.   **39.** increasing

41. increasing   **43.** decreasing   **45.** critical number: 3, relative minimum: $6 - 6 \ln 3$

47. critical number: e; relative maximum: $\dfrac{2}{e}$ **49.** critical number: $\dfrac{1}{\sqrt{e}}$; relative minimum: $-\dfrac{1}{2e}$

51. critical number: 1; relative maximum: 0

53.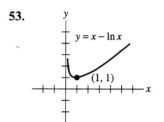

55.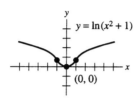

points of inflection $(\pm 1, \ln 2)$

57. $\dfrac{dy}{dx} = \dfrac{-\dfrac{3}{x} - y}{x + 1} = \dfrac{-3 - xy}{x^2 + x}$ **59.** $\dfrac{dy}{dx} = \dfrac{-y - 2x^2y}{2xy + x}$ **61.** $\dfrac{dy}{dx} = \dfrac{\dfrac{y}{x} - \ln y}{\dfrac{x}{y} - \ln x} = \dfrac{y^2 - xy \ln y}{x^2 - xy \ln x}$

63. $\dfrac{dy}{dx} = \dfrac{3y - 1 - e^x \ln y}{\dfrac{e^x}{y} - 3x} = \dfrac{3y^2 - y - ye^x \ln y}{e^x - 3xy}$ **65.** $y' = \dfrac{1}{x \ln 10}$ **67.** $y' = \dfrac{1}{x \ln 2}$

69. $y' = \log_{10} (1 - 3x) - \dfrac{3x}{(1 - 3x) \ln 10}$ **71.** $y' = \dfrac{\dfrac{1}{\ln 10} - \log_{10}x}{x^2}$ **73.** $\dfrac{dy}{dx} = x^{2x}(2 + 2 \ln x)$

75. $\dfrac{dy}{dx} = (x + 1)^x \left[\dfrac{x}{x + 1} + \ln(x + 1) \right]$ **77.** $\dfrac{dy}{dx} = x^{1/x} \left(\dfrac{1}{x^2} - \dfrac{1}{x^2} \ln x \right)$ **79.** $\dfrac{dy}{dx} = (3x)^{x + 1} \left(\dfrac{x + 1}{x} + \ln 3x \right)$

81. (a) $\dfrac{dy}{dx} = 3^x \ln 3$ **(b)** $\dfrac{dy}{dx} = 2^x \ln 2$ **(c)** $\dfrac{dy}{dx} = 5^x \cdot 3 \ln 5$ **(d)** $\dfrac{dy}{dx} = 4^{x^2} \cdot 2x \ln 4$ **83.** 0

85. No, the expression is $\dfrac{1}{2} \ln x$, a constant times a function. There is no need to use the quotient (or product) rule.

87. increasing   **89.** The only possible candidates for x values associated with relative extrema are the critical numbers—x such that $f'(x) = 0$ or $f'(x)$ is undefined when $f(x)$ is defined. Since $f'(x) = 1/x$, there are no x values for which $f'(x) = 0$. (The numerator is always 1.) Although $f'(x)$ is undefined when $x = 0$, so is the original function $f(x) = \ln x$ undefined when $x = 0$. Thus, f has no critical numbers and therefore $f(x) = \ln x$ has no relative extrema.

91. As x gets larger and larger, the slope of the tangent line gets closer and closer to zero. However, the slope can never be zero. After all, the slope is $1/x$, and $1/x$ is never equal to zero.   **93.** $f^{(40)}(x) = -1 \cdot 2 \cdot 3 \cdot 4 \cdot 5 \cdots \cdots 39x^{-40}$

Technology Exercises   (page 298)

1. (a) $(1.1, 5.0)$ **(b)** $(0, \infty)$ **3. (a)** positive **(b)** positive   **5.** 1.79

REVIEW EXERCISES FOR CHAPTER 5   (page 299)

1. $\frac{1}{7} \ln 6$ **3.** $\frac{1}{4}e^6$ **5.** $\frac{\ln .5}{.03}$ **7.** e^5 **9.** -7 **11.** -2 **13.** $\frac{dy}{dx} = 4e^4x^3$ **15.** $f'(x) = -7e^x(3 - e^x)^6$

17. $f'(x) = 3x^2e^{-3x} - 3x^3e^{-3x} = 3x^2e^{-3x}(1 - x)$ **19.** $f'(x) = e^{3x}\left(\frac{1}{x} + 3 \ln x\right)$ **21.** $y' = 2x \ln x + 2x(\ln x)^2$

23. $f'(x) = -\frac{2}{x}$ **25.** $y' = \ln x$ **27.** $\ln \frac{4}{3}$ **29.** 10   **31.** $\frac{dy}{dx} = \frac{2}{\frac{5}{y} + 3e^{3y}} = \frac{2y}{5 + 3ye^{3y}}$

33. \$7408   **35.** approximately 24   **37.** 14,112–14, 146   **39. (a)** \$356 billion   **(b)** \$267 billion   **41.** 38%

43. (a) 100 **(b)** 5317 **(c)** 200,000   **45. (a)** $P = 10^{a-b \log A}$ **(b)** $A = 10^{(a-\log P)/b}$

47. (ii) is the only function that is decreasing.

49. The calculator indicates an error, because ln 0 and ln(-1) are not defined. Specifically, ln x is defined only for $x > 0$.

51. 0   **53.** $f''(x) = 1/x^2$ is positive for all x in the domain of f.   **55. (a)** 50 feet **(b)** 56.4 feet **(c)** 6.4 feet

(d) $y' = 0$ leads to $x = 0$, and $y'' > 0$ at $x = 0$.

SECTION 6.1   (page 310)

1. $4x^2 + C$ **3.** $2x^3 + C$ **5.** $\frac{t^4}{4} + C$ **7.** $\frac{5x^6}{3} + C$ **9.** $-\frac{1}{x} + C$ **11.** $-\frac{1}{x^3} + C$ **13.** $-\frac{1}{4x^4} + C$ **15.** $-\frac{4}{z^5} + C$

17. $\frac{2x^{3/2}}{3} + C$ **19.** $\frac{4x^{7/4}}{7} + C$ **21.** $3x^{1/3} + C$ **23.** $3x + C$ **25.** $\frac{x^3}{3} + 3x^2 + C$ **27.** $\frac{2x^{3/2}}{3} - x^3 + C$

29. $2\sqrt{x} + 9x + C$ **31.** $\frac{t^3}{3} - 4t^2 + t + C$ **33.** $e^x + C$ **35.** $x^2 - e^x + C$ **37.** $e^x + x + C$ **39.** $\ln |z| + C$

41. $4 \ln |x| + 3x^2 + C$ **43.** $\frac{1}{5} \ln |x| + C$ **45.** $3x + \ln |x| + C$ **47.** $\frac{1}{7}e^{7x} + C$ **49.** $5e^x + C$ **51.** $20e^{.05t} + t + C$

53. $-\frac{1}{6}e^{-6x} + C$ **55.** $-100e^{-.01x} + C$ **57.** $\ln |x| + x^2 + C$ **59.** $\frac{2}{3}t^{3/2} + 2t^{1/2} + C$ **61.** $\frac{2}{5}x^{5/2} + \frac{2}{3}x^{3/2} + C$

63. $x - e^{-x} + C$ **65.** $\frac{x^3}{3} + \frac{x^4}{4} + C$ **67.** (ii)   **69.** (iv)

71. (a) Yes. **(b)** No. The integration leaves you with a ''+ C'' term. In particular, the function $f(x) + 5$ (after differentiation and integration) becomes $f(x) + C$, where C is *any* constant.

73. Yes. Use the power rule for all n except -1. For $n = -1$, the result is a natural logarithm.

75. The graph will have the same appearance, except it will be translated up 2 units.

Technology Exercises   (page 312)

1. (a) The graph of f crosses the x axis. **(b)** The graph of f is below the x axis to the left and above the x axis to the right.

3. (a) The slope of the tangent line is the same for each of them. **(b)** The derivative is the same: $f(-2)$ in each case.

SECTION 6.2   (page 317)

1. $f(x) = x^3 - x^2 + 5x + 3$ **3.** $f(x) = \dfrac{1}{x^3} + 2$ **5.** $f(x) = x + 2x^{3/2} - 4$ **7.** $f(x) = \ln |x| + 5$

9. $f(x) = \dfrac{1}{2}e^{2x} + 4x^2 + \dfrac{3}{2}$ **11.** $y = x^2 + 5$ **13.** $y = \dfrac{2}{3}x^{3/2} + 1$ **15.** $y = e^x$ **17.** $C(x) = 40x - .03x^2 + 200$

19. $C(x) = 20\sqrt{x} + 50$ **21.** $\$1015$ **23.** $R(x) = 50x - .2x^2$ **25.** $R(x) = 10x - 20e^{.05x} + 20$

27. $P(x) = 100x + .2x^2 - .02x^3$ **29.** $P(x) = 70x - 100e^{.01x} + 70$

31. (a) $v(t) = -32t$ **(b)** $s(t) = -16t^2 + 576$ **(c)** 128 feet per second **(d)** 6 seconds

33. (a) $v(t) = -5.3t + 120$ **(b)** $s(t) = -2.65t^2 + 120t$ **35. (a)** $\dfrac{dn}{dt} = 5t^{2/3} + 22$ **(b)** $n = 3t^{5/3} + 22t + 50$ **(c)** 322

37. (a) $n = t^2 + 30t + 2000$ **(b)** 2099   **39.** 102 milligrams   **41. (a)** $d = 30e^{-.001t} - 29.6$ **(b)** .1 centimeter

43. $P = 14.7e^{-.21x}$ **45.** 288π cubic centimeters   **47. (a)** the profit when no units are sold **(b)** a loss

49. You need a specific value of x and the corresponding $f(x)$ value.

Technology Exercises   (page 320)

1. (a) $y = .75x^2 + 2$ **(b)** The lines are tangent to the curve.
(c) The slope is -3, the same as that of tangent line $y = -3x - 1$.
(d) The slope is 1.5, the same as that of tangent line $y = 1.5x + 1.25$.   **3.** 58 units

SECTION 6.3   (page 327)

1. 55   **3.** 48   **5.** 100   **7.** 29/12   **9.** $\displaystyle\sum_{i=1}^{9} i$ **11.** $\displaystyle\sum_{i=4}^{n} i$ **13.** $\displaystyle\sum_{i=1}^{49} \dfrac{i}{i+1}$ **15.** $\displaystyle\sum_{i=1}^{10} a_i x_i$ **17.** $\displaystyle\sum_{i=0}^{n} f(x_i)$

19. 36   **21.** 70   **23.** 9   **25.** 11.25   **27.** 8.25   **29.** 8.12   **31.** The larger the n, the smaller the Δx.
33. If $f(x) < 0$, the area is negative.

Technology Exercises   (page 328)

1. (a) 9 **(b)** 7.75, 7.08, 6.7472, 6.7068, 6.674672   **3.** 18.16359544, 17.62622098, 17.44718718

SECTION 6.4   (page 335)

1. the total revenue from the sale of x units   **3.** the total amount of gasoline consumed in the United States from 1964 to 1976

5. the total interest paid by a bank on its money market account from 1984 to 1992

7. the total amount of growth (in milligrams) of the yeast this week   **9.** 36   **11.** 21   **13.** 6   **15.** 95/6   **17.** 3

19. $e - 2$ **21.** 3/10   **23.** 76   **25.** $\ln 3$ **27.** $20(e^5 - 1)$ **29.** $\dfrac{9}{2} + 4\ln 2$ **31.** $\dfrac{1}{e} - \dfrac{5}{4} + \ln 4$ **33.** 64/3

35. 9   **37.** 20/3   **39.** 10/3   **41.** 45/4   **43.** ln 6   **45.** $2e - 2$ **47.** 6   **49.** 16/3

51. *Sample:* $\int_2^2 6x\,dx = [3x^2]_2^2 = 12 - 12 = 0$ **53.** There is no area (zero area) under a point.   **55.** $2 - e$

57. 9/2   **59.** 8   **61.** The function is not continuous on [1, 5]. There is a discontinuity at 3.

Technology Exercises   (page 337)

1. 27/2   **3.** 7.812   **5. (a)** 80.115, 85.6446, 86.32365 **(b)** 87

SECTION 6.5   (page 346)

1. $197.75   **3.** $145,634   **5.** No. There will be a loss of $3000 from the additional 300 computers.   **7.** 23.85 feet

9. 109   **11.** 378,000 cubic meters   **13.** 1292 million barrels   **15.** 736   **17.** 13/3   **19.** 10   **21.** 2/7   **23.** $e - 1$

25. 43 centimeters per second   **27.** 80 feet per second   **29.** 17.6 feet   **31.** $4596

33. The average value is 5, which can be determined by noting that f is 5 at every number in the interval.   **35.** 6π

37. $124\pi/3$ **39.** $28\pi/15$ **41.** 48π **43.** $\dfrac{\pi}{4}(e^{12} - 1)$ **45.** $\pi(\ln 10 - 1)$ **47.** $\pi\left(\dfrac{3}{2} + 2\ln 2\right)$

49. 1.1956π or 3.756   **51.** $V = \displaystyle\int_0^h \pi\left(\dfrac{r}{h}x\right)^2 dx = \left[\dfrac{\pi r^2}{h^2} \cdot \dfrac{x^3}{3}\right]_0^h = \dfrac{\pi r^2 h}{3}$

53. (a) Determine the area of the trapezoid formed between the line segment and the x axis. **(b)** 9.2 billion barrels

Technology Exercises   (page 349)

1. yes   **3. (a)** $(-1, 3)$ **(b)** 4/3

SECTION 6.6   (page 352)

1. (a) $(11, 29)$ **(b)** $60.50 **(c)** $121   **3. (a)** $(13, 23.5)$ **(b)** $42.25 **(c)** $126.75   **5. (a)** $(28, 8)$ **(b)** $98 **(c)** $98

7. (a) $(5, 3.5)$ **(b)** $25 **(c)** $8.33   **9. (a)** $(16, 9)$ **(b)** $21.33 **(c)** $42.67   **11. (a)** $(3, 10)$ **(b)** $4.50 **(c)** $18

13. The unshaded region between the demand curve and the top ($y = p_e$) of the shaded rectangle.

Technology Exercises   (page 353)

1. $(6.0, 5.5)$ **3. (a)** $(5, 6)$ **(b)** consumer's surplus

SECTION 6.7   (page 360)

1. 66   **3.** 68/3   **5.** 47/6   **7.** 52/3   **9.** 35/6   **11.** 8/3   **13.** 9/2   **15.** 4/3   **17.** 1/12   **19.** 1/3   **21.** 4/3

23. $e - 2$ **25.** 34/3   **27.** 59/3   **29.** 2   **31.** 8   **33.** 1/2   **35.** 1/2   **37.** 9/2   **39.** 4/15   **41.** $\displaystyle\int_0^{x_e} [D(x) - p_e]\,dx$

43. 71/6   **45.** $\dfrac{2}{e} - \ln 2$ **47.** 7/3   **49.** 45/2

51. Negative. The region below the x axis is larger than the region above the x axis.

Technology Exercises   (page 362)

1. $f(x) = 2\sqrt{x + 6}$ **3.** $f(x) = 10 - .5x^2$ **5.** 2.3 and 5.9   **7.** .8 and 6.2; area $= 26.028$

REVIEW EXERCISES FOR CHAPTER 6   (page 363)

1. $4x^2 + 2x + C$ **3.** $2x^5 - \dfrac{1}{3}x^3 + C$ **5.** $x + \dfrac{2}{3}x^{3/2} + C$ **7.** $-\dfrac{3}{t} + C$ **9.** $2 \ln |x| + C$ **11.** $-50e^{-.02x} + C$

13. 10   **15.** 5/2   **17.** $\ln 6$ **19.** $25(e^{.4} - e^{.04})$ **21.** 15   **23.** $\dfrac{9}{2} - e$ **25.** 64/3   **27.** \$35   **29.** 225 feet

31. 18 billion barrels   **33.** 4800 gallons   **35.** 110.6   **37.** 633/95   **39.** $2\pi\left(1 - \dfrac{1}{e^2}\right)$ **41.** (20, 11); \$40; \$80

43. $\displaystyle\sum_{i=1}^{n} x_i f(x_i)$ **45. (a)** 1/3 **(b)** 1/3 **(c)** 1/3 **(d)** Each is 1/3.   **47.** $y = x^2 - 6$ **49. (a)** 7/2 **(b)** 3/2 **(c)** 29/2

SECTION 7.1   (page 375)

1. $\dfrac{(x^2 + 3)^6}{6} + C$ **3.** $\dfrac{2(x^2 - 6)^{3/2}}{3} + C$ **5.** $\dfrac{(3x - 2)^7}{21} + C$ **7.** $\dfrac{(x^2 - 3)^{3/2}}{3} + C$ **9.** $\dfrac{(5x^3 + 1)^5}{75} + C$

11. $\dfrac{-1}{14(7x + 2)^2} + C$ **13.** $\dfrac{2}{3}\sqrt{3x + 2} + C$ **15.** $\dfrac{3}{8}(x + 2)^8 + C$ **17.** $\dfrac{(x^2 - 4x + 1)^6}{12} + C$ **19.** $\dfrac{2}{5}(x^{1/2} + 1)^5 + C$

21. 21/2   **23.** 39   **25.** 1/3   **27.** 104/3   **29.** 2   **31.** 38/3   **33.** $e^{x^3} + C$ **35.** $e^{x+1} + C$ **37.** $-e^{-x} + C$

39. $\dfrac{1}{6}e^{3t^2} + C$ **41.** $e^x - e^{-x} + C$ **43.** $\ln |x + 1| + C$ **45.** $\dfrac{1}{5}\ln |5x + 2| + C$ **47.** $\ln |1 + x^3| + C$

49. $\dfrac{2}{3}\ln |1 + x^{3/2}| + C$ **51.** $\dfrac{1}{3}\ln |x^3 + 6x^2 - 15| + C$ **53.** $\dfrac{1}{2}\ln |1 + x^2| + C$ **55.** $t + \dfrac{1}{3}e^{3t} + C$

57. $\ln |x| + x + C$ **59.** $-\dfrac{1}{2}\ln |1 - e^{2x}| + C$ **61.** $\dfrac{1}{5}(\ln x)^5 + C$ **63.** $-\dfrac{1}{\ln x} + C$ **65.** $x + \dfrac{1}{e^x} + C$

67. $(\ln x)^2 + C$ **69.** $\dfrac{1}{3}(\ln x)^3 + C$ **71.** $\ln 2$ **73.** $\ln(1 + e) - \ln 2$ **75.** $\dfrac{1}{2} - \dfrac{1}{2e}$ **77.** 1   **79.** 1/2   **81.** $\dfrac{1}{2}\ln 3$

83. $e^2 x + C$ **85.** $\dfrac{1}{4}(\ln x)^2 + C$ **87.** $\dfrac{x^2}{2} + x + 3 \ln |x + 1| + C$ **89.** $3x + 3 \ln |x - 1| + C$

91. $y = 2e^{x^2} + 3$ **93.** 49/12   **95.** 45/28   **97.** $2\pi/77$ **99.** 10 feet   **101.** 316 gallons

103. (a) The second integral can be evaluated by the methods studied thus far. Insert a factor of 2 into the integral (and 1/2 in front of the integral). The integrand then has the form $u^n du$, where $u = 2x + 1$ and $du = 2x\, dx$.

(b) The first integral cannot be evaluated by the methods studied thus far. The integrand is *almost* $u^n du$, but it is missing a factor of x (because $u = x^2 + 1$ and $du = 2x\,dx$). Unfortunately, we cannot insert *variable* factors (such as x) into the integrand.

Technology Exercises (page 377)

1. 0 and 3; area $= \dfrac{85}{6} - \dfrac{2}{3}(5.5)^{3/2} \approx 5.5676$ **3. (a)** 53.018, 50.937, 50.669 **(b)** 50.4

SECTION 7.2   (page 383)

1. $\dfrac{1}{2}xe^{2x} - \dfrac{1}{4}e^{2x} + C$ **3.** $\dfrac{x^2}{2}\ln x - \dfrac{x^2}{4} + C$ **5.** $\dfrac{x^3}{3}\ln x - \dfrac{x^3}{9} + C$ **7.** $xe^x + C$ **9.** $-\dfrac{1}{x}\ln x - \dfrac{1}{x} + C$

11. $\dfrac{x(x+3)^5}{5} - \dfrac{(x+3)^6}{30} + C$ **13.** $\dfrac{-x}{2(x+7)^2} - \dfrac{1}{2(x+7)} + C$ **15.** $2x^{1/2}\ln x - 4x^{1/2} + C$

17. $x^3e^x - 3x^2e^x + 6xe^x - 6e^x + C$ **19.** $\dfrac{-x}{2(x+2)^2} - \dfrac{1}{2(x+2)} + C$ **21.** e^2 **23.** 1   **25.** 3/2   **27.** -1

29. 12,149   **31.** $\dfrac{1}{2}e^{x^2} + C$ **33.** $\dfrac{(\ln x)^2}{2} + C$ **35.** $x \ln 2x - x + C$ **37.** $\dfrac{2x}{3}(1+x)^{3/2} - \dfrac{4}{15}(1+x)^{5/2} + C$

39. $\dfrac{1}{3}(1+x^2)^{3/2} + C$ **41.** $-25xe^{-.04x} - 625e^{-.04x} + C$ **43.** $-150xe^{-.08x} - 1875e^{-.08x} + C$

45. $-20xe^{-.05x} - 400e^{-.05x} + C$ **47.** \$93,535   **49.** \$29,410   **51.** $p = 60 + t \ln t$ **53.** 59.4 milligrams

55. 1   **57.** $y = x \ln x - x$ **59.** $2e^{-1} - 4e^{-3}$ **61.** $\dfrac{\pi}{4}(e^2 - 1)$

63. The choice is not a good one, because it produces the same integral that we are trying to evaluate. Nothing is accomplished by using $u = 1$ and $dv = \ln x\,dx$.

Technology Exercises (page 385)

1. 0. Use symmetry: the y values on $[-2, 0]$ are the negatives of the y values on $[0, 2]$.

SECTION 7.3   (page 388)

1. $\dfrac{x}{2}\sqrt{x^2 + 16} + 8 \ln |x + \sqrt{x^2 + 16}| + C$ **3.** $\dfrac{x}{2}\sqrt{9x^2 + 5} + \dfrac{5}{6}\ln |3x + \sqrt{9x^2 + 5}| + C$ **5.** $\dfrac{1}{14}\ln \left|\dfrac{x-7}{x+7}\right| + C$

7. $\dfrac{1}{90}\ln \left|\dfrac{5x-9}{5x+9}\right| + C$ **9.** $x - \dfrac{1}{7}\ln(1 + e^{7x}) + C$ **11.** $x + \dfrac{1}{4}\ln(1 + e^{-4x}) + C$ **13.** $\ln |x + \sqrt{x^2 + 25}| + C$

15. $\dfrac{1}{3}\ln |3x + \sqrt{9x^2 + 16}| + C$ **17.** $-\dfrac{\sqrt{x^2 + 1}}{x} + C$ **19.** $-\dfrac{\sqrt{4x^2 + 3}}{12x} + C$ **21.** $-\dfrac{\sqrt{4x^2 + 3}}{3x} + C$

23. $\dfrac{1}{6}\ln \left|\dfrac{x-3}{x+3}\right| + C$ **25.** $\dfrac{1}{6}\ln \left|\dfrac{3x-1}{3x+1}\right| + C$ **27.** $\dfrac{x^3}{3}\ln x - \dfrac{x^3}{9} + C$ **29.** $\dfrac{x^6}{6}\ln x - \dfrac{x^6}{36} + C$

31. $-\ln\left|\dfrac{1+\sqrt{x^2+1}}{x}\right| + C$ **33.** $-\dfrac{1}{10}\ln\left|\dfrac{5+\sqrt{4x^2+25}}{2x}\right| + C$ **35.** $-\dfrac{1}{2}\ln\left|\dfrac{2+\sqrt{9x^2+4}}{3x}\right| + C$

37. $x(\ln x)^3 - 3x(\ln x)^2 + 6x\ln x - 6x + C$ **39.** $x\ln x - x + C$ **41.** $xe^x - e^x + C$ **43.** $x^2e^x - 2xe^x + 2e^x + C$

45. $\ln\dfrac{e^u}{1+e^u} = \ln e^u - \ln(1+e^u) = u - \ln(1+e^u)$ **47.** $\dfrac{81}{8}\ln 3 - \dfrac{5}{2}$ **49.** $3\ln(7+\sqrt{40}) - 3\ln 9$

SECTION 7.4   (page 395)

1. $\Delta x = 1$; $x_0 = 0$, $x_1 = 1$, $x_2 = 2$, $x_3 = 3$, $x_4 = 4$ **3.** $\Delta x = 1$; $x_0 = 1$, $x_1 = 2$, $x_2 = 3$, $x_3 = 4$, $x_4 = 5$, $x_5 = 6$, $x_6 = 7$

5. $\Delta x = .5$; $x_0 = 2$, $x_1 = 2.5$, $x_2 = 3$, $x_3 = 3.5$, $x_4 = 4$, $x_5 = 4.5$, $x_6 = 5$

7. $\Delta x = .5$; $x_0 = 2$, $x_1 = 2.5$, $x_2 = 3$, $x_3 = 3.5$, $x_4 = 4$, $x_5 = 4.5$, $x_6 = 5$, $x_7 = 5.5$, $x_8 = 6$

9. $\Delta x = .25$; $x_0 = 3$, $x_1 = 3.25$, $x_2 = 3.50$, $x_3 = 3.75$, $x_4 = 4$; $x_5 = 4.25$, $x_6 = 4.50$, $x_7 = 4.75$, $x_8 = 5$

11. 2.75   **13.** 5.6724   **15.** 2.0214 or 2.0215   **17.** 80.5657 or 80.5658   **19.** 3.9827 or 3.9828   **21.** 53.3333

23. 9.3004   **25.** 4.0299 to 4.0307   **27.** 1.0983 to 1.0987   **29.** .6445 or .6446

31. (a) 22 (b) 64/3 or 21.3333 (c) 64/3   **33.** (a) 64.6875 (b) 63.75 (c) 63.75

35. (a) 4.6615 (b) 4.6665 or 4.6666 (c) 14/3 or 4.6667   **37.** (a) .8959 (b) .8610 (c) $\dfrac{e-1}{2}$ or .8592 or .8591

39. (a) 2.5543 (b) 2.6249 or 2.6250 (c) 8/3 or 2.6667   **41.** (a) 2.9957 or 2.9958 (b) 3.0836 (c) 3.1416

43. 31,500 square feet   **45.** (a) 2 (b) .0167   **47.** (a) .0026 (b) .000033   **49.** (a) .0052 (b) .000022

51. 64   **53.** 566   **55.** The graph is a parabola, and Simpson's rule uses parabolas to approximate the area.

Technology Exercises   (page 397)

1. (a) 3.982772787 (b) 4.039815165; 4.044527255; 4.046763008; 4.047082903

3. (a) 1.098725349 (b) 1.098636168; 1.098615505; 1.098612373   **5.** .1159119   **7.** .2027326   **9.** .3923840

SECTION 7.5   (page 404)

1. 0   **3.** 0   **5.** ∞   **7.** 0   **9.** ∞   **11.** ∞   **13.** ∞   **15.** 3   **17.** ∞   **19.** ∞   **21.** 2   **23.** 1/2   **25.** 1/3

27. divergent   **29.** divergent   **31.** divergent   **33.** 1/e   **35.** divergent   **37.** divergent   **39.** divergent   **41.** divergent

43. 2   **45.** 1   **47.** 1/8   **49.** 1   **51.** 50 pounds   **53.** $50,000   **55.** $71,000   **57.** −1/2   **59.** 1/3

61. divergent   **63.** divergent   **65.** −1/8   **67.** 1/6   **69.** 1/e   **71.** 1/3   **73.** 1/32   **75.** divergent   **77.** divergent

79. divergent   **81.** 0   **83.** 0   **85.** divergent   **87.** 1 square unit   **89.** π

Technology Exercises   (page 406)

1. The magnitude of the area between the curve and the x axis is the same on $(-\infty, 0)$ as it is on $(0, \infty)$. However, between $-\infty$ and 0, the curve is *below* the x axis. This means that the integral from $-\infty$ to 0 will be negative. Because the integral from 0 to ∞ is positive, the two integrals will add up to 0.

REVIEW EXERCISES FOR CHAPTER 7   (page 407)

1. $\frac{1}{3}(1 + x^2)^{3/2} + C$ **3.** $x(1 + 2x)^{1/2} - \frac{1}{3}(1 + 2x)^{3/2} + C$ or $\frac{x-1}{3}\sqrt{1 + 2x} + C$ **5.** $\frac{(x-2)^4}{4} + C$

7. $\frac{x(x-2)^4}{4} - \frac{(x-2)^5}{20} + C$ **9.** $\frac{1}{2}e^{x^2} + C$ **11.** $\frac{1}{3}xe^{3x} - \frac{1}{9}e^{3x} + C$ **13.** $\sqrt{x^2 + 1} + C$ **15.** $\ln\left|x + \sqrt{x^2 + 1}\right| + C$

17. $x \ln 2x - x + C$ **19.** $\frac{(\ln 2x)^2}{2} + C$ **21.** $\frac{1}{2}\ln(1 + e^{2x}) + C$ **23.** $x - \frac{1}{2}\ln(1 + e^{2x}) + C$

25. (a) 5.5013 **(b)** 5.5196   **27. (a)** .323 **(b)** .3217   **29.** 1/3   **31.** divergent   **33.** divergent   **35.** divergent

37. $P(x) = (x + 1)\ln(x + 1) - x - 120$ **39.** \$150,817   **41.** $4 \ln 4 - 3$ **43.** 70   **45.** 49/6   **47.** $y = xe^x - e^x + 7$

SECTION 8.1   (page 416)

1. (a) .3 **(b)** .4 **(c)** .7 **(d)** 1   **3. (a)** .4 **(b)** .5 **(c)** 1 **(d)** .6   **5.** $\frac{1}{30}x \geq 0$ for x in $[2, 8]$ and $\int_2^8 \frac{1}{30}x\, dx = 1$

7. $\frac{1}{12}(3x^2 + 2x) \geq 0$ for x in $[0, 2]$ and $\int_0^2 \frac{1}{12}(3x^2 + 2x)\, dx = 1$ **9.** $\frac{3}{38}\sqrt{x} \geq 0$ for x in $[4, 9]$ and $\int_4^9 \frac{3}{38}\sqrt{x}\, dx = 1$

11. $\frac{10}{9x^2} \geq 0$ for x in $[1, 10]$ and $\int_1^{10} \frac{10}{9x^2}\, dx = 1$ **13. (a)** 63/64 **(b)** 1/8   **15. (a)** 1/2 **(b)** 3/10

17. (a) $\ln 2$ **(b)** $1 - \ln 2$ **19.** $g(x) = \frac{2x}{63}$ **21.** $g(x) = 4x^3$ **23.** $g(x) = \frac{1}{12}(x - 5)$ **25.** .36   **27.** 1/5

29. (a) $1 - \frac{1}{e}$ **(b)** .2858   **31. (a)** 9/13 **(b)** 1/13

33. No, f cannot be a probability density function. For f to be a probability density function, it must be true that

$\int_0^{10} f(x)\, dx = 1$, yet we already have 2.5 on the subinterval $[1, 4]$. The integrals over the remaining portions of the interval

$[0, 10]$ cannot be negative, because $f(x) \geq 0$ on $[0\ 10]$. Consequently, $\int_0^{10} f(x)\, dx$ will be greater than 2.5 and thus not equal to 1 as needed for a probability density function.

35. The candle will burn between 3 and 5 hours.

Technology Exercises   (page 418)

1. $P(2.5 \leq x \leq 4)$ is greater, because the area under the curve is greater over the interval $[2.5, 4]$ than over the interval $[1, 2.5]$.

SECTION 8.2   (page 425)

1. 7   **3.** 4   **5.** 3.04   **7.** 7   **9.** 1.2   **11.** e **13.** f **15.** d **17.** $\mu = 7$, Var$(x) = 3$, $\sigma = 1.73$

19. $\mu = 2.8$, Var$(x) = .66$, $\sigma = .81$ **21.** $\mu = 1.33$, Var$(x) = .89$, $\sigma = .94$ **23.** $\mu = 12.33$, Var$(x) = 4.17$, $\sigma = 2.04$

25. 13 minutes, 20 seconds   **27. (a)** 3 years, 4 months **(b)** 5.56 or 5.58

29. (a) 4.375 **(b)** The average life expectancy of such a tree is 4.375 years. **(c)** Var$(x) = 7.53$; $\sigma = 2.74$

Technology Exercises   (page 426)

1. 2   **3.** 3

SECTION 8.3   (page 429)

1. .25   **3. (a)** $f(x) = \frac{1}{3} \geq 0$ for $5 \leq x \leq 8$ and $\int_5^8 \frac{1}{3}\,dx = \left[\frac{x}{3}\right]_5^8 = 1$ **(b)** 1/3 **(c)** uniform   **5.** $f(x) = \frac{1}{25}, 0 \leq x \leq 25$

7. $f(x) = \frac{1}{6}, 4 \leq x \leq 10$ **9. (a)** .4512 **(b)** .4541   **11. (a)** .3935 **(b)** .2492 *or* .2493 **(c)** .1353   **13.** .9817

15. (a) 5 minutes **(b)** $f(x) = .125e^{-.125x}, x \geq 0$ **17.** $f(x) = .25e^{-.25x}, x \geq 0$

19. $\mu = \int_a^b x \cdot \frac{1}{b-a}\,dx = \frac{1}{b-a}\left[\frac{x^2}{2}\right]_a^b = \cdots = \frac{1}{2}(a+b)$ **21.** No. Since $\int_0^\infty f(x)\,dx = .5 \neq 1, f$ is not a probability

density function.

SECTION 8.4   (page 438)

1. .3643   **3.** .2673   **5.** .6628   **7.** .9265   **9.** .4452   **11.** .4821   **13.** .2005   **15.** .0427   **17.** .7321

19. .7723   **21.** .2426   **23.** .0897   **25.** .2061   **27.** .1151   **29.** .9332   **31.** .9332   **33.** .2088   **35.** .5859

37. .4772   **39.** .1587   **41.** .5   **43.** .2486   **45.** 84%   **47. (a)** .0668 **(b)** .1587   **49.** 3.6%   **51.** .4837

53. $f(x) = \frac{1}{1 \cdot \sqrt{2\pi}} e^{-(x-0)^2/(2 \cdot 1^2)} = \frac{1}{\sqrt{2\pi}} e^{-x^2/2}$

55. 1. The probability is 1 that z takes on a value that is a real number; it *must* happen.

57. (a) The integral must have the value 1 if f is a probability density function. **(b)** The $1/\sqrt{2\pi}$ is needed so that the integral will have the value 1. See the answer to part (a).

Technology Exercises   (page 439)

1. (a) .24 **(b)** .05

REVIEW EXERCISES FOR CHAPTER 8   (page 440)

1. $f(x) = \frac{1}{42} x \geq 0$ for $4 \leq x \leq 10$ and $\int_4^{10} \frac{1}{42} x\,dx = \left[\frac{x^2}{84}\right]_4^{10} = 1$ **3.** .9375   **5. (a)** .0225 **(b)** .91

7. .51   **9.** 5.0667   **11.** $\mu = 2.25$, Var$(x) = .3375$, $\sigma = .5809$ **13.** 5 minutes   **15. (a)** .7769 **(b)** .0498

17. .2157   **19.** .9479   **21.** .2335   **23.** .0808   **25.** .3891   **27.** .9987

29. Since f is a probability density function, the integral from 0 to 8 must be equal to 1. The integral from 0 to 3 must be equal to .25, because the integral from 3 to 8 is .75 (and .25 + .75 = 1).

SECTION 9.1   (page 447)

1. $x(10x) = 2(5x^2)$ leads to $10x^2 = 10x^2$.   **3.** $4e^{4x} - 4(e^{4x}) = 0$ **5.** $x(6x^{1/2}) - 1.5(4x^{3/2} - 2) = 3$ leads to $3 = 3$.

7. $2 - 3(2x + 6) + (x^2 + 6x + 16) = x^2$ leads to $x^2 = x^2$.   **9.** $(-2)^2 - 4(1 - 2x) - 8x = 0$ leads to $0 = 0$.

11. $y = 3x^2 + 19x + C$ **13.** $y = e^x + x + C$ **15.** $f(x) = 2x + \dfrac{2}{3}x^{3/2} + C$ **17.** $y = -\dfrac{1}{2}e^{-2t} + C$

19. $f(t) = t + 3\ln|t| + C$ **21.** $y = 2x^3 - x^2 + 5$ **23.** $f(x) = \dfrac{x^8}{8} + 3x + 14$ **25.** $y = 5x^2 - e^x + 1$

27. $y = 2x^{3/2} - 5$ **29.** $y = 8\ln|t| + 3$ **31.** $C(x) = 50x - .03x^2 + 150$ **33.** $R(x) = 5x + .0001x^2$

35. $P(x) = 80x - .2x^{3/2} - 50$ **37.** Yes, $y = 3$ is a solution of such differential equations as $y' = 0$ and $y' + 5y = 15$.

39. (a) $\dfrac{dy}{dx} = 3x^2$; $y(2) = 11$ **(b)** $y = x^3 + 3$ **41. (a)** $2y\dfrac{dy}{dx} - 2x = 0$ or $\dfrac{dy}{dx} = \dfrac{x}{y}$ **(b)** implicit differentiation

Technology Exercises   (page 448)

1. (a) $y = x^2 + C$
(b) For $C = 3$, the graph is translated 3 units up from the graph for $C = 0$. For $C = -2$, it is translated 2 units down from the graph for $C = 0$. The C value indicates how many units up $(+)$ or down $(-)$ it is translated compared with the graph for $C = 0$.

3. (a) $y = x^3 + C$ **(b)** The C value is the amount the graph is translated up or down compared with the graph for $C = 0$.

SECTION 9.2   (page 452)

1. $y = x^2 + C$ **3.** $\ln|y| = \dfrac{x^2}{2} + C$ **5.** $e^y = \dfrac{t^2}{2} + C$ **7.** $-\dfrac{1}{y} = 3x^2 + 5x + C$ **9.** $-\ln|y| = \ln|x| + C$

11. $e^y = e^x + C$ **13.** $y = -\dfrac{1}{x} + C$ **15.** $-\dfrac{1}{y^2} = \ln|t| + C$ **17.** $\dfrac{1}{3}\ln|1 + x^3| = \dfrac{y^5}{5} + C$ **19.** $\ln|y| = x^2 + C$

21. $y^2 = x^2 + 16$ **23.** $\ln|y| = x^2 + \ln 2$ **25.** $e^y = 2x^2 + 1$ **27.** $\ln|y| = \ln|x| + 1$ **29.** $3y = 2x^2 + 3$

31. $\dfrac{dy}{dx} = x - 3$ **33.** $\dfrac{dB}{dt} = .05B$ **35.** $\dfrac{dM}{dt} = -.02M$ **37. (a)** $\dfrac{dA}{dt} = .09A$ **(b)** $A = Ce^{.09t}$ **(c)** $C = 3000$

39. (a) $\dfrac{dA}{dt} = .03A$; $A(0) = 100{,}000{,}000$ **(b)** $A = 100{,}000{,}000e^{.03t}$ **41. (a)** $\dfrac{dA}{dt} = -.08A$; $A(0) = 10$ **(b)** $A = 10e^{-.08t}$

43. 61¢   **45. (a)** $\dfrac{dA}{dt} = -.081A$ **(b)** $A = Ce^{-.081t}$ **(c)** 8.6 days

47. The solution is an equation involving x, y, and C. The initial condition provides a specific x value and the corresponding y value. Substituting the known x and y values into the (solution) equation leaves an equation that contains only C and known values, from which C is readily determined.

49. $4x^2 + 9y^2 = 36$

Technology Exercises   (page 454)

1. (a) Just change it to logarithmic notation. **(b)** yes **(c)** yes, 0

3. (a) $\dfrac{dy}{dx} = -.04y$ **(b)** $y(0) = 1$ **(c)** $y = e^{-.04x}$ **(d)** 6.5 years

SECTION 9.3 (page 464)

1. (a) $\dfrac{dA}{dt} = .08A + 500$; $A = 9250e^{.08t} - 6250$ **(b)** $12,753 or $12,754

3. (a) $\dfrac{dA}{dt} = .05A - 200,000$ **(b)** $A = 6,000,000e^{.05t} + 4,000,000$ **(c)** $11,328,416 or $11,328,417 **(d)** The debt is increasing because the country's annual payments are less than the interest due each year.

5. (a) $\dfrac{dA}{dt} = .05A + 200,000$ **(b)** $A = 14,000,000e^{.05t} - 4,000,000$ **(c)** $13,099,639

7. $p = 20 - 10 \ln x$ **9. (a)** $\dfrac{dT}{dt} = k(T - 70)$ **(b)** $T = -50e^{-.051t} + 70$ **11.** 6.6 minutes

13. (a) $y = \dfrac{40,000}{1 + 199e^{-.14t}}$ **(b)** 24 days **15.** Approximately 6 days

Technology Exercises (page 466)

1. (a) down **(b)** false

3. (a) No; x must be a number between 0 and 54. If $x \geq 55$, then price p is negative. **(b)** increases **(c)** decreases

5. (a) 1444 fish **(b)** at 27 months

SECTION 9.4 (page 472)

1. 5.9674 **3.** 1.5282 **5.** 1.8370 **7.** 2.5010 or 2.5011 **9.** 1.6413 **11.** 1.6499 **13.** 2.5424 or 2.5425

15. 1, 1, 1.02, 1.0604, 1.1222, 1.2071 **17.** 3, 2.85, 2.71, 2.5795, 2.4580, 2.3451, 2.2403

19. 2, 2.2, 2.36, 2.488, 2.5904, 2.6723, 2.7378 **21.** 1, 1.1, 1.232, 1.4045, 1.6292, 1.9225 **23.** $n(0) = 357$

25. After 3 hours, there are 40 milligrams of mold. **27.** 847 or 848 **29.** $y = e^{x^2}$; $f(.6) = e^{.6^2} = 1.4333$

Technology Exercises (page 473)

1. 1, 1.02, 1.0608, 1.124448, 1.21440384, 1.335844224, 1.496145531 **3.** 1, 1.02, 1.0604, 1.122212, 1.20710048

5. 2.2, 2.36, 2.488, 2.5904, 2.67232, 2.737856

REVIEW EXERCISES FOR CHAPTER 9 (page 474)

1. $x(-12x) = 2(1 - 6x^2) - 2$, or $-12x^2 = -12x^2$. **3.** $y = x - \dfrac{x^4}{4} + C$ **5.** $y = -\dfrac{1}{2x^2} + C$ **7.** $\ln |y| = \ln |x| + C$

9. $y^2 = t^2 + C$ **11.** $y = 4\sqrt{x} + 1$ **13.** $4\sqrt{y} = x^2 + 12$ **15. (a)** $\dfrac{dA}{dt} = .08A$ **(b)** $A = Ce^{.08t}$ **(c)** $C = 2000$

17. $R(x) = 12x + .02x^2$ **19.** $p = 50 - 50 \ln x$ **21.** 1, 1, 1.04, 1.1265, 1.2788, 1.5405

23. (a) The rate at which the population is changing is equal to the birth rate times the population *minus* the death rate times the population. **(b)** Obtain $\dfrac{dN}{N} = (b - d)\, dt$ and then integrate. **(c)** The population decreases. **(d)** The population increases.

SECTION 10.1   (page 485)

1. 20, 37, 4, 1, 1   **3.** 2/3, −1/5, 0, 1, 0   **5.** −5, −4, −1, 0, 0   **7.** 34, −39, −14, 3, −7   **9.** 5, $\sqrt{42}$, 3, $\sqrt{6}$, $\sqrt{6}$

11. 0, 0   **13.** 4, e **15.** 4   **17.** 1/2   **19. (a)** \$1173.51 **(b)** \$6041.26   **21.** 65,215

23. (a) 130 **(b)** 80 **(c)** The person's mental age and actual age are the same.   **25.** $P(x, y, z) = x + 2y + 3z$

27. (a) $4k$, $64k$ **(b)** The resistance becomes 16 times as great.   **29. (a)** $R(x, y) = 6.5x + 5y$ **(b)** $P(x, y) = 2.5x + 2y$

31. (a) $V(x, y, z) = xyz$ **(b)** $V(x, y) = 2xy^2$ **33.** all (x, y) **35.** all (x, y) **37.** all (x, y) in which $y \geq x$

39. all (x, y) in which $y \neq 1$ **41.** all (x, y) in which $x \neq y$ **43.** all (x, y) in which $x \geq 0$ and $y \neq -3/2$ **45.** all (x, y)

47. all (x, y) in which $x > 1$

49.

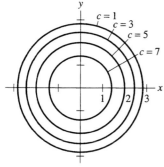

The radii are $\sqrt{8}$, $\sqrt{6}$, 2, $\sqrt{2}$.

51.

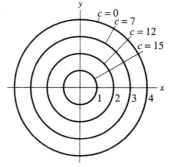

The radii are 4, 3, 2, 1.

53.

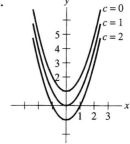

The parabolas
$y = x^2 + 1$,
$y = x^2$, $y = x^2 - 1$

55.

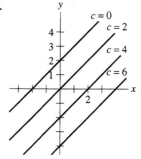

The lines $y = x + 2$,
$y = x$, $y = x - 2$,
$y = x - 4$

57.

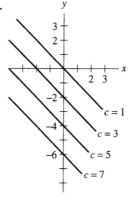

The lines $y = -x$,
$y = -x - 2$,
$y = -x - 4$,
$y = -x - 6$

59.

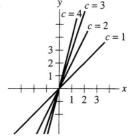

The lines $y = x$, $y = 2x$,
$y = 3x$, $y = 4x$

61.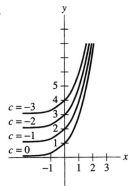

The graphs of $y = e^x + 3$,
$y = e^x + 2, y = e^x + 1, y = e^x$

63.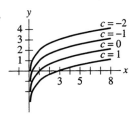

The graphs of $y = 2 + \ln x$,
$y = 1 + \ln x, y = \ln x, y = -1 + \ln x$

65. (a) 2.8 **(b)** increases   **67.** The limit of $f(x, y)$ as x approaches 0 and y approaches 1 is 2.5

Technology Exercises   (page 487)

1. $y = 1 - 2x$ **3. (a)** y_1 **(b)** y_3

SECTION 10.2   (page 494)

1. $\partial f/\partial x = 2; \partial f/\partial y = 5$ **3.** $\partial f/\partial x = 3x^2; \partial f/\partial y = -8y$ **5.** $\partial f/\partial x = 1/y; \partial f/\partial y = -x/y^2$ **7.** $\partial f/\partial x = y/x; \partial f/\partial y = \ln x$

9. $\partial f/\partial x = 3ye^{3xy}; \partial f/\partial y = 3xe^{3xy}$ **11.** $\partial f/\partial x = \sqrt{y}; \partial f/\partial y = \dfrac{x}{2\sqrt{y}}$ **13.** $\partial f/\partial x = x/\sqrt{x^2 + y^2}; \partial f/\partial y = y/\sqrt{x^2 + y^2}$

15. $\partial f/\partial x = y/(x + y)^2; \partial f/\partial y = -x/(x + y)^2$ **17.** $f_x = 3x^2y^5; f_y = 5x^3y^4$ **19.** $f_x = \dfrac{2x}{x^2 + y^2}; f_y = \dfrac{2y}{x^2 + y^2}$

21. $f_x = e^{-y}; f_y = -xe^{-y}$ **23.** y **25.** $2x$ **27.** 0   **29.** $2xy^2$ **31.** x **33.** 0   **35.** 3   **37.** $2x^2y$

39. (a) 157 **(b)** 18 **(c)** 47 **(d)** 2   **41. (a)** 12 **(b)** 1 **(c)** $1 + e$ **(d)** $2 + 2e$ **43.** $f_x = 2x; f_y = 2y; f_z = 2z$

45. $f_x = yz - 1; f_y = xz + 1; f_z = xy$ **47.** $f_x = ye^z; f_y = xe^z; f_z = xye^z$

49. $f_x = \dfrac{1}{y + z}; f_y = -x/(y + z)^2; f_z = -x/(y + z)^2$ **51.** $f_{xx} = 2; f_{xy} = 1; f_{yx} = 1; f_{yy} = 2$

53. $f_{xx} = -y/x^2; f_{xy} = 1/x; f_{yx} = 1/x; f_{yy} = 0$ **55.** $g_{xx} = 0; g_{xy} = 3e^y; g_{yx} = 3e^y; g_{yy} = 3xe^y$

57. $h_{xx} = 2 \ln y; h_{xy} = 2x/y; h_{yx} = 2x/y; h_{yy} = -x^2/y^2$

59. $f_{xx} = -1/(x + y^2)^2; f_{xy} = -2y/(x + y^2)^2; f_{yx} = -2y/(x + y^2)^2; f_{yy} = (2x - 2y^2)/(x + y^2)^2$

61. (a) \$148.40 **(b)** \$96.40   **63. (a)** $\partial f/\partial x = .8x^{-.6}y^{.6}$ **(b)** $\partial f/\partial y = 1.2x^{.4}y^{-.4}$ **65.** $135/64 \approx 2.1$

67. (a) 350° **(b)** The square of any $x \neq 0$ and the square of any $y \neq 0$ will be subtracted from 350°. Thus, $T(x, y) < 350°$ for any point other than $(0, 0)$. **(c)** -20 **(d)** -12 **(e)** The temperature *decreases* as you move away from the origin.

69. πr^2

71. (a) k/V **(b)** $-kT/V^2$
(c) $\partial P/\partial V$ is the rate of change of pressure with respect to volume, assuming the temperature is kept constant.
73. (a) 1.98 **(b)** $S_w = .00306w^{-.575}h^{.725}; \; S_h = .00522w^{.425}h^{-.275}$ **(c)** .01, .008
(d) S_w is the rate of change of body surface area with respect to body weight, assuming the body height is kept constant. S_h is the rate of change of body surface area with respect to body height, assuming the body weight is kept constant.   **75.** 9/25

SECTION 10.3   (page 503)

1. $(3, -1)$ **3.** $(-2, 5), (2, 5)$ **5.** $(-1, 4), (0, 4)$ **7.** $(-1, -3), (-1, 3), (1, -3), (1, 3)$ **9.** $(-3, 2)$
11. $(-1, 0), (-1, 2), (3, 0), (3, 2)$ **13.** $(0, 0), (1, 1)$ **15.** relative minimum value is -12, at $(-4, 1)$
17. relative maximum value is 14, at $(2, -3)$ **19.** relative maximum value is 7, at $(-2, -2)$
21. relative minimum value is -7, at $(4, 2)$
23. relative maximum value is 9, at $(-1, 0)$; relative minimum value is -27, at $(3, 2)$ **25.** none
27. $1000 on radio, $4000 on newspaper   **29.** 13 at $1200 and 14 at $1500   **31.** 9, 9, 9
33. 14 inches wide, 28 inches long, 14 inches high   **35.** 4 feet long, 4 feet wide, 8 feet high
37. The shape indicated by the lowest-cost approach would not be visually appealing, nor would it give the fish a long portion in which to swim.

SECTION 10.4   (page 509)

1. $f(x, y) = 25$, from $x = 5$ and $y = 5$ **3.** $f(x, y) = 8$, from $x = 2$ and $y = 1$ **5.** $f(x, y) = -16$, from $x = 4$ and $y = 2$
7. $f(x, y) = 4$, from $x = 2$ and $y = 0$ **9.** $f(x, y) = 50$, from $x = 5$ and $y = 7$ **11.** $f(x, y) = 300$, from $x = 10$ and $y = 10$
13. 500, 500   **15.** 2500 square meters   **17.** 70 units labor, 70 units capital; $21,000 minimum cost
19. 240 units labor, 60 units capital; $9600 minimum cost   **21.** 50 units labor, 50 units capital
23. radius $= \sqrt[3]{100/\pi} \approx 3.17$ inches, height $= 2\sqrt[3]{100/\pi} \approx 6.34$ inches

SECTION 10.5   (page 514)

1. $y = \dfrac{19}{14}x + 4$ **3.** $y = \dfrac{10}{7}x - \dfrac{73}{7}$ **5.** $y = \dfrac{6}{5}x + 3$ **7.** $y = 2x + \dfrac{5}{3}$ **9.** $y = \dfrac{53}{35}x + \dfrac{18}{5}$ **11.** $y = -\dfrac{3}{2}x + \dfrac{15}{2}$

13. (a) $y = -\dfrac{43}{35}x + \dfrac{69}{7}$ **(b)** 26/7 **(c)** 205/43 $\approx$ 4.7674   **15. (a)** $y = \dfrac{15}{113}x - \dfrac{1}{565}$ **(b)** 3.05

17. (a) $y = \dfrac{3}{5}x + 54$ **(b)** 75 grams **(c)** 43.3°C   **19.** $b = \dfrac{\Sigma \, y_i - m \, \Sigma \, x_i}{n} = \dfrac{\Sigma \, y_i}{n} - \dfrac{m \, \Sigma \, x_i}{n} = \bar{y} - m \cdot \bar{x}$

21. They might predict the amount of a tip based on the amount of the bill.

Technology Exercises   (page 516)

1. (a) $(3, 7)$ **(b)** $(7, 8)$ **3.** $y = .8284x + 4.2239$ **5.** $y = .1327x - .00177$

SECTION 10.6 (page 519)

1. $dz = 2x\,dx + 2y\,dy$ **3.** $dz = (y^2 + 6x)\,dx + (2xy - 4y)\,dy$ **5.** $dz = (e^y + ye^x)\,dx + (xe^y + e^x)\,dy$

7. $dz = \left(-\dfrac{y}{x^2} - 8\right)dx + \left(\dfrac{1}{x} + 3\right)dy$ **9.** $dz = (\ln y - 2x)\,dx + \dfrac{x}{y}\,dy$ **11.** 777.6   **13.** .22   **15.** .1275

17. 163.22   **19.** 2   **21.** 15.56   **23.** \$30,000   **25.** R(21.5, 13) − R(20, 12) = 806.9375 − 784 = \$22,937.50

27. $-4.4\pi \approx 13.8$ cubic inches   **29.** \$118.60   **31.** 44.4

33. No; the exact change Δz can be calculated, but dz offers a good, fast approximation.

SECTION 10.7 (page 528)

1. $104y$ **3.** $36x$ **5.** $3 + 9x$ **7.** $21 + 6y$ **9.** $2x^2 + 6$ **11.** 56   **13.** 120   **15.** 63   **17.** 10/3

19. 76   **21.** $e^3 - e^2 - e + 1$ **23.** 32   **25.** $\int_0^2 \int_1^3 (2x + 6y)\,dy\,dx = \int_0^2 (4x + 24)\,dx = 56$

27. $\int_1^3 \int_2^4 (x + 2y)\,dx\,dy = 28$ **29.** 12   **31.** 22/3   **33.** 40/3   **35.** 9   **37.** 20   **39.** 97.5   **41.** 17/3 or 5.67

43. $\int_2^6 \int_3^5 3xy\,dy\,dx$ or $\int_3^5 \int_2^6 3xy\,dx\,dy$ **45.** $\int_1^2 \int_{x/2}^{2x+1} 3xy\,dy\,dx$ **47.** $e - 2$ **49.** 55   **51.** 25/3   **53.** $e^4 - 1$

55. 55.8   **57.** 1/12   **59.** −4/21

61.

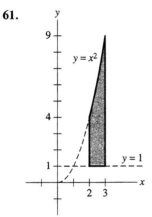

63.

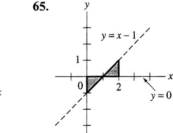

65.

67. 346°

Technology Exercises (page 530)

1. See Example 8 (drawing).   **3.** See Exercise 46 (drawing).

REVIEW EXERCISES FOR CHAPTER 10 (page 531)

1. 10, −3   **3.** all (x, y) in which $x \neq 1$

5.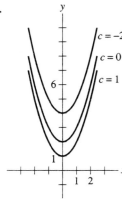

7.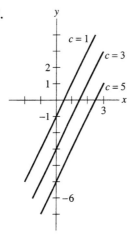

The graphs of $y = x^2 + 4$, $y = x^2 + 2$, $y = x^2 + 1$

The graphs of $y = 2x - 1$, $y = 2x - 3$, $y = 2x - 5$

9. $f_x = 4x^3 + 2xy^2$; $f_y = 2x^2y - 4y^3$ **11.** $f_x = 3e^{3x} + \ln y$; $f_y = x/y$ **13.** $f_x = e^y$; $f_y = xe^y$; $f_z = 15z^4$

15. $f_{xx} = 10$; $f_{yy} = 6y$; $f_{xy} = -1$; $f_{yx} = -1$ **17.** $(2, -6)$ **19.** none   **21. (a)** 2.25 **(b)** 0

23. 300 regular, 700 deluxe   **25.** $f(4, 3) = 31$ **27.** $y = \dfrac{17}{12}x + \dfrac{595}{12}$ $(952/672 = 17/12)$ **29.** 110,400 cubic centimeters

31. $2\sqrt{2}$ feet by $2\sqrt{2}$ feet   **33.** -84 **35.** $10(e - 1)$ **37.** 72   **39.** 90   **41.** $-4/15$

INDEX

INDEX OF APPLICATIONS